Datsun Owners Workshop Manual

Ian Coomber

Models covered
UK: Datsun 'new' Cherry models (N10 Series) with ohv and ohc engines
USA: Datsun 310 models with ohv and ohc engines
Covers 4- and 5-speed manual transmission; semi and fully automatic transmissions

ISBN 0 85696 955 9 (Hardback)
ISBN 0 85696 977 X (Softback)

ABCDE
FGHIJ

Printed in England   *(679-5J2)*

THE
BOOK

AUTOMOTIVE
PARTS &
ACCESSORIES
ASSOCIATION MEMBER

HAYNES PUBLISHING GROUP
SPARKFORD YEOVIL SOMERSET BA22 7JJ ENGLAND
distributed in the USA by
HAYNES PUBLICATIONS INC
861 LAWRENCE DRIVE
NEWBURY PARK
CALIFORNIA 91320
USA

Acknowledgements

Thanks are due to the Nissan Motor Company Limited of Japan for the provision of technical information and certain illustrations. The Champion Sparking Plug Company supplied the illustrations showing the various spark plug conditions. The bodywork repair photographs used in this manual were provided by Holt Lloyd Limited who supply 'Turtle Wax', 'Dupli-Color Holts', and other Holts range products.

About this manual

Its aim

The aim of this manual is to help you get the best from your car. It can do so in several ways. It can help you decide what work must be done (even should you choose to get it done by a garage), provide information on routine maintenance and servicing, and give a logical course of action and diagnosis when random faults occur. However, it is hoped that you will use the manual by tackling the work yourself. On simpler jobs it may even be quicker than booking the car into a garage and going there twice to leave and collect it. Perhaps most important, a lot of money can be saved by avoiding the costs the garage must charge to cover its labour and overheads.

The manual has drawings and descriptions to show the function of the various components so that their layout can be understood. Then the tasks are described and photographed in a step-by-step sequence so that even a novice can do the work.

Its arrangement

The manual is divided into thirteen Chapters, each covering a logical sub-division of the vehicle. The Chapters are each divided into Sections, numbered with single figures, eg 5; and the Sections into paragraphs (or sub-sections), with decimal numbers following on from the Section they are in, eg 5.1. 5.2 etc.

It is freely illustrated, especially in those parts where there is a detailed sequence of operations to be carried out. There are two forms of illustration: figures and photographs. The figures are numbered in sequence with decimal numbers, according to their position in the Chapter – Fig. 6.4 is the fourth drawing/illustration in Chapter 6. Photographs carry the same number (either individually or in related groups) as the Section or sub-section to which they relate.

There is an alphabetical index at the back of the manual as well as a contents list at the front. Each Chapter is also preceded by its own individual contents list.

References to the 'left' or 'right' of the vehicle are in the sense of a person in the driver's seat facing forwards.

Unless otherwise stated, nuts and bolts are removed by turning anti-clockwise, and tightened by turning clockwise.

Vehicle manufacturers continually make changes to specifications and recommendations, and these, when notified, are incorporated into our manuals at the earliest opportunity.

Whilst every care is taken to ensure that the information in this manual is correct, no liability can be accepted by the authors or publishers for loss, damage or injury caused by any errors in, or omissions, from the information given.

Introduction to the Datsun Cherry and 310 Series

The Datsun models covered by this manual are the 'new' Cherry for the European markets and the 310 Series for the USA and Canadian markets.

Introduced in 1979, both the Cherry and the 310 Series are updated variants of the Cherry F-II model (UK market) and the Datsun F10 model (USA market). They have the same basic mechanics but have revised body styling and fittings.

The New Cherry is available with one of two engine types depending on model, these being the 988 cc (A10) engine or the 1171 cc (A12) engine. Both engine types are mounted transversely and are of conventional ohv, water-cooled design.

Again dependent on model and engine type, either a 4-speed or 5-speed manual transmission is fitted, or a 3-speed selective automatic transmission is also available (on A12 engine models only).

The 1979 and 1980 310 Series models have the 1397 cc (A14) engine fitted, whilst the 1981 models have the 1488 cc (A15) engine. Both engine types are of ohv, water-cooled design and are transversely mounted.

The 310 Series vehicles are fitted with a 4-speed or 5-speed manual transmission, with full synchromesh on all forward gears.

The body styles available comprise 3 and 5-door Hatchbacks, a 4-door Saloon, a 5-door Estate car and for the more sporty minded, the Hatchback Coupe.

Models manufactured for the USA and Canada have a wider range of accessories available and in order to comply with the regulations, a sophisticated emission control system is fitted to reduce the poisonous exhaust gases being freely released into the atmosphere. The emission control equipment fitted to California models differs slightly to comply with the additional regulations of that State.

In October 1981 the Cherry and 310 series was again revised and all models were equipped with a new E-series ohc engine, improved four and five-speed transmissions and other detail refinements. As well as a new fully automatic three-speed transmission available as an option, many previous options have now become standard equipment on the new model.

The Cherry and 310 models continued unchanged in this form until September 1982 when the model was discontinued. The changes to these later models are covered in the Supplement at the end of this manual.

Contents

Datsun Cherry 5-door Hatchback

Datsun Cherry 3-door Hatchback with later style front grille

Datsun 310 2-door Sedan Hatchback GX

Datsun 310 Coupe Hatchback GX

General dimensions, weights and capacities

Overall length
UK models:
  Saloon, Hatchback and Coupe:
    Standard .... 153.1 in (3.890 m)
    With headlight washer .... 154.3 in (3.920 m)
  Estate .... 157.1 in (3.990 m)
North American models:
  1980 .... 159.4 in (4.050 m)
  1981 .... 160.6 in (4.080 m)

Overall width .... 63.8 in (1.600 m)

Overall height
Saloon/Hatchback .... 53.5 in (1.360 m)
Coupe .... 52.0 in (1.320 m)
Estate .... 54.5 in (1.384 m)

Ground clearance .... 7.1 in (180 mm)

Kerb weights (approximate)
UK models:
  Saloon .... 1720 lb (780 kg)
  3-door Hatchback (A10 engine) .... 1710 lb (775 kg)
  3-door Hatchback (A12 engine) .... 1765 lb (800 kg)
  5-door Hatchback .... 1775 lb (805 kg)
  Coupe .... 1810 lb (820 kg)
  Estate .... 1841 lb (836 kg)
North American models:
  2-door Sedan .... 1985 lb (902 kg)
  4-door Sedan .... 2015 lb (916 kg)
  Coupe .... 2015 lb (916 kg)

Capacities
Fuel tank .... 11 Imp gal (13.25 US gal, 50 litre)
Engine oil:
  Without filter change .... 4.75 Imp pint (2.88 US quart, 2.7 litre)
  With filter change .... 5.75 Imp pint (3.38 US quart, 3.2 litre)
Cooling system (with heater):
  Manual transmission .... 9.75 Imp pint (5.88 US quart, 5.5 litre)
  Automatic transmission .... 10.5 Imp pint (6.25 US quart, 5.9 litre)
Transmission lubricant:
  Manual .... 4 Imp pint (2.44 US quart, 2.3 litre)
  Automatic .... 8 Imp pint (4.75 US quart, 4.5 litre)

Use of English

As this book has been written in England, it uses the appropriate English component names, phrases, and spelling. Some of these differ from those used in America. Normally, these cause no difficulty, but to make sure, a glossary is printed below. In ordering spare parts remember the parts list will probably use these words:

English	American	English	American
Aerial	Antenna	Layshaft (of gearbox)	Countershaft
Accelerator	Gas pedal	Leading shoe (of brake)	Primary shoe
Alternator	Generator (AC)	Locks	Latches
Anti-roll bar	Stabiliser or sway bar	Motorway	Freeway, turnpike etc
Battery	Energizer	Number plate	License plate
Bodywork	Sheet metal	Paraffin	Kerosene
Bonnet (engine cover)	Hood	Petrol	Gasoline
Boot lid	Trunk lid	Petrol tank	Gas tank
Boot (luggage compartment)	Trunk	'Pinking'	'Pinging'
Bottom gear	1st gear	Propeller shaft	Driveshaft
Bulkhead	Firewall	Quarter light	Quarter window
Cam follower or tappet	Valve lifter or tappet	Retread	Recap
Carburettor	Carburetor	Reverse	Back-up
Catch	Latch	Rocker cover	Valve cover
Choke/venturi	Barrel	Roof rack	Car-top carrier
Circlip	Snap-ring	Saloon	Sedan
Clearance	Lash	Seized	Frozen
Crownwheel	Ring gear (of differential)	Side indicator lights	Side marker lights
Disc (brake)	Rotor/disk	Side light	Parking light
Drop arm	Pitman arm	Silencer	Muffler
Drop head coupe	Convertible	Spanner	Wrench
Dynamo	Generator (DC)	Sill panel (beneath doors)	Rocker panel
Earth (electrical)	Ground	Split cotter (for valve spring cap)	Lock (for valve spring retainer)
Engineer's blue	Prussian blue	Split pin	Cotter pin
Estate car	Station wagon	Steering arm	Spindle arm
Exhaust manifold	Header	Sump	Oil pan
Fast back (Coupe)	Hard top	Tab washer	Tang; lock
Fault finding/diagnosis	Trouble shooting	Tailgate	Liftgate
Float chamber	Float bowl	Tappet	Valve lifter
Free-play	Lash	Thrust bearing	Throw-out bearing
Freewheel	Coast	Top gear	High
Gudgeon pin	Piston pin or wrist pin	Trackrod (of steering)	Tie-rod (or connecting rod)
Gearchange	Shift	Trailing shoe (of brake)	Secondary shoe
Gearbox	Transmission	Transmission	Whole drive line
Halfshaft	Axleshaft	Tyre	Tire
Handbrake	Parking brake	Van	Panel wagon/van
Hood	Soft top	Vice	Vise
Hot spot	Heat riser	Wheel nut	Lug nut
Indicator	Turn signal	Windscreen	Windshield
Interior light	Dome lamp	Wing/mudguard	Fender

Miscellaneous points

An 'oil seal' is fitted to components lubricated by grease!

A 'damper' is a 'shock absorber', it damps out bouncing, and absorbs shocks of bump impact. Both names are correct, and both are used haphazardly.

Note that British drum brakes are different from the Bendix type that is common in America, so different descriptive names result. The shoe end furthest from the hydraulic wheel cylinder is on a pivot; interconnection between the shoes as on Bendix brakes is most uncommon. Therefore the phrase 'Primary' or 'Secondary' shoe does not apply. A shoe is said to be 'Leading' or 'Trailing'. A 'Leading' shoe is one on which a point on the drum, as it rotates forward, reaches the shoe at the end worked by the hydraulic cylinder before the anchor end. The opposite is a 'Trailing' shoe, and this one has no self servo from the wrapping effect of the rotating drum.

Buying spare parts
and vehicle identification numbers

For modifications, and information applicable to later models, see Supplement at end of manual

Buying spare parts

Spare parts are available from many sources, for example: Datsun garages, other garages and accessory shops, and motor factors. Our advice regarding spare parts is as follows:

Officially appointed Datsun garages – This is the best source of parts which are peculiar to your car and otherwise not generally available (eg complete cylinder heads, internal gearbox components, badges, interior trim etc). It is also the only place at which you should buy parts if your car is still under warranty; non-Datsun components may invalidate the warranty. To be sure of obtaining the correct parts it will always be necessary to give the storeman your car's engine and chassis number, and if possible to take the old part along for positive identification. Remember that many parts are available on a factory exchange scheme – any parts returned should always be clean! It obviously makes good sense to go straight to the specialists on your car for this type of part for they are best equipped to supply you.

Other garages and accessory shops – These are often very good places to buy material and components needed for the maintenance of your car (eg oil filters, spark plugs, bulbs, fan belts, oils and grease, touch-up paint, filler paste etc). They also sell general accessories, usually have convenient opening hours, charge lower prices and can often be found not far from home.

Motor factors – Good factors will stock all of the more important components, (eg pistons, valves, exhaust systems, brake cylinder/pipes/hoses/seals/shoes and pads etc). Motor factors will often provide new or reconditioned components on a part exchange basis – this can save a considerable amount of money.

Vehicle identification numbers

Modifications are a continuing and unpublished process in vehicle manufacture quite apart from major model changes. Spare parts manuals and lists are compiled upon a numerical basis, the individual vehicle numbers being essential to correct identification of the component required.

The car identification number plate is located on the engine bulkhead on the right-hand side (photo).

The engine serial number is stamped on the right-hand side of the cylinder block.

The transmission serial number is stamped into the top face of the transmission casing.

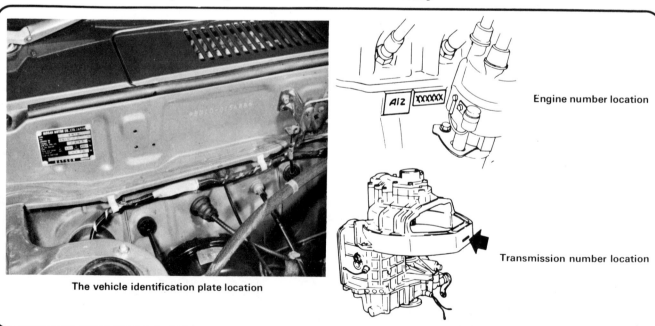

The vehicle identification plate location

Engine number location

Transmission number location

Tools and working facilities

Introduction

A selection of good tools is a fundamental requirement for anyone contemplating the maintenance and repair of a motor vehicle. For the owner who does not possess any, their purchase will prove a considerable expense, offsetting some of the savings made by doing-it-yourself. However, provided that the tools purchased are of good quality, they will last for many years and prove an extremely worthwhile investment.

To help the average owner to decide which tools are needed to carry out the various tasks detailed in this manual, we have compiled three lists of tools under the following headings: *Maintenance and minor repair, Repair and overhaul,* and *Special.* The newcomer to practical mechanics should start off with the *Maintenance and minor repair* tool kit and confine himself to the simpler jobs around the vehicle. Then, as his confidence and experience grow, he can undertake more difficult tasks, buying extra tools as, and when, they are needed. In this way, a *Maintenance and minor repair* tool kit can be built-up into a *Repair and overhaul* tool kit over a considerable period of time without any major cash outlays. The experienced do-it-yourselfer will have a tool kit good enough for most repair and overhaul procedures and will add tools from the *Special* category when he feels the expense is justified by the amount of use these tools will be put to.

It is obviously not possible to cover the subject of tools fully here. For those who wish to learn more about tools and their use there is a book entitled *How to Choose and Use Car Tools* available from the publishers of this manual.

Maintenance and minor repair tool kit

The tools given in this list should be considered as a minimum requirement if routine maintenance, servicing and minor repair operations are to be undertaken. We recommend the purchase of combination spanners (ring one end, open-ended the other); although more expensive than open-ended ones, they do give the advantages of both types of spanner.

> Combination spanners - 6, 7, 8, 9, 10, 11, & 12 mm
> Adjustable spanner - 9 inch
> Transmission filler/level and drain plug key
> Spark plug spanner (with rubber insert)
> Spark plug gap adjustment tool
> Set of feeler gauges
> Brake bleed nipple spanner
> Screwdriver - 4 in long x $\frac{1}{4}$ in dia (flat blade)
> Screwdriver - 4 in long x $\frac{1}{4}$ in dia (cross blade)
> Combination pliers - 6 inch
> Hacksaw (junior)
> Tyre pump
> Tyre pressure gauge
> Oil can
> Fine emery cloth (1 sheet)
> Wire brush (small)
> Funnel (medium size)

Repair and overhaul tool kit

These tools are virtually essential for anyone undertaking any major repairs to a motor vehicle, and are additional to those given in the *Maintenance and minor repair* list. Included in this list is a comprehensive set of sockets. Although these are expensive they will be found invaluable as they are so versatile - particularly if various drives are included in the set. We recommend the $\frac{1}{2}$ in square-drive type, as this can be used with most proprietary torque spanners. If you cannot afford a socket set, even bought piecemeal, then inexpensive tubular box wrenches are a useful alternative.

The tools in this list will occasionally need to be supplemented by tools from the *Special* list.

> Sockets (or box spanners) to cover range in previous list
> Reversible ratchet drive (for use with sockets)
> Extension piece, 10 inch (for use with sockets)
> Universal joint (for use with sockets)
> Torque wrench (for use with sockets)
> Self-grip wrench - 8 inch
> Ball pein hammer
> Soft-faced hammer, plastic or rubber
> Screwdriver - 6 in long x $\frac{5}{16}$ in dia (flat blade)
> Screwdriver - 2 in long x $\frac{5}{16}$ in square (flat blade)
> Screwdriver - 1$\frac{1}{2}$ in long x $\frac{1}{4}$ in dia (cross blade)
> Screwdriver - 3 in long x $\frac{1}{8}$ in dia (electricians)
> Pliers - electricians side cutters
> Pliers - needle nosed
> Pliers - circlip (internal and external)
> Cold chisel - $\frac{1}{2}$ inch
> Scriber (this can be made by grinding the end of a broken hacksaw blade)
> Scraper (this can be made by flattening and sharpening one end of a piece of copper pipe)
> Centre punch
> Pin punch
> Hacksaw
> Valve grinding tool
> Steel rule/straight-edge
> Allen keys
> Selection of files
> Wire brush (large)
> Axle-stands
> Jack (strong scissor or hydraulic type)

Special tools

The tools in this list are those which are not used regularly, are expensive to buy, or which need to be used in accordance with their manufacturers' instructions. Unless relatively difficult mechanical jobs are undertaken frequently, it will not be economic to buy many of these tools. Where this is the case, you could consider clubbing together with friends (or joining a motorists' club) to make a joint purchase, or borrowing the tools against a deposit from a local garage or tool hire specialist.

The following list contains only those tools and instruments freely available to the public, and not those special tools produced by the vehicle manufacturer specifically for its dealer network. You will find occasional references to these manufacturers' special tools in the text of this manual. Generally, an alternative method of doing the job without the vehicle manufacturers' special tool is given. However, sometimes, there is no alternative to using them. Where this is the case and the relevant tool cannot be bought or borrowed you will have to entrust the work to a franchised garage.

> Valve spring compressor
> Piston ring compressor
> Balljoint separator
> Universal hub/bearing puller
> Impact screwdriver

Micrometer and/or vernier gauge
Carburettor flow balancing device (where applicable)
Dial gauge
Stroboscopic timing light
Dwell angle meter/tachometer
Universal electrical multi-meter
Cylinder compression gauge
Lifting tackle (photo)
Trolley jack
Light with extension lead

Buying tools

For practically all tools, a tool dealer is the best source since he will have a very comprehensive range compared with the average garage or accessory shop. Having said that, accessory shops often offer excellent quality tools at discount prices, so it pays to shop around.

Remember, you don't have to buy the most expensive items on the shelf, but it is always advisable to steer clear of the very cheap tools. There are plenty of good tools around at reasonable prices, so ask the proprietor or manager of the shop for advice before making a purchase.

Care and maintenance of tools

Having purchased a reasonable tool kit, it is necessary to keep the tools in a clean serviceable condition. After use, always wipe off any dirt, grease and metal particles using a clean, dry cloth, before putting the tools away. Never leave them lying around after they have been used. A simple tool rack on the garage or workshop wall, for items such as screwdrivers and pliers is a good idea. Store all normal spanners and sockets in a metal box. Any measuring instruments, gauges, meters, etc, must be carefully stored where they cannot be damaged or become rusty.

Take a little care when tools are used. Hammer heads inevitably become marked and screwdrivers lose the keen edge on their blades from time to time. A little timely attention with emery cloth or a file will soon restore items like this to a good serviceable finish.

Working facilities

Not to be forgotten when discussing tools, is the workshop itself. If anything more than routine maintenance is to be carried out, some form of suitable working area becomes essential.

It is appreciated that many an owner mechanic is forced by circumstances to remove an engine or similar item, without the benefit of a garage or workshop. Having done this, any repairs should always be done under the cover of a roof.

Wherever possible, any dismantling should be done on a clean flat workbench or table at a suitable working height.

Any workbench needs a vice: one with a jaw opening of 4 in (100 mm) is suitable for most jobs. As mentioned previously, some clean dry storage space is also required for tools, as well as the lubricants, cleaning fluids, touch-up paints and so on which become necessary.

Another item which may be required, and which has a much more general usage, is an electric drill with a chuck capacity of at least $\frac{5}{16}$ in (8 mm). This, together with a good range of twist drills, is virtually essential for fitting accessories such as wing mirrors and reversing lights.

Last, but not least, always keep a supply of old newspapers and clean, lint-free rags available, and try to keep any working area as clean as possible.

Spanner jaw gap comparison table

Jaw gap (in)	Spanner size
0.250	$\frac{1}{4}$ in AF
0.276	7 mm
0.313	$\frac{5}{16}$ in AF
0.315	8 mm
0.344	$\frac{11}{32}$ in AF; $\frac{1}{8}$ in Whitworth
0.354	9 mm
0.375	$\frac{3}{8}$ in AF
0.394	10 mm
0.433	11 mm
0.438	$\frac{7}{16}$ in AF

Jaw gap (in)	Spanner size
0.445	$\frac{3}{16}$ in Whitworth; $\frac{1}{4}$ in BSF
0.472	12 mm
0.500	$\frac{1}{2}$ in AF
0.512	13 mm
0.525	$\frac{1}{4}$ in Whitworth; $\frac{5}{16}$ in BSF
0.551	14 mm
0.563	$\frac{9}{16}$ in AF
0.591	15 mm
0.600	$\frac{5}{16}$ in Whitworth; $\frac{3}{8}$ in BSF
0.625	$\frac{5}{8}$ in AF
0.630	16 mm
0.669	17 mm
0.686	$\frac{11}{16}$ in AF
0.709	18 mm
0.710	$\frac{3}{8}$ in Whitworth, $\frac{7}{16}$ in BSF
0.748	19 mm
0.750	$\frac{3}{4}$ in AF
0.813	$\frac{13}{16}$ in AF
0.820	$\frac{7}{16}$ in Whitworth; $\frac{1}{2}$ in BSF
0.866	22 mm
0.875	$\frac{7}{8}$ in AF
0.920	$\frac{1}{2}$ in Whitworth; $\frac{9}{16}$ in BSF
0.938	$\frac{15}{16}$ in AF
0.945	24 mm
1.000	1 in AF
1.010	$\frac{9}{16}$ in Whitworth; $\frac{5}{8}$ in BSF
1.024	26 mm
1.063	$1\frac{1}{16}$ in AF; 27 mm
1.100	$\frac{5}{8}$ in Whitworth; $\frac{11}{16}$ in BSF
1.125	$1\frac{1}{8}$ in AF
1.181	30 mm
1.200	$\frac{11}{16}$ in Whitworth; $\frac{3}{4}$ in BSF
1.250	$1\frac{1}{4}$ in AF
1.260	32 mm
1.300	$\frac{3}{4}$ in Whitworth; $\frac{7}{8}$ in BSF
1.313	$1\frac{5}{16}$ in AF
1.390	$\frac{13}{16}$ in Whitworth; $\frac{15}{16}$ in BSF
1.417	36 mm
1.438	$1\frac{7}{16}$ in AF
1.480	$\frac{7}{8}$ in Whitworth; 1 in BSF
1.500	$1\frac{1}{2}$ in AF
1.575	40 mm; $\frac{15}{16}$ in Whitworth
1.614	41 mm
1.625	$1\frac{5}{8}$ in AF
1.670	1 in Whitworth; $1\frac{1}{8}$ in BSF
1.688	$1\frac{11}{16}$ in AF
1.811	46 mm
1.813	$1\frac{13}{16}$ in AF
1.860	$1\frac{1}{8}$ in Whitworth; $1\frac{1}{4}$ in BSF

A Haltrac hoist and gantry in use during a typical engine removal sequence

Jacking and towing

Jacking points

The pantograph type jack (photo), supplied with the car when new, is designed to be used at the four lifting positions shown in the illustration. Other types of jack should be located below the front crossmember or centrally at the rear where indicated.

The axle stand supporting locations are also shown and it is most important that these be used whenever repair work is being carried out under the vehicle.

Use only the lifting points shown, as no other positions are suitable. Always jack the car up on firm level ground and chock a wheel on the opposite side to that being worked on, in front and behind it.

Towing points

If the vehicle is to be towed, first ensure that the tow-rope is adequate for the job and then only attach it to the front tow hooks. Ensure that the steering is unlocked, and also check that the gear lever is in the neutral position. Remember that increased braking effort will be needed if the engine is not running.

Rear tow hooks are not fitted; the eyes at the rear are lash-down points (photo) and are only meant for securing the vehicle on a transporter or similar.

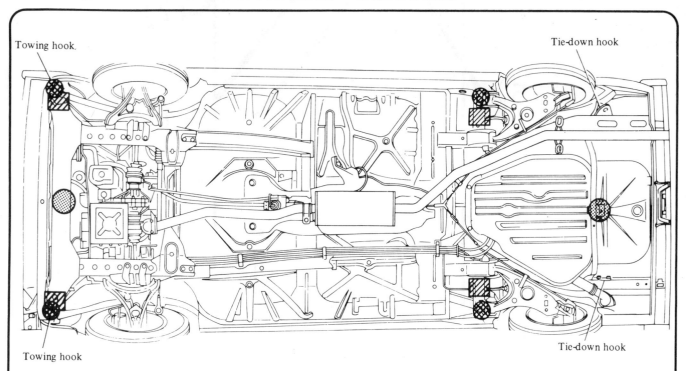

Underside of vehicle showing jacking and towing eye locations front and rear

 : Jack-up point for pantograph jack   : Jack-up point for garage jack   : Supportable point for safety stand

The pantograph jack in position

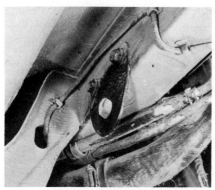

Rear lash-down eye is not meant for towing

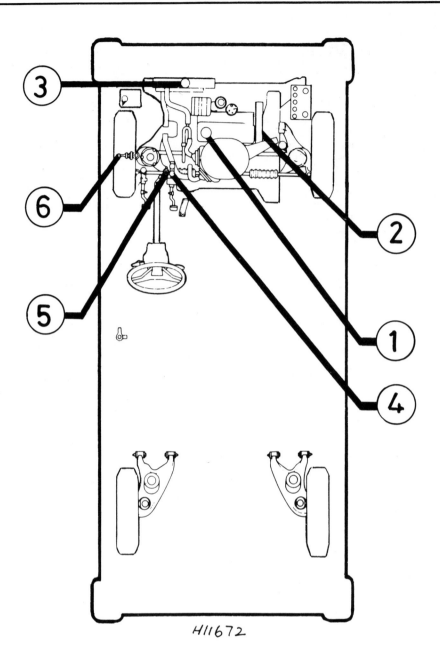

H11672

Recommended lubricants and fluids

Component or system	Lubricant type or specification	Castrol product
1 Engine	Multigrade engine oil	**GTX**
2 Manual transmission	Hypoid gear oil SAE 80 EP	**Hypoy Light**
2 Automatic transmission	ATF Dexron® type	**TQ Dexron® II**
3 Engine coolant	Antifreeze to BS 3151	**Anti-freeze**
4 Brake hydraulic fluid	Hydraulic fluid to DOT 3	**Universal Brake and Clutch Fluid**
5 Steering gear (manual) .... Power steering	Hypoid gear oil SAE 80 EP ATF Dexron® type	**Hypoy Light** **TQ Dexron® II**
6 Wheel bearings	Multi-purpose grease	**LM grease**

Safety first!

Professional motor mechanics are trained in safe working procedures. However enthusiastic you may be about getting on with the job in hand, do take the time to ensure that your safety is not put at risk. A moment's lack of attention can result in an accident, as can failure to observe certain elementary precautions.

There will always be new ways of having accidents, and the following points do not pretend to be a comprehensive list of all dangers; they are intended rather to make you aware of the risks and to encourage a safety-conscious approach to all work you carry out on your vehicle.

Essential DOs and DON'Ts

DON'T rely on a single jack when working underneath the vehicle. Always use reliable additional means of support, such as axle stands, securely placed under a part of the vehicle that you know will not give way.

DON'T attempt to loosen or tighten high-torque nuts (e.g. wheel hub nuts) while the vehicle is on a jack; it may be pulled off.

DON'T start the engine without first ascertaining that the transmission is in neutral (or 'Park' where applicable) and the parking brake applied.

DON'T suddenly remove the filler cap from a hot cooling system — cover it with a cloth and release the pressure gradually first, or you may get scalded by escaping coolant.

DON'T attempt to drain oil until you are sure it has cooled sufficiently to avoid scalding you.

DON'T grasp any part of the engine, exhaust or catalytic converter without first ascertaining that it is sufficiently cool to avoid burning you.

DON'T syphon toxic liquids such as fuel, brake fluid or antifreeze by mouth, or allow them to remain on your skin.

DON'T inhale brake lining dust — it is injurious to health.

DON'T allow any spilt oil or grease to remain on the floor — wipe it up straight away, before someone slips on it.

DON'T use ill-fitting spanners or other tools which may slip and cause injury.

DON'T attempt to lift a heavy component which may be beyond your capability — get assistance.

DON'T rush to finish a job, or take unverified short cuts.

DON'T allow children or animals in or around an unattended vehicle.

DO wear eye protection when using power tools such as drill, sander, bench grinder etc, and when working under the vehicle.

DO use a barrier cream on your hands prior to undertaking dirty jobs — it will protect your skin from infection as well as making the dirt easier to remove afterwards; but make sure your hands aren't left slippery.

DO keep loose clothing (cuffs, tie etc) and long hair well out of the way of moving mechanical parts.

DO remove rings, wristwatch etc, before working on the vehicle — especially the electrical system.

DO ensure that any lifting tackle used has a safe working load rating adequate for the job.

DO keep your work area tidy — it is only too easy to fall over articles left lying around.

DO get someone to check periodically that all is well, when working alone on the vehicle.

DO carry out work in a logical sequence and check that everything is correctly assembled and tightened afterwards.

DO remember that your vehicle's safety affects that of yourself and others. If in doubt on any point, get specialist advice.

IF, in spite of following these precautions, you are unfortunate enough to injure yourself, seek medical attention as soon as possible.

Fire

Remember at all times that petrol (gasoline) is highly flammable. Never smoke, or have any kind of naked flame around, when working on the vehicle. But the risk does not end there — a spark caused by an electrical short-circuit, by two metal surfaces contacting each other, or even by static electricity built up in your body under certain conditions, can ignite petrol vapour, which in a confined space is highly explosive.

Always disconnect the battery earth (ground) terminal before working on any part of the fuel system, and never risk spilling fuel on to a hot engine or exhaust.

It is recommended that a fire extinguisher of a type suitable for fuel and electrical fires is kept handy in the garage or workplace at all times. Never try to extinguish a fuel or electrical fire with water.

Fumes

Certain fumes are highly toxic and can quickly cause unconsciousness and even death if inhaled to any extent. Petrol (gasoline) vapour comes into this category, as do the vapours from certain solvents such as trichloroethylene. Any draining or pouring of such volatile fluids should be done in a well ventilated area.

When using cleaning fluids and solvents, read the instructions carefully. Never use materials from unmarked containers — they may give off poisonous vapours.

Never run the engine of a motor vehicle in an enclosed space such as a garage. Exhaust fumes contain carbon monoxide which is extremely poisonous; if you need to run the engine, always do so in the open air or at least have the rear of the vehicle outside the workplace.

If you are fortunate enough to have the use of an inspection pit, never drain or pour petrol, and never run the engine, while the vehicle is standing over it; the fumes, being heavier than air, will concentrate in the pit with possibly lethal results.

The battery

Never cause a spark, or allow a naked light, near the vehicle's battery. It will normally be giving off a certain amount of hydrogen gas, which is highly explosive.

Always disconnect the battery earth (ground) terminal before working on the fuel or electrical systems.

If possible, loosen the filler plugs or cover when charging the battery from an external source. Do not charge at an excessive rate or the battery may burst.

Take care when topping up and when carrying the battery. The acid electrolyte, even when diluted, is very corrosive and should not be allowed to contact the eyes or skin.

If you ever need to prepare electrolyte yourself, always add the acid slowly to the water, and never the other way round. Protect against splashes by wearing rubber gloves and goggles.

Mains electricity

When using an electric power tool, inspection light etc which works from the mains, always ensure that the appliance is correctly connected to its plug and that, where necessary, it is properly earthed (grounded). Do not use such appliances in damp conditions and, again, beware of creating a spark or applying excessive heat in the vicinity of fuel or fuel vapour.

Ignition HT voltage

A severe electric shock can result from touching certain parts of the ignition system, such as the HT leads, when the engine is running or being cranked, particularly if components are damp or the insulation is defective. Where an electronic ignition system is fitted, the HT voltage is much higher and could prove fatal.

Routine maintenance

For modifications, and information applicable to later models, see Supplement at end of manual

Maintenance is essential for ensuring safety and desirable for the purpose of getting the best in terms of performance and economy from the car. Over the years the need for periodic lubrication – oiling, greasing and so on – has been drastically reduced if not totally eliminated. This has unfortunately tended to lead some owners to think that because no such action is required, the items either no longer exist, or will last for ever. This is certainly not the case and it is essential to carry out regular visual examination as comprehensively as possible in order to spot any possible defects at an early stage before they develop into major and expensive repairs.

The maintenance information given in this Section is not of a detailed nature. Further information is to be found in the appropriate Chapters throughout this manual.

Cleanliness

Whenever you do any work allow time for cleaning. When something is in pieces or components removed to improve access to other areas, give an opportunity for a thorough clean. This cleanliness will allow you to cope with a crisis on the road without getting yourself dirty. During bigger jobs when you expect a bit of dirt it is less extreme and can be tolerated at least whilst removing a component. When an item is being taken to pieces there is less risk of ruinous grit finding its way inside. The act of cleaning focuses your attention onto parts and you are more likely to spot trouble. Dirt on the ignition components is a common cause of poor starting. Large areas such as the engine compartment, inner wings or bulkhead should be brushed thoroughly with grease solvent, allowed to soak and then very carefully hosed down. Water in the wrong places, particularly the carburettor or electrical components, will do more harm than dirt. Use petrol or paraffin and a small paintbrush to clean the more inaccessible places.

Waste disposal

Old oil and cleaning paraffin must be destroyed. Although it makes a good base for a bonfire the practice is dangerous. It is also illegal to dispose of oil and paraffin down domestic drains. By buying your new engine oil in one gallon cans you can refill them with old oil and take them to the local garage who have facilities for disposal.

Long journeys

Before taking the car on long journeys, particularly such trips as continental holidays, make sure that the car is given a thorough check in the form of the next service due, plus a full visual inspection well in advance so that any faults found can be rectified in time.

Service intervals

The service intervals are those recommended by the manufacturer. They are necessarily something of a compromise since no two vehicles operate under identical conditions. Stop-start driving, especially in dusty conditions or in climatic extremes, takes a heavier toll of the vehicle components than highway cruising. The style and sensitivity of the driver also has an important influence.

It will be noted that the major service intervals differ for UK and North American models. This may be more a reflection of market forces than of different driving habits or lubricant qualities. The home mechanic, who does not have the cost of his or her labour to consider, may be well advised to adopt shorter intervals than those specified.

Every 250 miles (400 km) or weekly – whichever comes first

With the car standing on level ground, check the oil level on the dipstick. If necessary, top up through the filler neck in the rocker cover (photo). Do not overfill.

Check the radiator coolant level and top up if necessary.

Check the battery electrolyte levels and top up if necessary as given in Chapter 10.

Check the tyre pressures (photo), including the spare, and if necessary adjust the pressures to those specified in Chapter 8.

Examine the tyres for wear or damage.

Check the brake hydraulic fluid reservoir fluid level(s) and top up if necessary, using only the recommended fluid type. Do not allow dirt to enter the system and wash any fluid spillage from surrounding paintwork and fittings (photo).

Check that all lights work at the front and rear.

Check the windscreen wipers for correct operation, and the washer fluid level in the reservoir – top up if necessary (photo).

Check that the horns operate.

Every 6000 miles (10 000 km) – UK model, or 7500 models (12 000 km) – North American models, or six-monthly (whichever comes first)

Engine

Change oil. (If short distance driving, extensive idling or driving in dusty conditions, change oil every 3000 miles) (photo).

Renew engine oil filter (photo).

Clean and check spark plugs.

Check distributor cap, rotor and contact points/air gap as applicable (photo).

Lubricate distributor shaft and cam.

Check and if necessary adjust the ignition timing (see Chapter 4).

Check drive belts for cracks, fraying, wear and correct tension.

Check battery terminals for security.

Check for coolant, oil and fuel leaks.

Check and if necessary adjust the idle speed and mixture setting as given in Chapter 3.

Transmission

On models fitted with the selective automatic transmission, check the fluid level.

Check clutch adjustment as described in Chapter 5 according to clutch type.

On models fitted with a hydraulic clutch, check and if necessary top up the hydraulic fluid level in the reservoir.

On models fitted with manual transmission, check and if necessary adjust the oil level.

Brakes

Examine disc pads and drum shoes for wear. Renew if necessary.

Examine all hydraulic pipes, hoses and unions for chafing, cor-

Topping up the engine oil level (A10 engine)

Check the tyre pressures

Check the hydraulic fluid level in the reservoir

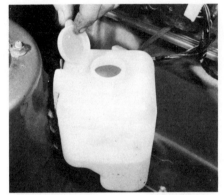
Check the windscreen washer fluid level

The engine oil drain plug in the sump

Renew the oil filter

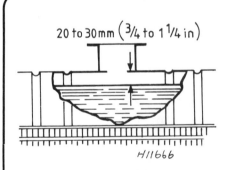
20 to 30mm (3/4 to 1 1/4 in)

H11666

Correct radiator coolant level

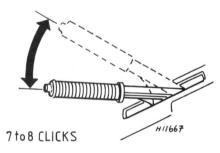
7 to 8 CLICKS

H11667

Check the handbrake efficiency

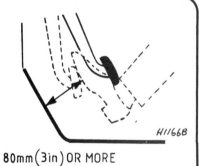
80mm (3in) OR MORE

H11668

Check the brake pedal free travel

APPROXIMATELY 15mm (1/2 in)

H11669

Check the clutch pedal free play

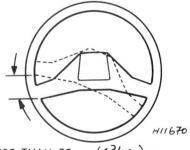
LESS THAN 35mm (1 3/8 in)

H11670

Check the steering wheel for excessive play

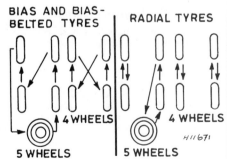
BIAS AND BIAS-BELTED TYRES   RADIAL TYRES

4 WHEELS   4 WHEELS

5 WHEELS   5 WHEELS

H11671

Rotate the tyre positions to even out the wear

Check and if necessary adjust the distributor contact points gap

Check cooling system hoses for condition and security

Transmission/final drive oil drain plug

Transmission/final drive oil filler/level plug

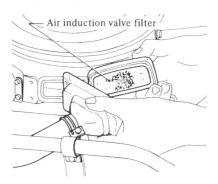

Renew the air induction filter (if fitted)

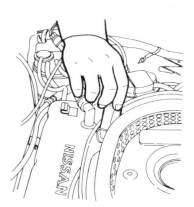

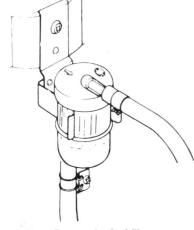

Renew the fuel filter

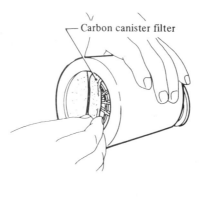

Renew the carbon canister filter

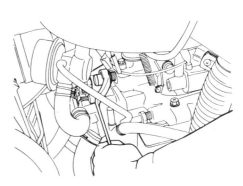

Renew the PCV filter and valve

rosion or dents. Check for any signs of leaks.
Check brake pedal and handbrake adjustments as given in Chapter 9.

General maintenance

Make a general check of the steering and suspension components for signs of wear or damage, also the driveshaft gaiters.
Check the roadwheel retaining nuts for security.
Lubricate the door locks and hinges, also the bonnet and boot lid/rear door/hatchback hinges and locks, also the release cables as applicable.

Every 12 000 miles (20 000 km) or annually, whichever comes first – UK models

---

In addition to, or instead of, the items specified in the previous Schedule:

Engine

Check and adjust the valve clearances – refer to Chapter 1.
Check the tension and condition of all drivebelts as applicable and adjust or renew as necessary.
Check all cooling system hoses and connections for security and signs of leaks (photo).
Renew and adjust the distributor contact points (Chapter 4).
Renew the spark plugs.
Inspect the condition of the positive crankcase ventilation (PCV) system, the details of which are given in Chapter 1.

Brakes

Change the brake fluid (Chapter 9).
Check the brake system for lining wear and/or hydraulic leaks.

Steering and suspension

Check all steering assembly components and joints for signs of excessive wear and insecurity.

Check the front wheel alignment.
Inspect the suspension components and bushes for signs of excessive wear or damage.
Interchange the wheel/tyre positions if wished to even out the wear.

General

Check the seat belts for defects and the anchorage points for security.

Every 15 000 miles (24 000 km) or annually, whichever comes first – North American models

In addition to, or instead of, the items specified in the 7500-mile and the UK 12 000-mile Schedules:

Emission control system

Refer to Chapter 3 and check the choke plate setting and linkage.
Check the operation of the automatic temperature control air cleaner.
Inspect the various vacuum hoses and fittings for security and condition.

Steering

Inspect the power steering lines and hoses for condition and security.
Check the power steering fluid level in the reservoir and top up if necessary with new fluid of the specified type.

Every 24 000 miles (40 000 km) or two years, whichever comes first – UK models

In addition to, or instead of, the items specified in the 6000-mile and 12 000-mile Schedules:

Engine

Renew the carburettor air filter, referring to Chapter 3.
Inspect all fuel lines and hoses for security, condition and signs of leakage.
Renew the fuel filter.
Renew the cooling system antifreeze mixture (see Chapter 2).
Clean and inspect the ignition system HT and LT wiring and connections.

Transmission

Renew the transmission oil/fluid (manual/automatic) (photos).

Brakes

Inspect the brake servo hoses and connections for condition and security, also the check valve.

Driveshafts

Check the driveshafts for security and signs of wear.

Steering

Dismantle, clean and repack the front wheel bearings with grease. Reassemble and adjust the bearing endplay, referring to Chapter 11 for details. Renew the bearings if worn or damaged.

Every 30 000 miles (48 000 km) or two years, whichever comes first – North American models

In addition to, or instead of, the items specified in the previous Schedules

Air conditioning

Check the respective air conditioning system hoses and connections for condition and security. Where renewal is found to be necessary, entrust the task to your Datsun dealer or a refrigeration engineer – see Chapter 10 for further details and precautions.

Emission control system

Renew the air induction valve or air pump filter. In dusty driving conditions this filter should be renewed at more frequent intervals.
Renew the positive crankcase ventilation (PCV) filter, and valve.
Check all fuel and vapour lines for condition and security.
Renew the carbon canister filter.
Check all vacuum and ventilation hoses for condition and security.

Every 48 000 miles (80 000 km) or four years, whichever comes first (all models)

Braking system

Renew all rubber seals and flexible hoses in the braking system components (if not previously done during maintenance or repair work).

Fault diagnosis

Introduction

The car owner who does his or her own maintenance according to the recommended schedules should not have to use this section of the manual very often. Modern component reliability is such that, provided those items subject to wear or deterioration are inspected or renewed at the specified intervals, sudden failure is comparatively rare. Faults do not usually just happen as a result of sudden failure, but develop over a period of time. Major mechanical failures in particular are usually preceded by characteristic symptoms over hundreds or even thousands of miles. Those components which do occasionally fail without warning are often small and easily carried in the car.

With any fault finding, the first step is to decide where to begin investigations. Sometimes this is obvious, but on other occasions a little detective work will be necessary. The owner who makes half a dozen haphazard adjustments or replacements may be successful in curing a fault (or its symptoms), but he will be none the wiser if the fault recurs and he may well have spent more time and money than was necessary. A calm and logical approach will be found to be more satisfactory in the long run. Always take into account any warning signs or abnormalities that may have been noticed in the period preceding the fault – power loss, high or low gauge readings, unusual noises or smells, etc – and remember that failure of components such as fuses or spark plugs may only be pointers to some underlying fault.

The pages which follow here are intended to help in cases of failure to start or breakdown on the road. There is also a Fault Diagnosis Section at the end of each Chapter which should be consulted if the preliminary checks prove unfruitful. Whatever the fault, certain basic principles apply. These are as follows:

Verify the fault. This is simply a matter of being sure that you know what the symptoms are before starting work. This is particularly important if you are investigating a fault for someone else who may not have described it very accurately.

Don't overlook the obvious. For example, if the car won't start, is there petrol in the tank? (Don't take anyone else's word on this particular point, and don't trust the fuel gauge either!) If an electrical fault is indicated, look for loose or broken wires before digging out the test gear.

Cure the disease, not the symptom. Substituting a flat battery with a fully charged one will get you off the hard shoulder, but if the underlying cause is not attended to, the new battery will go the same way. Similarly, changing oil-fouled spark plugs for a new set will get you moving again, but remember that the reason for the fouling (if it wasn't simply an incorrect grade of plug) will have to be established and corrected.

Don't take anything for granted. Particularly, don't forget that a 'new' component may itself be defective (especially if it's been rattling round in the boot for months), and don't leave components out of a fault diagnosis sequence just because they are new or recently fitted. When you do finally diagnose a difficult fault, you'll probably realise that all the evidence was there from the start.

Electrical faults

Electrical faults can be more puzzling than straightforward mechanical failures, but they are no less susceptible to logical analysis if the basic principles of operation are understood. Car electrical wiring exists in extremely unfavourable conditions – heat, vibration and chemical attack – and the first things to look for are loose or corroded connections and broken or chafed wires, especially where the wires pass through holes in the bodywork or are subject to vibration.

All metal-bodied cars in current production have one terminal of the battery 'earthed', ie connected to the car bodywork, and in nearly all modern cars it is the negative (–) terminal. The various electrical components motors, bulb holders etc – are also connected to earth, either by means of a lead or directly by their mountings. Electric current flows through the component and then back to the battery via the car bodywork. If the component mounting is loose or corroded, or if a good path back to the battery is not available, the circuit will be incomplete and malfunction will result. The engine and/or gearbox are also earthed by means of flexible metal straps to the body or subframe; if these straps are loose or missing, starter motor, generator and ignition trouble may result.

Assuming the earth return to be satisfactory, electrical faults will be due either to component malfunction or to defects in the current supply. Individual components are dealt with in Chapter 10. If supply wires are broken or cracked internally this results in an open-circuit, and the easiest way to check for this is to bypass the suspect wire temporarily with a length of wire having a crocodile clip or suitable connector at each end. Alternatively, a 12V test lamp can be used to verify the presence of supply voltage at various points along the wire and the break can be thus isolated.

If a bare portion of a live wire touches the car bodywork or other earthed metal part, the electricity will take the low-resistance path thus formed back to the battery: this is known as a short-circuit. Hopefully a short-circuit will blow a fuse, but otherwise it may cause burning of the insulation (and possibly further short-circuits) or even a fire. This is why it is inadvisable to bypass persistently blowing fuses with silver foil or wire.

Spares and tool kit

Most cars are only supplied with sufficient tools for wheel changing; the *Maintenance and minor repair* tool kit detailed in *Tools and working facilities*, with the addition of a hammer, is probably sufficient for those repairs that most motorists would consider attempting at the roadside. In addition a few items which can be fitted without too much trouble in the event of a breakdown should be carried. Experience and available space will modify the list below, but the following may save having to call on professional assistance:

Spark plugs, clean and correctly gapped
HT lead and plug cap
Distributor rotor, condenser and contact breaker points (as applicable)
Drivebelt(s) – emergency type may suffice
Spare fuses
Tyre valve core
Tube of filler paste
Set of principal light bulbs
Tin of radiator sealer and hose bandage
Exhaust bandage
Roll of insulating tape
Length of soft iron wire
Length of electrical flex
Torch or inspection lamp (can double as test lamp)
Battery jump leads
Tow-rope
Ignition waterproofing aerosol
Litre of engine oil
Sealed can of hydraulic fluid
Emergency windscreen

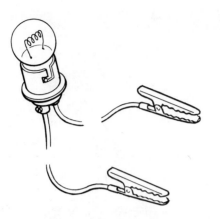

A simple test lamp is useful for tracing electrical faults

If spare fuel is carried, a can designed for the purpose should be used to minimise risks of leakage and collision damage. A first aid kit and a warning triangle, whilst not at present compulsory in the UK, are obviously sensible items to carry in addition to the above.

When touring abroad it may be advisable to carry additional spares which, even if you cannot fit them yourself, could save having to wait while parts are obtained. The items below may be worth considering:

Clutch and throttle cables (as applicable)
Cylinder head gasket
Alternator brushes
Fuel pump repair kit

One of the motoring organisations will be able to advise on availability of fuel etc in foreign countries.

Engine will not start

Engine fails to turn when starter operated
Flat battery (recharge, use jump leads, or push start)
Battery terminals loose or corroded
Battery earth to body defective

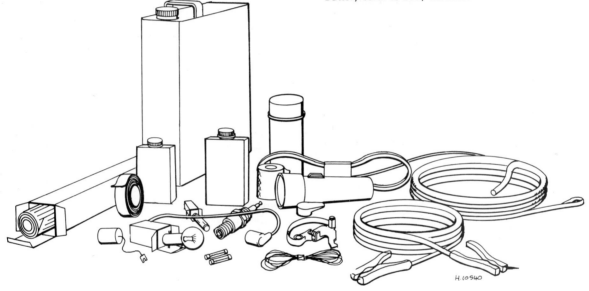

Carrying a few spares can save you a long walk!

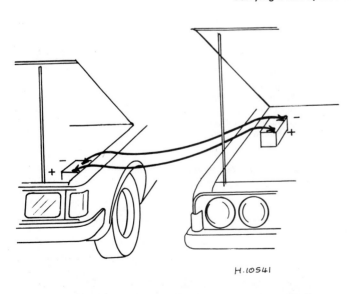

Correct way to connect jump leads. Do not allow car bodies to touch!

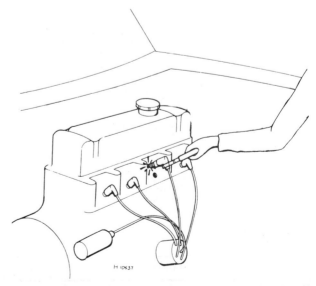

Crank engine and check for spark. Note use of insulated tool!

Check for fuel delivery by looking in carburettor sight glass
(arrowed). Fuel pipe is immediately above

A slack drivebelt can cause overheating and battery charging
problems

Engine earth strap loose or broken
Starter motor (or solenoid) wiring loose or broken
Automatic transmission selector in wrong position, or inhibitor
switch faulty
Ignition/starter switch faulty
Major mechanical failure (seizure) or long disuse (piston rings
rusted to bores)
Starter or solenoid internal fault (see Chapter 10)

Starter motor turns engine slowly
Partially discharged battery (recharge, use jump leads, or push
start)
Battery terminals loose or corroded
Battery earth to body defective
Engine earth strap loose
Starter motor (or solenoid) wiring loose
Starter motor internal fault (see Chapter 10)

Starter motor spins without turning engine
Flywheel gear teeth damaged or worn
Starter motor mounting bolts loose

Engine turns normally but fails to start
Damp or dirty HT leads and distributor cap (crank engine and
check for spark)
Dirty or incorrectly gapped CB points (if applicable)
No fuel in tank (check for delivery at carburettor) (photo)
Excessive choke (hot engine) or insufficient choke (cold engine)
Fouled or incorrectly gapped spark plugs (remove, clean and
regap)
Other ignition system fault (see Chapter 4)
Other fuel system fault (see Chapter 3)
Poor compression (see Chapter 1)
Major mechanical failure (eg camshaft drive)

Engine fires but will not run
Insufficient choke (cold engine)
Air leaks at carburettor or inlet manifold
Fuel starvation (see Chapter 3)
Ballast resistor defective, or other ignition fault (see Chapter 4)

Engine cuts out and will not restart

Engine cuts out suddenly – ignition fault
Loose or disconnected LT wires

Wet HT leads or distributor cap (after traversing water splash)
Coil or condenser failure (check for spark)
Other ignition fault (see Chapter 4)

Engine misfires before cutting out – fuel fault
Fuel tank empty
Fuel pump defective or filter blocked (check for delivery)
Fuel tank filler vent blocked (suction will be evident on releasing
cap)
Carburettor needle valve sticking
Carburettor jets blocked (fuel contaminated)
Other fuel system fault (see Chapter 3)

Engine cuts out – other causes
Serious overheating
Major mechanical failure (eg camshaft drive)

Engine overheats

Ignition (no-charge) warning light illuminated
Slack or broken drivebelt (photo) – retension or renew (Chapter 2)

Ignition warning light not illuminated
Coolant loss due to internal or external leakage (see Chapter 2)
Thermostat defective
Low oil level
Brakes binding
Radiator clogged externally or internally
Electric cooling fan not operating correctly
Engine waterways clogged
Ignition timing incorrect or automatic advance malfunctioning
Mixture too weak

Note: *Do not add cold water to an overheated engine or damage may
result*

Low engine oil pressure

Gauge reads low or warning light illuminated with engine running
Oil level low or incorrect grade
Defective gauge or sender unit
Wire to sender unit earthed
Engine overheating

Oil filter clogged or bypass valve defective
Oil pressure relief valve defective
Oil pick-up strainer clogged
Oil pump worn or mountings loose
Worn main or big-end bearings

Note: *Low oil pressure in a high-mileage engine at tickover is not ncessarily a cause for concern. Sudden pressure loss at speed is far more significant. In any event, check the gauge or warning light sender before condemning the engine.*

Engine noises

Pre-ignition (pinking) on acceleration
Incorrect grade of fuel
Ignition timing incorrect
Distributor faulty or worn
Worn or maladjusted carburettor
Excessive carbon build-up in engine

Whistling or wheezing noises
Leaking vacuum hose
Leaking carburettor or manifold gasket
Blowing head gasket

Tapping or rattling
Incorrect valve clearances
Worn valve gear
Worn timing chain
Broken piston ring (ticking noise)

Knocking or thumping
Unintentional mechanical contact (eg fan blades)
Worn fanbelt
Peripheral component fault (generator, water pump etc)
Worn big-end bearings (regular heavy knocking, perhaps less under load)
Worn main bearings (rumbling and knocking, perhaps worsening under load)
Piston slap (most noticeable when cold)

Chapter 1 Engine

For modifications, and information applicable to later models, see Supplement at end of manual

Contents

Specifications

General

Engine type ....

Four-cylinder in line (Transverse), overhead valve with pushrod operation, water-cooled

Engine designation:
    UK models ....

A10 and A12

    USA models ....

A14 and A15

Engine data:

	A10	A12	A14	A15
Capacity cc (cu in)	998 (60.3)	1171 (71.5)	1397 (85.24)	1488 (90.80)
Bore in (mm)	2.87 (73.0)	2.87 (73.0)	2.99 (76.0)	2.99 (76.0)
Stroke in (mm)	2.32 (59.0)	2.76 (70.0)	3.03 (77.0)	3.22 (82.0)
Compression ratio:				
All except California models	9.0 to 1	9.0 to 1	8.5 to 1	8.9 to 1
California models	–	–	8.9 to 1	–

Firing order 1-3-4-2

Location of No 1 cylinder .... Timing cover end

Lubrication system

Type .... Pressure feed

Engine oil capacity:
    With filter .... 5.75 Imp pint (3.2 litre 7.75 US pint)
    Less filter .... 4.750 Imp pint (2.7 litre 5.75 US pint)

Filter .... Canister – disposable type

Oil pump .... Rotor, camshaft gear driven

Oil pressure:
    At idle speed .... 11 lbf/in^2 (0.8 kgf/cm^2)
    At 3000 rpm .... 54 to 74 lbf/in^2 (3.8 to 5.2 kgf/cm^2)

Oil pressure relief valve spring free length .... 1.712 in (43.49 mm)

Oil pump tolerances:
    Rotor side clearance:
        Standard .... 0.002 to 0.004 in (0.05 to 0.12 mm)
        Wear limit .... 0.0078 in (0.20 mm)
    Rotor tip clearance:
        Standard .... Less than 0.0047 in (0.12 mm)
        Wear limit .... 0.0078 in (0.20 mm)
    Body-to-outer rotor clearance:
        Standard .... 0.0059 to 0.0083 in (0.15 to 0.21 mm)
        Wear limit .... 0.0196 in (0.050 mm)
    Body-to-rotor gap:
        Standard .... 0.002 in (0.05 mm)
        Wear limit .... 0.0078 in (0.20 mm)

Cylinder head

Surface flatness (maximum limit) .... 0.004 in (0.10 mm)
Resurfacing limit .... 0.008 in (0.20 mm)

Valves

Valve clearances:
    Inlet and exhaust (cold) .... 0.010 in (0.25 mm)
    Inlet and exhaust (hot) .... 0.014 in (0.35 mm)

Valve head diameter – in (mm):	Inlet	Exhaust
A10, A12 and A14 engines	1.457 to 1.465 (37.0 to 37.2)	1.181 to 1.189 (30.0 to 30.2)
A15 engine	1.378 (35.0)	1.181 (30.0)
Valve stem diameter – in (mm):		
A10, A12 and A14 engines	0.3138 to 0.3144 (7.97 to 7.98)	0.3128 to 0.3134 (7.94 to 7.96)
A15 engine	0.3130 to 0.3140 (7.96 to 7.97)	0.3128 to 0.3134 (7.94 to 7.96)

Valve length (inlet and exhaust) – in (mm):
    A10 and A12 engines .... 4.030 to 4.041 (102.3 to 102.6)
    A14 engine .... 4.079 to 4.094 (103.6 to 104.0)
    A15 engine .... 3.917 to 3.937 (99.5 to 100.0)
Valve spring free length:
    A10 engine 1.799 (45.7)
    A12, A14 and A15 engines 1.831 (46.5)

Valve guides

Length – in (mm):
    A10, A12 and A14 (except California) engines 1.929 (49.0)
    A14 (California) engine 2.090 (53.0)
Fitted height from head surface – in (mm) 0.709 (18.0)
Inner diameter – in (mm) .... 0.3150 to 0.3156 (8.00 to 8.01)
Outer diameter – in (mm) .... 0.481 to 0.482 (12.23 to 12.24)
Guide-to-stem clearance – in (mm):
    Inlet .... 0.0006 to 0.0018 (0.015 to 0.045) ± 0.004 (0.1)
    Exhaust .... 0.0016 to 0.0028 (0.040 to 0.070) ± 0.004 (0.1)

Valve seats

Valve seat angle (all engines) .... 45°30'

Valve seat width – in (mm):	Inlet	Exhaust
A10 and A12 engines	0.051 (1.3)	0.071 (1.8)
A14 engine	0.059 (1.5)	0.059 (1.5)
A15 engine	0.059 (1.5)	0.075 (1.9)

Cylinder block

	A10 and A12	A14 and A15
Bore diameter – in (mm)	2.874 to 2.876 (73.000 to 73.050)	2.9921 to 2.9941 (76.000 to 76.050)
Bore wear limit – in (mm)	0.008 (0.20)	0.008 (0.20)
Maximum allowable bore ovality – in (mm)	0.006 (0.015)	0.008 (0.20)
Surface flatness (maximum limit) – in (mm)	0.004 (0.10)	0.004 (0.10)

Pistons

Diameter – in (mm):	A10 and A12	A14 and A15
Standard	2.8735 to 2.8755 (72.987 to 73.037)	2.9908 to 2.9927 (75.967 to 76.017)
Oversize (0.50)	2.8924 to 2.8944 (73.467 to 73.517)	3.0105 to 3.0124 (76.467 to 76.517)
Oversize (1.00)	2.9121 to 2.9140 (73.967 to 74.017)	3.0301 to 3.0321 (76.967 to 77.017)
Oversize (1.50)	2.9318 to 2.9337 (74.467 to 74.517)	–

Piston rings

Number	Two compression and one oil control

	A10 and A12	A14 and A15
Side clearance – in (mm):		
Top ring	0.0016 to 0.0028 (0.04 to 0.07)	0.0016 to 0.0028 (0.04 to 0.07)
2nd ring	0.0016 to 0.0028 (0.04 to 0.07)	0.0012 to 0.0024 (0.03 to 0.06)
Oil ring	0.0118 to 0.0354 (0.30 to 0.90)	Combined ring
Ring gap – in (mm):		
Top ring	0.0079 to 0.0138 (0.20 to 0.35)	0.0079 to 0.0138 (0.20 to 0.35)
2nd ring	0.0079 to 0.0138 (0.20 to 0.35)	0.0059 to 0.0118 (0.15 to 0.30)
Oil ring	0.0118 to 0.0354 (0.30 to 0.90)	0.0118 to 0.0354 (0.30 to 0.90)

Gudgeon pin

	A10 and A12	A14 and A15
Diameter – in (mm)	0.6869 to 0.6871 (17.447 to 17.452)	0.7478 to 0.7480 (18.995 to 19.000)
Clearance in piston at 20°C (68°F) – in (mm)	0.00004 to 0.00051 (0.001 to 0.013)	0.0003 to 0.0005 (0.008 to 0.012)
Interference fit in connecting rod – in (mm)	0.0008 (0.020)	0.0007 to 0.014 (0.017 to 0.035)

Connecting rods and big-end bearings

Bearng thickness – in (mm)	0.0591 to 0.0594 (1.500 to 1.508)
Big-end endplay	0.008 to 0.012 (0.2 to 0.3)
Endplay wear limit – in (mm)	0.016 (0.40)
Big-end clearance – in (mm)	0.0008 to 0.0020 (0.020 to 0.050)
Weight difference between rods	0.18 oz (5 g) maximum

Crankshaft and main bearings

Number of main bearings:	
A10 engine	3
A12, A14 and A15 engines	5
Journal diameter – in (mm)	1.9666 to 1.9671 (49.951 to 49.964)
Main journal ovality (maximum) – in (mm)	0.0004 (0.01)
Crankpin diameter – in (mm)	1.7701 to 1.7706 (44.961 to 44.974)
Maximum crankpin ovality – in (mm):	
A10 and A12	0.0004 (0.01)
A14 and A15	0.0012 (0.03)
Main bearing thickness – in (mm)	0.0719 to 0.0722 (1.827 to 1.835)
Main bearing clearance – in (mm)	0.0008 to 0.0024 (0.020 to 0.062)
Main bearing clearance wear limit – in (mm)	0.0059 (0.15)
Crankshaft endplay – in (mm)	0.0020 to 0.0059 (0.05 to 0.15)
Endplay wear limit – in (mm)	0.0118 (0.30)
Flywheel run-out limit – in (mm)	0.006 (0.15)

Camshaft

	A10	A12	A14/A15
Number of bearings	Five, bored in line	Five, bored in line	Five, bored in line
Endplay – in (mm)	0.0004 to 0.0020 (0.01 to 0.05)	0.0004 to 0.0020 (0.01 to 0.05)	0.0004 to 0.0020 (0.01 to 0.05)
Endplay – in (mm)	0.0039 (0.10)	0.0039 (0.10)	0.0039 (0.10)
Lobe lift – in (mm):			
Intake	0.211 (5.35)	0.222 (5.65)	0.2224 (5.65)
Exhaust	0.211 (5.35)	0.222 (5.65)	0.2331 (5.92)
Journal diameter (standard) – in (mm):			
1st	1.7237 to 1.7242 (43.783 to 43.796)	1.7237 to 1.7242 (43.783 to 43.796)	1.7237 to 1.7242 (43.783 to 43.796)
2nd	1.7041 to 1.7046 (43.283 to 43.296)	1.7041 to 1.7046 (43.283 to 43.296)	1.7041 to 1.7046 (43.283 to 43.296)
3rd	1.6844 to 1.6849 (42.783 to 42.796)	1.6844 to 1.6849 (42.783 to 42.796)	1.6844 to 1.6849 (42.783 to 42.796)
4th	1.6647 to 1.6652 (42.283 to 42.296)	1.6647 to 1.6652 (42.283 to 42.296)	1.6647 to 1.6652 (42.283 to 42.296)
5th	1.6224 to 1.6299 (41.208 to 41.221)	1.6224 to 1.6299 (41.208 to 41.221)	1.6224 to 1.6299 (41.208 to 41.221)
Bearing inner diameter (standard) – in (mm):			
1st	1.7257 to 1.7261 (43.833 to 43.843)	1.7257 to 1.7261 (43.833 to 43.843)	1.7257 to 1.7261 (43.833 to 43.843)
2nd	1.7056 to 1.7060 (43.323 to 43.333)	1.7056 to 1.7060 (43.323 to 43.333)	1.7056 to 1.7060 (43.323 to 43.333)
3rd	1.6865 to 1.6868 (42.836 to 42.846)	1.6865 to 1.6868 (42.836 to 42.846)	1.6865 to 1.6868 (42.836 to 42.846)

4th	1.6663 to 1.6667 (42.323 to 42.333)	1.6663 to 1.6667 (42.323 to 42.333)	1.6663 to 1.6667 (42.323 to 42.333)
5th	1.6242 to 1.6247 (41.258 to 41.268)	1.6264 to 1.6247 (41.258 to 41.268)	1.6242 to 1.6247 (41.258 to 41.268)
Camshaft sprocket runout limit – in (mm)	0.006 (0.15)	0.006 (0.15)	0.006 (0.15)
Timing chain type	Double roller	Double roller	Double roller

Torque wrench settings

	lbf ft	kgf m
Cylinder head bolts:		
A10	43 to 47	6 to 6.5
A12, A14 and A15	51 to 54	7 to 7.5
Rocker shaft pillar bolts	14 to 18	2 to 2.5
Connecting rod big-end nuts:		
A10	22 to 26	3 to 3.6
A12, A14 and A15	23 to 27	3.2 to 3.8
Flywheel bolts:		
A10	41 to 43	5.6 to 6
A12	47 to 54	6.5 to 7.5
A14 and A15	58 to 65	8.0 to 9.0
Main bearing cap bolts	36 to 43	5 to 6
Camshaft sprocket bolt	29 to 35	4 to 4.8
Oil sump bolts:		
A10 and A12	11 to 14	1.5 to 2
A14 and A15	3 to 4	0.4 to 0.6
Oil pump bolts	7 to 10	0.9 to 1.4
Sump drain plug	14 to 22	2 to 3
Camshaft plate bolts	3 to 4	0.4 to 0.5
Water pump bolts	7 to 10	0.9 to 1.4
Timing chain cover bolts	4 to 5	0.5 to 0.7
Crankshaft pulley bolt	108 to 145	15 to 20
Engine mounting bolts	14 to 18	1.9 to 2.5
Locating plate bolt	3.6 to 5.8	0.5 to 0.8
Manifold nut	6.5 to 10	0.9 to 1.4
Front cover bolts	3.6 to 5.1	0.5 to 0.7
Valve rocker adjustment nuts	12 to 16	1.6 to 2.2

1 General description

The engine fitted to the UK market models is either the A10 series of 998 cc or the A12 series of 1171 cc. The Saloon is only available with the A10 engine and the Coupe is only available with the A12 engine; the Hatchback and Estate models are available with either engine.

The engine fitted to the USA market models is either the A14 series of 1397 cc or the A15 series of 1488 cc.

All four engine types are based on the same basic design but the following main differences apply. The A10 engine crankshaft runs in three main bearings whilst the other engine types have a five-bearing crankshaft. The camshafts also differ, as do the locations of the distributor, and the oil filter installation direction.

All the engines are of the four-cylinder, in-line overhead valve, water-cooled design. The pistons are made of aluminium with flat crowns on the A10 engine, and with concave crowns on the A12, A14 and A15 engines. The connecting rods are of forged steel with gudgeon pins which are an interference fit in the connecting rod small ends but fully floating in the pistons.

The crankshaft is supported by renewable bearings, the number depending on engine type, and drives the camshaft by a double roller chain. The cylinder head is of aluminium with pressed in valve seats. The overhead valve mechanism comprises conventional camshaft operated tappets, pushrods and rocket shaft and arms. The valves are fitted with single coil springs, and split cotters are employed to retain the valve spring caps.

The inlet manifold is aluminium and the exhaust manifold is cast-iron and incorporates a quick warm-up valve.

The power unit is mounted at three points, one at the sump, one at the clutch housing and one on the transmission housing. The mountings are of bonded rubber/metal acting under compression of steel brackets.

Unless otherwise stated, the photographs in the ensuing Sections are of the A10 engine, but because of the close similarities, are nearly all applicable to the A12, A14 and A15 engine types also.

2 Major operations possible with engine in the car

The following major operations can be carried out on the engine with it in place in the bodyframe:

(a) Removal and refitting of the cylinder head assembly
(b) Removal and refitting the oil pump
(c) Removal and refitting the clutch assembly

3 Major operations requiring engine removal

The following major operations require the removal of the engine/transmission assembly from the bodyframe

(a) Removal and refitting of the main bearings
(b) Removal and refitting of the crankshaft
(c) Removal and refitting of the flywheel
(d) Removal and refitting of the crankshaft rear bearing oil seal
(e) Removal and refitting of the timing chain
(f) Removal and refitting of the camshaft
(g) Removal and refitting of the big-end bearings, pistons and connecting rods

4 Engine removal – general

The engine and transmission are removed as an assembly. The engine cannot be removed as a separate unit because of the method of utilizing the clutch housing as part of the transmission casing and the limited access to split them when fitted in the vehicle.

Before beginning work it would be worthwhile getting all the dirt and oil cleaned off the engine, either by a service station, using steam cleaning equipment, or doing it yourself using a grease solvent and a garden hose. This will make dismantling the engine that much more pleasant, and cleaner.

A good hoist will be required, and two axle stands if an inspection

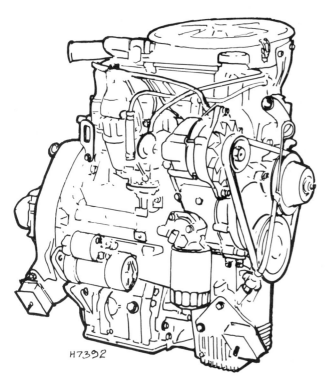

Fig. 1.1 The A12 engine and transmission assembly (Sec 1)

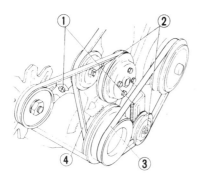

Fig. 1.2 On USA market models remove the items indicated where applicable (Sec 5)

| 1 | Adjuster bolts | 3 | Compressor belt |
| 2 | Idler pulley locknut | 4 | Air pump belt |

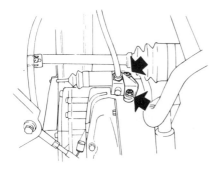

Fig. 1.3 Remove the clutch operating cylinder where applicable (Sec 5)

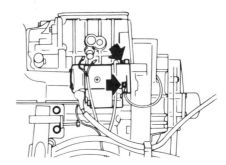

Fig. 1.4 Remove the starter motor retaining bolts (arrowed) (Sec 6)

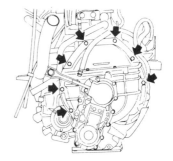

Fig. 1.5 Engine-to-transmission bolt locations (Sec 6)

pit is not available. Removal will be much easier if there is someone to assist, especially during the later stages.

In most cases, it is better to lift out the engine with all the ancillaries (alternator, distributor, carburettor, starter motor and exhaust manifold) still attached as they are easier to remove with the engine out of the car.

On USA models fitted with air conditioning, the air compressor unit **must not** be discharged by the home mechanic; therefore do not disconnect its line hoses. Consult your refrigeration specialist if disconnection becomes necessary. In general the removal and refitting details refer to manual transmission models, but automatic transmission details are included where applicable.

5 Engine – removal

1   Using a pencil, mark the outline of the bonnet hinge on either side to act as a datum point for refitting. With the help of an assistant, undo and remove the two bolts and washers securing the bonnet to the hinge on each side (photo) and carefully lift the bonnet up and then over the front of the car. Store it in a safe place where it will not get damaged. Push the hinges down out of the way.
2   Protect the top surface of the front wings with covers to prevent damage to the paintwork during the removal operations.
3   Disconnect the earth lead from the negative (–) terminal of the battery. On USA models fitted with air conditioning, disconnect both battery leads and remove the battery.
4   Drain the cooling system and remove the radiator as described in Chapter 2.
5   Remove the air cleaner unit from the carburettor, referring to Chapter 3 if necessary for full details. Cover the carburettor air intake to prevent the ingress of dirt. On USA models the following emission control items must also be detached or removed as applicable:

(a)   Hot air duct
(b)   Sensor and idle compensator-to-inlet manifold vacuum hose
(c)   The air inlet hoses
(d)   The AB valve-to-air cleaner hose
(e)   The air cleaner-to-throttle opener or vacuum switching valve hose
(f)   The air cleaner-to-rocker cover blowby hose
(g)   The air cleaner-to-solenoid valve hoses

5.1 Remove the bonnet hinge retaining bolts

5.6 Disconnect the throttle and (where applicable) choke cables at the points indicated

5.7a Disconnect the coil LT and HT leads ...

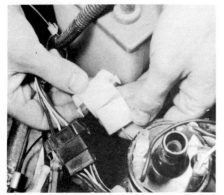

5.7b ... and the harness connectors

5.7c Detach the heater hoses

5.12 Disconnect the speedometer cable

5.15 Exhaust pipe and retaining bracket to differential housing

5.16a Remove the lower shift rod retaining spring clip ...

5.16b ... and the upper link spring clip (from above)

5.18 Disconnect the exhaust downpipe flange

5.19 Detach and remove the front buffer rod

5.21 Remove the front mounting nuts

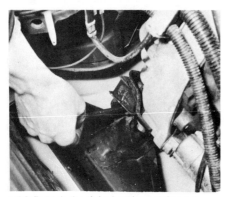

5.22 Detach the right-hand mounting nut

5.25 Lifting sling and hoist in position to raise the engine and transmission from the car. Note fabricated lifting eye attachment point at the front (arrowed)

5.26 The A10 engine and transmission removed and ready for dismantling

6   Disconnect the accelerator and (if applicable) the choke cables from the carburettor (photo).
7   Disconnect the following electrical wiring and hoses:

   (a)   *Coil-to-distributor HT lead*
   (b)   *Coil lead to clutch housing. Remove the coil on automatic transmission models*
   (c)   *The starter motor, anti-diesel solenoid valve, distributor LT, oil pressure switch and water temperature lead harness at the common connector attached to the right-hand inner wing (photo).*
   (d)   *The reversing light switch lead*
   (e)   *Alternator leads*
   (f)   *Heater inlet and outlet hoses (photo)*
   (g)   *Fuel hoses at the fuel pump. Plug hose when detached to prevent leakage*
   (h)   *Brake servo vacuum hose at the inlet manifold*
   (j)   *The stroke switch harness – automatic transmission model only.*

On USA models the following additional items must be disconnected:

   (k)   *Fuel return hose from the carburettor*
   (l)   *Carbon canister hose*
   (m)   *Air pump cleaner hose*

8   On USA models with air conditioning, remove the washer tank and then unbolt and remove the air compressor unit from the engine. **Do not** detach the hoses of this system. Support the compressor out of the way. Also remove the condenser together with the receiver/drier and locate them on the battery bracket.
9   On models fitted with power steering, refer to Chapter 11 and remove the power steering pump, but do not detach the hoses. Suspend the pump out of the way.
10   On cable-operated clutch models, remove the two bolts securing the cable location bracket to the clutch housing and then disconnect the cable from the clutch lever. Tie the cable and bracket back out of the way.
11   On hydraulic clutch models, remove the slave cylinder securing bolts after disconnecting the operating rod from the clutch release arm. The slave cylinder may then be swung up out of the way without disturbing the hydraulic circuit (which would necessitate subsequent bleeding of the clutch hydraulic system).
12   Disconnect the speedometer cable from the transmission (photo).
13   It is now necessary to work underneath the vehicle; therefore jack it up and support it with axle stands or other equally secure support.
14   Unbolt and remove the exhaust pipe retaining bracket from the differential housing (three bolts). Also remove the two bolts and nuts attaching the exhaust to the bracket (photo).
15   Remove the gearchange linkage bracket to the differential housing.
16   Extract the spring pins and detach the lower and upper shift rods, noting the washer positions. You may find it easier to disconnect the upper shift rod by working downwards through the engine compartment (photos).
17   Remove the respective driveshaft attachment bolts (three on each side). Lower the shafts and allow them to rest on the subframe.

18   Unscrew and remove the exhaust downpipe-to-manifold retaining nuts (photo).
19   Working from above again, remove the buffer rod upper and lower retaining nuts and withdraw the buffer rod from the front engine mounting (photo).
20   Remove the two bolts securing the right-hand buffer rod to the engine and then pivot the rod towards the wing out of the way, complete with bracket.
21   Unscrew and remove the front and rear engine mounting nuts (photo).
22   Unscrew and remove the lower right-hand engine mounting nut (photo).
23   On automatic transmission models, disconnect the clutch control solenoid harness at its connector.
24   The engine should now be ready for lifting out, but before attaching the lifting sling, make a check to ensure that there are no more items to be disconnected from the engine or transmission. Also position surrounding cables, leads and hoses out of the way so that they will not snag the unit as it is being lifted out.
25   If the lifting sling is being attached to lifting eyes, you will have to bolt one into position on the front right-hand side of the engine as shown (photo). The other lifting eye is already fitted to the rear left hand side. If the sling is being fitted completely round the unit, ensure that it is securely located and will allow an even lift.
26   With suitable lifting tackle connected securely to the engine, carefully raise it clear. An assistant should be at hand if possible to guide it clear of surrounding fittings and components. When the sump is clear of the front grille panel the engine can be fully withdrawn (photo).

6   Engine – separation from transmission

1   Having lifted the engine and transmission from the car, lower the combined unit to the floor, but leave the lifting sling in position so that when the engine is detached from the transmission it can be withdrawn and lifted clear.

Manual transmission

2   Disconnect the reversing light switch leads.
3   Unbolt and remove the starter motor, noting the earth strap location under the head of the upper bolt.
4   Disconnect the main loom wires as applicable.
5   Unscrew and remove the differential housing-to-engine steady bracket bolt and nut (photo).
6   Remove the respective engine-to-transmission bolts. Note the cable location bracket position under one of the bolts (Fig. 1.5).
7   Check that the weight of the engine is suitably supported by the sling and hoist and carefully withdraw the engine (photo).

Automatic transmission model

8   Detach the vacuum tube at the vacuum diaphragm unit.
9   Unbolt and remove the starter motor (note the earth strap location).
10   Unscrew and remove the eight driveplate-to-converter retaining

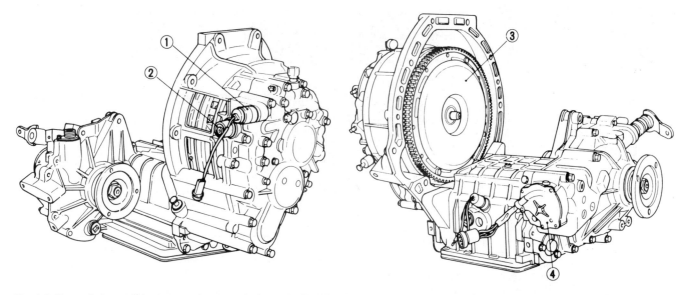

Fig. 1.6 General views of the automatic transmission unit showing the clutch control solenoid (1), the vacuum diaphragm (2), the torque converter (3) and the shift stroke switch (4) (Sec 6)

bolts using a suitable socket and extension bar inserted through the starter motor location aperture. As each bolt is removed, turn the engine progressively for access to the next bolt. Removal of the spark plugs enables the engine to be turned more easily.

11 Unscrew and remove the engine-to-transmission housing retaining bolts. Note the filler pipe connection to these bolts.

12 The engine is now ready for removal. Check that the hoist and sling have it suitably supported. Pull the engine from the transmission about 0.5 in (12 mm) and then lift it clear. As it is lifted, check that the torque converter remains engaged in the transmission. *Do not remove or partially withdraw the torque converter from the transmission housing once the engine is removed.* To ensure that it stays in position, bolt a suitable bar across the face of the torque converter housing, using a couple of the engine-to-transmission bolt holes as attachment points.

---
7 Engine dismantling – general

1 It is best to mount the engine on a dismantling stand but if one is not available, then stand the engine on a strong bench so as to be at

a comfortable working height. Failing this, the engine can be stripped down on the floor.

2 During the dismantling process the greatest care should be taken to keep the exposed parts free from dirt. As an aid to achieving this, it is a sound scheme to thoroughly clean down the outside of the engine, removing all traces of oil and congealed dirt, if it has not been done already.

3 Use paraffin or a good grease solvent. The latter compound will make the job much easier, as, after the solvent has been applied and allowed to stand for a time, a vigorous jet of water will wash off the solvent and all the grease and filth. If the dirt is thick and deeply embedded, work the solvent into it with a wire brush.

4 Finally wipe down the exterior of the engine with a rag and only then, when it is quite clean, should the dismantling process begin. As the engine is stripped, clean each part in a bath of paraffin or petrol.

5 Never immerse parts with oilways in paraffin, eg the crankshaft, but to clean, wipe down carefully with a petrol-dampened rag. Oilways can be cleaned out with wire. If an air line is present all parts can be blown dry and the oilways blown through as an added precaution.

6 Re-use of old engine gaskets is false economy and can give rise to oil and water leaks, if nothing worse. To avoid the possibility of trouble

6.5 Remove the transmission-to-engine bracket securing bolt

6.7 Separating the transmission from the engine

after the engine has been reassembled **always** use new gaskets throughout.

7 Do not throw the old gaskets away as it sometimes happens that an immediate replacement cannot be found and the old gasket is then very useful as a template. Hang up the old gaskets as they are removed on a suitable hook or nail.

8 To strip the engine it is best to work from the top down. The sump provides a firm base on which the engine can be supported in an upright position. When the stage where the sump must be removed is reached, the engine can be turned on its side and all other work carried out with it in this position.

9 Wherever possible, refit nuts, bolts and washers finger tight from wherever they were removed. This helps avoid later loss and muddle. If they cannot be refitted then lay them out in such a fashion that it is clear from where they came.

8 Ancillary components – removal

1 With the engine removed from the vehicle and separated from the gearbox, the ancillary components should now be removed before dismantling of the engine unit commences.

2 Unscrew and remove the main wiring loom location clip retaining screw from the clutch (torque converter) housing, then disengage the loom from the clip.

3 Loosen the alternator mounting bolts and the adjustment strap bolt. Push the alternator in towards the engine and remove the drivebelt. Remove the alternator mounting bolts and adjustment strap bolt and lift the unit away (photo).

4 On USA models equipped with an air pump used in conjunction with the emission control system (See Chapter 3), remove the idler pulley, the air pump drivebelt and the idler pulley bracket. Remove the pump and its mounting bracket.

5 Remove the oil level dipstick.

6 Unscrew and remove the cartridge type oil filter (photo). It may be necessary to employ a small chain or strap wrench where the filter is stuck tight. Allow for a certain amount of oil spillage.

7 Unscrew and remove the bolts which secure the oil pump body to the exterior of the crankcase. Withdraw the oil pump complete with drivegear.

8 Unscrew and remove the spark plugs.

9 Disconnect and remove the vacuum tube which runs between the distributor vacuum capsule and the carburettor.

10 Unscrew and remove the setscrew which retains the distributor plate to the engine crankcase. Withdraw the distributor from its crankcase location.

11 Disconnect the fuel line between the carburettor and fuel pump.

12 Unscrew and remove the carburettor-to-inlet manifold flange nuts and washers and lift the carburettor clear. As an alternative the carburettor can be left in position on the manifold and removed later with the inlet and exhaust manifolds.

13 Unscrew and lift clear the rocker cover screws, then carefully prise the cover free from the cylinder head.

14 Unscrew and remove the thermostat housing retaining bolts and note the fuel line retaining clip position. Pull the housing clear. If it is stuck do not insert a blade and attempt to prise it off as this will damage the mating faces. Tap it sideways with a plastic-faced hammer until it is free,

15 Withdraw the thermostat. If it is stuck in its seating, do not try and pull it out with a pair of pliers but cut round its periphery with a sharp pointed knife to free it.

16 On USA engines (A14 and A15), remove the EGR valve.

17 Unbolt and remove the inlet and exhaust manifolds, complete with carburettor if this has been left on. Carefully remove the manifold gasket(s).

18 On USA models, remove the PCV hose (pipe connector to control valve).

19 Unscrew the water pump pulley securing bolts (use a strap wrench to hold the pulley) and remove it.

20 Unscrew and remove the nuts which secure the water pump to the upper front face of the timing cover.

21 Unscrew and remove the securing nuts from the fuel pump and lift it from its crankcase location. Carefully note the exact number and sequence of gaskets and spacers between the pump and crankcase.

22 Remove the clutch assembly as described in Chapter 5.

9 Cylinder head – removal with engine in car

1 If the cylinder head is to be removed with the engine in the car, refer to Section 5 and carry out the operations given in paragraphs 2 to 6 inclusive, but do not remove the radiator. It is not necessary to remove the bonnet, simply raise and support it.

2 In addition to the above items, disconnect the spark plug HT leads, the fuel line at the fuel pump (to the carburettor), the coolant temperature sender lead, the brake servo vacuum hose at the inlet manifold, and the distributor vacuum timing control tube.

3 The carburettor can be left in position on the inlet manifold and the inlet and exhaust manifolds detached from the cylinder head. Do not detach the exhaust manifold from the downpipe in this instance. If the carburettor, inlet and exhaust manifolds are to be removed together with the cylinder head, disconnect the exhaust manifold-to-downpipe flange, also the accelerator and choke cables, the automatic choke wire (where applicable) and the anti-diesel solenoid valve lead.

4 Where comprehensive emission control components are fitted it will be necessary to disconnect those items which directly affect the cylinder head removal – refer to Chapter 3.

5 Unscrew and remove the rocker cover screws and lift the cover free.

6 Now proceed as given in Section 10.

10 Cylinder head – removal with engine out of the car

1 Unscrew the rocker shaft pillar securing bolts. Lift the rocker shaft assembly from the cylinder head (photo).

2 Unscrew each of the cylinder head bolts a turn or two each at a time in the sequence shown in Fig. 1.7, finally removing them.

3 Withdraw each of the pushrods and keep them in sequence so that they can be returned to their original positions. A piece of wood with two rows of holes drilled in it and numbered will provide a very useful rack for both pushrods and valves.

4 Lift off the cylinder head. Should it be stuck, **do not** attempt to prise it from the engine block but tap it all round using a hardwood block or plastic faced mallet. Remove the cylinder head gasket.

8.3 Remove the alternator (A10 engine shown)

8.6 Remove the oil filter

10.1 Lift off the rocker shaft assembly

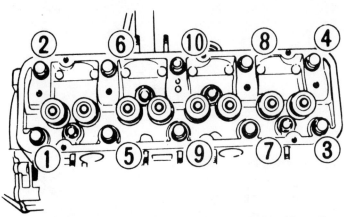

Fig. 1.7 Loosening sequence of cylinder head bolts (Sec 10)
Note: *The sequence must be reversed when tightening (Sec 38)*

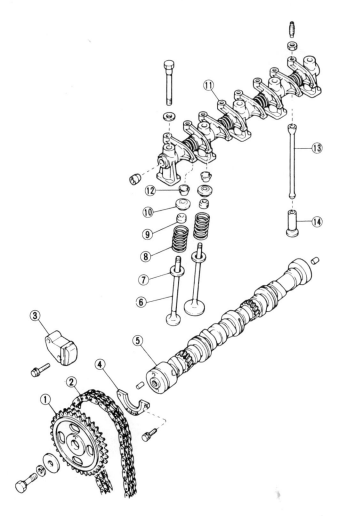

Fig. 1.8 Valve assembly, rocker assembly and camshaft assembly components (Sec 11)

1	Sprocket	8	Valve spring
2	Timing chain	9	Seal
3	Chain tensioner	10	Spring retainer
4	Camshaft plate	11	Rocker arm
5	Camshaft	12	Collet
6	Valve	13	Pushrod
7	Spring seat	14	Tappet

11 Inlet and exhaust valves – removal

1   The valves can be removed from the cylinder head by the following method. Compress each spring in turn with a valve spring compressor until the two halves of the collet can be removed (photo). Release the compressor and remove the spring and spring retainer.
2   If, when the valve spring compressor is screwed down, the valve spring retaining cap refuses to free to expose the split collet, do not continue to screw down on the compressor as there is a likelihood of damaging it.
3   Gently tap the top of the tool directly over the cap with a light hammer. This will free the cap. To avoid the compressor jumping off the valve spring retaining cap when it is tapped, hold the compressor firmly in position with one hand.
4   Slide the rubber oil control seal off the top of each valve stem and then drop out each valve through the combustion chamber.
5   It is essential that the valves are kept in their correct sequence unless they are so badly worn that they are to be renewed.

12 Rocker unit – dismantling

1   Remove the bolts from the rocker pillars and slide the rocker pillars, rocker arms and springs off the rocker shaft.
2   If the original components are to be refitted, identify their fitting sequence with a piece of masking tape.

13 Engine oil sump – removal

1   If not already done, unscrew and remove the sump drain plug, catching the oil in a container of adequate capacity. Refit the plug.
2   Invert the engine. Unscrew and remove the sump retaining bolts and lift the sump away (photo).
3   The gauze strainer and oil suction pipe are now exposed and can be detached by removing the two suction pipe flange securing bolts (photo).

14 Timing cover, gears and chain – removal

1   Unscrew the crankshaft pulley securing bolt. To do this it will be necessary to restrain the crankshaft from turning by wedging the flywheel (see photo). One or two heavy blows with a club hammer on the end of the spanner should loosen the nut.
2   Lever off the crankshaft pulley, using two screwdrivers or similar levers.
3   Unscrew the timing cover securing bolts and remove the timing cover.
4   Withdraw the oil thrower disc from the crankshaft. Unscrew the securing bolts and remove the timing chain tensioner from the front of the engine block (photo).
5   Unscrew and remove the camshaft sprocket securing bolt.
6   Remove the camshaft and crankshaft sprockets simultaneously, complete with double roller chain (photo). Use tyre levers behind each gear and lever them equally and a little at a time. If they are stuck on their shafts, the use of a puller may be required.
7   When the sprockets and chain are removed, extract the two Woodruff keys from the crankshaft and retain safely.

15 Pistons and connecting rods – removal

1   With the cylinder head and sump removed, undo the big-end retaining bolts.
2   The connecting rods and pistons are lifted out from the top of the cylinder block, after the carbon or 'wear' ring at the top of the bore has been scraped away.
3   Remove the big-end caps one at a time, taking care to keep them in the right order and the correct way round. Also ensure that the shell bearings are kept with their correct connecting rods and caps unless they are to be renewed. Normally, the numbers 1 to 4 are stamped on adjacent sides of the big-end caps and connecting rods, indicating which cap fits on which rod and which way round the cap fits (photo).

11.1 Removing the valve collets

13.2 Remove the oil sump and ...

13.3 ... then the oil strainer

14.1 Method of preventing the flywheel from turning

14.4 Remove the timing chain tensioner retaining bolt

14.6 Withdraw the camshaft and crankshaft sprockets together with the timing chain

If no numbers or lines can be found, then, with a sharp screwdriver or file, scratch mating marks across the joint from the rod to the cap. One line for connecting rod No 1, two for connecting rod No 2 and so on. This will ensure there is no confusion later as it is most important that the caps go back in the correct position on the connecting rods from which they were removed.

4   If the big-end caps are difficult to remove they may be gently tapped with a soft hammer.

5   To remove the shell bearings, press the bearing opposite the groove in the connecting rod and the connecting rod caps, and the bearings will slide out easily.

6   Withdraw the pistons and connecting rods upwards and ensure they are kept in the correct order for refitting in the same bore. Refit the connecting rod caps to the rods to prevent the caps and rods getting mixed up. Keep the bearing shells with their respective rods and cap if they are to be re-used.

16 Piston rings – removal

1   If the same piston rings are to be refitted, care must be taken that the rings are not broken when being removed. Starting with the top ring (all rings must be removed from the top of the piston), ease one end out of its groove and place a thin piece of metal (eg an old feeler blade) behind it.

2   Then move the metal strip carefully behind the ring, at the same time easing the ring upward so that it rests on the surface of the piston above the groove, until the whole ring is clear and can be slid off. With the second and third rings which must come off from the top, arrange the strip of metal to carry them over the other grooves.

3   Identify the rings so that they can be refitted to the same pistons, by piercing a piece of paper with each ring, showing its location, top 1, middle 1, etc.

17 Gudgeon pins – removal

1   The gudgeon pins are an interference fit in the connecting rod small ends.

2   To separate the pistons from the connecting rods considerable pressure is required to press out the gudgeon pins and this requires a proper press. Attempts with other methods will probably result in bent connecting rods or broken pistons. Therefore this is a job best left to your local Datsun dealer, as in the event of new pistons being needed it is necessary to heat the connecting rod when refitting the gudgeon pins and this requires experience to prevent distortion of the connecting rod.

18 Flywheel – removal

1   Unscrew and remove the flywheel retaining bolts (photo). It will be necessary to restrain the crankshaft from turning while undoing the bolts. To do this wedge the flywheel (refer to Section 14, paragraph 1) or place a block of wood between a crankshaft web and the side of the crankcase.

2   Lift the flywheel off the crankshaft flange.

3   The endplate behind the flywheel can now be removed.

19 Main bearings and crankshaft – removal

1   Unscrew and remove the securing bolts from the main bearing caps (photo). Gradually loosen the bolts in two or three stages in the sequence shown in Fig. 1.9. On the three-bearing crankshaft fitted to the A10 engine, the main bearing cap at the timing case end has a raised circular flange in the centre. The other two bearing caps can easily be confused so it is as well to identify them before dismantling. On the five-bearing crankshaft fitted to the A12, A14 and A15 engines the caps are numbered 1 to 5, starting from the timing cover end of the engine, and arrows marked on the caps, point towards the timing cover to ensure correct orientation of the caps when refitting.

2   Withdraw the bearing caps complete with the shell bearings.

3   Remove the rear oil seal.

4   Lift the crankshaft out of the crankcase and then remove the shell bearings (photo).

5   Remove the baffle plate and the steel mesh screen from the crankcase (A12, A14 and A15 engines only).

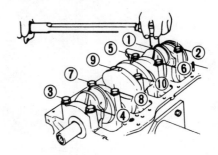

Fig. 1.9 Loosen main bearing cap bolts in sequence shown – A12, A14 and A15 engine (Sec 19)

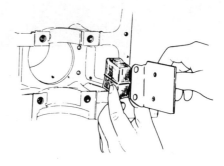

Fig. 1.10 Remove the baffle plate and steel mesh screen on A12, A14 and A15 engines (Sec 19)

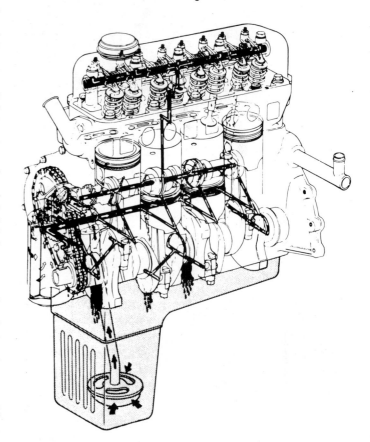

Fig. 1.11 The engine lubrication circuit diagram (A12 engine shown) (Sec 21)

15.3 The connecting rods and caps are numbered

18.1 Remove the flywheel retaining bolts

19.1 Remove the main bearing caps and retaining bolts

19.4 Extract the bearing shells

20.2 Withdrawing the camshaft

22.3 Removing the oil pressure regulator plug, spring and valve

20 Camshaft and tappets – removal

1   Remove the two bolts which secure the camshaft endplate and take off the plate.
2   Carefully withdraw the camshaft (photo). Rotate the camshaft during the removal operation and take particular care not to damage the camshaft bearings as the lobes of the camshaft pass through them.
3   The tappets can now be removed from the crankcase. Identify the tappets so that they can be refitted in their original positions.

21 Lubrication system – description

The engine lubrication system is of the pressure feed type. An oil pump mounted on the right-hand side of the cylinder block is driven by a meshing gear on the camshaft which also drives the distributor drive shaft. Oil is drawn from the sump through a filter screen and tube, by the rotor type pump through the full flow oil filter to the main crankcase oil gallery.

The main oil gallery supplies oil to the crankshaft main bearings and big-end bearings through drillings, and a regulated quantity of oil ejected from small holes in the connecting rods lubricates the gudgeon pins and cylinder walls.

The timing chain is fed with oil from the main gallery and the chain tensioner is held against the timing chain partly by oil pressure and partly by a coil spring.

The camshaft bearings are lubricated with oil from the main gallery, and the rocker shaft and valve gear obtain their lubrication through a drilling from the camshaft centre bearing.

22 Oil pump – inspection and servicing

1   Having removed the oil pump as described in Section 8, unscrew and remove the bolt securing the pump cover to the pump body.
2   Slide out the outer rotor from the pump body.
3   Remove the oil pressure regulator plug, washer, shim, spring and valve (photo).
4   Thoroughly clean all parts in cleaning solvent. Use a brush to clean the inside of the pump housing and pressure regulator valve chamber.
5   Examine all the parts for damage and excessive wear.
6   Check the inner rotor shaft for looseness in the pump body, the regulator valve for wear or scoring and the spring for chafing or a permanent set.
7   Check the following clearances using a feeler gauge and straight edge, see Fig. 1.12:

(a)   Side clearance between inner and outer rotors
(b)   Clearance between outer rotor and the pump body
(c)   Rotor tip clearance
(d)   Gap between body and rotor

If the clearances exceed the limits given in the Specifications at the beginning of this Chapter, the pump must be renewed as a complete assembly, as individual parts are not available.
8   The oil pressure relief valve, located in the oil pump cover, bypasses the oil into the main oil gallery when the oil filter element is excessively clogged. With the regulator valve removed check the valve operation.
9   Reassembly of the oil pump is the reverse of the dismantling procedure. Always use a new gasket between the pump cover and pump body.

23 Inspection and renovation – general

Having dismantled the engine and thoroughly cleaned all the parts, everything should now be examined and checked for damage and wear. The following Sections describe the inspection procedure and the renovation or renewal operations as necessary.

Renew shell bearings as a matter of course unless they are known to have covered only a very small mileage – not to do so is false economy. Similarly, renew all gaskets and oil seals. If in doubt as to whether a component needs renewing, consider the additional work that will be caused if the old component is refitted and fails within a short time, against the cost of renewal. The expected life remaining for the vehicle as a whole must also be considered.

24 Crankshaft and main bearings – inspection and renovation

1   Examine the crankpin and main journal surfaces for signs of scoring or scratches. Check the ovality of the crankpins at different positions with a micrometer (photo). If more than the specified maximum out of round the crankpin will have to be reground. It will also have to be reground if there are any scores or scratches present. Check the journals in the same fashion.
2   If it is necessary to regrind the crankshaft and fit new bearings, your local Datsun garage or engineering works will be able to decide how much metal to grind off and the size of new bearing shells.
3   The main bearing clearances may be established by using a strip of Plastigage between the crankshaft journals and the main bearing shell. Tighten the bearing cap bolts to the specified torque setting. Do not turn the crankshaft while the Plastigage is in place. Remove the cap and compare the flattened Plastigage strip with the scale printed on the Plastigage envelope. Check that the clearance is within the limit specified at the beginning of this Chapter (Fig. 1.14).
4   Temporarily fit the crankshaft in the crankcase, with main bearing shells, and tighten the bearing caps to their specified torque setting. Push the crankshaft as far as possible to one end and, inserting a feeler gauge as shown in Fig. 1.15, measure the crankshaft endplay between the crankshaft thrust face and the flange of the centre main bearing (photo). Check that the endplay is within the specified limit.
5   On A12, A14 and A15 engines check the crankshaft pilot bush at the rear end of the crankshaft for wear or damage (photo). Renew the bush if defective. When fitting a new bush, press the bush in so that its height above the flange end is 0.11 in (2.8 mm) – see Fig. 1.16. Do **not** oil the bush.

25 Connecting rods and bearings – inspection and renovation

1   Big-end failure is indicated by a knocking from within the crankcase and a slight drop in oil pressure.
2   Examine the big-end bearing surfaces for pitting and scoring (photo). Renew the shells unless they are in perfect condition. Where the crankshaft has been reground, the correct undersize big-end shell bearings will be supplied with the crank.
3   Should there be any suspicion that a connecting rod is bent or twisted, or the small-end bush no longer provides an interference fit for the gudgeon pin, then the rod(s) should be straightened as necessary and/or new bush(es) fitted if required. These tasks are best entrusted to your Datsun dealer or automotive repair shop, as specialised equipment is required. If renewing the rod(s), ensure that their respective weights are within the specified tolerance.
4   Measurement of the big-end bearing clearances may be carried out in a similar manner to that described for the main bearings in the previous Section.

26 Cylinder bores and crankcase – inspection and renovation

1   The cylinder bores must be examined for taper, ovality, scoring and scratches. Start by carefully examining the top of the cylinder bores. If they are at all worn, a very slight ridge will be found on the thrust side. This marks the top of the piston ring travel. The owner will have a good indication of the bore wear prior to dismantling the engine, or removing the cylinder head. Excessive oil consumption accompanied by blue smoke from the exhaust is a sure sign of worn cylinder bores and piston rings.
2   Measure the bore diameter just under the ridge with an internal micrometer and compare it with the diameter at the bottom of the bore, which is not subject to wear. If the difference between the two measurements is more than 0.008 in (0.20 mm) then it will be necessary to fit special pistons and rings, or to have the cylinders rebored and fit oversize pistons.
3   Oversize pistons are available as listed in the Specifications. These are accurately machined to just below the indicated measurements so as to provide correct running clearances in bores machined out to the exact oversize dimensions.
4   If the bores are slightly worn but not so badly worn as to justify

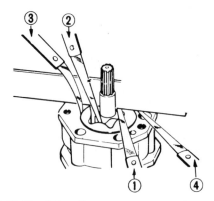

Fig. 1.12 Check the oil pump rotor clearances (Sec 22)

1   Side clearance   clearance
2   Tip clearance   4   Gap between body and rotor
3   Outer rotor to body

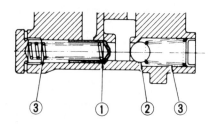

Fig. 1.13 Oil system regulator valve and relief valve (Sec 22)

1   Regulator valve   3   Valve spring
2   Relief valve

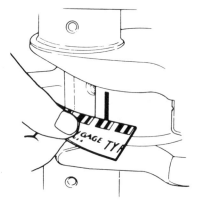

Fig. 1.14 Using Plastigage to measure the main bearing clearance
(Sec 24)

Fig. 1.15 Check the crankshaft endplay (Sec 24)

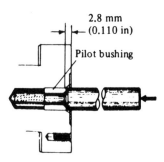

Fig. 1.16 Crankshaft pivot bush fitting showing correct location
when installed – A12, A14 and A15 engines (Sec 24)

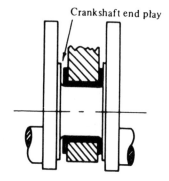

Fig. 1.17 Check cylinder bores for wear (Sec 26)

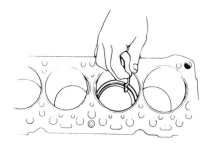

Fig. 1.18 Check the piston ring end gap (Sec 27)

Fig. 1.19 Check the piston ring side clearance in the piston groove
(Sec 27)

24.1 Check connecting rod journal for ovality and wear using a micrometer. In this instance the crankshaft is still in position in the crankcase

24.4 Use a feeler gauge to check crankshaft endplay

24.5 Check the pilot bush (when fitted) in the rear end of the crankshaft

25.2 Piston and connecting rod assembly

reboring them, then special oil control rings and pistons can be fitted which will restore compression and stop the engine burning oil. Several different types are available and the manufacturer's instructions concerning their fitting must be followed closely.

5   If new pistons are being fitted and the bores have not been rebored, it is essential to slightly roughen the hard glaze on the sides of the bores with fine glass paper so that the new piston rings will have a chance to bed in properly.

27 Piston and piston rings – inspection and renovation

1   If the original pistons are to be refitted, carefully remove the piston rings as described in Section 16.
2   Clean all carbon off the rings and grooves, taking care not to scratch the aluminium surface of the pistons. Protect your fingers – piston rings are sharp! Ensure that the oil slots in the bottom land of the oil ring groove are cleaned out.
3   Before fitting the rings to the pistons, check the ring gap. Place the ring in the cylinder bore and press it down to the bottom of the cylinder with a piston, and using a feeler gauge, check that the gap is as given in the Specifications at the beginning of this Chapter. If the ring gap is too large the ring will have to be renewed, if too small the gap can be

increased by filing one end of the ring with a fine file. Be careful not to break the rings as they are very brittle. Ensure that the gap is not less than that specified; if it closes under normal operating temperatures the ring will break.
4   Check that each ring gives a side clearance in the piston groove as given in the Specifications. If the gap is too large, new pistons and rings will be required if Datsun spares are used. However, independent specialist manufacturers of pistons and rings can normally provide the rings required separately. If new Datsun pistons and rings are being obtained it will be necessary to have the ridge ground away from the top of the cylinder bores. If specialist oil control rings are being obtained from an independent supplier the ridge removal will not be necessary as the top rings will be stepped to provide the necessary clearance. If the top ring of a new set is not stepped, it will hit the ridge made by the previous ring and break.
5   If new pistons are obtained the rings will be included, so it must be emphasised that the top ring be stepped if fitted to a cylinder which has not been rebored, or had the ridge at the top removed.
6   The groove clearance of new rings on old pistons should be within the specified tolerance. If it is not enough the rings could stick in the grooves, causing loss of compression and oiling-up. If it is too loose, this accelerates wear on the sides of the ring grooves.
7   If the piston appears slack on the gudgeon pin, then both the

piston and the gudgeon pin should be renewed. This is a job for the local Datsun dealer as mentioned in Section 17.

28 Camshaft and camshaft bearings – inspection and renovation

1   Carefully examine the camshaft bearings for wear. If the bearings are obviously worn or pitted then they must be renewed. This is an operation for your local Datsun dealer or local engineering works as it demands the use of specialized equipment. The bearings are removed with a special drift after which new bearings are pressed in, and in-line bored, care being taken to ensure the oil holes in the bearings line up with those in the block.
2   The camshaft itself should show no signs of wear, but, if very slight scoring on the cams is noticed, the score marks can be removed by very gently rubbing down with a fine emery cloth. The greatest care should be taken to keep the cam profiles smooth.
3   Examine the skew gear for wear, chipping teeth or other damage.
4   Check the camshaft endplay by fitting the camshaft thrust plate and camshaft sprocket in their respective positions. Measure the endplay with a feeler gauge. If the endplay exceeds the maximum specified, renew the thrust plate.

29 Valves and valve seats – inspection and renovation

1   Examine the heads of the valves for pitting and burning, especially the heads of the exhaust valves. The valve seats should be examined at the same time. If the pitting on valve and seat is very slight the marks can be removed by grinding the seats and valves together with coarse, and then fine, valve grinding paste.
2   Where bad pitting has occurred to the valve seats it will be necessary to recut them and fit new valves. If the valve seats are so worn that they cannot be recut, then it will be necessary to fit new valve seat inserts. These latter two jobs should be entrusted to the local Datsun agent or engineering works. In practice it is very seldom that the seats are so badly worn for refitting, and the owner can easily purchase a new set of valves and match them to the seats by valve grinding.
3   Valve grinding is carried out as follows. Smear a trace of coarse carborundum paste on the seat face and apply a suction grinder tool to the valve head. With semi-rotary motion, grind the valve head to its seat, lifting the valve occasionally to redistribute the grinding paste. When a dull matt even surface finish is produced on both the valve seat and the valve, wipe off the paste and repeat the process with fine carborundum paste, lifting and turning the valve to redistribute the paste as before. A light spring placed under the valve head will greatly ease this operation. When a smooth unbroken ring of light grey matt finish is produced, on both valve and valve seat faces, the grinding operation is completed.
4   Scrape away all carbon from the valve head and the valve stem. Carefully clean away every trace of grinding compound, taking great care to leave none in the ports or in the valve guides. Clean the valves and valve seats with a paraffin soaked rag, then with a clean rag, and finally, if an air line is available, blow the valves, valve guides and valve ports clean.

30 Valve guides – inspection and renewal

1   Check each valve in its guide for wear. After a considerable mileage, the valve guide bore may wear oval.
This can best be checked by inserting a new valve in the guide and moving it from side to side. If the top of the valve stem deflects by more than 0.008 in (0.20 mm) then it must be assumed that the tolerance between the stem and guide is greater than the permitted maximum.
2   New valve guides (oversize available – see Specifications) may be pressed or drifted into the cylinder head after the worn ones have been removed in a similar manner. The cylinder head must be heated to 200°C (392°F) before carrying out these operations and although this can be done in a domestic oven, it must be remembered that the new guide will have to be reamed after installation and it is therefore preferable to leave this work to your Datsun dealer.
3   If new valve guides are fitted, the valve seats must be recut or renewed as appropriate, otherwise the valves may not seat properly.

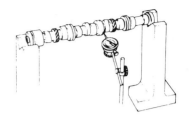

Fig. 1.20 Check the camshaft for bend (Sec 28)

31 Rockers and rocker shaft – inspection and renewal

1   Thoroughly clean the rocker shaft and then check the shaft for straightness by rolling it on plate glass. It is most unlikely that it will deviate from normal, but if it does, purchase a new shaft. The surface of the shaft should be free from any worn ridges, caused by the rocker arms. If any wear is present, renew the shaft.
2   Check the rocker arms for wear of the rocker bushes, for wear at the rocker arm face which bears on the valve stem, and for wear of the adjusting ball-ended screws. Wear in the rocker arm bush can be checked by gripping the rocker arm tip and holding the rocker arm in place on the shaft, noting if there is any lateral rocker arm shake. If shake is present, and the arm is very loose on the shaft, a new bush or rocker arm must be fitted.
3   Check the top of the rocker arm where it bears on the valve head for cracking or serious wear on the case hardening. If none is present re-use the rocker arm. Check the lower half of the ball on the end of the rocker arm adjusting screw.
4   Reassemble the rocker arms, springs and pillars on the rocker shaft and retain with the rocker pillar bolts.

32 Tappets and pushrods – inspection and renewal

1   Examine the bearing surface of the mushroom tappets which lie on the camshaft. Any indentation in this surface or any cracks indicate serious wear and the tappets should be renewed. Thoroughly clean them out, removing all traces of sludge. It is most unlikely that the sides of the tappets will prove worn, but, if they are a very loose fit in their bores and can readily be rocked, they should be exchanged for new units. It is very unusual to find any wear in the tappets, and any wear is likely to occur only at very high mileages.
2   Check the pushrods for straightness by rolling them on a piece of glass. Check the ends for roughness or excessive wear. Renew any that are bent or worn.

33 Cylinder head – decarbonising, inspection and renovation

1   With the cylinder head removed, use a blunt scraper to remove all traces of carbon deposits from the combustion spaces and ports. Remember that the cylinder head is aluminium alloy and can be damaged easily during the decarbonising operations. Scrape the cylinder head free from scale or old pieces of gasket or jointing compound. Clean the cylinder head by washing it in paraffin and take particular care to pull a piece of rag through the ports and cylinder head bolt holes. Any grit remaining in these recesses may well drip onto the gasket or cylinder block mating surface as the cylinder head is lowered into position and could lead to a gasket leak after reassembly is complete.
2   With the cylinder head clean, test for distortion if a history of coolant leakage has been apparent. Carry out this test using a straight edge and feeler gauge or a piece of plate glass. If the surface shows any warping in excess of 0.0039 in (0.10 mm) then the cylinder head will have to be resurfaced which is a job for a specialist engineering company.
3   Clean the pistons and top of the cylinder bores. If the pistons are still in the block then it is essential that great care is taken to ensure that no carbon gets into the cylinder bores as this could scratch the cylinder walls or cause damage to the piston and rings. To ensure this does not happen, first turn the crankshaft so that two of the pistons are

at the top of their bores. Stuff rag into the other two bores or seal them off with paper and masking tape. The waterways should also be covered with small pieces of masking tape to prevent particles of carbon entering the cooling system and damaging the water pump.

4   There are two schools of thought as to how much carbon should be removed from the piston crown. One school recommends that all carbon should be removed from the piston head. The other recommends that a ring of carbon should be left round the edge of the piston and on the cylinder bore wall as an aid to low oil consumption. Although this is probably true for older engines with worn bores, on newer engines the thought of the first school can be applied; which is that for effective decarbonisation all traces of carbon should be removed.

5   If all traces of carbon are to be removed, press a little grease into the gap between the cylinder walls and the two pistons which are to be worked on. With a blunt scraper carefully scrape away the carbon from the piston crown, taking great care not to scratch the aluminium. Also scrape away the carbon from the surrounding lip of the cylinder wall. When all carbon has been removed, scrape away the grease which will now be contaminated with carbon particles, taking care not to press any into the bores. To assist prevention of carbon build-up, the piston crown can be polished with a metal polish. Remove the rags or masking tape from the other two cylinders and turn the crankshaft so that the two pistons which were at the bottom are now at the top. Place rag or masking tape in the cylinders which have been decarbonised and proceed as just described.

6   If a ring of carbon is going to be left round the piston then this can be helped by inserting an old piston ring into the top of the bore to rest on the piston and ensure that the carbon is not accidentally removed. Check that there are no particles of carbon in the cylinder bores. Decarbonising is now complete.

34 Timing chain, tensioner and sprockets – inspection and renovation

1   Examine the teeth on both the crankshaft sprocket and the camshaft sprocket for wear or damage. If any sign of wear is present the sprockets must be renewed.

2   Check the timing chain for wear on the rollers or any other damage. Check the links of the chain for side slackness. Renew the chain if any defect is apparent. It is normal to renew the chain at time of major overhaul.

3   Check the chain tensioner slipper head for wear and grooving. Check that the spring loaded plunger is free in its bore and that the spring is not distorted or damaged.

35 Flywheel ring gear – inspection and renewal

1   If the teeth on the flywheel starter ring are badly worn, or if some are missing, then it will be necessary to remove the ring and fit a new one, or preferably exchange the flywheel for a reconditioned unit.

2   Either split the ring with a cold chisel after making a cut with a hacksaw blade between two teeth, or use a soft-headed hammer (not steel) to knock the ring off, striking it evenly and alternately at equally spaced points. Take great care not to damage the flywheel during this process.

3   Heat the new ring in an electric oven to about 200°C (392°F) or immerse in a pan of boiling oil.

4   Hold the ring at this temperature for five minutes and then quickly fit it to the flywheel so the chamfered portion of the teeth faces the gearbox side of the flywheel.

5   The ring should be tapped gently down onto its register and left to cool naturally when the contraction of the metal on cooling will ensure that it is a secure and permanent fit. Great care must be taken not to overheat the ring, indicated by it turning light metallic blue, as if this happens the temper of the ring will be lost.

36 Engine reassembly – general

1   To ensure maximum life with minimum trouble from a rebuilt engine, not only must everything be correctly assembled, but everything must be spotlessly clean: all the oilways must be clear, locking washers and spring washers must always be fitted where indicated

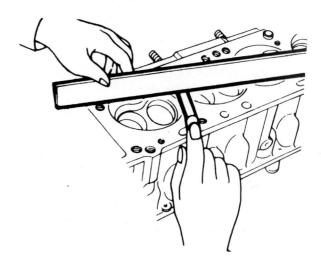

Fig. 1.21 Check the cylinder head for distortion (Sec 33)

and all bearing and other working surfaces must be thoroughly lubricated during assembly.

2   Before assembly begins renew any bolts or studs the threads of which are in any way damaged, and whenever possible use new spring washers.

3   Apart from your normal tools, a supply of clean rags, an oil can filled with engine oil (an empty plastic detergent bottle, thoroughly cleaned and washed out, will do just as well); a new supply of assorted spring washers, a set of new gaskets and a torque wrench should be collected together.

37 Cylinder head – reassembly

1   Oil the valve guides and fit the valves to the seats into which they have been previously ground (Section 29) (photo).

2   Fit a valve spring seat and a new oil seal (photo), then the valve spring and valve spring retainer on each valve (photo).

3   Fit the base of the spring compressor tool on the valve head and compress the valve spring until the collets can be fitted in the grooves of the valve stem. Release the compressor tool and repeat for the remaining valves. When all the collets have been fitted, tap the valve stems with a hammer to ensure all the parts are seated correctly.

38 Engine – reassembly

1   Check the cylinder block for cracks, probe the oil passages and holes with a piece of wire and clean the external surfaces.

2   Renew all gaskets and seals and use plenty of clean engine oil to lubricate the components as they are fitted. Observe absolute cleanliness.

Camshaft and tappets

3   Lubricate and refit the tappet blocks to their original locations with the engine block in the inverted position (photo).

4   Oil the camshaft bearings and gently slide the camshaft into position, taking care not to scratch or damage the bearing surfaces as the cam lobes pass through.

5   Fit the camshaft locking plate so that the word 'lower' is to the bottom when the engine is the right way up (photo). Tighten the securing bolts to the specified torque wrench setting, then check that the camshaft endfloat is within the specified limits. Fit a new lockplate to adjust if required.

Crankshaft and main bearings

6   Install the main bearing shells into their crankcase locations and into the bearing caps (photo). Oil the bearing surfaces and carefully lower the crankshaft into position in the crankcase (photos). Apply

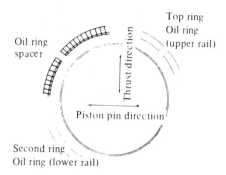

Fig. 1.22 Piston ring gap locations when fitted (Sec 38)

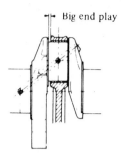

Fig. 1.23 Check the connecting rod big-end float (Sec 38)

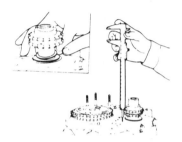

Fig. 1.24 Check the sprockets for alignment – adjust with washers if necessary (inset) (Sec 38)

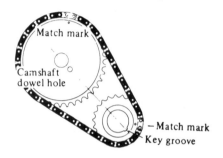

Fig. 1.25 Timing chain and sprocket engagement positions (Sec 38)

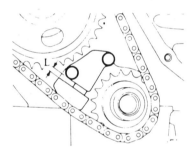

Fig. 1.26 Check the tensioner body-to-slipper rear face clearance (L) (Sec 38)

11 The piston will slide into the cylinder only as far as the piston ring clamp. Gently tap the piston into the bore with a hammer shaft (photo). This should drive the piston and rod assembly into the bore. If this action does not have the desired effect then either the piston rings have not been sufficiently compressed with the piston ring compressor, or the connecting rod has jammed on the crankshaft.

12 Connect each big-end to its appropriate crankshaft journal and fit the big-end cap complete with shells (photo). The caps and rods are numbered 1 to 4 commencing at the timing gear end of the engine and when correctly fitted will have the cap and rod numbers adjacent. Tighten the big-end bolt nuts to the torque given in the Specifications (photo). Use plenty of oil when fitting the connecting rods to the crankshaft and turn the crankshaft so that each big-end bearing is engaged when the respective crankshaft journal is at its lowest point.

13 Check the endfloat of each connecting rod big-end after refitting; this should be within the specified limits (Fig. 1.23).

14 Refit the crankshaft baffle and gauze filter screen (if applicable).

Timing sprockets and chain components

15 Fit the crankshaft sprocket keys and temporarily refit the camshaft and crankshaft sprockets to check their fitted heights. The difference in height between the sprockets must not exceed 0.020 in (0.5 mm). If required, fit an alternative washer under the sprocket(s) to align the two, then remove both sprockets.

16 Place the crankshaft and camshaft sprockets within the timing chain and fit both sprockets, complete with timing chain, to the crankshaft and camshaft simultaneously. When correctly installed, a line drawn through the sprocket centres should also pass through the camshaft dowel hole and the crankshaft sprocket keyway. A double check is the alignment of the sprocket dot punch marks and the bright links on the chain (Fig. 1.25) (photo). Installation of the timing gear will call for rotation of the camshaft and the crankshaft and repositioning of the camshaft sprocket within the loop of the chain on a trial and error basis until the alignment is correct.

17 With the sprockets and chain correctly aligned and located on their shafts, fit the camshaft sprocket retaining bolt and washers and then tighten the bolt to the specified torque (photo).

18 Fit the timing chain tensioner and tighten the securing bolts (photo).

19 Check that the gap between the body of the tensioner and the rear face of the slipper does not exceed 0.59 in (15 mm), dimension L in Fig. 1.26. If the gap is greater than specified, either the chain has stretched badly or the tensioner slipper has worn away and in either

some lithium-based grease to the inner face of the rear oil seal. It can now be positioned approximately on the crankshaft boss.

7   Fit the main bearing caps, complete with shells. Refer to Section 19 for the difference between the main bearing caps of the A10 engine and the A12, A14 and A15 engines. Ensure that the caps are refitted in their original locations. Tighten the main bearing caps bolts, in four stages in the reverse order to Fig. 1.9, to the specified torque setting (photo). When fitting the rear main bearing cap, apply gasket sealant to each contact corner of the crankcase as shown in photo 38.24a.

8   Check that the crankshaft rotates smoothly and recheck the crankshaft endfloat (Section 24).

9   Check that the rear oil seal is located correctly, then fit the endplate in position. Fit the flywheel on the crankshaft and tighten the retaining bolts to the specified torque (photos).

Pistons and connecting rods

10 The pistons, piston rings, and connecting rods, having been assembled with new big-end bearings and gudgeon pins as required, can now be fitted in the cylinders. Arrange the piston ring gaps as shown in Fig. 1.22. Liberally lubricate the rings and pistons. Fit a piston ring compressor on the piston to compress the rings and insert the connecting rod and piston into the cylinder bore. Ensure that it is the correct piston/connecting rod assembly for that particular bore and that the number stamped on the piston head faces to the front of the engine (photos).

37.1 Insert valves into their original locations ...

37.2a ... and fit new seal onto the stems

37.2b Fit valve spring and retainer

38.3 Insert the tappets into their original locations

38.5 Fit the camshaft locking plate with the word 'lower' towards the bottom of the engine (sump end)

38.6a Locate the main bearing shells into their positions in the crankcase. Bearings with oil holes must be fitted to crankcase

38.6b Oil the bearing surfaces ...

38.6c ... and lower the crankshaft into position. The A10 three-bearing crankshaft is shown

38.7a Fitting the rear main bearing cap

38.7b Tighten the main bearing caps using a torque wrench

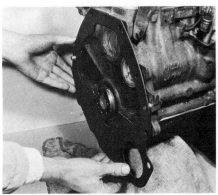

38.9a Locating the rear plate (on the A12 engine), followed by ...

38.9b ... the flywheel ...

38.9c ... and its retaining bolts

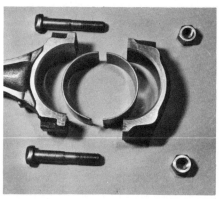
38.10a Connecting rod big-end and bearing assembly

38.10b Insert the piston and connecting rod down into the cylinder bore

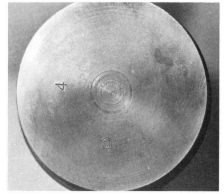
38.10c Check that the number on the piston crown faces to the front of the engine

38.11 Tap the piston into the cylinder with a hammer shaft

38.12a Fit the big-end bearing caps ...

38.12b ... and tighten them with a torque wrench

38.16 The punch mark on the sprocket must align with the bright link on the chain

38.17 Tighten the camshaft sprocket retaining bolt

38.18 Fit the timing chain tensioner

38.20 Fit the oil thrower disc with projecting rim towards the timing chain cover

38.22 Fit the timing chain cover

38.23 Fit the oil pump intake pipe and strainer

38.24a The sump gasket and rear main bearing seal fitted (A12 engine). Note sealant applied to points arrowed

38.24b Carefully refit the sump (A12 engine shown)

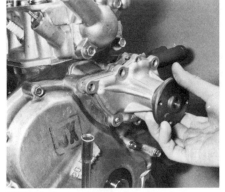

38.25 Refit the water pump

38.26 Refit the crankshaft pulley

38.28 Always fit a new cylinder head gasket

38.30 Lower the cylinder head into position

38.31 Fit the small diameter bolt in the centre hole on the spark plug side of the head

38.32 Tighten the cylinder head bolts to the specified torque

38.33 Insert the pushrods into their original locations

38.35a Fit the new manifold gasket into position over the studs ...

38.35b ... and then refit the manifold assembly

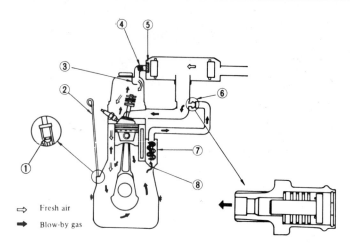

Fig. 1.27 The positive crankcase ventilation (PCV) system (Sec 39)

1	O-ring	5	Filter
2	Dipstick	6	PCV valve
3	Baffle plate	7	Steel net
4	Flame arrester	8	Baffle plate

event the component must be renewed.

20 Fit the oil thrower disc to the crankshaft, ensuring that the projecting rim is towards the timing chain cover (photo).

21 Drift out the timing cover oil seal using a piece of tubing for this purpose. Fit a new seal, ensuring that the lips face inwards. Renew the chain slipper if it is worn.

22 Apply a thin film of gasket cement to the mating surfaces of the timing cover and the cylinder block. Use a new gasket and fit the cover (photo). Secure the cover with the retaining bolts and tighten them to the specified torque.

Sump, water pump and crankshaft pulley

23 Refit the oil pump intake pipe and gauze filter (photo).

24 Apply a thin film of gasket cement to the lower face of the crankcase and stick a new sump gasket into position, so that the holes in the gasket are in alignment with the bolt holes of the crankcase. Apply more gasket cement to the mating surfaces of the sump, being particularly liberal with it at the front and rear and in the corners adjacent to the main bearing caps and timing cover. Offer up the sump and insert the securing bolts. Tighten them progressively in a diametrically opposite sequence (photos).

25 Fit the water pump (photo). Always use a new gasket. Tighten the attaching bolts to the specified torque.

26 Fit the Woodruff key on the crankshaft and then fit the crankshaft pulley (photo). Tighten the pulley securing bolt to the specified torque. Restrain the crankshaft from turning by wedging the flywheel during the tightening operation.

Cylinder head

27 After checking that both the cylinder block and cylinder head mating faces are perfectly clean, lubricate each cylinder bore with engine oil.

28 Always use a new cylinder head gasket as the old gasket will be compressed and not capable of giving a good seal (photo).

29 The cylinder head gasket is of the laminated type, having a steel sheet surface on one face, and this surface should make contact with the face of the cylinder block. Due to the possibility of oil leakage from the cylinder head gasket on the pushrod side, the gasket has been partially treated with sealant in this area only. It is recommended however, that both the mating faces of head and block are smeared with a thin coat of non-setting gasket cement as this will help to protect the surface of the alloy head against corrosion as well as providing a reliable seal.

30 Place the gasket in position on the block (steel side down, jointing material visible). Lightly smear the threads of the cylinder head bolts with grease and push two of the bolts through the head so that as the head is gently lowered into position they will serve as locating dowels to locate the gasket and head (photo).

31 Note that one of the cylinder head bolts is smaller in diameter than the others and has a hollow head. It must be fitted in the centre hole on the spark plug side of the head (photo).

32 Fit the remaining bolts and then tighten them in two or three steps, in the reverse sequence to that shown in Fig. 1.7, to the specified torque (photo).

33 Refit the pushrods in their original positions (photo).

34 Refit the rocker shaft assembly, tightening the pillar bolts to the specified torque. Tighten the centre bolt first and work outwards.

35 Fit a new manifold gasket and then fit the inlet and exhaust manifold assembly (photos). Tighten the securing nuts to their respective torque settings according to engine type.

36 Fit the EGR control valve (A14 and A15 engines).

Valve clearance adjustment

37 The valve clearances should now be adjusted. Rotate the engine during the adjustment procedure by using a spanner or socket on the crankshaft pulley bolt.

38 The valve clearances obviously will have to be set with the engine cold to start with but when the unit is refitted to the vehicle and run up to normal operating temperature, then they should be checked and readjusted when the engine is hot.

39 The valve adjustments may be made with the engine cold but are more accurate when the engine is hot. The importance of correct rocker arm/valve stem clearances cannot be overstressed as they vitally affect the performance of the engine. If the clearances are set too open, the efficiency of the engine is reduced as the valves open later and close earlier than was intended. If, on the other hand, the clearances are set too close there is a danger that the stem will expand upon heating and not allow the valves to close properly which will cause burning of the valve head and seat and possible warping.

40 It is important that the valve clearance is set when the tappet of the valve being adjusted is on the heel of the cam (the lowest point) so that the valve is fully seated. One of two methods may be employed; first place a finger over No 1 spark plug hole, turn the engine and as soon as compression is felt, either observe the piston crown until it reaches its highest point (TDC) and descends about $\frac{1}{8}$ inch (3.175 mm) or using a length of wire as a measure, stop rotating the engine when the wire has passed its highest point and descended about $\frac{1}{8}$ in (3.175 mm). Both the valves for No 1 cylinder may then be set to the specified clearances, and the procedure repeated for the other cylinders.

41 The alternative method of valve clearance adjustment, which avoids the necessity of turning the engine excessively, is to apply the adjustment sequence shown in the following table:

Valve fully open	Check & Adjust
Valve No 8	Valve No 1
Valve No 6	Valve No 3
Valve No 4	Valve No 5
Valve No 7	Valve No 2
Valve No 1	Valve No 8
Valve No 3	Valve No 6
Valve No 5	Valve No 4
Valve No 2	Valve No 7

Counting from the timing cover end of the engine, inlet valves are Nos 2-3-6-7, exhaust valves are Nos 1-4-5-8.

42 Adjustment of the clearance is made by conventional screw and locknut. Insert the feeler blade between the rocker arm face and the valve stem end face. Loosen the locknut, turn the screw until the blade cannot be withdrawn and then loosen the screw until the blade can be just withdrawn (stiffly), by a hard pull. Holding the slotted adjustment screw quite still, tighten the locknut with a ring spanner (photo). When all the valve clearances have been adjusted, recheck them before fitting the rocker box cover complete with a new sealing gasket.

Oil pump and filter

43 Using a new gasket, fit the oil pump to the crankcase, checking that the drivegear meshes correctly (photo).

44 Screw a new oil filter cartridge into position. Lightly grease the rubber sealing ring before fitting it and tighten it by hand pressure only.

Engine ancillary components

45 Using new gaskets, fit the thermostat and thermostat cover. Fit the drivebelt pulley on the water pump (photo). Hold the pulley with a strap or chain wrench when tightening the bolts.

46 Fit the alternator to its mountings and reconnect the slotted adjustment strap. Refit any shim washers located between the alternator and mounting bracket to take up the clearance if required.
47 Locate the drivebelt over the crankshaft, water pump and alternator pulleys and then prise the alternator away from the engine until the belt has a total deflection of $\frac{1}{2}$ in (12 mm) at the centre of its longest run. Tighten the adjustment strap bolt and mounting bolts of the alternator.
48 Fit the carburettor to the manifold (if not previously fitted with the manifold) and the fuel pump to the crankcase, ensuring that new gaskets similar to those originally fitted are used.
49 Reconnect the fuel pipe between the pump and the carburettor.
50 The distributor can now be refitted; the details of this are given in Chapter 4. It is essential that the distributor be correctly installed to ensure the correct timing.
51 Fit the spark plugs, cleaned and correctly gapped (refer to Chapter 4).
52 Fit the distributor cap and HT leads. Connect the HT leads to the spark plugs.
53 Fit the pipe connector to PCV control valve hose and the right-hand engine mounting bracket.
54 Fit the distributor vacuum hose.
55 Fit the oil level dipstick.
56 Fit the clutch assembly to the flywheel and assemble the

transmission to the engine as described in Chapter 5 and 6.
57 On A14 and A15 engines with the air injection emission control system, fit the air pump bracket, air pump and air pump pulley. Fit the idler pulley bracket, air pump drivebelt and idler pulley. Adjust the air pump belt tension so that a deflection of 0.31 to 0.47 in (8 to 12 mm) is obtained when a pressure of 22 lb (10 kg) is applied midway between the crank pulley and the air pump pulley.

39 Positive crankcase ventilation (PCV) system – description and maintenance

1 The closed type of crankcase ventilation system fitted to models covered by this manual draws air from the air cleaner and passes it through a mesh type flame trap to a hose connected to the rocker cover. The air is then passed through the inside of the engine and back to the inlet manifold via a hose and control valve. This means that fumes in the crankcase are drawn into the combustion chambers, burnt and passed to the exhaust system.
2 When the car is being driven at full throttle conditions, the inlet manifold depression is not sufficient to draw all the fumes through the control valve and into the inlet manifold. Under these operating conditions the crankcase ventilation flow is reversed with the fumes passing into the air cleaner instead of the inlet manifold.

38.42 Adjust the valve clearances

38.43 Fit the oil pump with a new filter

38.45 Fit the drivebelt pulley on the water pump

38.50 Crankshaft pulley and timing cover marks in alignment (TDC)

3   To prevent engine oil being drawn into the inlet manifold a baffle plate and steel mesh is positioned in the crankcase.
4   Maintenance of the system simply involves inspection and renewal of any suspect parts. Check the condition of the rocker cover to air cleaner hose and crankcase to inlet manifold hose. Check for blockage, deterioration or collapse of the hoses and renew as necessary.
5   Inspect the seats on the engine oil filler and dipstick. If defective renew the seals.
6   Operation of the control valve may be checked by running the engine at a steady idle speed and disconnecting the hose from the control valve. Listen for a hissing noise from the valve when the hose has been detached. Now place a finger over the valve inlet: a strong suction should be felt immediately as the finger closes the inlet.
7   If the valve is faulty it must be renewed as it is not practical to dismantle it.

40 Engine/transmission refitting – general

1   Although the engine can be refitted by one man using a suitable winch, it is easier if two are present: one to lower the assembly into the engine compartment and the other to guide the assembly into position and to ensure it does not foul anything.
2   At this stage one or two tips may come in useful. Ensure all the loose leads, cables, etc are tucked out of the way. If not it is easy to trap one and so cause much additional work after the engine is refitted.
3   Two pairs of hands are better than one when refitting the bonnet. Do not tighten the bonnet securing bolts fully until it is ascertained that the bonnet is on straight.

41 Engine/transmission – refitting

1   Raise the engine/transmission unit and either roll the vehicle forward under it or if the hoist is mobile roll it forward, so that the unit is suspended above the engine compartment.
2   Lower the assembly into the engine compartment. Ensure that nothing is fouled during the operation.
3   The engine is installed by following, in the reverse order, the procedures given for removal. The following points must be noted.
4   With the engine in position and located on its mountings, refit the respective retaining bolts and nuts with washers as applicable.
5   Refit the buffer rods and if necessary adjust their lengths as required so that the rubbers are not distorted when fully fitted. Tighten all mounting and buffer retaining nuts and bolts to their specified torque wrench settings.
6   On models fitted with air conditioning, refit the compressor before reattaching the driveshafts and gearshift linkages.
7   Working underneath, reattach the driveshafts on each side.
8   Relocate and insert the retaining bolts to secure the gearshift location plate to the differential housing, three bolts at the rear and one on the left-hand side.
9   Re-engage the gearshift rods and secure with clips. If the rod rubber bushes are worn or defective, they must be renewed before fitting the rods. Each rod is fitted with a flat washer against its flange, the rod is inserted into its bush and then a spring and flat washer fitted before inserting the spring clip to secure (photo).
10 Reattach the exhaust pipe mounting plate to the differential housing (two bolts), and the downpipe to the manifold (two nuts).
11 Working from above, reattach the speedometer cable and the clutch cable and bracket.
12 Reconnect the respective wiring connectors, ensuring that the lead colours are aligned and the respective connections are secure.
13 Reconnect the fuel line to the fuel pump.
14 Reconnect the heater hoses.
15 Reconnect the carburettor throttle and (if applicable) choke cables, referring to Chapter 3 for adjustment.
16 On USA models, reconnect the various emission control hoses and wiring connectors – refer to Chapter 3 if necessary.
17 On power steering equipped models, relocate the pump and adjust

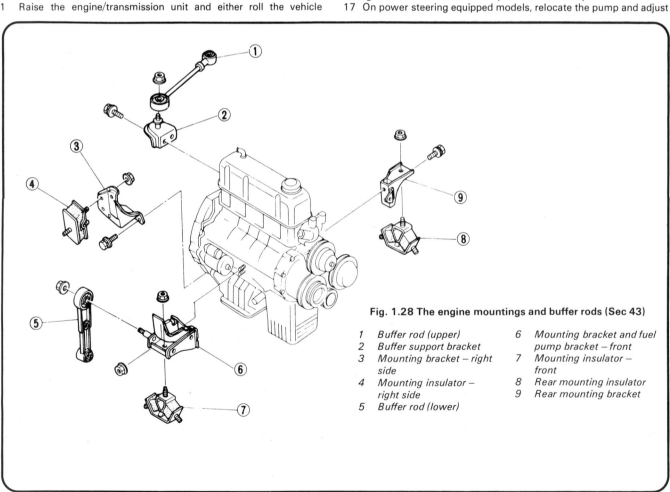

Fig. 1.28 The engine mountings and buffer rods (Sec 43)

1 Buffer rod (upper)	6 Mounting bracket and fuel
2 Buffer support bracket	pump bracket – front
3 Mounting bracket – right	7 Mounting insulator –
side	front
4 Mounting insulator –	8 Rear mounting insulator
right side	9 Rear mounting bracket
5 Buffer rod (lower)	

the drivebelt.

18 Refit the air filter onto the carburettor, ensuring that the rubber seal is in good condition, and refit the three retaining bolts to secure the unit. Do not forget to engage the brake vacuum hose location clip under the filter attachment bolts at the rear. Insert a new element and fit the lid.

19 Refit the radiator and reattach the top and bottom hoses, also the fan lead. Do not forget to connect the oil cooler pipes to their fixings below the radiator on automatic transmission models.

20 Top up the engine and transmission oil levels using the correct grade and quantity of lubricant, but make sure that the drain plugs have been refitted first!

21 Refill the cooling system as given in Chapter 2.

22 The engine should now be ready for restarting, but make a final check to ensure that all fittings and associated components are reassembled and secure.

23 Refit the bonnet and check its alignment.

42 Engine – adjustment after major overhaul

1 With the engine refitted to the vehicle, give a final visual check to see that everything has been reconnected and that no loose rags or tools have been left within the engine compartment.

2 Turn the engine idle speed adjusting screw in about ½ turn (to

41.9 Gearshift rod-to-bracket location showing washer positions

43.5a The rear engine mounting removal

43.5b General view of the rear engine mounting unit (engine removed for clarity)

43.5c Front engine mounting unit (engine removed)

43.5d Removing the side mounting

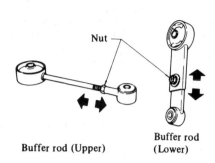

Fig. 1.29 Adjust length of buffer rod to prevent rubber distortion
(Sec 43)

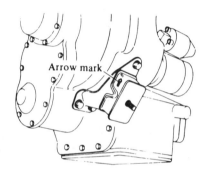

Fig. 1.30 Arrow mark location on front insulator to point upwards
(Sec 43)

increase slow running once the engine is started) (Chapter 3).
3   Restarting the engine may take a little longer than usual as the
fuel pump and carburettor will be empty and need initial filling.
4   As soon as the engine starts, push the choke in (manual choke
models) until the engine runs at a fast tickover and examine the engine

for leaks. Check particularly the water hoses and oil filter and fuel hose
unions.
5   Run the vehicle on the road until normal operating temperature is
reached. Check the valve clearances while the engine is hot, as
described in Section 38 of this Chapter. Readjust the engine idling
speed (Chapter 3).
6   If many new internal components have been fitted, the engine
should be treated as if it were new and run-in at reduced revolutions
for the first 500 miles (800 km) or so.
7   After 500 miles (800 km) running, the   engine oil should be
changed (particularly where the majority of the internal components
have been renewed or reconditioned).
8   At the same time check the torque setting of the cylinder head
bolts with the cylinder head **cold**. Follow the sequence given in Fig.
1.7.

43 Engine mountings – renewal

1   With time the bonded rubber insulators will perish, causing undue
vibration and noise from the engine. Severe juddering when reversing
or when moving off from rest is also likely and is a further sign of worn
mounting rubbers.
2   The mounting rubber insulators can be changed with the engine in
the car.
3   Apply the handbrake firmly, jack up the front of the car, and place
stands under the front of the car.
4   Lower the jack, and place the jack under the sump to take the
weight of the engine. Use a block of wood to spread the load.
5   Undo the large bolt which holds each of the engine mountings to
the subframe (photo).
6   Raise the engine sufficiently high to enable the mounting insulator
brackets to be disconnected from the sump, clutch housing and
transmission. If the engine is raised too high the buffer rods and
exhaust pipe could be damaged. If you are uncertain it is better to
disconnect them.
7   Fitting new flexible insulators is a reversal of removal, but on
reassembly and with the engine lowered, check that the buffer rod
rubbers are not distorted. If they are then loosen off the locknut(s) and
adjust the length of the rod(s) to suit, then retighten the locknuts to
secure.
8   Note that when in position the front insulation must be fitted so
that the arrow marks point upwards (Fig. 1.30).

44 Fault diagnosis – engine

Note: *When investigating starting and uneven running faults do not be tempted into snap diagnosis. Start from the beginning of the check procedure and follow it through. It will take less time in the long run. Poor performance from an engine in terms of power and economy is not normally diagnosed quickly. In any event the ignition and fuel systems must be checked first before assuming any further investigation needs to be made.*

Symptom	Reasons
Engine will not turn over when starter switch is operated	Flat battery Bad battery connections Bad connections at solenoid switch and/or starter motor Starter motor jammed Defective starter solenoid Starter motor defective 'N' or 'P' not selected – automatic transmission models
Engine turns over normally but fails to start	No spark at plugs Too much fuel reaching the engine (flooding)
Engine starts but runs unevenly and misfires	Ignition and/or fuel system faults Incorrect valve clearances Burnt out valves Worn out piston rings
Lack of power	Ignition and/or fuel system faults Incorrect valve clearances Burnt out valves Worn out piston rings
Excessive oil consumption	Oil leaks from crankshaft rear oil seal, timing cover gasket and oil seal, rocker cover gasket, oil filter gasket, sump gasket, sump plug washer. Worn piston rings or cylinder bores resulting in oil being burnt by engine Worn valve guides and/or defective valve stem seals
Excessive mechanical noise from engine	Wrong valve clearances Worn crankshaft bearings Worn cylinder (piston slap) Slack or worn timing chain and sprockets

Chapter 2 Cooling system

For modifications, and information applicable to later models, see Supplement at end of manual

Contents

Specifications

System type .... Thermo-syphon with pump assistance

Radiator type .... Corrugated fin

Filler cap opening pressure .... 13 lbf/in² (0.9 kgf/cm²)

Thermostat
Type .... Wax pellet
Opening temperature:
    Standard .... 177° to 182°F (80.5° to 83.5°C)
    Cold climates .... 188° to 193°F (86.5° to 89.5°C)

Fan motor
Voltage 12
Wattage 85
Speed .... 2350 to 2650 rpm

Temperature sensing switch
Radiator cooling fan:
    On .... 181° to 189°F (83° to 87°C)
    Off .... 169° to 183°F (76° to 84°C)
Auxiliary cooling fan (A14 and A15 engines):
    On .... 158° to 165°F (70° to 74°C)
    Off .... 145° to 160°F (63° to 91°C)

Water pump drivebelt deflection .... 0.31 to 0.47 in (8 to 12 mm)

Coolant capacity
A10 and A12 with manual transmission and heater .... 9.75 Imp pint (11.75 US pint) (5.5 litre)
A10 and A12 with automatic transmission and heater .... 10.5 Imp pint (12.5 US pint) (5.9 litre)
A14 and A15 engines with heater .... 10.5 Imp pint (12.5 US pint) (5.9 litre)

Torque wrench settings

	lbf ft	kgf m
Water pump retaining bolts	6.5 to 10.1	0.9 to 1.4
Water outlet retaining bolt	5.8 to 8.0	0.8 to 1.1
Temperature sensing switches	14 to 18	2 to 2.5

1 General description

The cooling system comprises the radiator, top and bottom water hoses, water pump, cylinder head and block water jackets, radiator cap with pressure relief valve and flow and return heater hoses. An electrically operated and controlled fan is mounted directly on the radiator with a coolant temperature sensing switch fitted at the radiator outlet. A thermostat is located in a recess at the front of the cylinder head.

The A14 and A15 engine models have an auxiliary fan fitted behind the engine near the carburettor. The function of this fan is to eliminate problems encountered when restarting the engine in very hot weather. The auxiliary cooling fan is activated by a coolant temperature sensing switch located in the radiator outlet hose.

The pressure type radiator filler cap operates the cooling system at higher than atmospheric pressure. The higher pressure raises the boiling point of the coolant and increases the cooling efficiency of the system.

The principle of the system is that cold coolant in the bottom of the radiator circulates through the bottom radiator hose to the water pump, where the pump impeller pushes the coolant round the cylinder block and head, through the various passages to cool the cylinder bores, combustion areas and valve seats. When sufficient heat has been absorbed by the coolant, and the engine has reached an efficient working temperature, the coolant passes from the cylinder head past the open thermostat into the top radiator hose and then into the radiator header tank. The coolant then travels down the radiator tubes where it is rapidly cooled by the in-rush of air, when the vehicle is in motion, and by the cooling fan. The coolant, now cooled, reaches the bottom of the radiator and the cycle is repeated.

When the engine is cold the thermostat remains closed until the coolant reaches a pre-determined temperature (see Specifications). This assists the rapid warm-up of the engine.

Water temperature is measured by an electro-sensitive capsule located immediately below the thermostat housing. Connection between the transmitter capsule and the temperature gauge is made by a single lead and connector. The cooling system also provides heat for the heating system. The heater matrix is fed directly with coolant from the hottest part of the cooling system, the cylinder head, returning through a connection on the bottom radiator hose.

The auxiliary cooling fan fitted to A14 and A15 (USA models) is designed to reduce the temperature within the fuel lines and carburettor above a given engine temperature (162°F – 72°C) when the ignition is turned off. The fan will operate for approximately 17 minutes, unless the ignition is switched on during this period in which case it will automatically cut off. A fan motor timer unit is fitted and this is mounted on the clutch pedal bracket.

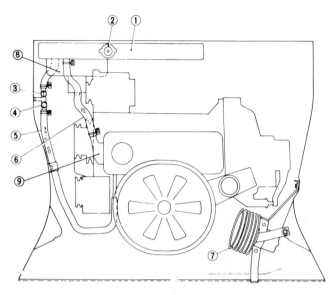

Fig. 2.1 Cooling system (Sec 1)

1	Radiator	5	Inlet hose
2	Filler cap	6	Outlet hose
3	Temperature sensing switch (cooling fan)	7	Auxiliary electric cooling fan (if fitted)
4	Temperature sensing switch (auxiliary fan) (A14 and A15 engines)	8	Radiator electric cooling fan
		9	Thermostat

2 Cooling system – draining

1   Should it be necessary to drain the cooling system, it can be partially drained via the radiator drain tap or fully drained from both the radiator and cylinder block drain taps, dependent on the job at hand. Should the system have to be left empty for any reason, both the cylinder block and radiator must be drained, otherwise with a partly drained system corrosion of the water pump impeller seal face may occur with subsequent early failure of the pump seal and bearing.

2   Place the car on a level surface and have ready a container having a capacity of two gallons which will slide beneath the radiator and sump.

3   Move the heater control on the facia to 'warm' and remove the radiator cap. If hot, remove the cap very slowly, first covering it with a cloth to remove the danger of scalding when the pressure in the system is released.

2.4a Radiator drain tap

2.4b Coolant drain plug on cylinder block

4   Unscrew the radiator drain tap (photo) at the base of the radiator and then when coolant ceases to flow into the receptacle, repeat the operation by unscrewing the cylinder block plug located on the engine (photo). If the coolant has recently been renewed, retain it for further use. The coolant should be renewed every 24 000 miles (40 000 km) or two years.

3   Cooling system – flushing

1   The radiator and waterways in the engine after some time may become restricted or even blocked with scale or sediment which reduce the efficiency of the cooling system. When this condition occurs or the coolant appears rusty or dark in colour the system should be flushed. In severe cases reverse flushing may be required as described later.
2   Fully drain the coolant as described in the previous Section.
3   Insert a water hose into the radiator filler neck and allow water to flow through the system and out of the drain cocks.
4   In severe cases of cooling system contamination it will be necessary to reverse flush the system. To do this first remove the radiator as given in Section 6.
5   With the radiator removed, invert it and insert a water hose into its bottom outlet pipe. Continue flushing until clear water emerges from the radiator top tank.
6   To flush the engine water jackets, set the heater controls to the 'warm' position, remove the thermostat as described in Section 7 and insert the water hose into the thermostat location. Run water through the system until clean water emerges from the water pump inlet. During this operation take particular care not to splash water over the ignition system or it will require drying out before restarting the engine.
7   Whilst the thermostat is removed you may wish to test its efficiency as described in Section 7.
8   Refit the thermostat and radiator as given in Sections 6 and 7 and refill the cooling system as described in Section 4.
9   In extremely bad cases of blockage a proprietary flushing compound may be used in accordance with the maker's instructions. Make sure that such a compound is suitable for the engine in your car.

4   Cooling system – filling

1   Check that the heater control is set in the 'warm' position.
2   Screw in the radiator drain tap and the cylinder block drain plug.
3   Pour coolant slowly into the radiator so that air can pass through the thermostat bleed hole without being trapped in a coolant passage.
4   Fill to the correct level, which is 1 inch (25.4 mm) below the base of the radiator filler neck, and refit the filler cap.
5   Run the engine to normal operating temperature, check for leaks and recheck the coolant level.

5   Antifreeze mixture

1   The cooling system should be filled with antifreeze coolant (ethylene glycol base) or fresh soft water and a corrosion inhibitor. The antifreeze solution should be renewed every 2 years. Antifreeze solutions of good quality will prevent corrosion and rusting.
2   Before adding antifreeze to the system, check all hose connections and check the tightness of the cylinder head bolts as such solutions are searching. The cooling system should be drained and refilled with clean water as previously explained, before adding antifreeze.
3   The quantity of antifreeze which should be used for various levels of protection is given in the table below:

Minimum temperature	Antifreeze requirement		
	Imp qt	litres	US qt
14°F (–10°C)	1	1.1	1.12
5°F (–15°C)	1.37	1.5	1.62
–4°F (–20°C)	1.67	1.9	2
–13°F (–25°C)	2	2.2	2.37
–22°F (–30°C)	2	2.3	2.37
–31°F (–35°C)	2.25	2.5	2.62
–40°F (–40°C)	2.37	2.7	2.87

4   Where the cooling system contains an antifreeze solution any topping-up should be done with a solution made up in similar proportions to the original in order to avoid dilution.

Fig. 2.2 Testing the thermostat – check lift height 'H' (Sec 7)

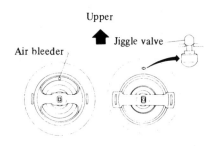

Fig. 2.3 Thermostat air bleed hole to face upwards when fitted (Sec 7)

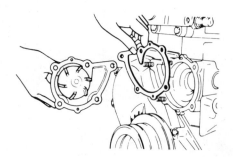

Fig. 2.4 Refit the water pump using a new gasket (Sec 9)

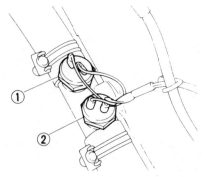

Fig. 2.5 The auxiliary cooling fan (1) and radiator fan (2) sensor switch positions (A14 and A15 engines) (Sec 12)

6.2 Radiator top hose

6.3 The fan shroud-to-radiator retaining bolts (arrowed)

6.4a Remove grille panel retaining screws from top edge ...

6.4b .. and from the front ...

6.4c ... then remove the grille panel

6.6 Lift the radiator unit out wth care

6 Radiator – removal, inspection and refitting

1   Drain the cooling system as described in Section 2.
2   Disconnect the radiator upper and lower hoses (photo).
3   The fan motor unit can be left attached to the radiator and removed with it, or removed separately if preferred. In this instance detach the wiring to the fan motor, unscrew and remove the fan unit retaining bolts from the radiator (photo) and withdraw the fan unit with its shroud.
4   To gain access to the radiator retaining bolts, remove the outer grille panel which is secured by six self-tapping screws (photos).
5   On automatic transmission models, disconnect the oil cooler inlet and outlet hoses from the base of the radiator, allowing for spillage. Plug or clamp the pipes to prevent spillage.
6   Remove the radiator retaining bolts and lift out the radiator, taking care not to damage its core (photo).
7   Clean the exterior of the radiator matrix by using a compressed air jet or a strong jet of water to clean away road dirt, flies or other foreign matter.
8   With the radiator removed from the car and the fan and its shroud detached, the radiator can be inspected for any signs of leaks or damage. Minor leaks may be repaired by soldering but this is best left to a specialist. Clean the inside of the radiator by flushing, particularly reverse flushing, as described in Section 3.
9   Inspect the radiator hoses for cracks, internal and external deterioration and damage by overtightening of the securing clips. Check that the overflow pipe is clear. Renew any suspect hoses and hose clips.
10 Refitting of the radiator is the reverse of the removal procedure. Take care not to damage the radiator fins and core tubes when refitting the radiator in the car.
11 Ensure that the respective hoses are fully located and secured. The hose arrow marks should be visible from above when fitted, (where applicable), and each hose must have a clearance of 1.18 in (30 mm) between itself and surrounding components. On models fitted with air conditioning a clearance of at least 0.71 in (18 mm) must be kept between the compressor and hose.
12 When the fan is refitted, ensure that its wires are engaged under the location clip on the shroud and also that the fan-to-shroud clearance is equal all round.
13 Where applicable, reconnect the oil cooler hoses and on completion check the automatic transmission oil level as given in Chapter 6. Top up if required.
14 Refill the cooling system and check for any signs of leaks on completion with the engine running and at its normal operating temperature.

7 Thermostat – removal, testing and refitting

1   The wax pellet type thermostat is located in the thermostat housing at the cylinder head coolant outlet. The thermostat controls the flow of coolant, facilitating fast engine warm-up and regulating coolant temperature. The thermostat is designed to open and close at predetermined temperatures, and if suspect, should be removed and tested as described below.
2   Drain off enough coolant through the radiator drain tap so that the coolant level is below the thermostat housing joint face. A good indication that the correct level has been reached is when the cooling tubes are exposed when viewed through the radiator filler cap.
3   Disconnect the upper radiator hose at the coolant outlet and on engines with an air injection system, disconnect the air hose at the check valve. Unscrew the retaining bolts and remove the thermostat cover, gasket and thermostat (photo).
4   To test whether the unit is serviceable, suspend the thermostat by a piece of string in a pan of water being heated. Using a thermometer, with reference to the opening and closing temperature in Specifications, its operation may be checked. The thermostat should be renewed if it is stuck open or closed or it fails to operate at the specified temperature. The operation of a thermostat is not instantaneous and sufficient time must be allowed for movement during testing. Never refit a faulty unit – leave it out if no new unit is available immediately.
5   Refitting of the thermostat is a reversal of the removal procedure. Ensure the mating faces of the housing are clean. Use a new gasket

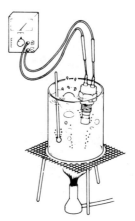

Fig. 2.6 Sensor switch test method (Sec 12)

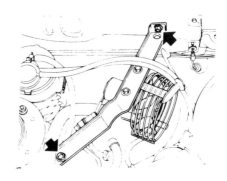

Fig. 2.7 Auxiliary cooling fan location. Securing bolts arrowed (Sec 13)

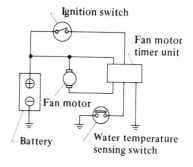

Fig. 2.8 Auxiliary cooling fan electrical circuit diagram (Sec 13)

with jointing compound. The word 'TOP' which appears on the thermostat face must be visible from above (with the air leak hole or jiggle valve facing upwards as in Fig. 2.3).
6   Top up the cooling system and check for leaks.

8 Water pump – description

The water pump is of the conventional impeller type, driven by a pulley belt from the crankshaft. The impeller chamber is built into, and forms part of, the timing cover. The water pump detachable body is of die-cast aluminium in which runs the shaft. The shaft is fitted with bearings which are a shrink fit in the body, therefore the water pump should not be dismantled. In the event of leakage or failure of the water pump, it must be renewed as an assembly on an exchange basis.

7.3 Remove the thermostat cover and thermostat

11.4 The radiator cooling fan sensor switch (A10 and A12 engines)

15.2 Water temperature gauge transmitter unit position in the cylinder head

If the pump is squeaky in operation, try using a proprietary water pump seal lubricant before deciding to remove it. Sometimes a teaspoonful of hydraulic fluid will suffice for this purpose.

9 Water pump – removal and refitting

1   Drain the cooling system as described in Section 2.
2   Slacken the alternator mountings and adjustment strap bolt, push the alternator in towards the engine and slip the belt from the driving pulleys.
3   Unscrew and remove the four bolts which secure the pulley to the hub. Hold the pulley from turning with a strap wrench, or by gripping an old drivebelt around it.
4   Unscrew and remove the securing nuts and bolts from the water pump housing flange and withdraw the water pump. Should the pump be stuck to the face of the timing cover, do not attempt to prise the mating flange apart as this will damage the soft aluminium and cause leaks after refitting. Grip the shaft extension housing firmly and lever from side to side to break the seal.
5   If on inspection the pump shows signs of advanced corrosion and/or there is excessive bearing wear, the unit must be renewed.
6   Refitting is a reversal of removal, but ensure that the mating faces are clean and free from old pieces of gasket. Use a new gasket coated both sides with jointing compound and tighten the securing nuts to the specified torque.
7   Adjust the tension of the drivebelt, as described in Section 10.
8   Refill the cooling system (Section 4).

10 Drivebelt – adjustment and renewal

1   The correct drivebelt tension must be maintained. If it is over-tightened the bearings in the water pump and the alternator may wear prematurely. If it is slack, it will slip and cause overheating and a discharged battery through low alternator output.
2   The drivebelt is correctly tensioned when a total movement of $\frac{1}{2}$ in (12 mm) can be obtained at the centre of the longest run of the belt. Always adjust the drivebelt with the engine cold. Slacken the alternator mounting bolts and the slotted adjustment strap bolt. Prise the alternator away from the engine until the correct tension is obtained. It will be easier to achieve the correct tension if the alternator bolts are only slackened sufficiently to permit it to move stiffly. Always apply leverage to the drive end housing when tilting the alternator and never to the diode end housing, or the alternator will be damaged at the casing. Always recheck the drivebelt tension after the alternator mounting and adjustment strap bolts have been tightened.
4   Where the drivebelt is to be removed, which is normally only necessary where it is found to be cracked or badly worn and stretched, loosen off the adjustment completely as described and disengage the old belt from its pulleys. On some models it will also be necessary to remove the compressor drive pulley belt (air conditioned models) and (on models with power steering) the steering pump drivebelt.
5   Locate the new belt and adjust as given above. After a small initial mileage has been covered, recheck the belt tension and take up any slack caused by the new belt stretching.

11 Radiator cooling fan – testing, removal and refitting

1   If the water temperature gauge is showing a high reading then one obviously suspects the thermostat or cooling fan, if nothing more obvious like coolant leaks are the cause. Check the gauge for accuracy also (Section 15).
2   In the case of an electrical cooling fan it is not easy to determine when, or if, it is working, especially since it is thermostatically controlled by the thermostatic sensor switch and is not always running.
3   Obviously, if the engine has been working hard (eg after climbing a longish hill), then one simply looks at the fan and sees whether it is working or not. If it is, then you have some other reason for the high temperature, and should check the fault diagnosis chart in this Chapter.
4   Having decided the fan is not working, proceed as follows. First, turn on the ignition and then short-circuit the thermostat switch; this is in the insert pipe in the bottom hose on the left-hand side, and stands up like a tee-piece (photo). If the fan now runs, the thermostat switch is faulty and should be renewed. If not, check that the feed cable to the thermostat switch is live, using a test lamp or voltmeter. For the circuit wiring diagram refer to Chapter 10.
5   If all is satisfactory so far, check the relay unit outlet feed wire to the thermoswitch, which should be live when the switch is short-circuited, and the main feed wire, which should be permanently live whilst the ignition is on. If not, check the fused end of the cable at the fuse box.
6   If all tests are still satisfactory next check the blue wire at the fan relay: this should only be live when the thermostat is short-circuited. If it is all right it indicates that the fan motor is probably defective: this must be removed and renewed.
7   Disconnect the connectors to the fan and then remove the bolts that secure it to the radiator. The fan can now be lifted out. Refitting is the reverse of removal.

12 Water temperature sensing switch (radiator fan) – removal, testing and refitting

1   The water temperature sensing switch for controlling the radiator cooling fan is located in the insert pipe in the bottom radiator hose. On A14 and A15 engines there are two sensing switches, one for the radiator fan and the other for the auxiliary cooling fan. Both are removed and tested in the same manner.
2   Drain the cooling system as described in Section 2.
3   Disconnect the leads and unscrew the water temperature sensing switch.
4   Check the operation of the switch by submerging the temperature sensing unit in water as shown in Fig. 2.6. Gradually heat the water to 194°F (90°C). Never boil the water.
5   Check that the switch comes on in the range given in the Specifications at the beginning of this Chapter and goes off when the temperature is outside the specified range. Renew a defective switch.
6   Refitting is the reverse of the removal procedure. Tighten the switch to the specified torque setting.

7   Refill the cooling system and check for leaks as described in Section 4.

13 Auxiliary (carburettor cooling) fan – removal, testing and refitting

1   Detach the lead wires to the fan at their connectors.
2   Unscrew and remove the two fan unit-to-support bracket bolts and remove the fan unit.
3   To test the fan motor first check for continuity between the lead wires.
4   Connect one terminal to a test lead running from the battery positive terminal and ground (earth) the other terminal. If the fan fails to operate then it is defective and must be renewed.
5   Refit the fan in the reverse order to removal.
6   If the fan timer unit is suspected of malfunction, its test procedures are given in Chapter 10.

14 Auxiliary fan sensing switch – removal, testing and refitting

1   The auxiliary fan sensing switch is activated according to the coolant temperature. It is similar to, and mounted in line with, the radiator cooling fan sensor switch.

2   The auxiliary fan sensor switch is removed, tested and refitted in the same manner as the radiator cooling fan sensor switch (see Section 12), but note that the switch operating temperatures are different.

15 Water temperature gauge – fault finding

1   Correct operation of the water temperature gauge is very important as the engine can otherwise overheat without it being observed.
2   The gauge is an electrically operated instrument comprising a transmitter unit screwed into the front of the cylinder head (photo) and transmitting through a cable to the dial mounted on the instrument panel. The instrument only operates when the ignition is switched on.
3   Where the water temperature gauge reads high-low intermittently, or not at all, then first check the security of the connecting cable between the transmitter unit and the gauge.
4   Disconnect the connector from the transmitter unit and switch on the ignition, when the gauge should read COLD. Now earth the cable to the engine block, when the gauge needed should indicate HOT. This test proves the gauge to be functional and the fault must therefore lie in the cable or transmitter unit. Renew as appropriate.
5   If the fuel gauge shows signs of malfunction at the same time as the water temperature gauge then a fault in the voltage stabilizer may be the cause.

16 Fault diagnosis – cooling system

Symptom	Reason(s)
Overheating	Electric fan faulty Low coolant level Pump drivebelt slack Thermostat not operating Radiator pressure cap faulty or of wrong type Defective water pump Cylinder head gasket blowing Radiator core clogged Radiator blocked Binding brakes
Engine running too cool	Defective or missing thermostat Faulty water temperature gauge Faulty temperature sensing switch
Loss of coolant	Leaking radiator or hoses Cylinder head gasket leaking Leaking cylinder block core plugs Faulty radiator filler cap or wrong type fitted

Chapter 3 Fuel, exhaust and emission systems

For modifications, and information applicable to later models, see Supplement at end of manual

Contents

Specifications

Air cleaner type .... Disposable element type, with air temperature control device on some models

Fuel pump .... Diaphragm type, mechanically driven by camshaft eccentric

Fuel tank
Location .... Rear mounted
Capacity .... 11.0 Imp gal (13.25 US gal) (50 litres)

Carburettor type
A10 engine .... Hitachi DCG 286-6D
A12 engine .... Hitachi DCG 306-6D
A14 engine (1979 models):
    California models .... Hitachi DCH 306-75
    Non-California models .... Hitachi DCH 306-76
    Canada models .... Hitachi DCH 306-74
A14 engine (1980 models):
    California models .... Hitachi DCH 306-75
    Non-California models .... Hitachi DCH 306-76
    Canada models .... Hitachi DCH 306-74

A14 engine (1980 models):
  California models .... DCH 306-112
  Non-California models .... DCH 306-102
  Canada models .... DCH 306-74
A15 engine (1981 models):
  California models .... DCR 306-113
  Non-California models .... DCR 306-103
  Canada models .... DCR 306-123

Carburettor specifications

A10 and A12 engines

	DCG 286-6D		DCG 306-6D	
	Primary	Secondary	Primary	Secondary
Choke diameter in (mm)	1.024 (26)	1.102 (28)	1.024 (26)	1.181 (30)
Venturi diameter in (mm)	0.748 (19)	0.945 (24)	0.787 (20)	1.024 (26)
Main jet	92	140	96	150
Main air bleed	80	80	80	80
Slow air bleed	220	100	220	100
Power jet	45		60	
Main nozzle in (mm)	0.083 (2.1)	0.091 (2.3)	0.083 (2.1)	0.110 (2.8)
Engine idle speed (all models)	700 rpm			

A14 engine (1979 models)

	DCH 306-75		DCH 306-76/DCH 306-74	
	Primary	Secondary	Primary	Secondary
Choke diameter in (mm)	1.02 (26)	1.181 (30)	1.02 (26)	1.181 (30)
Venturi diameter in (mm)	0.906 (23)	1.063 (27)	0.906 (23)	1.063 (27)
Main jet	107	145	105	145
Main air bleed	95	80	95	80
Slow jet	45	50	45	50
Power jet	43		40	
Engine idle speed/CO% (air off) (all models)	700 rpm/CO2 $\pm$ 1%			
Fast idle speed (at 2nd cam stop)*	1900 to 2700 rpm			

A14 engine (1980 models)

	DCH 306-112		DCH 306-102	
	Primary	Secondary	Primary	Secondary
Choke diameter in (mm)	1.02 (26)	1.18 (30)	1.02 (26)	1.18 (30)
Venturi diameter in (mm)	0.91 (23)	1.06 (27)	0.87 (22)	1.06 (27)
Main jet	107	145	107	143
Main air bleed	80	80	65	60
Slow jet	45	50	45	50
Power jet	38		43	

Engine idle speed* .... 750 $\pm$ 50 rpm
Fast idle speed (at 2nd cam stop):*
  California models .... 2300 to 3100 rpm
  Non-California models .... 2400 to 3200 rpm
  Canada models .... 1900 to 2700 rpm

A15 engine (1981 models)

	DCR 306-113		DCR 306-103	
	Primary	Secondary	Primary	Secondary
Choke diameter in (mm)	1.02 (26)	1.18 (30	1.02 (26)	1.18 (30)
Venturi diameter in (mm)	0.91 (23)	1.06 (27)	0.91 (23)	1.06 (27)
Main jet	113	125	114	125
Main air bleed	60	80	80	80
Slow jet	45	50	45	50
Slow air bleed	190	80	190	100
Power jet	35		35	

	DCR 306-123	
Choke diameter in (mm)	1.02 (26)	1.18 (30)
Venturi diameter in (mm)	0.83 (21)	1.06 (27)
Main jet	100	145
Main air bleed	70	80
Slow jet	43	70
Slow air bleed	170	100
Power jet	40	

Engine idle speed* .... 750 $\pm$ 50 rpm
Fast idle speed (at 2nd cam stop):*
  California models .... 2300 to 3100 rpm
  Non-California models .... 2400 to 3200 rpm
  Canada models .... 1900 to 2700 rpm

*Refer also to vehicle decal; follow decal information if different from above

Torque wrench settings

	lbf ft	kgf m
Anti-diesel solenoid valve	13 to 16	1.8 to 2.2
Catalytic converter bolts	23 to 31	3.2 to 4.3
Catalytic converter guard plate bolts	4.6 to 6.1	0.6 to 0.8

1 General description

The fuel system comprises a fuel tank at the rear of the vehicle, a mechanical fuel pump driven from the engine and a Hitachi carburettor. A disposable type fuel filter is fitted in the fuel line between the tank and the fuel pump.

The fuel pump draws petrol from the fuel tank and delivers it to the carburettor. The level of the petrol in the carburettor float chamber controlled by a float operated needle valve. Petrol flows past the needle valve until the float rises sufficiently to close the valve. The pump will then freewheel under the slight back pressure until the petrol level drops. The needle valve will open and petrol will again flow past the needle valve until the level in the float chamber rises again to close the needle valve.

Three types of emission control system may be fitted. The crankcase emission control system is used on all vehicles. The exhaust emission control and evaporative emission control systems are used on models exported to Canada and USA.

Vehicles operated in areas controlled by the US Federal Regulations on air pollution must have their engines and ancillary equipment modified and accurately tuned so that carbon monoxide, hydrocarbons and nitrogen oxides produced by the engine are within finely controlled limits. To achieve this there are several systems used. Depending on the anti-pollution standard required, the systems may be fitted singly or as a combination of them all. This is achieved by modifying various parts of the engine and fuel system.

American market models are also equipped with a carburettor cooling fan. Its description and other details are given in Chapter 2.

2 Standard air cleaner – servicing

1 The standard air cleaner comprises a body in which is housed a paper element type filter, a lid and the necessary connecting hoses and brackets.
2 Every 24 000 miles (40 000 km) the element should be renewed (photo). Other than renewal, no servicing is required.
3 Unscrew and remove the wing nut which secures the air cleaner lid in position, remove the lid and extract the paper element.
4 Wipe the interior of the air cleaner body free from oil and dirt and install the new element.
5 On some models a WINTER/SUMMER selector lever is used on the air inlet (photo). The lever should be set accordingly and in winter will admit air heated from the proximity of the exhaust manifold.

3 Automatic temperature control (ATC) air cleaner – description and checking

1 The ATC air cleaner fitted to A14 and A15 engines is designed to reduce hydrocarbon emission when the engine compartment temperature is below 38°C (100°F). The automatic temperature control system maintains the temperature of air being drawn into the carburettor at 40°C (110°F), thus allowing a weaker mixture setting for the carburettor. In addition the automatic temperature control system effectively improves the warm-up characteristics of the engine and prevents the carburettor icing-up.
2 The ATC air cleaner consists of the following devices:

  (a) *A viscous paper type filter which should be renewed at the specified mileage intervals. It cannot be cleaned*
  (b) *The air control valve which is actuated by inlet manifold vacuum to control the intake airflow circuit. The temperature sensor detects the intake air temperature and opens or closes the vacuum passage accordingly*
  (c) *A hot air duct mounted on the exhaust manifold. The air warmed up between the exhaust manifold and the hot air duct passes to the air cleaner*
  (d) *A blow-by gas filter which removes dirt and oil from the blow-by gas sucked into the air cleaner from the engine rocker cover*
  (e) *An idle compensator which introduces the air directly from the air cleaner to the inlet manifold to compensate for abnormal enrichment of the mixture in high idling temperature*
  (f) *An altitude compensator (California models only)*

3 In warm weather, it is difficult to detect malfunction of the hot air control system. In cold weather, however, malfunction of the air control valve, due to a defective or disconnected vacuum hose between the inlet manifold and the vacuum motor, or a faulty control valve, will result in poor engine performance, such as engine stalling, lack of power and an increase in fuel consumption. If these faults become apparent, check the hot air control system before checking the carburettor.
4 Check that the vacuum hoses are securely connected in the correct position and that they are in good condition.
5 With the engine switched off and in cold condition, disconnect the fresh air duct (where fitted). Position a mirror at the end of the air cleaner inlet (Fig. 3.2) and check that the cold air inlet is open and the hot air inlet shut.
6 Now start the engine and check that the cold air inlet is shut and

2.2 Renew the air filter element at the specified intervals

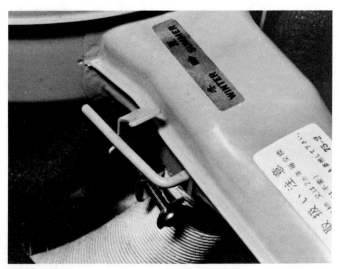

2.5 The Winter/Summer selector lever

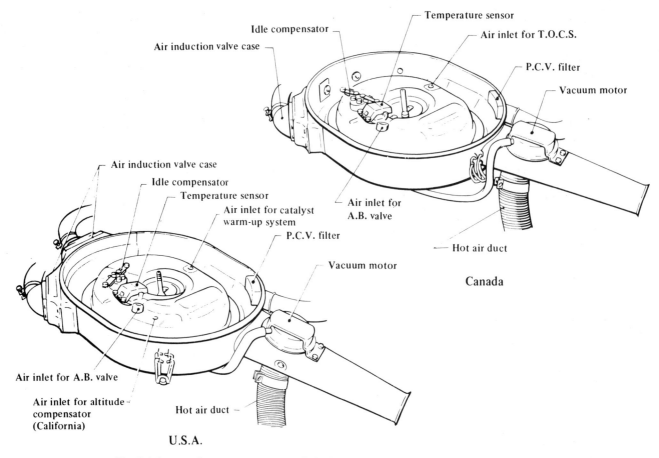

Fig. 3.1 Automatic temperature control air cleaner for USA and Canadian models (Sec 3)

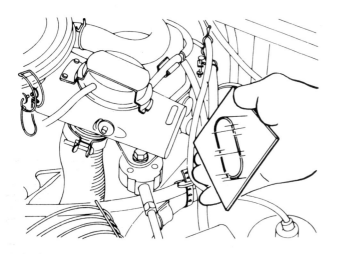

Fig. 3.2 Use mirror to check valve position (Sec 3)

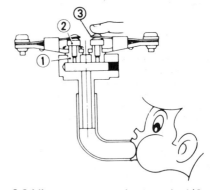

Fig. 3.3 Idle compensator check method (Sec 3)

1	Orifice	3	Bi-metal strip
2	Rubber valve		

motor as an assembly.

8   To check the idle compensator, disconnect the hose leading to the compensator and connect another piece of hose. Blow or suck at the end of the hose. If excessive air leakage is found at the valve, renew the idle compensator as an assembly. Note that two idle compensators are fitted to the air cleaner and it is necessary to plug the valve of one while checking the other. The idle compensator operates in response to the under-bonnet air temperature as follows:

Bi-metal	Intake air temperature	Idle compensator operation
No 1	Below 60°C (140°F)	Fully closed
	60° to 70°C (140° to 158°F)	Close to open
	Above 70°C (158°F)	Fully open

the hot air inlet open. As the engine warms up, the cold air inlet should gradually open. Should a malfunction be observed in these tests, proceed as follows.

7   Disconnect the vacuum motor inlet vacuum hose and connect another piece of hose to the inlet, then apply vacuum by sucking the end of the hose. Using a mirror, check that the cold air inlet is closed and the hot air inlet open. Pinch the hose to cut off the vacuum and check that the hot air inlet remains open for more than 30 seconds. If the diaphragm spring actuates the air control valve by spring force to open the under-bonnet air inlet within 30 seconds, renew the vacuum

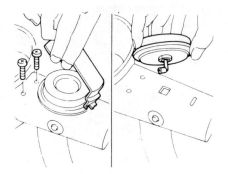

Fig. 3.4 Removal of the vacuum motor (Sec 5)

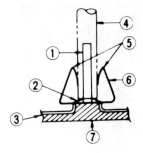

Fig. 3.5 Air cleaner temperature sensor hose connection (Sec 5)

1	Pipe	5	Tab
2	Catch	6	Clip
3	Adhesive	7	Gasket
4	Hose		

No 2	Below 70°C (158°F)	Fully closed
	70° to 80°C (158° to 176°F)	Close to open
	Above 80°C (176°F)	Fully open

4 ATC air cleaner – removal and refitting

1   Remove the bolts securing the air cleaner to the air cleaner bracket.
2   Disconnect the following hoses when removing the air cleaner from the carburettor (as applicable):

(a) Air inlet hose
(b) Hot air inlet hose
(c) Sensor/idle compensator-to-inlet manifold vacuum hose
(d) AB valve-to-air cleaner hose
(e) Air induction hoses (except California/Canada models)
(f) Air cleaner-to-throttle opener or vacuum switching valve
(g) Blow-by hose – air cleaner-to-rocker cover
(h) Air cleaner-to-solenoid valve hoses

3   Refitting is the reversal of the removal procedure. Renew any hoses or retaining clips which are defective.

5 ATC air cleaner components – removal and refitting

1   Removal and refitting of the component parts is straightforward after removing the top cover and filter element from the air cleaner. **Note**: *The gasket between the temperature sensor and air cleaner is bonded to the air cleaner and should not be removed.*
2   When refitting the temperature sensor ensure that the vacuum hose is fitted correctly. The correct position is: right-hand side to 'Nissan' mark at the top face of the sensor for inlet manifold – left-hand side for vacuum motor.

6 Fuel filter – renewal

1   The fuel filter is located in the tank-to-pump hose and is of the sealed paper element type.
2   The filter must be renewed at the specified mileage intervals (photo). It is preferable to carry out this operation when the fuel tank level is low, otherwise when the fuel hoses are disconnected from the filter, the tank line will have to be plugged to prevent loss of fuel.

7 Fuel pump – description

The fuel pump is a diaphragm type, consisting of a body, rocker arm and link assembly, diaphragm, diaphragm spring, seal, inlet and outlet valves.
The diaphragm is made of specially treated rubber, which is not affected by petrol, held together by two metal discs and a pull-rod.
The fuel pump is actuated by the movement of the rocker arm on

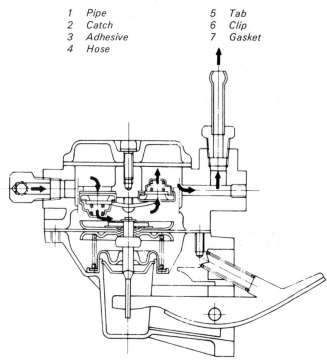

Fig. 3.6 Sectional view of fuel pump (Sec 7)

a camshaft eccentric. This movement is transferred to the flexible diaphragm which draws the fuel from the tank and delivers it under pressure to the carburettor float chamber. The inlet and outlet valves control the flow of fuel.

8 Fuel pump – checking operation

Assuming that the fuel lines and unions are in good condition and that there are no leaks anywhere, check the performance of the fuel pump in the following manner. Disconnect the fuel pipe at the carburettor inlet union, and the high tension lead to the coil, and with a suitable container or a large rag in position to catch the ejected fuel, turn the engine on the starter motor. A good spurt of petrol should emerge from the end of the pipe every second revolution.

9 Fuel pump – removal and refitting

1   Disconnect the fuel pipe unions on the fuel pump, which is located on the front of the engine (photos). Where the fuel tank contains more than a small amount of fuel it will probably be necessary to plug the inlet from the tank.
2   Remove the two nuts which secure the fuel pump to the crankcase. Lift away the pump, noting carefully the number and position of gaskets used between the pump and crankcase mating faces.
3   Refitting is the reverse of removal. Always use new gaskets.

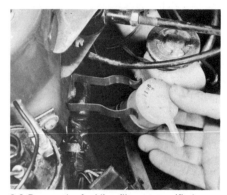

6.2 Renew the fuel line filter at specified intervals

9.1a The A10 engine fuel pump

9.1b The A12 engine fuel pump

10 Fuel pump – dismantling, inspection and reassembly

1   Before dismantling, clean the exterior of the pump then make a mark across the centre and base mating flanges so that they can be refitted in their original position.
2   Remove the screws securing the cap to the upper body and take off the cap and cap gasket.
3   Separate the upper and lower body by removing the securing screws and lifting off the upper body. It is possible for the diaphragm to stick to the mating flanges; if this happens use a sharp knife to free it.
4   To remove the diaphragm, diaphragm spring, lower body seal washer and lower body seal from the lower body, press down on the diaphragm to counter the action of the diaphragm spring and while doing this, tilt the diaphragm so that the rectangular part in the lower end of the pull-rod is unhooked from the rocker arm link.
5   Check the upper and lower bodies for cracks or damage.
6   Check the valve assembly for wear of valve and valve spring.
7   Hold the diaphragm up to the light and examine for splits or pin holes.
8   Check the rocker arm pin for wear, as a worn pin may cause oil leakage. Check the rocker arm for wear on the mating face with the camshaft.
9   Renew defective parts as necessary. Always use a new gasket.
10   Reassembly is the reverse of the dismantling procedure. Before refitting the pump to the engine, lubricate the rocker arm link and rocker arm pin.
11   After the pump has been reassembled, functionally test it either by placing a finger over the inlet and actuating the rocker arm, when a good suction noise should be heard, or by connecting it to the tank fuel line and after actuating the rocker arm a few times, each successive stroke should be accompanied by a spurt of fuel from the pump outlet. Collect the fuel in a container.

11 Fuel tank and fuel lines – decription and servicing

1   The fuel tank is mounted at the rear of the vehicle. The tank filler, tube, vent pipes and fuel lines are connected to the tank by flexible tubing. The fuel gauge sender unit is mounted in the top face of the fuel tank and a drain plug is conveniently located underneath.
2   To remove the fuel tank, first disconnect the battery earth lead.
3   Drain the contents of the tank into a suitable container, then disconnect the fuel gauge sender unit wires and the fuel supply line, the fuel return line and evaporation line (as applicable) at the tank end.
4   Detach the fuel filler tube and hose from the tank, also the breather tube and check valve hoses.
5   Release the handbrake lever and detach the cable from the clamp-to-tank connection.
6   Supporting the tank underneath, remove its retaining bolts and then carefully lower it from the vehicle and withdraw it.
7   If the tank contains a lot of sediment or sludge, shake it vigorously using two or three changes of paraffin and then allow it to drain thoroughly. Remove the gauge sender unit first – see Section 12.

8   If the tank is damaged and/or leaks, do not be tempted to solder over the hole. Fuel tank repair is a specialist job and unless lengthy safety precautions are observed, can be a very dangerous procedure.
9   Refitting the fuel tank is a reversal of removal, but check that the vent tubes which are connected to the filler neck are not trapped and are securely clipped in position. Do not forget to install spring and plain washers on the tank mounting bolts, since the mounting holes in the tank flange are elongated to provide for adjustment.
10   Under certain damp or dusty operating conditions it is a good idea to occasionally drain the tank when there is very little fuel in it so that any accumulated water or sediment will be flushed out and discarded. This action will safeguard the tank against corrosion and help to prevent clogging of the fuel line filter.

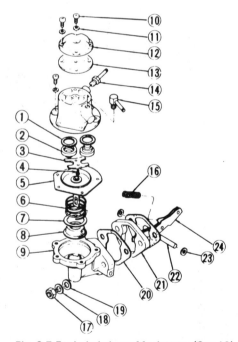

Fig. 3.7 Exploded view of fuel pump (Sec 10)

1	Packing	13	Cap gasket
2	Valve assembly	14	Inlet connector
3	Retainer	15	Outlet connector
4	Screw	16	Rocker arm spring
5	Diaphragm assembly	17	Nut
6	Diaphragm spring	18	Spring washer
7	Retainer	19	Plain washer
8	Oil seal	20	Gasket
9	Lower body	21	Spacer
10	Screw	22	Rocker pin
11	Spring washer	23	Spacer
12	Fuel pump cap	24	Rocker arm

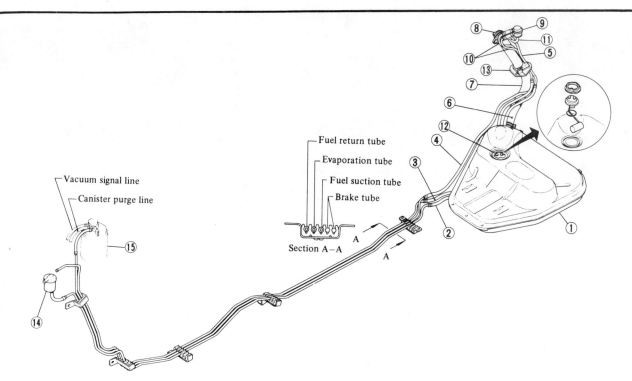

Fig. 3.8 Fuel tank and supply lines – North American models (Sec 11)

1	Fuel tank	6	Filler hose	11	Drain hose
2	Fuel suction hose	7	Filler tube	12	Fuel tank gauge unit
3	Fuel return hose	8	Filler cap	13	Grommet
4	Evaporation hose	9	Fuel check valve	14	Fuel filter
5	Vent tube	10	Breather tube	15	Carbon canister

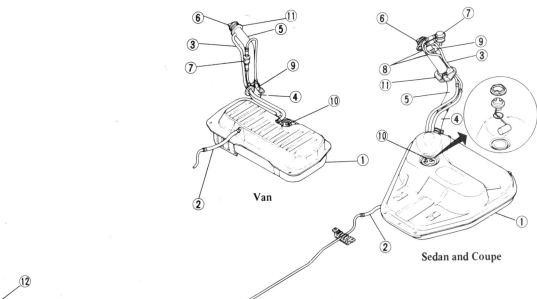

Van

Sedan and Coupe

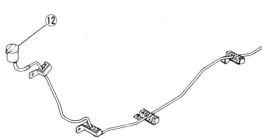

Fig. 3.9 Fuel tank and supply lines – A10 and A12 engines (Sec 11)

1	Fuel tank	7	Fuel check valve
2	Suction hose	8	Breather tube
3	Vent tube	9	Drain hose
4	Filler hose	10	Fuel tank gauge unit
5	Filler tube	11	Grommet
6	Filler cap	12	Fuel filter

15.1 The DCG286 carburettor fitted to the A10 engine (air cleaner removed)

16.1 Carburettor adjusting screws showing idle mixture screw (1) and idle speed (throttle stop) screw (2)

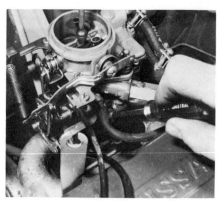

16.4 Adjusting the idle mixture screw

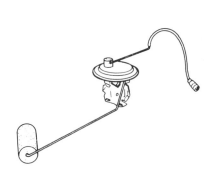

Fig. 3.10 Fuel tank gauge sender unit (Sec 12)

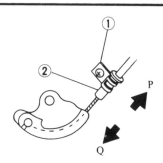

Fig. 3.12 Accelerator cable adjustment. For P and Q see text (Sec 13)

1   Clamp   2   Socket

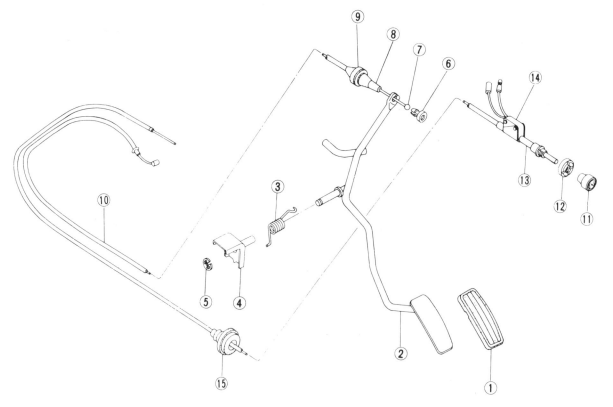

Fig. 3.11 The accelerator linkage and manual choke cable components (Sec 13)

1 Accelerator pedal	5 Snap-ring	9 Grommet	13 Choke cable
2 Accelerator arm	6 Nylon collar	10 Accelerator cable	14 Micro-switch
3 Return spring	7 Cable end	11 Choke knob	15 Grommet
4 Accelerator pedal bracket	8 Cable casing end	12 Escutcheon nut	

12 Fuel gauge sender unit – removal and refitting

1 Remove the fuel tank as described in Section 11.
2 Turn the lockplate with a screwdriver, then remove the gauge unit (bayonet type).
3 To refit the fuel gauge sender unit, align the notches and then turn the lockplate. Always use a new gasket.
4 Refit the fuel tank as described in Section 11.

13 Accelerator cable – removal and refitting

1 Remove the outer casing clamp and accelerator cable on the carburettor end. Before removing the cable, hold the throttle valve fully open so as to slacken the cable.
2 From inside the car, the accelerator cable is disconnected from the pedal by pushing the nylon collar towards the wire so that the wire can be detached from the pedal and collar.
3 The accelerator cable can now be withdrawn through the engine compartment together with the grommet.
4 Refit in the reverse order to removal, but grease the cable-to-pedal connection, the return spring-to-piping components at the pedal and the pedal lever shaft and piping at the pedal bracket.
5 Adjust the accelerator cable as follows. Refer to Fig. 3.12.
6 On automatic choke models, open the choke flap fully by hand and pull the throttle lever up to release the automatic choke.
7 Pull the cable outer casing in direction P until the throttle shaft just starts to move, then return it in direction Q by 1 to 6 mm (0.4 to 0.12 in) and tighten the clamp.
8 Have an assistant depress the accelerator pedal and check for correct operation.

14 Choke control (manual) – removal and refitting

1 Remove the choke knob by holding the inner wire with a pair of pliers and push the knob in, then rotate the knob through 90° and pull it off.
2 Disconnect the choke control wire from the choke control lever at the carburettor.
3 Remove the escutcheon from the dash panel and pull the choke cable assembly clear to remove it.
4 The choke warning light switch can be removed from the choke

control by unscrewing and withdrawing the retaining screws.
5 Refitting the choke cable assembly is the reverse of the removal sequence.
6 Adjust the choke valve so that it opens fully when the choke knob is pushed in all the way and closes when the knob is pulled out.

15 Carburettor (DCG types) – description

The carburettor is of the downdraught twin choke type (photo). Full specifications are given at the beginning of this Chapter.
The carburettor is conventional in operation and incorporates a primary and main jet system and mechanically operated accelerator pump.
The manually operated choke comprises a butterfly valve which closes one of the venturi choke tubes and is so synchronized with the throttle valve plate that the latter opens sufficiently to provide a rich mixture and an increased slow running speed for easy starting.
For idling and slow running, the fuel passes through the slow running jet, the primary slow air bleed and the secondary slow air bleed. The fuel is finally ejected from the bypass and idle holes.
The accelerator pump is synchronized with the throttle valve. During periods of heavy acceleration, the pump which is of simple piston and valve construction, provides an additional metered quantity of fuel to enrich the normal mixture. The quantity of fuel metered can be varied according to operating climatic conditions by adjusting the stroke of the pump linkage.
The secondary system provides a mixture for normal motoring conditions by means of a main jet and air bleed.
The float chamber is fed with fuel pumped by the mechanically operated pump on the crankcase. The level in the chamber is critical and must at all times be maintained as specified.
The power valve system utilizes the vacuum in the intake manifold to open or close the valve. During the light load running the valve is closed, but is opened during full load running or acceleration, thus furnishing more fuel.

16 Idling speed – adjustment (DCG carburettors)

1 Run the engine to normal operating temperatures and then set the idle speed (throttle stop) screw to provide an engine speed of 700 rpm.
2 If the vehicle is fitted with a tachometer then the setting of engine

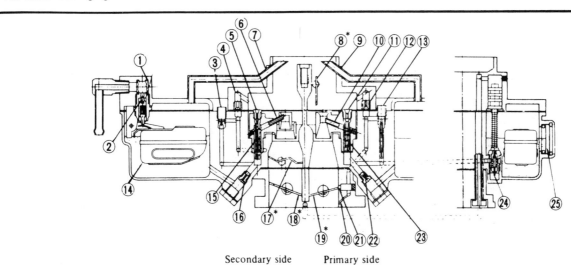

Fig. 3.13 Sectional view of the DCG type carburettor (Sec 15)

1 Filter	7 Secondary air vent	13 Primary slow jet	19 *Primary throttle valve
2 Needle valve	8 *Choke valve	14 Float	20 Idle hole
3 Secondary slow jet	9 Primary air vent	15 Secondary emulsion tube	21 Bypass hole
4 Secondary slow air bleed	10 Primary main nozzle	16 Secondary main jet	22 Primary main jet
5 Secondary main air bleed	11 Primary main air bleed	17 *Auxiliary valve	23 Primary emulsion tube
6 Secondary main nozzle	12 Primary slow air bleed	18 *Secondary throttle valve	24 Power valve
		*Do not remove these parts	25 Level gauge

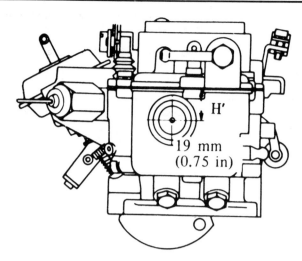

Fig. 3.14 Fuel level check (Sec 17)

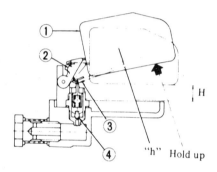

Fig. 3.15 Float adjustment. For H and h see text (Sec 17)

1   Float   3   Float seat
2   Float stop   4   Needle valve

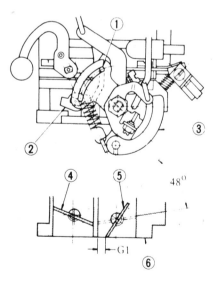

Fig. 3.16 Adjusting the interlock opening of the primary and
secondary throttle valves (Sec 18)

G1 = 0.23 in (5.83 mm)

1   Connecting rod   4   Secondary throttle valve
2   Secondary connecting lever   5   Primary throttle valve
3   Throttle lever   6   Throttle chamber

speed will be no problem. Where an instrument is not available then a useful guide may be obtained from the state of the ignition warning lamp. This should be just going out at the correct idling speed.
3   Setting of the mixture screw may be carried out using a 'Colortune'. Follow the equipment manufacturer's instructions.
4   In certain territories, the use of a CO meter is essential and if this is used then the throttle adjusting screw and the mixture screw must be turned to provide a reading on the meter of 2 ± 1% at the specified engine idling speed (photo).
5   As a temporary measure, the adjustment screws may be rotated progressively, first one and then the other, until the engine idles at the correct speed without any 'hunting' or stalling. Turning the mixture screw clockwise weakens the mixture and anti-clockwise richens it.
6   If the idle mixture is too rich, the tickover will be lumpy with a tendency to 'hunt'. If the mixture is too weak, the tickover will be fast and misfiring may occur.

17   Float chamber fuel level – checking and adjustment

Float chamber fuel level check
1   The fuel level can be checked in the float chamber sight glass.
2   The level should be maintained within the range of 0.71 to 0.79 in (18 to 20 mm) as shown in Fig. 3.14.

Float level – adjustment
3   If the fuel level is found to be incorrect and/or there is evidence of fuel starvation or conversely, flooding or excessively rich mixture, the float level must be checked and adjusted accordingly.
4   Remove the carburettor, as described in Section 19.
5   Disconnct the choke connecting rod, accelerator pump lever and return spring.
6   Unscrew and remove the five securing screws which secure the upper choke chamber to the main body.
7   Turn the choke chamber upside down and check the dimension 'H' in Fig. 3.15 with the float hanging upside down under its own weight. This should be 0.47 in (12.0 mm).
8   Now gently push the float upwards to the full extent of its travel and check the clearance between the endface of the inlet needle valve and the float tongue. This should be 0.051 to 0.067 in (1.3 to 1.7 mm) when the float is fully raised, dimension 'h' in Fig. 3.15. Adjustment to correct either of these dimensions is carried out by bending the float seat or stopper tag.

18   Interlock opening of primary and secondary throttle valves – checking and adjustment

1   Open the primary side throttle valve 48° from the fully closed posiiton and measure the clearance, G1 in Fig. 3.16, between the throttle valve and throttle chamber inner wall.
2   Retaining the throttle valve in this position, bend the rod connecting the two throttle valves as required to set the secondary valve in the just about to open position.
3   After the adjustment has been made, check that the link system operates smoothly.

19   Carburettor – removal and refitting

1   Remove the air cleaner unit complete from the carburettor.
2   Disconnect the fuel and vacuum hoses from the carburettor, also the choke and accelerator controls (as applicable).
3   Remove the four nuts and washers which secure the carburettor to the inlet manifold.
4   Lift the carburettor from the manifold and discard the flange gasket.
5   Refitting is a reverse of removal, but always use a new flange gasket.

20   Carburettor dismantling and reassembly – general

1   With time the component parts of the carburettor will wear and petrol consumption will increase. The diameter of drillings and jets

may alter, and air and fuel leaks may develop round spindles and other moving parts. Because of the high degree of precision involved it is recommended that an exchange rebuilt carburettor is purchased. This is one of the few instances where it is better to buy a new component rather than to rebuild the old one.

2   The accelerator pump itself may need attention and gaskets may need renewal. Providing care is taken there is no reason why the carburettor may not be completely reconditioned at home, but ensure a full repair kit can be obtained before you strip the carburettor down. **Never** poke out jets with wire or similar to clean them but blow them out with compressed air or air from a car tyre pump.

21 Carburettor (DCG types) – dismantling and reassembly

Before dismantling the carburettor, clean its external surfaces and prepare an area where the respective components can be laid out in order of appearance as they are removed.

1   The main jets are accessible from the exterior of the carburettor.
2   These should be unscrewed, removed and cleaned by blowing

them through with air from a tyre pump; **never** probe a jet with wire.
3   Detach the choke chamber by removing the connecting rod accelerator pump lever, return spring and the five securing screws.
4   The primary and secondary emulsion tubes are accessible after removing the main air bleeds.
5   Remove the accelerator pump cover, retaining the spring, piston and ball carefully.
6   Separate the float chamber from the throttle housing by unscrewing and removing the three securing screws. Slide out the float pivot pin and remove the float. Remove the needle valve.
7   Unless imperative, do not dismantle the throttle butterfly valves from their spindles.
8   Take great care when disconnecting the interlock rods that they are not bent or twisted, or the settings and adjustments will be upset.
9   With the carburettor dismantled, clean all components in a suitable solvent and blow through the internal body passages with air from a tyre pump.
10 Inspect all components for wear and the body and chamber castings for cracks.
11 Clean the small gauze filter and if corroded or clogged, renew it.

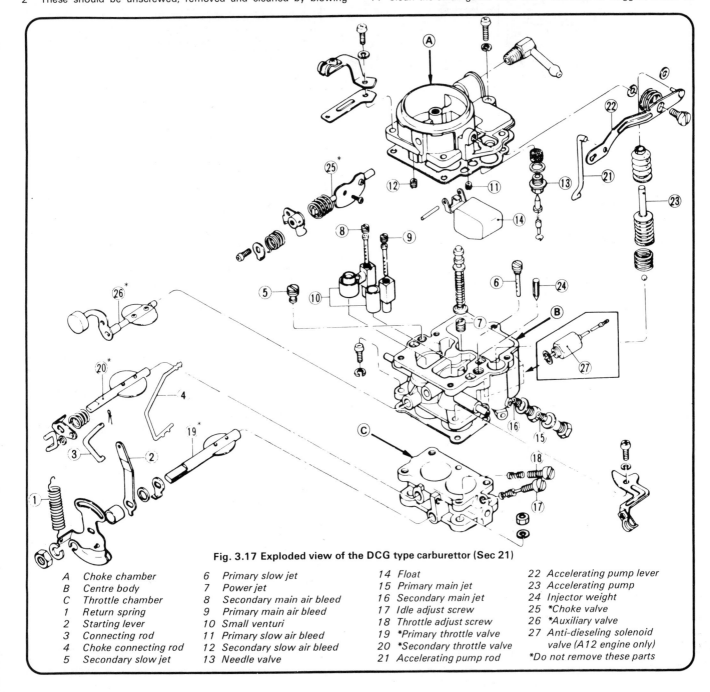

Fig. 3.17 Exploded view of the DCG type carburettor (Sec 21)

A	Choke chamber	6	Primary slow jet	14	Float	22	Accelerating pump lever
B	Centre body	7	Power jet	15	Primary main jet	23	Accelerating pump
C	Throttle chamber	8	Secondary main air bleed	16	Secondary main jet	24	Injector weight
1	Return spring	9	Primary main air bleed	17	Idle adjust screw	25	*Choke valve
2	Starting lever	10	Small venturi	18	Throttle adjust screw	26	*Auxiliary valve
3	Connecting rod	11	Primary slow air bleed	19	*Primary throttle valve	27	Anti-dieseling solenoid
4	Choke connecting rod	12	Secondary slow air bleed	20	*Secondary throttle valve		valve (A12 engine only)
5	Secondary slow jet	13	Needle valve	21	Accelerating pump rod		*Do not remove these parts

.12 If wear is evident in the throttle spindle, the carburettor should be renewed on an exchange basis.

13 Check all jet and air bleed sizes with those given in the Specifications in case a previous owner has changed them for ones of an incorrect size.

14 Check the ejection of fuel when the accelerator pump is actuated.

15 Reassembly is a reversal of dismantling, using all the items supplied in the repair kit.

16 When the carburettor is being reassembled, check the float movement (Section 17) and when it is refitted to the engine, carry out all the checks and adjustments described in this Chapter.

22 Carburettor (DCH and DCR types) – description

Both the DCH 306 carburettor (A14 engine) and the DCR 306 carburettor (A15 engine) are basically similar in design and function to the DCG 306 type carburettor described in Section 15. The main differences is the choke mechanism, which is automatically operated, and this is described in the following Section. A throttle opener control system is fitted to some models to reduce hydrocarbon emissions and a dashpot is fitted to the DCH 306 model to ensure smooth deceleration.

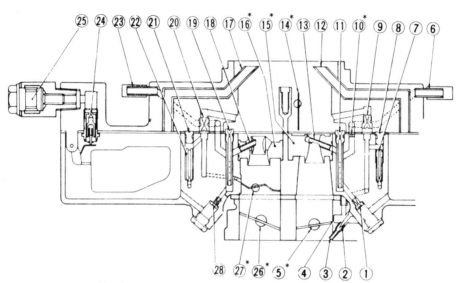

Fig. 3.18 Sectional view of the DCH type carburettor (Sec 22)

1 Primary main jet	7 Primary slow jet	15 *Primary small venturi	23 Secondary altitude
2 Idle adjust screw	8 Plug	16 *Secondary small venturi	compensator pipe (for
3 Idle nozzle	9 Primary slow air bleed	17 Secondary air vent pipe	California)
4 Bypass hole	10 *Safe orifice	18 Secondary main nozzle	24 Needle
5 *Primary throttle valve	11 Primary main air bleed	19 Secondary main air bleed	25 Fuel filter
6 Primary altitude	12 Primary air vent pipe	20 Secondary slow air bleed	26 *Secondary throttle valve
compensator pipe (for	13 Primary main nozzle	21 Plug	27 *Auxiliary valve
California)	14 *Choke valve	22 Secondary slow jet	28 Secondary main jet
			*Do not remove these parts

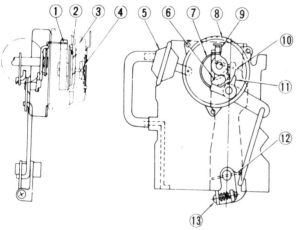

Fig. 3.19 Sectional view of automatic choke (Sec 23)

1 Bi-metal spring	8 Bi-metal index mark
2 Heater	9 Choke shaft lever
3 Bi-metal cover	10 Choke valve
4 Bi-metal switch	11 Unloader tang
5 Vacuum diaphragm	12 Throttle valve
6 Fast idle cam	13 Fast idle adjusting screw
7 Bi-metal spring	

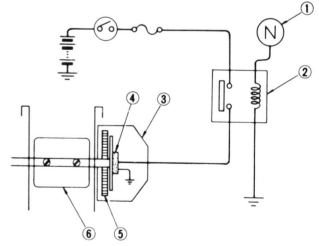

Fig. 3.20 Circuit diagram of automatic choke heater (Sec 23)

1 Alternator	4 Choke heater
2 Automatic choke relay	5 Bi-metal spring
3 Automatic choke cover	6 Choke valve

An altitude compensator is fitted to California models and this corrects the fuel/air mixture at higher altitudes.

23 Automatic choke (DCH and DCR carburettors) – description

1   An electric heater warms a bi-metal, interconnected to the choke valve, and this then controls the position of the choke valve and throttle valve according to the time elapsed, the warm-up condition of the engine and the ambient temperature. The function of each part is as follows.

2   *Bi-metal and heater in thermostat cover:* When the engine starts, electric current flows through the heater and warms up the bi-metal. The movement of the bi-metal coil is transferred to the choke valve by the lever.

3   *Fast idle cam:* This regulates the throttle valve spring to adjust the mixture in accordance with the choke valve opening (dependent on engine warm-up condition).

4   *Fast idle adjuster screw:* This screw adjusts the throttle valve opening by the fast idle cam.

5   *Unloader:* The function of the unloader is to force open the choke valve a fraction to adjust the fuel/air mixture when accelerating a cool engine (where the choke valve is not yet opening fully).

6   *Vacuum diaphragm:* This diaphragm opens the choke valve accordingly when the engine is started.

7   *Bi-metal case index marking:* This indicates the setting of the bi-metal coil movement for controlling the fuel/air mixture ratio when the engine is started.

24 Automatic choke (DCH and DCR carburettors) – checking

1   Before starting the engine, fully depress the accelerator pedal to ensur that the choke valve closes.

2   Push the choke valve with a finger to check for binding.

3   Check that the bi-metal cover index mark is set at the centre of the choke housing index as shown in Fig. 3.21. Do not set the bi-metal cover index mark at any position other than the centre of the choke housing index marks.

4   Check the automatic choke heater wiring connections, then start the engine.

5   After warming up the engine, check that the choke valve is fully open.

6   If the automatic choke heater wiring is in order and the choke valve does not operate after warm-up, renew the bi-metal cover. Refer also to Section 30.

7   Note that on DCR carburettors the bi-metal cover may be riveted in place. **Do not** remove the cover in this case except for renewal, when the rivets will have to be drilled out.

25 Fast idle adjustment – automatic choke (DCH and DCR carburettors)

DCH-306

1   Remove the carburettor from the engine.

2   Remove the bi-metal cover.

3   Place the fast idle arm on the second step of the fast idle cam and then adjust the fast idle screw (Fig. 3.22). The clearance at 'A' should be 0.0287 to 0.0343 in (0.73 to 0.87 mm).

4   Refit the carburettor, run the engine and check that the specified fast idle speed is obtained.

DCR-306

5   Warm up the engine, and connect up the tachometer.

6   Manually operate the throttle valve and the choke valve to set the fast idle arm on the second step of the fast idle cam.

7   Check the engine speed against that given in the Specifications. Adjust if necessary by turning the fast idle screw.

8   If the correct speed cannot be obtained, remove the carburettor and proceed as described for the DCH 306 carburettor above, but do not remove the bi-metal cover if it is riveted in place.

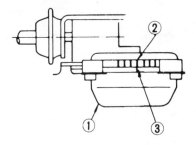

Fig. 3.21 Position of bi-metal cover (Sec 24)

1   *Bi-metal cover*   3   *Bi-metal cover index marks*
2   *Choke housing index marks*

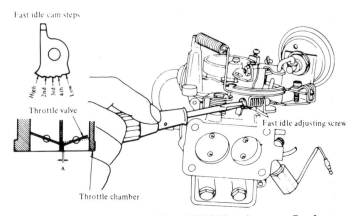

Fig. 3.22 Adjusting the fast idle – DCH 306 carburettor. For A see text (Sec 25)

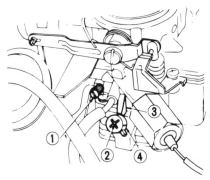

Fig. 3.23 The throttle stop and idle mixture adjustment screws on the DCH carburettor (Sec 26)

1   *Idle speed (throttle stop)*   3   *Stopper*
2   *Idle mixture screw*   4   *Idle limiter cap*

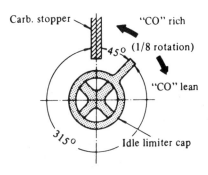

Fig. 3.24 Setting the idle limiter cap (Sec 27)

Fig. 3.25 Removal and refitting methods for the later model idle mixture seal cap (Sec 27)

Fig. 3.26 Adjusting the vacuum break – DCH 306 carburettor (Sec 28)

1 Rubber band
2 Vacuum break stem
3 Vacuum break rod
4 Choke valve
5 Vacuum break stem
B See text

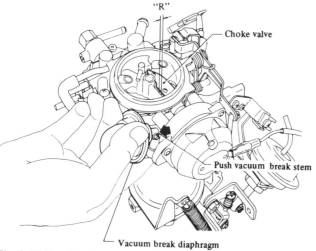

Fig. 3.27 Checking the vacuum break choke valve clearance on the DCR 306 carburettor. Note automatic choke bimetal cover is left in position. For R see text (Sec 28)

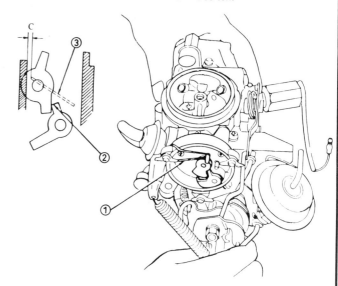

Fig. 3.28 Adjusting the choke unloader – DCH 306 carburettor (Sec 29)

1 Rubber band
2 Unloader tongue
3 Choke valve
C See text

Fig. 3.29 Adjusting the choke unloader – DCR 306 carburettor. For C see text (Sec 29)

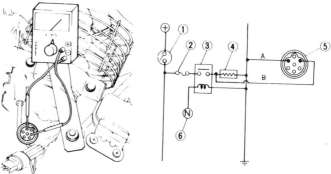

Fig. 3.30 Checking the choke heating circuit (Sec 30)

1 Ignition key
2 Fuse
3 Automatic choke relay
   Engine stop: OFF
   Engine start: ON
4 Automatic choke heater
5 Function test connector
6 'N' terminal of alternator

26 Idle speed and mixture ratio – adjustment (DCH and DCR carburettors)

1   The engine must be at normal operating temperature and the ignition timing must be correct. Switch off the air conditioning (if fitted).
2   The use of a tachometer and a CO meter will be required. Insert the CO meter probe at least 16 in (40 cm) into the tailpipe.

DCH 306-75 and DCH 306-76

3   Disconnect the air hose from the air check valve and fit a cap on the air check valve.
4   Run the engine up to 1500 to 2000 rpm two or three times (under no load), then allow it to idle for one minute. Read the idle speed on the tachometer.
5   Turn the idle speed (throttle stop) adjuster screw if necessary to achieve the correct idle speed.
6   CO percentage should be checked after the engine has been idling for about 10 minutes. Turn the idle mixture screw if necessary to achieve a CO percentage within the specified limits.
7   If a CO meter is not available, the following procedure may be used (local regulations permitting):

(a)   *Proceed as above but adjust the throttle screw until the engine speed is 740 rpm, then adjust the idle mixture until maximum rpm is obtained*
(b)   *Repeat the procedures at (a) above until the engine speed, at best idle mixture, is 740 rpm*
(c)   *Turn the idle adjustment clockwise until the engine speed drops off to the specified rpm, if the idle limiter cap prevents correct adjustment, remove it. To refit the idle limiter cap refer to Section 27*
(d)   *If the engine speed rises when the air hose is reconnected to the air check valve, readjust to the specified speed*

DCH 306-102

8   Proceed as described above, with the following minor differences:

(a)   *At paragraph 3, disconnect the air induction hose from the air pipe, and cap the pipe*
(b)   *At paragraph 4, run the engine up to 2000 to 3000 rpm*
(c)   *Note that the specified idling speed is different*

DCH 306-112, DCR 306-103 and DCR 306-113

9   The idle mixture screw on these carburettors is sealed with a plug and should not normally be disturbed – see Section 27.
10   If adjustment is necessary, proceed as described in paragraph 8.

27 Idle limiter cap – removal and refitting

Do not remove the idle limiter cap unless necessary, and satisfy yourself that you are not contravening local or national emission control regulations by so doing. Once removed, the cap should be refitted as follows.
1   After adjusting the throttle or idle speed adjusting screws, check that the CO percentage in the exhaust gases is within the specified limit.
2   Fit the idle limiter cap in position, making sure that the adjusting screw can rotate a further ⅛ turn in the CO-Rich direction, see Fig. 3.24.
3   Later models are fitted with a plug type seal cap and it can only be removed by drilling and prising free (with care). After the idle CO is adjusted, carefully insert a new cap as shown in Fig. 3.25.

28 Vacuum break (DCH and DCR carburettors) – choke valve clearance check

1   To check this clearance the engine must be cold and the air cleaner removed.

DCH 306-75/DCH 306-76/DCH 306-74 carburettors

2   Close the choke valve plate completely with the fingers and retain the valve plate in this position using a rubber band connected between the choke piston lever and carburettor body (Fig. 3.26).
3   With a pair of pliers, grip the end of the vacuum diaphragm capsule operating rod and withdraw it as far as it will go without straining it. Now bend the connecting rod (if necessary) to provide a 0.070 to 0.078 in (1.80 to 1.98 mm) clearance between the edge of the choke valve and plate and the carburettor body (B in Fig. 3.26).

DCR 306-113/DCR 306-103/DCR 306-123 carburettors

4   With the vacuum break stem pushed fully straight check the choke valve-to-carburettor body clearance (R in Fig. 3.27). The clearance should be as follows:

(a)   *Clearance R for USA models*   = 0.0669 ± 0.0035 in (1.70 ± 0.09 mm)
(b)   *Clearance R for Canada models* = 0.0587 ± 0.0035 in (1.49 ± 0.09 mm)

5   On USA models, adjust by removing the plastic plug from the adjuster screw and hold, turn the adjuster screw accordingly and then insert the plastic plug to reseal.
6   On Canadian models adjust the clearance by bending the connecting rod to suit.

29 Choke unloader (DCH and DCR carburettors) – adjustment

1   Repeat the operations in paragraph 2 or 4 of Section 28 as applicable.
2   Pull the throttle lever to fully open the throttle and then adjust the clearance, C in Fig. 3.28 or 3.29, between the choke valve and the carburettor body to 0.0929 in (2.36 mm) by bending the unloader tongue.
3   Ensure that the throttle valve opens fully when the carburettor is fitted on the engine. If the throttle valve fails to open fully, the unloader becomes inoperative and results in poor acceleration.

30 Automatic choke (DCH and DCR carburettors) – heater circuit check

1   Connect a circuit tester as shown in Fig. 3.30 and check for continuity between 'A' and 'B' with the engine stationary. If continuity exists the heater is functioning. If there is no continuity, check for disconnected connector or open heater circuit.
2   With the engine idling check for voltage across 'A' and 'B'. If voltmeter reading is 12 volts the heater circuit is functioning. If voltmeter reading is zero, check for disconnected connector, open circuit or faulty automatic choke relay.
3   If the above checks indicate a faulty part or unit, renew as necessary.

31 Dashpot – checking and adjustment

1   The dashpot is interlinked with the primary throttle valve and its function is to dampen the effect of sudden deceleration to reduce the HC emissions. On automatic transmission models it prevents the engine from stalling caused by sudden braking.
2   For checking and adjusing of this unit a tachometer will be required. If a tachometer is not available, get your Datsun dealer to carry out this check.
3   Start the engine and run it until it reaches its normal running temperature.
4   Gradually increase the engine speed until the tachometer reads 2300 to 2500 rpm (1900 to 2100 for California models). At this speed the dashpot stem should be in contact with the primary throttle lever. (Fig. 3.31).
5   Should the dashpot not be in contact with the throttle lever, then release the dashpot locknut and adjust the dashpot until the stem just touches the primary throttle lever. Retighten the locknuts.
6   With the engine running and the tachometer registering the specified rpm, (paragraph 4 above), release the throttle suddenly and

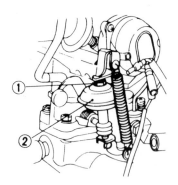

Fig. 3.31 Dashpot adjustment (Sec 31)

1   Locknut   *2   Dashpot*

check that the engine speed drops smoothly to 1000 rpm in approximately 3 seconds.
7   If necessary, slacken the locknuts once more and readjust the dashpot until the required action is obtained.

32 Throttle opening control system (TOCS) – description and operation (DCH and DCR carburettors)

1   The throttle opener is designed to open the throttle valve of the carburettor slightly during deceleration. During deceleration, manifold vacuum rises and the quantity of mixture in the engine is not sufficient for normal combustion, resulting in increased emission of hydrocarbon gases in the exhaust.

2   Carburettors equipped with the throttle opener supply the engine with an adequate charge of mixture to maintain correct combustion during deceleration and thereby reduce the HC emission.
3   The system for the manual transmission model consists of servo diaphragm, vacuum control valve, throttle opener solenoid valve, speed detecting switch and amplifier. An altitude connector fitted to the vacuum control serves to regulate automatically the operating pressure in the system with variation of atmospheric pressure.
4   When the manifold vacuum increases on deceleration, the vacuum control valve opens to transfer the manifold vacuum to the servo diaphragm chamber and the throttle valve opens slightly. Under this condition the correct amount of fresh air is sucked into the combustion chamber. This additional air assists in the complete combustion of the fuel and the amount of HC in the exhaust gases is reduced.
5   The throttle opener solenoid valve is controlled by a speed detecting switch which is actuated by the speedometer needle. As the car speed falls below 10 mph (16 km/h), this switch is actuated and produces a signal which is led to the amplifier and amplified to actuate the throttle opener solenoid valve. The throttle opener solenoid valve is actuated and the servo-diaphragm chamber is opened to the atmosphere. In this case the servo-diaphragm does not operate.
6   Generally, the throttle opener control system does not require adjusting, but should it become suspect, the vehicle should be taken to a Datsun dealer for checking and adjusting.

33 Altitude compensator (California models) – description

1   The higher the altitude, the richer the air-fuel mixture ratio and therefore the higher exhaust gas emissions, even with the engine correctly adjusted for low altitude driving.
2   At high altitudes, additional air is supplied to the carburettor by the altitude compensator. The compensator operates automatically.
3   Make sure that the altitude compensator hoses are securely connected and not cracked or blocked.

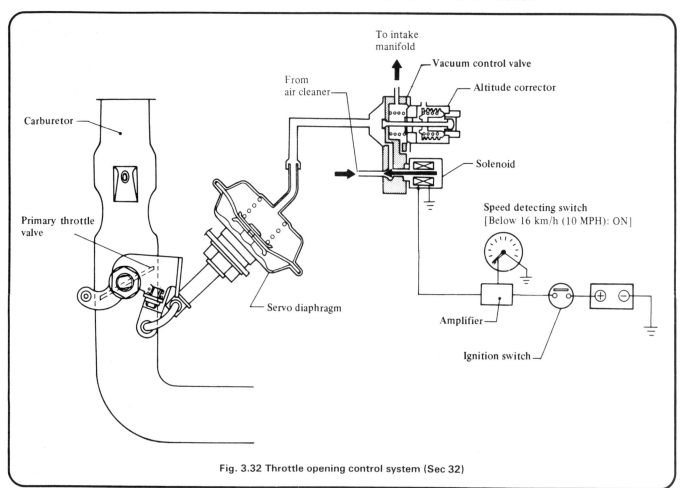

Fig. 3.32 Throttle opening control system (Sec 32)

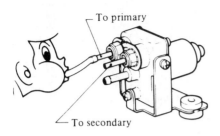

Fig. 3.33 Altitude compensator test method (Sec 33)

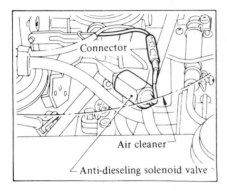

Fig. 3.34 Anti-diesel solenoid valve (Sec 34)

4   If the altitude compensator is suspected of malfunction a simple check can be made by disconnecting its hoses and connecting up a temporary tube to the primary and secondary outlet lines in turn – see Fig. 3.33. If air is able to pass freely through the unit when blowing or sucking the test hose, then the unit is faulty and must be renewed.

34 Anti-diesel solenoid valve – checking and renewal

1   This valve is designed to stop the fuel flow as soon as the ignition is switched off.
2   The valve operation is easily checked by starting the engine and running it at idle speed, then disconnecting the solenoid lead wire, (Fig. 3.34). When detached the engine should stop immediately; if not the valve must be stuck open and must therefore be renewed. Unscrew and remove the unit for renewal.
3   Screw the new unit into position and tighten to the specified torque setting, then run the engine and check for correct operation.

35 Carburettor (DCH and DCR types) – dismantling and re-assembly

1   The dismantling and reassembly procedures for the DCH and DCR carburettors are very similar to those for the DCG carburettor, in Section 21. Reference to that Section can therefore be made, but before starting to dismantle the carburettor, first read the general notes detailed in Section 20, which are also applicable.
2   Exploded views of the DCH and DCR carburettors are shown in Figs. 3.35, 3.36 and 3.37.
3   During assembly a check can be made to ensure that the accelerator pump is operating satisfactorily by pouring fuel into the float chamber and operating the throttle lever. Fuel should be ejected into the venturi from the fuel injection nozzle.
4   Check, and adjust if necessary, the accelerator pump limiter. To do this insert feeler gauges, or preferably a gauge rod of suitable thickness, between the carburettor throat and the throttle valve (Fig. 3.38). The required gauge thickness is as follows:

DCH carburettors   – 0.051 ± 0.004 in
                                  (1.3 ± 0.1 mm)

DCR carburettors   – 0.050 ± 0.008 in
                                  (1.27 ± 0.2 mm)

Holding the throttle open with the inserted gauge, check that the lever is only just contacting the pin and if necessary adjust accordingly by bending the limiter until they are only just touching.

36 Emission control systems – general

Three types of emission control systems may be used; a closed type crankcase emission control system, exhaust emission control system and an evaporative control system.
Periodic inspection and servicing of these systems should be carried out to maintain the reduction of air pollution by carbon monoxide, hydrocarbons and nitrogen gases. The following should also be checked regularly as they play an important part in reducing harmful emissions:

(a) Valve clearances
(b) Ignition timing
(c) Spark plugs
(d) Carburettor adjustments

37 Crankcase ventilation system – description

This system draws clean air from within the air cleaner and passes it through a mesh flame arrester and into a hose which is connected to the top of the rocker cover. This air is then passed through the engine and into the inlet manifold via an oil separator, hose and regulating valve. This means any crankcase vapours are passed back into the combustion chambers and burnt.
The oil dipstick and filler cap are sealed to prevent the passing of vapours to the atmosphere.
The operation of this system is most efficient under part throttle conditions when there is a relatively high induction vacuum in the inlet manifold so as to allow the regulation valve to open and allow all crankcase vapours to be drawn from the crankcase. Under full throttle conditions the inlet manifold vacuum is not sufficient to draw all vapours from the crankcase and into the inlet manifold. In this case the crankcase ventilation air flow is reversed, with the fumes being drawn into the air cleaner instead of the inlet manifold.
Positioned within the crankcase is a baffle plate and filter mesh which will prevent engine oil from being drawn back upwards into the inlet manifold.
Servicing information will be found in Chapter 1.

38 Exhaust emission control system – description

1   The exhaust emission control system consists of some of the following items, dependent on model, year and intended market:

(a) Early fuel evaporative system (EFE)
(b) Exhaust gas recirculation system (EGR)
(c) Mixture ratio rich-lean exchange system
(d) Fuel shut-off system
(e) Catalyst warm-up system
(f) Spark timing control system
(g) Throttle opener control system (TOCS)
(h) Catalytic converter
(i) Air induction system (AIS)
(j) Air injection system (AIS)

2   In addition to the above systems, the anti-dieseling solenoid, altitude compensator (if fitted) and temperature controlled air cleaner can be regarded as emission control items. These are referred to elsewhere in this Chapter.
3   A brief description of the above listed systems and their functions is given below.

Early fuel evaporative system (EFE)

4   This system utilizes a thermostatically controlled heat control valve in the exhaust manifold to heat the intake manifold during the

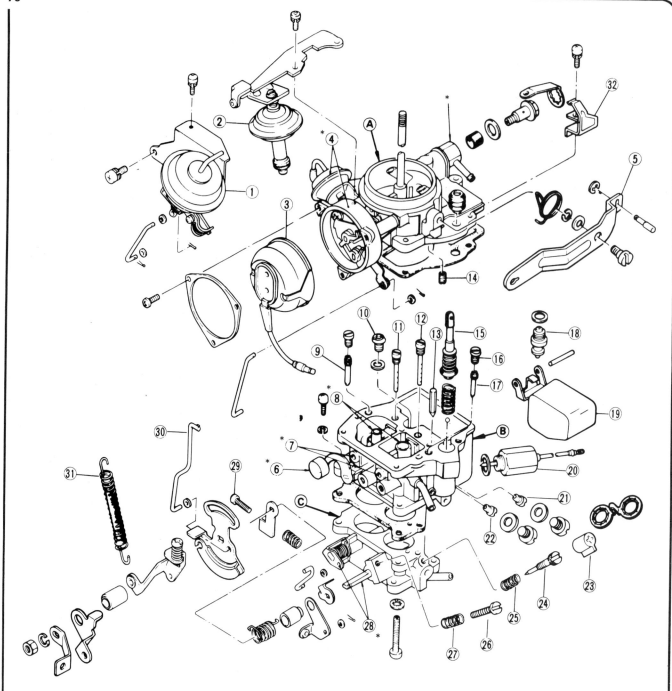

Fig. 3.35 Exploded view of the DCH carburettor – non-Californian and Canadian models (Sec 35)

A   Choke chamber
B   Central body
C   Throttle chamber
1   Throttle opener servo diaphragm
2   Dashpot
3   Automatic choke cover
4   Automatic choke body and diaphragm chamber*
5   Accelerator pump lever
6   Auxiliary valve*
7   Venturi stopper screws*
8   Primary and secondary small venturi*

9   Secondary slow jet
10 Power valve
11 Secondary main air bleed
12 Primary main air bleed
13 Injector weight
14 Primary slow air bleed
15 Accelerator pump
16 Plug
17 Primary slow jet
18 Needle valve
19 Float
20 Anti-dieseling solenoid valve
21 Primary main jet

22 Secondary main jet
23 Idle limiter cap
24 Idle mixture screw
25 Spring
26 Idle speed (throttle stop) screw
27 Spring
28 Primary and secondary throttle valves*
29 Fast idle adjuster screw
30 Accelerator pump rod
31 Throttle return spring
32 Stroke limiter
*Do not remove these parts

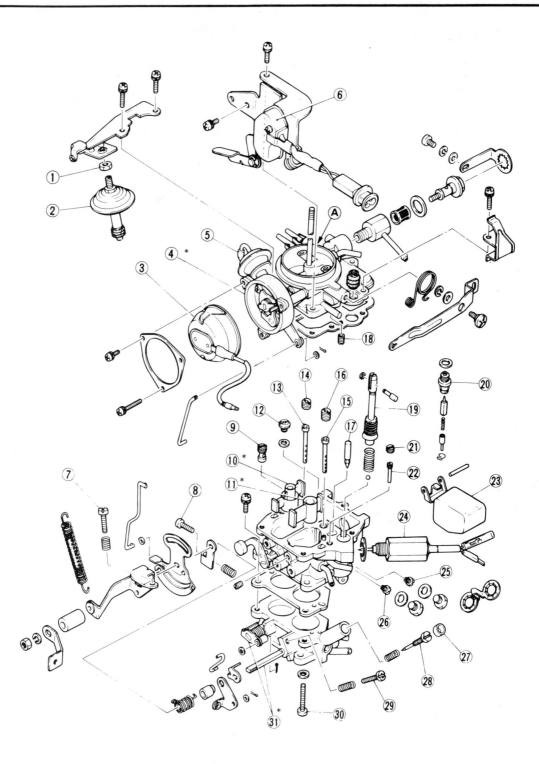

Fig. 3.36 Exploded view of the DCH carburettor fitted to California models (Sec 35)

A	Choke chamber	11*	Primary small venturi	22	Primary slow jet
1	Dashpot adjusting nut	12	Power valve	23	Float
2	Dashpot	13	Secondary main air bleed	24	Anti-dieseling solenoid valve
3	Automatic choke cover	14	Plug	25	Secondary main jet
4*	Automatic choke body	15	Primary main air bleed	26	Primary main jet
5	Automatic choke break diaphragm	16	Plug	27	Idle mixture screw blanking plug
6	Throttle valve switch assembly	17	Injector weight	28	Idle mixture screw
7	Throttle valve switch adjusting screw	18	Primary slow air bleed	29	Idle speed (throttle stop) screw
8	Fast idle adjusting screw	19	Accelerating pump	30	Vacuum screw
9	Secondary slow jet	20	Needle valve	31*	Primary and secondary throttle shaft
10*	Secondary small venturi	21	Plug		*Do not remove these parts

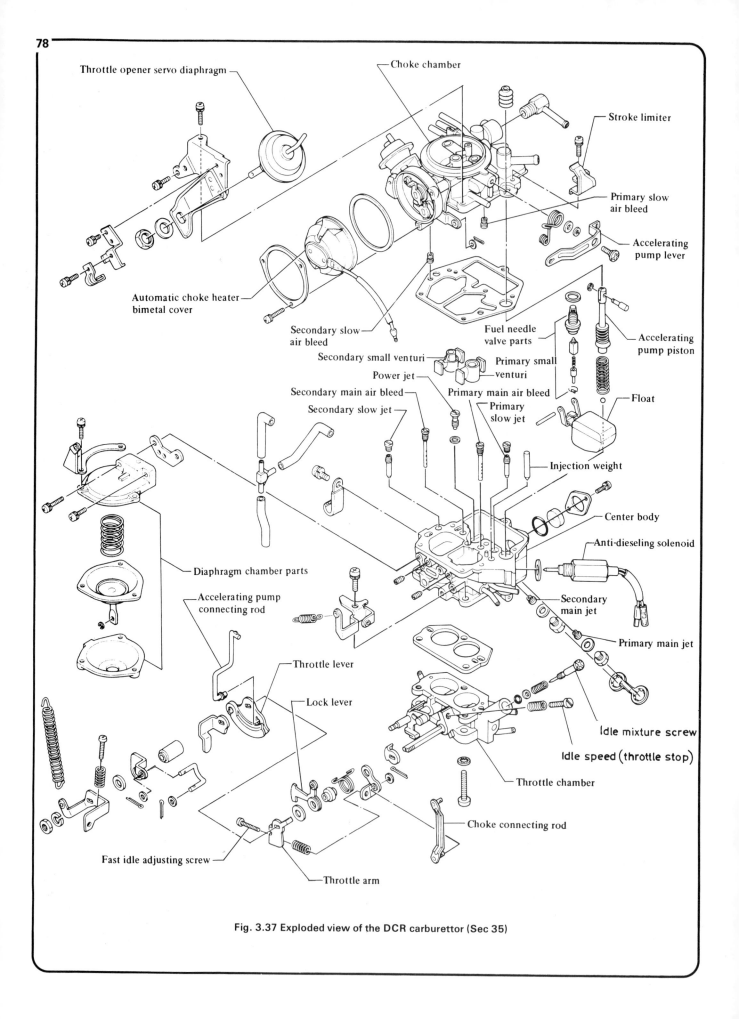

Fig. 3.37 Exploded view of the DCR carburettor (Sec 35)

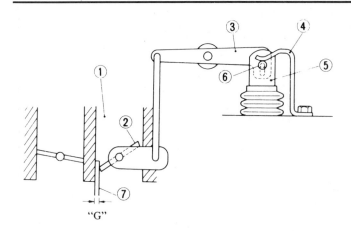

Fig. 3.38 Accelerator pump stroke limiter adjustment. For G see text (Sec 35)

1	Primary carburettor throat	5	Piston
2	Throttle valve	6	Pin
3	Lever	7	Feeler gauge
4	Limiter		

engine warm-up period. This improves the fuel atomization and results in lower hydrocarbon emissions from the exhaust. On some models the manifold is coolant-heated.

Exhaust gas recirculation system (EGR)
5   The function of this system is to lower the flame temperature during combustion, so reducing the nitrogen oxide content of the exhaust gases. This it achieves by returning a small amount of exhaust gas to the combustion chambers, the amount of gas being regulated by the EGR control valve. The gas being recirculated is directed to the inlet manifold and it is then drawn into the combustion chambers in the normal manner.

Mixture ratio rich-lean exchange system
6   This system controls the air to fuel mixture ratio to improve fuel economy and performance whilst reducing the harmful exhaust emissions. The operation of the system depends on the engine coolant temperature and the car speed. A diagram of the layout is shown in Fig. 3.41.

Fuel shut-off system
7   Fitted to certain models from 1981, the fuel shut-off system enables the fuel supply to be cut off during deceleration from high speeds and is actuated by high manifold vacuum. The system circuit is shown in Fig. 3.42. If it can be seen that the system works in conjunction with the anti-dieseling solenoid and speed detecting switch. When the vacuum within the inlet manifold drops below a certain level, the vacuum switch reactivates the anti-dieseling solenoid valve and the fuel flow is allowed to continue.

Catalyst warm-up system
8   A diagram of this system is shown in Fig. 3.43. Fitted from 1981 on, the system is designed to help reduce the CO emissions when the engine is cold by retarding the spark timing via the vacuum switching solenoid. This alters the valve control, operates the throttle opener and changes the spark timing accordingly. The system works in conjunction with the coolant temperature switches, the fuel shut-off system, the neutral switch and the vacuum delay valve. This last item regulates any sudden change of vacuum in the distributor vacuum advance line.

Spark timing control system
9   Shown in Fig. 3.44, this system utilizes a sintered steel flow restrictor and an umbrella type non-return valve in the vacuum line between the carburettor and the distributor. Its purpose is to delay the spark advance during rapid acceleration and to cut off spark advance immediately during deceleration.

Throttle opener control system
10   This is described in Section 32.

Catalytic converter
11   Fitted in the exhaust system of most vehicles destined for America, this device speeds up the chemical reaction of the hydrocarbons and carbon monoxide present in the exhaust gases so that they change into harmless carbon dioxide and water.

Air induction system
12   The function of the air induction system (which is an alternative to the air injection system) is to supply secondary air to the exhaust manifold during pulses of vacuum within the manifold. This then assists in reducing the harmful CO and HC exhaust emissions. The air induction valve is fitted to the air cleaner and when the exhaust pressure drops below the atmospheric pressure, the valve opens to provide the system with secondary air until the exhaust pressure rises above atmospheric pressure. The purpose of the AB (anti-backfire) valve is to prevent afterburning in the exhaust system during initial moments of deceleration.

Air injection system
13   The air injection system is an alternative to the air induction system. It is a method of injecting air (generated in an external compressor) into the exhaust manifold in order to reduce hydrocarbons and carbon monoxide in the exhaust gas by providing conditions favourable for recombustion. This system comprises an air cleaner, engine-driven air pump, relief valve, check valve, anti-backfire valve, air gallery and the associated hoses. Models for use in California also have an air control valve.
14   Air is drawn through the air pump air cleaner, compressed, and directed through the check valve to the air gallery and injection nozzles. During high speed operation, excessive pump pressure is vented through a relief valve in the carburettor air cleaner.
15   The check valve is fitted in the delivery line at the injection gallery. The function of this valve is to prevent any exhaust gases passing into the air pump should the manifold pressure be greater than the pump injection pressure. It is designed to close against the exhaust manifold pressure should the air pump fail as a result, for example, of a broken drivebelt.
16   During deceleration, intake manifold vacuum opens the anti-backfire valve to allow the fresh air to flow into the intake manifold. This ensures that the combustion cycle is more effective and reduces the amount of unburned gasses exhausted.
17   On California models, the combined air control (CAC) valve opens when the combined air pump pressure and intake manifold vacuum reach a predetermined level as happens during lightly loaded conditions. The air from the air pump is bled off to the air cleaner which means that the injection system is less effective, the exhaust gas temperature is lowered and the catalytic converter temperature can be maintained at the optimum operating temperature.

39 Emission control system – maintenance

1   The respective emission control components can only operate efficiently if the engine and its associate parts are in good condition and correctly adjusted. If the maintenance schedules given at the front of the book are closely adhered to then this should be the case but in particular check that the valve clearances are correct, the fuel lines are secure and the fuel filter is changed at the specified mileage. The carburettor air filter and air pump filter (if applicable) must also be renewed regularly and the carburettor correctly adjusted. In the ignition circuit, check that the timing is in correct adjustment, also the spark plug electrode clearances.
2   Check that all emission control vapour lines and their respective connections are secure and in good condition.
3   Check the condition of the air pump drivebelt and also its tension. Readjust if necessary as given in Section 46.
4   Renew the positive crankcase ventilation (PCV) valve and filter at the prescribed mileage/time interval.
5   Remove the ventilation hoses occasionally and blow through with an air line. This is most essential whenever the PCV valve has been renewed.
6   The fuel tank vacuum relief valve must be in good working condition. If defective renew together with the fuel filler cap.
7   The carbon canister filter in the evaporative control system must be removed at regular intervals.

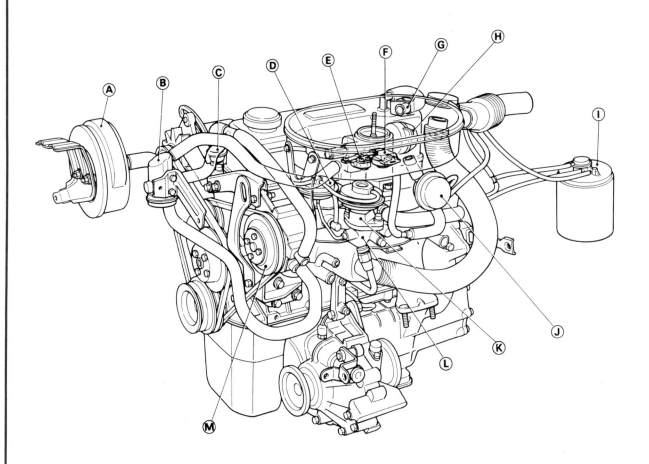

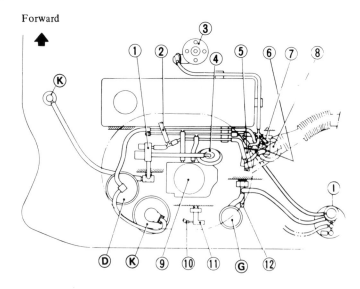

Forward

Fig. 3.39 The emission control components layout – 1979 USA models (Sec 38)

1	Throttle opener vacuum control valve	6	Thermal vacuum tube
2	From 3-way connector to air cleaner	7	From vacuum motor to temperature sensor
3	Distributor	8	Vacuum motor
4	Throttle opener servo diaphragm	9	Carburettor
5	Vacuum switching valve	10	From idle compensator to intake manifold
		11	From AB valve

12	From brake booster
A	Air pump air cleaner
B*	CAC valve
C	Check valve
D	BPT valve
E	Idle compensator
F	ATC air cleaner temperature sensor
G	PCV filter

H	Auto-choke heater
I	Carbon canister
J	AB valve
K*	EGR control valve
L	EGR passage
M	Air pump
*California models only	

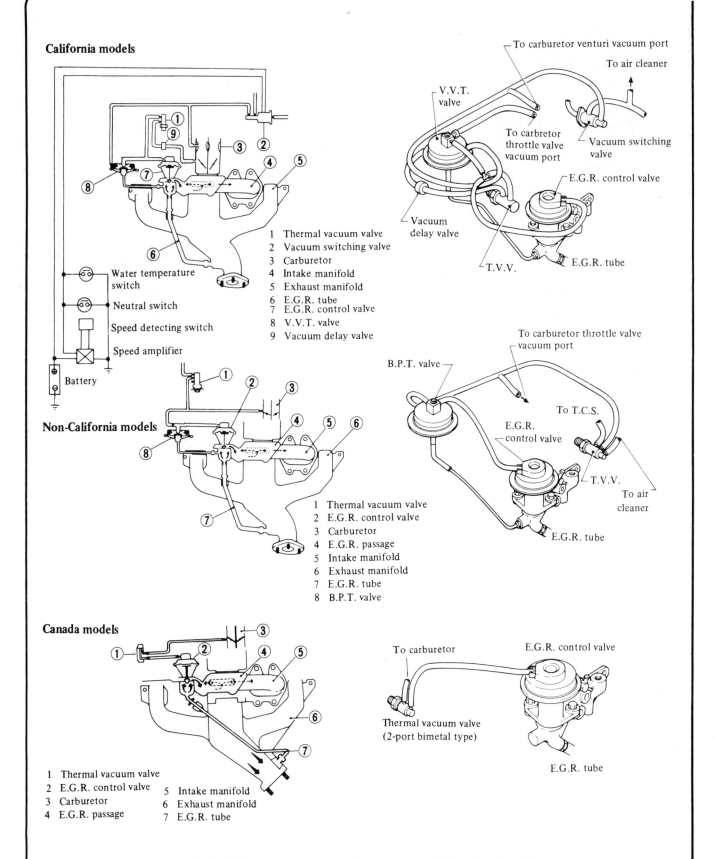

California models

- 1 Thermal vacuum valve
- 2 Vacuum switching valve
- 3 Carburetor
- 4 Intake manifold
- 5 Exhaust manifold
- 6 E.G.R. tube
- 7 E.G.R. control valve
- 8 V.V.T. valve
- 9 Vacuum delay valve

Water temperature switch
Neutral switch
Speed detecting switch
Speed amplifier
Battery

To carburetor venturi vacuum port
To air cleaner
V.V.T. valve
To carbretor throttle valve vacuum port
Vacuum switching valve
E.G.R. control valve
Vacuum delay valve
T.V.V.
E.G.R. tube

Non-California models

- 1 Thermal vacuum valve
- 2 E.G.R. control valve
- 3 Carburetor
- 4 E.G.R. passage
- 5 Intake manifold
- 6 Exhaust manifold
- 7 E.G.R. tube
- 8 B.P.T. valve

To carburetor throttle valve vacuum port
B.P.T. valve
E.G.R. control valve
To T.C.S.
T.V.V.
To air cleaner
E.G.R. tube

Canada models

- 1 Thermal vacuum valve
- 2 E.G.R. control valve
- 3 Carburetor
- 4 E.G.R. passage
- 5 Intake manifold
- 6 Exhaust manifold
- 7 E.G.R. tube

To carburetor
E.G.R. control valve
Thermal vacuum valve (2-port bimetal type)
E.G.R. tube

Fig. 3.40 The exhaust gas recirculation system – 1980 models (Sec 38)

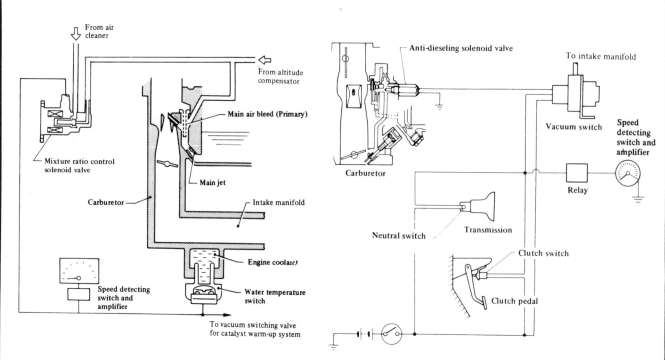

Fig. 3.41 Mixture ratio rich-lean exchange system (Sec 38)

Fig. 3.42 The fuel shut-off system – 1981 models (Sec 38)

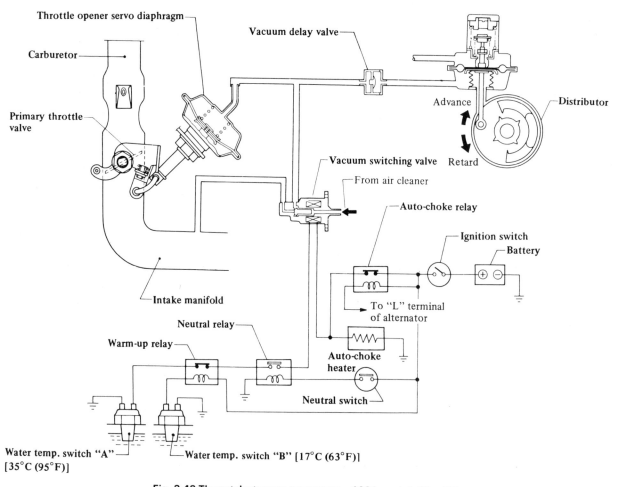

Fig. 3.43 The catalyst warm-up system – 1981 models (Sec 38)

California models

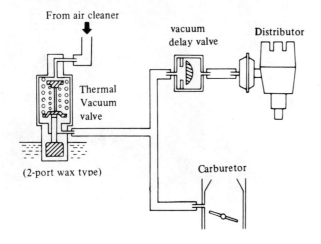

From air cleaner

vacuum delay valve

Distributor

Thermal Vacuum valve

(2-port wax type)

Carburetor

Non-California models

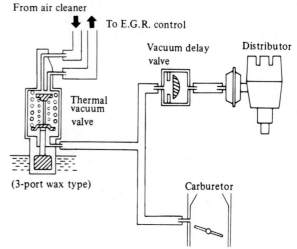

From air cleaner

To E.G.R. control

Vacuum delay valve

Distributor

Thermal vacuum valve

(3-port wax type)

Carburetor

Canada models

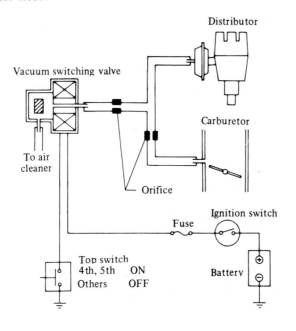

Distributor

Vacuum switching valve

Carburetor

To air cleaner

Orifice

Fuse

Ignition switch

Top switch
4th, 5th   ON
Others   OFF

Battery

Operation for U.S.A. models

Water temperature °C (°F)	Thermal vacuum valve	Spark timing
Below 15 (59)	Closed	Fully advanced
Between 15 and 60 (59 and 140)	Open	Partially advanced
Above 60 (140)	Closed	Fully advanced

Operation for Canada M/T models

Transmission gear position	Vacuum switching valve	Ignition timing
"Top" (4th and 5th)	Closed	Fully advanced
Other than "Top"	Open	Partially advanced

Fig. 3.44 The spark timing control system (Sec 38)

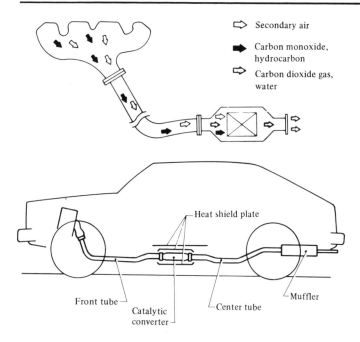

➪ Secondary air

➡ Carbon monoxide,
hydrocarbon

➪ Carbon dioxide gas,
water

Fig. 3.45 Operation and location of the catalytic converter
(Sec 8)

U.S.A. models

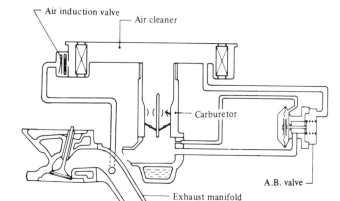

Canada models

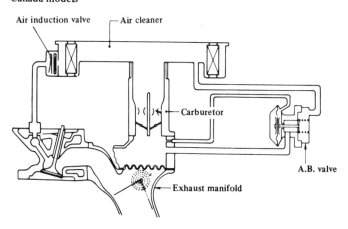

Fig. 3.46 The air induction system for later USA and Canada
models (Sec 38)

40.1 The early fuel evaporation system heat control valve unit

8   Specialised equipment is required to check the efficiency of the systems and also to enable accurate adjustment of the carburettor idle and ignition timing to suit. Therefore apart from the above mentioned items and the following service sections, any more complex repair or overhauls of the emission control system components are best left to your Datsun dealer who has the specialised knowledge and equipment to deal with such problems.

40 Early fuel evaporative (EFE) system – checking, removal and refitting

1   Periodically inspect the operation of the heat control valve. On starting with the engine cold, the counterweight should be in its extreme anti-clockwise position (photo).
2   During acceleration (engine still cold) the counterweight will rotate in a clockwise direction.
3   When the engine reaches normal operating temperature, the counterweight will have moved fully clockwise.
4   External components of the device can be renewed but as the internal valve plate is welded to the operating shaft, any fault or wear in these items will necessitate renewal of the complete manifold assembly.
5   The removable components can be dismantled as follows. Refer to Fig. 3.50.
6   Withdraw the circlip and remove the lockbolt. Remove the key, the counterweight, the thermostatic spring and the coil spring.
7   Refit in the reverse order to removal. Start and run the engine on completion and check the unit for satisfactory operation as the engine warms up.

41 Exhaust gas recirculation system – checking and maintenance

1   Check the complete system for insecure or damaged hoses. Tighten or renew as appropriate.
2   With the engine stationary, move the diaphragm of the EGR valve upwards with the fingers and check that it does not stick or bind.
3   Run the engine and with the temperature low, check that the EGR control valve does not operate as the engine speed is increased from idle to 3000 to 3500 rpm, again with a finger on the diaphragm.
4   With the engine coolant at its normal operating temperature, repeat this test (paragraph 3) and ensure that the valve operates at the given speed of between 3000 and 3500 rpm.
5   Should the valve fail to operate, detach the vacuum hose to the EGR control valve, at the thermal vacuum valve (Canada models), the BPT valve (non-California models) or the VVT valve (California models) as applicable.

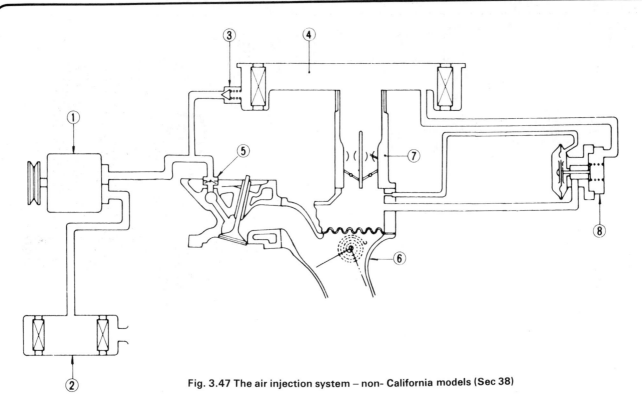

Fig. 3.47 The air injection system – non- California models (Sec 38)

1	Air pump	3	Air relief valve	5	Check valve	7	Carburettor
2	Air pump air cleaner	4	Air cleaner	6	Exhaust manifold	8	Anti-backfire valve

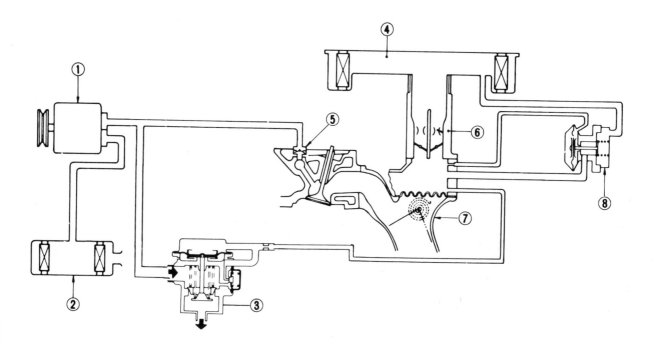

Fig. 3.48 Air injection system – California models (Sec 38)

1	Air pump	3	CAC valve	5	Check valve	7	Exhaust manifold
2	Air pump air cleaner	4	Air cleaner	6	Carburettor	8	Anti-backfire valve

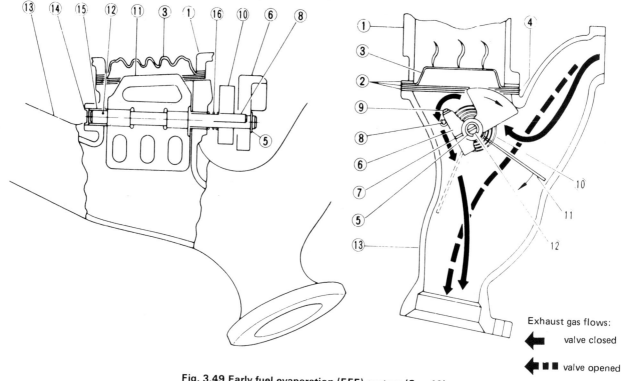

Fig. 3.49 Early fuel evaporation (EFE) system (Sec 40)

1 Intake manifold	5 Circlip	9 Screw	13 Exhaust manifold
2 Stove gasket	6 Counterweight	10 Thermostat spring	14 Cap
3 Manifold stove	7 Key	11 Heat control valve	15 Bushing
4 Heat shield plate	8 Stopper pin	12 Control valve shaft	16 Coil spring

Exhaust gas flows:

◀ valve closed

◀▬▬ valve opened

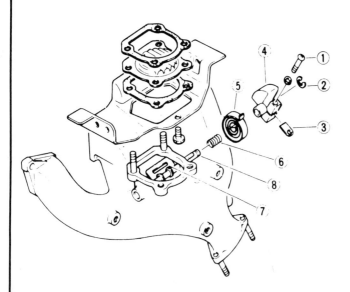

Fig. 3.50 Exploded view of the EFE components (Sec 40)

1 Lockbolt	5 Thermostat spring
2 Circlip	6 Coil spring
3 Key	7 Heat control valve
4 Counterweight	8 Valve shaft

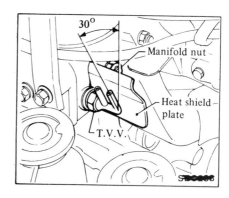

Fig. 3.51 Thermal vacuum valve fitting position (Sec 41)

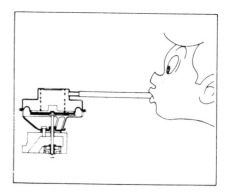

Fig. 3.52 EGR valve test (Sec 41)

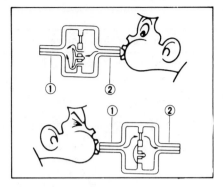

Fig. 3.53 Vacuum delay valve – test 1 (Sec 41)

1　Carburettor side　2　TVV side

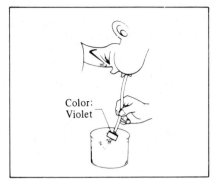

Fig. 3.54 Vacuum delay valve – test 2 (Sec 41)

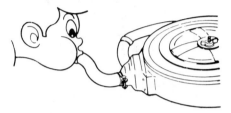

Fig. 3.55 Checking the air induction valve and filter (Sec 45)

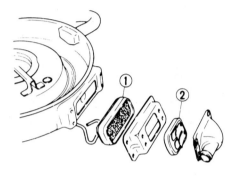

Fig. 3.56 The air induction valve and filter assembly (Sec 45)

1　Valve filter　　　2　Valve

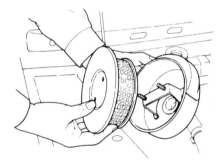

Fig. 3.57 Removing the air pump filter (Sec 47)

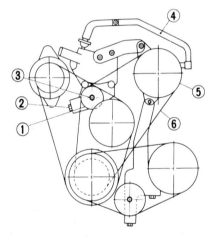

Fig. 3.58 The air pump drivebelt and fixings (Sec 47)

1　Idler pully　　　　4　Air pump hose
2　Belt adjustment bolt　5　Air pump
3　Locknut　　　　　6　Drivebelt

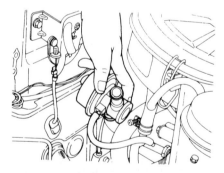

Fig. 3.59 AB valve removal (Sec 47)

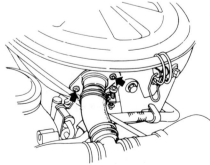

Fig. 3.61 Air pump relief valve removal (Sec 47)

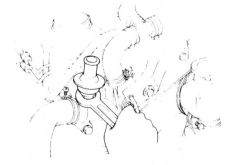

Fig. 3.60 Check valve removal (Sec 47)

6   On Canadian models, accelerate the engine from idle to 3000 to 3500 rpm and check that the thermal vacuum is open with vacuum present at the end of the vacuum hose (EGR valve side). If very little or no vacuum is felt, renew the thermal vacuum valve.

7   If renewal of the thermal vacuum valve is necessary you will need to partially drain the coolant (Chapter 2). When renewing the valve unit, take care as it is made of plastic and is easily damaged. When refitting the thermal vacuum valve, tighten it so that it is positioned 30° from vertical (Fig. 3.51).

8   On all models, to check the EGR control valve, remove it from the engine and then connect a piece of hose to its port and suck with the mouth (Fig. 3.52). The valve should move into its fully extended position and retain this attitude for at least 30 seconds after the vacuum ceases. Check the valve for any signs of damage. Clean the external surface of the valve with a wire brush and then clean using compressed air. If the EGR control valve or its packing are damaged in any way then they must be renewed.

9   On USA models, both the VVT valve and the BPT valve can be tested on removal from the engine but they are best checked by your Datsun dealer for their respective vacuum and pressure functions.

10 The vacuum delay valve can be tested by blowing air into the carburettor side port (Fig. 3.53). Air should flow through the valve. When blowing air through the opposing port, a resistance should be felt. If thought to be malfunctioning, immerse the valve in water and blow air through the side coloured violet. Small air bubbles should be seen; if not renew the valve.

42 Catalyst warm-up system – maintenance and testing

1   Maintenance of this system comprises a visual check to ensure that all the components are secure and in good condition. Actuate the throttle opener servo diaphragm by hand to ensure that it moves freely and correctly.

2   Detach the vacuum switching valve connector leads. Connect an independent 12V supply to the valve and check that the throttle opener diaphragm is operational.

3   To check the vacuum switching valve, leave the independent 12V supply connected and using a length of hose, check the airflow through the valve which should be as follows, depending on the switch position:

Switch on: Air flows from the vacuum delay valve into the switching valve port and out of the outlet port to the inlet manifold

Switch off: Air flows into the vacuum valve port and out of the air cleaner connecting pipe port

Refer to Fig. 3.43 for the system layout.

4   To check the vacuum delay valve operation, first remove it, then blow air into the distributor port side. The air should pass through the valve. Now blow air through the carburettor port side. There should be an increased resistance to the airflow through the valve.

5   Renew any defective components. Testing of the water temperature switches and the electrical relays is best entrusted to your Datsun dealer.

43 Spark timing control system – maintenance

1   Check that all the system wiring connections are secure and in good condition. Refer to Fig. 3.44 for the system layout.

2   Inspect the vacuum hoses for signs of deterioration, damage or insecurity.

3   Check that the distributor advance/retard control is operational.

4   Check the operation of the thermal vacuum valve or vacuum switching valve as given in the table in Fig. 3.44.

5   Check the top gear detaching switch (if fitted) for correct operation by using an ohmmeter and connecting it up to the switch. Engage top gear; continuity should only exist if the gear selected is 4th or 5th. In other gears there should be no continuity. When making this test, leave the ignition switched off or you may damage the tester.

44 Catalytic converter – checking, removal and refitting

The catalytic converter condition can be checked by noting the variation in CO percentage.

1   Visually inspect the catalytic converter for cracks or damage.

2   Remove the air hose from the air induction valve check and fit a cap on the valve.

3   Refer to Section 26 and adjust the throttle and idle adjusting screws to obtain the specified CO percentage.

4   Remove the cap and connect the air hose to the induction check valve. If the idling speed increases, readjust it to the specified speed.

5   Run the engine for about four minutes at 2000 rpm, then at idling speed for one minute, then check the CO percentage.

6   If the CO percentage is less than 0.3% the catalytic converter is serviceable.

7   If the CO percentage is more than 0.3%, check the air injection or induction system and renew the air induction/check valve (if fitted). Recheck the CO percentage; if it is still more than 0.3% the catalytic converter is defective and must be renewed. Remove as follows.

8   Apply the parking brake, jack up the car and support it on axle stands. *Ensure that the catalytic converter is cold.*

9   Undo the bolts securing the catalytic converter lower guard plate and remove the guard plate.

10 Undo the attaching bolts and remove the catalytic converter from the exhaust system.

11 Refitting is the reverse of the removal procedure. Tighten the catalytic converter attaching bolts and the guard plate bolts to the specified torque.

45 Air induction system – inspection, removal and refitting

1   Inspect the system hoses for security, distortion and general condition. Renew any hoses which are defective.

2   Check the air induction valve and filter by detaching the induction hose at the induction pipe and then blow or suck through the hose to ensure that the air only flows to the induction pipe side (Fig. 3.55).

3   Check the induction valve and filter by removing them from the air cleaner body, to which they are attached by retaining screws.

4   Extract the filter (Fig. 3.56) and if blocked or very dirty, renew it. The filter must be renewed at the specified mileage intervals irrespective of condition.

5   Inspect the induction reed valve for binding or signs of damage and renew it if necessary.

46 Air injection system (AIS) – checking

Air injection system hoses

1   Check the air system for loose connections, cracks or deterioration. Tighten or renew as necessary.

Air pump

2   Check and adjust the air pump drivebelt tension to obtain a deflection of 0.3 to 0.47 in (8 to 12 mm), with a load of 22 lb (10 kg) applied at the midpoint of the longest run of the belt.

3   To test the air pump, a special Datsun pressure test gauge and adaptor are required and this task should therefore be entrusted to your Datsun dealer. If the pump is diagnosed as being defective it should be removed and renewed or entrusted to your Datsun dealer for overhaul.

Check valve

4   Start the engine and warm it up to the normal operating temperature.

5   Disconnect the air supply hose from the check valve.

6   Run the engine at approximately 2000 rpm and then let it return to idling.

7   Check for any signs of leaks. If leaks are detected renew the check valve.

Air pump relief valve

8   Disconnect the check valve and air control valve hoses from the air hose connector. Blank off the connector.

9 With the engine running at approximately 3000 rpm place your hand on the air outlet of the air pump relief valve and check for a discharge of air. If no air is felt, renew the air pump relief valve.

Anti-backfire valve

10 With the engine at the normal operating temperature, disconnect the hose from the air cleaner and place a finger near the outlet.

11 Run the engine at approximately 3000 rpm then quickly return it to idling. A suction force should be felt on your finger if the valve is operating normally. If no suction is felt, the anti-backfire valve is defective and must be renewed.

CAC valve (California models)

12 A vacuum pump and test gauge is required for checking the CAC valve and it is recommended that the car is taken to the local Datsun dealer for this check to be carried out.

47 Air injection system components – removal and refitting

Air pump air cleaner

1 Remove the retaining nuts securing the air pump cleaner to its bracket and detach the cleaner. The air cleaner filter and lower body must be renewed as a unit (Fig. 3.57). Refit in reverse sequence.

Air pump

2 Disconnect the air hoses from the air pump.

3 Loosen the air pump adjusting bar securing bolts and the air pump mounting bolts, then remove the air pump drivebelt.

4 Remove the air pump from the mounting bracket.

5 Refit the pump in the reverse order to removal, but adjust the drivebelt tension as given in the previous Section before fully tightening the retaining bolts.

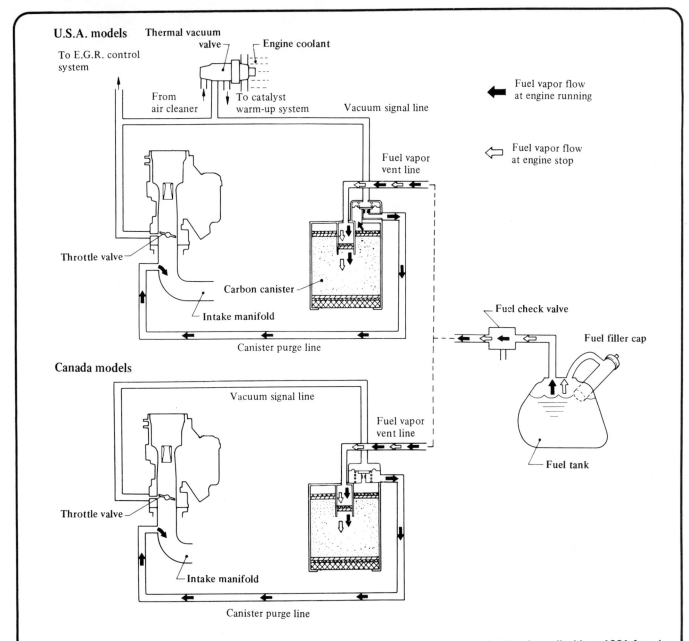

Fig. 3.62 The evaporative emission control system. Note that the thermal vacuum valve connection is only applicable to 1981 American market models (Sec 48)

Anti-backfire (AB) valve

6   This is located on the air cleaner rear side and can be withdrawn after the air hoses and vacuum tube have been disconnected – see Fig. 3.59. Refit in reverse order, and ensure that the hoses and vacuum tube are secure.

Check valve

7   The check valve is located in the cylinder head. To remove it, disconnect the air line and then unscrew and withdraw the valve (Fig. 3.60). Refit in the reverse order.

Air pump relief valve (non-California models)

8   Disconnect the air hose from the relief valve.
9   Remove the relief valve-to-air cleaner retaining screws and withdraw the valve (Fig. 3.61). Refit in the reverse order to removal.

CAC valve (California models)

10   Located beneath the air pump air cleaner, this valve can be withdrawn after the air hoses and vacuum tube are detached and the retaining screws removed. Refit in the reverse order to removal and ensure that the tube and hose connections are secure.

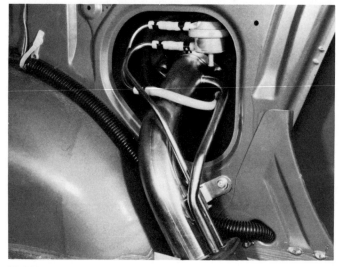

48.8 The fuel check valve unit and hoses

48 Evaporative emission control system – description and checking

1   This system is designed to prevent vapour from the tank escaping into the atmosphere and is fitted to vehicles operating in areas where stringent anti-pollution regulations are enforced.
2   The system comprises a positive sealing fuel tank filler cap, a fuel check valve, a vapour vent line, a carbon canister, a vacuum signal line and a canister purge line. The component connections are shown in Fig. 3.62.
3   The fuel vapours within the sealed fuel tank are directed to the carbon canister, which is filled with activated charcoal to absorb the vapours when the engine is idling or stopped.
4   When the engine speed increases, vacuum in the signal line opens the purge control line and the fuel vapours in the canister are drawn into the inlet manifold through the purge line.
5   To maintain and check the system, proceed as follows.
6   Periodic preventative maintenance of the system should be carried out. Inspect all hoses and the fuel filler cap for damage or deteriora-

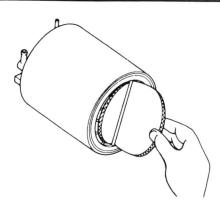

Fig. 3.63 Renew the carbon canister filter at specified intervals (Sec 48)

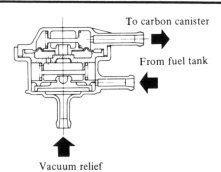

Fig. 3.64 Fuel check valve inspection (Sec 48)

To carbon canister

From fuel tank

Vacuum relief

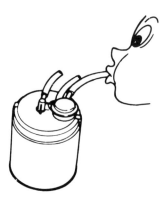

Fig. 3.65 Carbon canister purge control valve check method (Sec 48)

Fig. 3.66 Carbon canister purge control valve diaphragm unit (Sec 48)

| 1 | Cover | 3 | Retainer |
| 2 | Diaphragm | 4 | Spring |

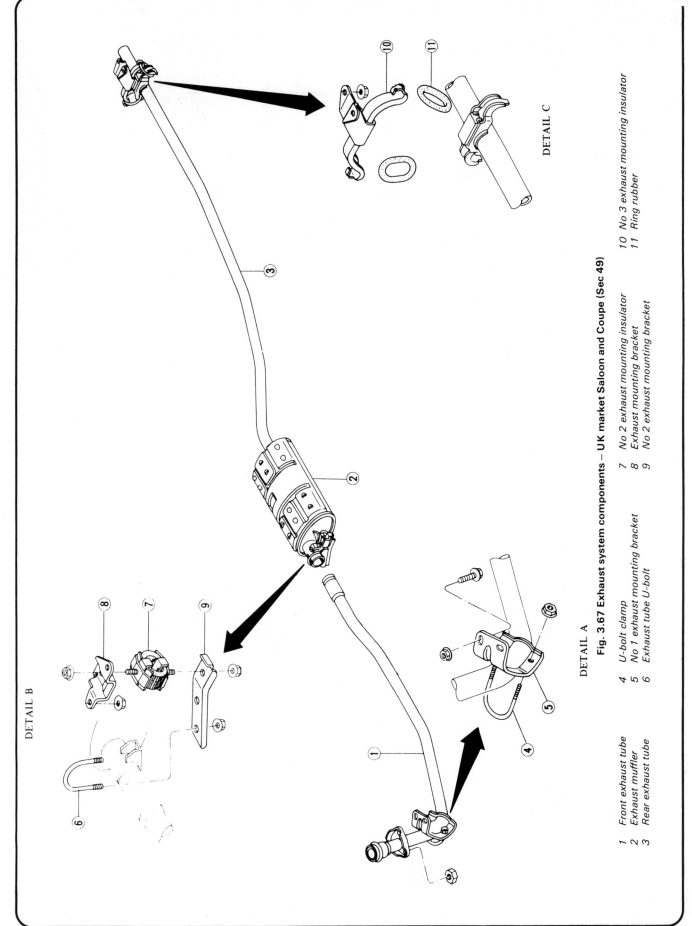

DETAIL B

DETAIL C

DETAIL A

Fig. 3.67 Exhaust system components – UK market Saloon and Coupe (Sec 49)

1 Front exhaust tube
2 Exhaust muffler
3 Rear exhaust tube

4 U-bolt clamp
5 No 1 exhaust mounting bracket
6 Exhaust tube U-bolt

7 No 2 exhaust mounting insulator
8 Exhaust mounting bracket
9 No 2 exhaust mounting bracket

10 No 3 exhaust mounting insulator
11 Ring rubber

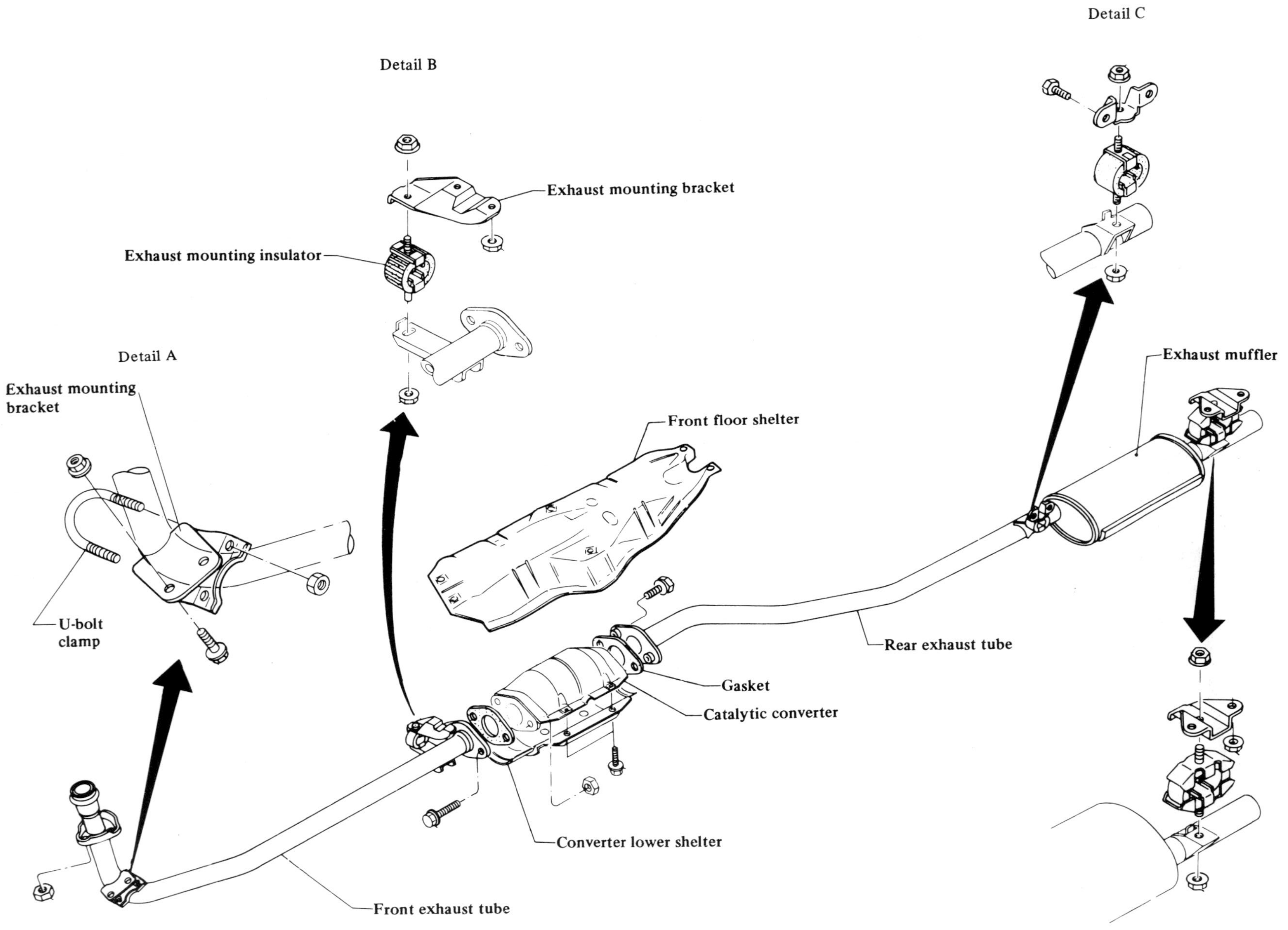

Detail C

Detail B

Detail A

Detail D

Exhaust muffler

Rear exhaust tube

Front floor shelter

Gasket

Catalytic converter

Converter lower shelter

Front exhaust tube

Exhaust mounting bracket

Exhaust mounting insulator

Exhaust mounting bracket

U-bolt clamp

Fig. 3.68 Exhaust system – USA models with catalytic converter (Sec 49)

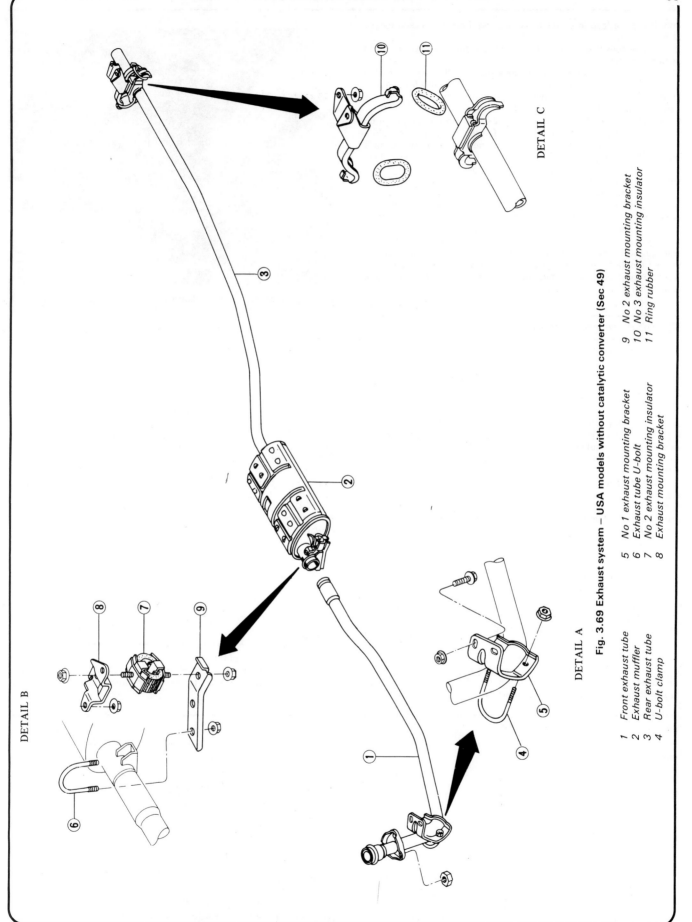

DETAIL C

DETAIL B

DETAIL A

Fig. 3.69 Exhaust system – USA models without catalytic converter (Sec 49)

1 Front exhaust tube
2 Exhaust muffler
3 Rear exhaust tube
4 U-bolt clamp

5 No 1 exhaust mounting bracket
6 Exhaust tube U-bolt
7 No 2 exhaust mounting insulator
8 Exhaust mounting bracket

9 No 2 exhaust mounting bracket
10 No 3 exhaust mounting insulator
11 Ring rubber

tion. If the fuel cap is suspected of leaking, have it checked by your Datsun dealer.

7   At the specified maintenance intervals, remove and renew the carbon canister filter.

8   The fuel check valve is fitted above the fuel filler pipe to the tank within the body side panel (photo). To remove the valve for checking, prise free the inner panel for access, then detach the respective hoses and withdraw the valve.

9   To check the valve, refer to Fig. 3.64 and blow through the fuel tank connector. A resistance should be felt whilst some air should be felt to emerge from the engine side connectors. Now blow the air through from the engine side connector and check that air exits freely from the fuel tank port connection. Renew the valve unit if it is suspected of malfunction.

10 Check the carbon canister purge control valve for signs of leakage. Check the distributor vacuum line and the purge control diaphragm also. To do this, detach the rubber hose in the line at the T-connector (to carbon canister) and suck air through a rubber hose connected to a vacuum port in the canister (Fig. 3.65). There should be no sign of leakage, but if there is, remove the purge control valve top cover and inspect the diaphragm for signs of cracks or damage. If the diaphragm is found to be defective it must be renewed together with its retainer and spring (Fig. 3.68).

49.4 Typical silencer-to-pipe clamp and support hanger

49 Exhaust system – removal and refitting

1   The type of exhaust system fitted is dependent on the territory to which the car was originally supplied.

2   The various system types are shown in the accompanying illustrations.

3   Examination of the exhaust pipe and silencer at regular intervals is worthwhile as small defects may be repairable when, if left, they will almost certainly require renewal of one of the sections of the system. Also, any leaks, apart from the noise factor, may cause poisonous exhaust gases to get inside the car which can be unpleasant, to say the least, even in mild concentrations. Prolonged inhalation could cause sickness and giddiness, or death.

4   As the sleeve connections and clamps are usually very difficult to separate (photo) it is quicker and easier in the long run to remove the complete system from the car when renewing a section. It can be expensive if another section is damaged when trying to separate a bad section from it.

5   To remove the system first remove the bolts holding the tail pipe bracket to the body. Support the tailpipe on something to prevent cracking or kinking the pipes elsewhere.

6   Disconnect the front pipe support brackets.

7   Disconnect the manifold-to-downpipe connecting flange and then

withdraw the complete exhaust system from below and out to the rear of the vehicle. If necessary, jack up the rear of the vehicle to provide more clearance.

8   When separating a damaged section to be renewed, cut away the damaged part from the adjoining good section rather than risk damaging the latter.

9   If small repairs are being carried out it is best, if possible, not to try to pull the sections apart.

10 Refitting should be carried out after connecting the two sections together. De-burr and grease the connecting socket and make sure that the clamp is in good condition and slipped over the front pipe, but do not tighten it at this stage.

11 Connect the system to the manifold and connect the rear support.

12 Tighten the pipe clamp, the manifold flange nuts and the rear suspension strap bolts. Check that the exhaust system will not knock against any part of the vehicle when deflected slightly in a sideways upward direction.

13 On models so equipped, the silencer box is located at the rear whilst the catalytic converter is fitted between the front and rear pipe sections. Particular care must be taken when handling this system not to drop or damage it or the effectiveness of the catalytic converter may well be reduced. Refer also to Section 44.

50 Fault diagnosis – fuel system and carburation

Unsatisfactory engine performance and excessive fuel consumption are not necessarily the fault of the fuel system or carburettor. In fact they more commonly occur as a result of ignition and timing faults. Before acting on the following it is necessary to check the ignition system first. Even thugh a fault may lie in the fuel system it will be difficult to trace unless the ignition is correct. The faults below, therefore, assume that this has been attended to first (where appropriate).

Symptom	Reason(s)
Smell of petrol when engine is stopped	Leaking fuel lines or unions Leaking fuel tank
Smell of petrol when engine is idling	Leaking fuel line unions between pump and carburettor Overflow of fuel from float chamber due to wrong level setting, ineffective needle valve or punctured float
Fuel consumption excessive	Leakage (see above) Air cleaner blocked Air cleaner winter/summer adjustment incorrect, or thermostatic air cleaner malfunction Generally worn carburettor Incorrect carburettor adjustment Excessive rolling resistance (tyres under-inflated, brake binding or wheel alignment incorrect)

Symptom	Reason(s)
Mixture too weak	Air cleaner element missing Carburettor or manifold gasket leaking Vacuum hose leaking Float chamber level too low Insufficient fuel delivery
Insufficient fuel delivery	Fuel pipe connections loose Fuel filter blocked Fuel pump defective
Erratic idle	Slow jet clogged Worn throttle valve shafts Throttle valve(s) not fully closing Secondary throttle valve function fault Carburettor-to-manifold gasket leaking TOCS (where fitted) incorrectly adjusted Dashpot stuck (where fitted) Damaged vacuum control solenoid
Reduced power	Blocked main jets Throttle valve not opening correctly Dirty fuel filter/air cleaner filter Fuel pump diaphragm damaged Power valve faulty Idle adjustment incorrect Binding brakes Ignition timing needs adjustment Worn engine
Poor starting	Main jets or slow jets blocked No fuel Idle speed adjustment incorrect Fast idle speed adjustment incorrect Faulty anti-diesel solenoid valve Faulty auxiliary cooling fan or sensor unit (A14 and A15 engines only – see Chapter 2 for details)
Engine hesitation	Main jet or slow jet blocked Emulsion tube blocked Idle speed adjustment incorrect Secondary throttle valve faulty

51 Fault diagnosis – emission control system

Symptom	Reason(s)
Erratic idle speed	Faulty anti-backfire valve Carbon canister purge line disconnected Faulty EGR valve Faulty throttle operner system Sticking throttle cable
Reduced power	EGR valve faulty

Chapter 4 Ignition system

For modifications, and information applicable to later models, see Supplement at end of manual

Contents

Specifications

General

System type:	
A10 and A12 engines	Contact breaker and coil
A14 and A15 engines	Breakerless, integrated circuit
Firing order	1–3–4–2
Location of No 1 cylinder	Timing cover end

Spark plugs

Type:	
A10 engine	Hitachi L46W, NGK B5ES or BR5ES, or equivalent
A12 engine	Hitachi L46PW, NGK BP5ES or BPR5ES, or equivalent
A14 and A15 engines:	
Standard plug	NGK BP5ES-11 or BPR5ES
Hot plug	NGK BP4ES-11 or BPR4ES
Cold plug	NGK BP6ES-11 or BPR6ES
Electrode gap:	
A10 engine	0.028 to 0.031 in (0.7 to 0.8 mm)
A12 engine	0.031 to 0.035 in (0.8 to 0.9 mm)
A14 and A15 engines	0.039 to 0.043 in (1.0 to 1.1 mm)

Coil

Make	Hitachi or Hanskin
Type:	
A10 and A12 engines	6CR-205 or HP5-13E11
A14 and A15 engines	CIT-30 or 5TC-30

Distributor – A10 and A12 engines

Make	Hitachi
Type	D413-67 or D411-89
Direction of rotation	Anticlockwise
Dwell angle	49° to 55°
Contact breaker points gap	0.018 to 0.022 in (0.45 to 0.55 mm)

Distributor – A14 and A15 engines

Make	Hitachi
Type:	
A14 engine, except California	D4K8-19 or 4DK9-05
A14 engine, California	D4K8-18 or 4D4K9-12
A15 engine, except California	D4K80-01
A15 engine, California	D4K80-02
Direction of rotation	Counterclockwise
Air gap	0.012 to 0.020 in (0.3 to 0.5 mm)

Ignition timing

A10 engine .... 8° BTDC at 700 rpm
A12 engine .... 7° BTDC at 700 rpm
A14 engine - except California (1979) .... 10° BTDC at 700 rpm
A14 engine - California (1979) .... 5° BTDC at 700 rpm
A14 engine - all models (1980) .... 8° ± 2° BTDC at 750 ± 50 rpm
A15 engine - all models .... 5° ± 2° BTDC at 750 ± 50 rpm

Torque wrench setting

	lbf ft	kgf m
Spark plugs	11 to 14	1.5 to 2.0

1 General description

In order that the engine can run correctly it is necessary for an electrical spark to ignite the fuel/air mixture in the combustion chamber at exactly the right moment in relation to engine speed and load. The ignition system is based on feeding low tension (LT) voltage from the battery to the coil where it is converted to high tension (HT) voltage. The high tension voltage is powerful enough to jump the spark plug gap in the cylinders many times a second under high compression pressures, providing that the system is in good condition and that all adjustments are correct.

The ignition system is divided into two circuits: the low tension circuit and the high tension circuit.

The low tension (sometimes known as the primary) circuit consists of the battery lead to the ignition switch, lead from the ignition switch to the low tension or primary coil windings (terminal +), and the lead from the low tension coil windings (coil terminal −) to the contact breaker points and condenser in the distributor. (See below for breakerless ignition).

The high tension circuit consists of the high tension or secondary coil windings, the heavy ignition lead from the centre of the coil to the centre of the distributor cap, the rotor arm, and the spark plug leads and spark plugs.

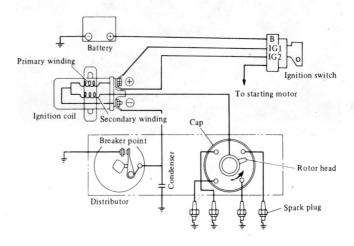

Fig. 4.1 Typical A10/A12 engine ignition circuit (Sec 1)

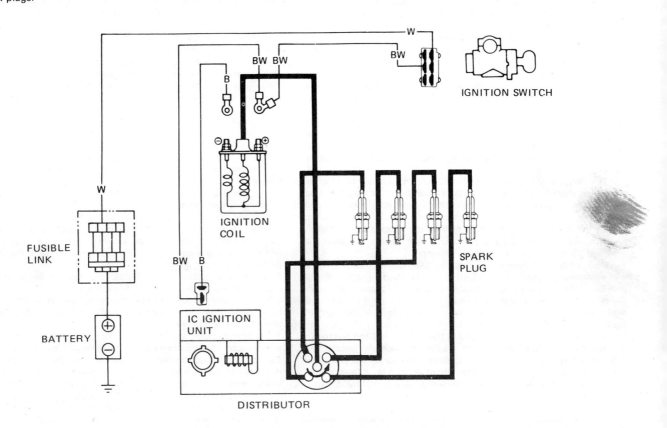

Fig. 4.2 The A14/A15 engine ignition circuit (Sec 1)

2.7 Loosen a contact breaker plate screw

2.8 Adjusting the contact points

The system functions in the following manner. Low tension voltage is changed in the coil into high tension voltage by the opening and closing of the contact breaker points in the low tension circuit. High tension voltage is then fed via the carbon brush in the centre of the distributor cap to the rotor arm of the distributor cap, and each times it comes in line with one of the four metal segments in the cap, which are connected to the spark plug leads, the opening and closing of the contact breaker points causes the high tension voltage to build up, jump the gap from the rotor arm to the appropriate metal segment and so via the spark plug lead to the spark plug, where it finally jumps the spark plug gap before going to earth.

The ignition is advanced and retarded automatically, to ensure the spark occurs at just the right instant for the particular load at the prevailing engine speed.

The ignition advance is controlled both mechanically and by a vacuum-operated system. The mechanical governor mechanism comprises two weights, which move out from the distributor shaft as the engine speed rises due to centrifugal force. As they move outwards they rotate the cam relative to the distributor shaft, and so advance the spark. The weights are held in position by two light springs and it is the tension of the springs which is largely responsible for correct spark advancement.

The vacuum control consists of a diaphragm, one side of which is connected via a small bore tube to the carburettor, and the other side to the contact breaker plate. Depression in the inlet manifold and carburettor, which varies with engine speed and throttle opening, causes the diaphragm to move, so moving the contact breaker plate, and advancing or retarding the spark. A fine degree of control is achieved by a spring in the vacuum assembly.

On A14 and A15 engine models a breakerless distributor is fitted and a transistor ignition unit is added to the circuit. In the conventional distributor the firing pulse is initiated by the cam and breaker arm; with the breakerless system it is initiated by the reluctor on the distributor shaft and the pick-up coil, which are fitted in place of the contact breaker.

An electrical signal is generated in the pick-up coil and passed to the transistor ignition unit which breaks the primary circuit and induces a high voltage in the secondary winding of the coil. The transistor unit re-makes the primary circuit again after a fixed time.

The centrifugal and vacuum advance mechanism is of the conventional type.

2 Distributor contact breaker points (A10 and A12 engines) – adjustment

1   To adjust the contact breaker points to the correct gap, first pull off the two clips securing the distributor cap to the distributor body, and lift away the cap. Clean the cap inside and out with a dry cloth. It is unlikely that the four segments will be badly burned or scored, but if they are the cap will have to be renewed.

2   Inspect the carbon brush contact located in the top of the cap – see that it is unbroken and stands proud of the plastic surface.

3   Check the contact spring on the top of the rotor arm. It must be clean and have adequate tension to ensure good contact.

4   Gently prise the contact breaker points open to examine the condition of their faces. If they are rough, pitted, or dirty, it will be necessary to remove them for resurfacing, or for new points to be fitted – see Section 3.

5   Assuming the points are satisfactory, or that they have been cleaned and refitted, measure the gap between the points by turning the engine until the heel of the breaker arm is on the highest point of the cam. (Turn the engine with a spanner on the crankshaft pulley bolt).

6   A clean 0.020 in (0.50 mm) feeler gauge should now just fit between the points. The specifications allow a tolerance of 0.018 in (0.45 mm) to 0.022 in (0.55 mm) but the optimum gap of 0.020 in (0.50 mm) should be set if possible. This will allow the normal changes in the gap due to wear, to still fall in the permitted tolerance.

7   If the gap varies from this amount, slacken the contact plate securing screws (photo).

8   Adjust the contact gap by moving the adjuster (photo) as required with a screwdriver. Turn clockwise to increase and anticlockwise to decrease the gap. When the gap is correct tighten the securing screws and check the gap again. Take care not to contaminate the points with oil from the feeler gauges.

9   Making sure the rotor is in position, refit the distributor cap and clip the spring blade retainers into position.

10 On modern engines, setting the points gap as described can only be regarded as a preliminary adjustment. Ideally the dwell angle should then be checked.

11 Dwell angle is the number of degrees through which the distributor cam rotates between the instants of closure and opening of the points. Various proprietary instruments are available for measuring dwell angle, either with the engine running or being cranked by the starter motor. The correct dwell angle is given in the Specifications.

12 Connect the dwell meter and measure the dwell angle in accordance with the meter manufacturer's instructions. If the dwell angle is too large, increase the points gap; if it is too small, reduce the gap.

13 If the dwell angle varies considerably as the distributor shaft rotates, wear in the cam or shaft should be suspected.

14 Disconnect the dwell meter on completion. If the points gap was altered, check the ignition timing as described in Section 9.

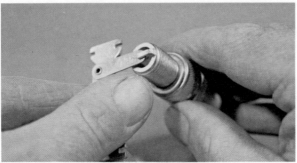

Measuring plug gap. A feeler gauge of the correct size (see ignition system specifications) should have a slight 'drag' when slid between the electrodes. Adjust gap if necessary

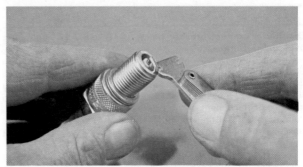

Adjusting plug gap. The plug gap is adjusted by bending the earth electrode inwards, or outwards, as necessary until the correct clearance is obtained. Note the use of the correct tool

Normal. Grey-brown deposits, lightly coated core nose. Gap increasing by around 0.001 in (0.025 mm) per 1000 miles (1600 km). Plugs ideally suited to engine, and engine in good condition

Carbon fouling. Dry, black, sooty deposits. Will cause weak spark and eventually misfire. Fault: over-rich fuel mixture. Check: carburettor mixture settings, float level and jet sizes; choke operation and cleanliness of air filter. Plugs can be re-used after cleaning

Oil fouling. Wet, oily deposits. Will cause weak spark and eventually misfire. Fault: worn bores/piston rings or valve guides; sometimes occurs (temporarily) during running-in period. Plugs can be re-used after thorough cleaning

Overheating. Electrodes have glazed appearance, core nose very white – few deposits. Fault: plug overheating. Check: plug value, ignition timing, fuel octane rating (too low) and fuel mixture (too weak). Discard plugs and cure fault immediately

Electrode damage. Electrodes burned away; core nose has burned, glazed appearance. Fault: pre-ignition. Check: as for 'Overheating' but may be more severe. Discard plugs and remedy fault before piston or valve damage occurs

Split core nose (may appear initially as a crack). Damage is self-evident, but cracks will only show after cleaning. Fault: pre-ignition or wrong gap-setting technique. Check: ignition timing, cooling system, fuel octane rating (too low) and fuel mixture (too weak). Discard plugs, rectify fault immediately

3   Distributor contact breaker points (A10 and A12 engines) – removal and refitting

1   Slip back the spring clips which secure the distributor cap in position. Remove the distributor cap and place it to one side, only removing one or two of the HT leads from the plugs, if necessary, to provide greater movement of the cap.
2   Pull the rotor from the distributor shaft.
3   Unscrew the contact breaker securing screws a turn or two and disconnect the LT lead from the contact breaker arm.
4   If necessary, unscrew the securing screws a turn or two more and slide the contact breaker arms sideways to remove them.
5   Inspect the faces of the contact points. If they are only lightly burned or pitted then they may be ground square on an oilstone or by rubbing a carborundum strip between them. Where the points are found to be severely burned or pitted, then they must be renewed. Rapid wear or burning of the points is most likely to be due to poor earth connections from the battery negative lead to body earth or the engine to earth strap. Remove the connecting bolts at these points, scrape the surfaces free from rust and corrosion and tighten the bolts using a star type lock washer. Other screws to check for security are: the baseplate-to-distributor body securing screws, the condenser securing screw and the distributor body-to-lockplate bolt. Looseness in any of these could contribute to a poor earth connection. Check the condenser (Section 4).
6   Refitting the contact breaker assembly is a reversal of removal and when fitted, adjust the points gap as described in the preceding Section.

4   Condenser (capacitor) – testing, removal and refitting

1   Fitted to the contact breaker points distributor (A10 and A12 engine models, the condenser ensures that with the contact breaker points open, the sparking between them is not excessive as this would cause severe pitting.
2   Testing for an unserviceable condenser may be effected by switching on the ignition and separating the contact points by hand. If this action is accompanied by a strong blue flash then condenser failure in the open-circuit mode is indicated. Difficult starting, missing of the engine after several miles running and badly pitted points are other indications of a faulty condenser.
3   If the condenser fails in the short-circuit mode, complete ignition failure will result, as the points will be prevented from interrupting the LT circuit.
4   The surest test is by substitution of a new unit.
5   Removal of the condenser is by means of withdrawing the screw which retains it to the distributor. Refitting is a reversal of this procedure.

5   Distributor (all types) – removal and refitting

1   To remove the distributor complete with cap from the engine, begin by pulling the plug lead terminals off the four spark plugs, but first mark the leads so that you know where to refit the HT lead from the centre of the coil to the centre of the distributor by undoing the lead retaining cap from the coil (photo).
2   Pull off the rubber pipe holding the vacuum tube to the distributor vacuum advance and retard take-off pipe.
3   Disconnect the low tension wire from the coil.
4   If the engine is not going to be turned whilst the distributor is removed, mark the relative positions of the distributor fixing plate and the cylinder block and of the rotor arm to the distributor body so that you have a positional guide when refitting the distributor.
5   Unscrew and remove the bolt retaining the distributor clamp plate in position and then withdraw the distributor.
6   Refitting the distributor is a reversal of the removal procedure but before inserting it into the cylinder block, the rotor must be correctly positioned. If the engine has not been turned and alignment marks were made, the distributor can be inserted so that when fully positioned the marks are aligned. Due to the meshing action of the distributor and camshaft drive gears however, the distributor drive shaft must be turned back (clockwise) by approximately 30 degrees from the position it will finally take up. Insert the distributor into its

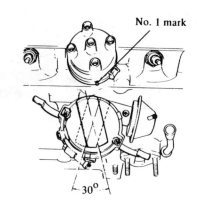

Fig. 4.3 Rotor alignment position (Sec 5)

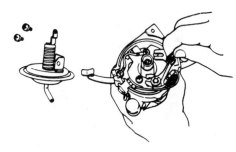

Fig. 4.4 Detach the vacuum control unit and remove the contact breaker points (Sec 6)

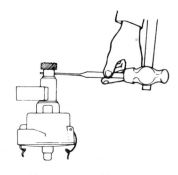

Fig. 4.5 Pinion retaining pin removal method (Sec 6)

5.1 The A10 engine distributor

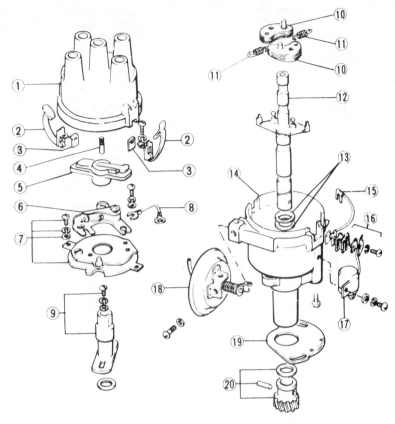

**Fig. 4.6 Exploded view of distributor – contact breaker type
(Sec 6)**

1 Cap assembly	6 Contact set	11 Governor springs	16 Terminal assembly
2 Cap clamp set	7 Breaker plate	12 Shaft assembly	17 Condenser
3 Dust seal	8 Earth wire	13 Thrust washers	18 Vacuum control assembly
4 Carbon brush	9 Cam set assembly	14 Housing	19 Fixing plate
5 Rotor arm	10 Governor weights	15 Lead wire	20 Pinion set

crankcase location and check the rotor alignment with the marks previously made.

7 To refit the distributor, if the engine has been rotated, turn the engine by hand using a spanner on the crankshaft pulley securing bolt until number one piston is at TDC on compression stroke. This position is indicated when the mark on the crankshaft pulley is in alignment with the 0° mark on the timing indicator on the front cover (compression stroke, both number one cylinder valves closed).

8 The distributor is now inserted with an allowance made for the previously mentioned distributor-to-camshaft mesh (paragraph 6) so that when fully fitted the rotor is in alignment with the No 1 cylinder mark on the distributor cap as shown in Fig. 4.3.

9 When in position refit and tighten the distributor plate retaining bolt.

10 Reconnect the HT and LT leads and then time the ignition as described in Section 9.

6 Distributor (contact breaker type) – dismantling, inspection and reassembly

1 Remove the distributor cap, rotor and contact breaker points as described in Section 3.

2 Remove the vacuum control assembly, which is secured to the distributor body by two setscrews (Fig. 4.4).

3 Remove the two securing screws and remove the breaker plate.

4 Remove the packing from the top of the cam assembly and unscrew the rotor shaft setscrew. Mark the cam and shaft so that they can be refitted in their original position.

5 Using a suitable drift, drive out the pin retaining the drive pinion on

the end of the shaft. Remove the pinion and washer.

6 Withdraw the distributor driveshaft complete with the mechanical advance assembly.

7 If it is necessary to dismantle this assembly, take care not to stretch the springs during removal and mark their respective positions; also mark the governor weights in relation to their pivots so that they can be refitted in their original locations.

8 With the distributor dismantled, clean all the parts and check for wear or damage. Check the distributor cap for signs of tracking, indicated by a thin black line between the segments. Renew the cap if evident. If wear in the shaft, bushes, governor weight pivots or holes is excessive, then the distributor should be renewed on an exchange basis.

9 Reassembly is the reverse of dismantling. Align the marks made so the parts are assembled to their original positions. Apply grease sparingly to the cam and wick. Adjust the points gap as described in Section 2.

10 When the distributor is refitted to the engine, retime the ignition as given in Section 9.

7 Air gap (breakerless distributor) – adjustment

1 Remove the distributor cap and rotor. Turn the engine to align a reluctor peak with a stator peak.

2 Using a feeler gauge measure the gap between the reluctor and pick-up coil, as shown in Fig. 4.7. The standard air gap is given in the Specifications.

3 Adjust, if necessary, by loosening the stator securing screws

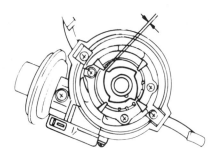

Fig. 4.7 Check the reluctor-to-stator air gap (Sec 7)

and repositioning the stator to obtain the specified gap. Tighten the stator securing screws.

4   Refit the rotor and distributor cap.

8   Distributor (breakerless type) – dismantling, inspection and reassembly

Refer to Fig. 4.8 for an exploded view of the distributor components.

1   Remove the distributor cap and lift the rotor head from the shaft.
2   Remove the retaining screws and withdraw the IC ignition unit from the distributor body.
3   Remove the retaining screws and lift out the stator and magnet.
4   Remove the retaining screw and withdraw the vacuum control unit.
5   Support the distributor and using two screwdrivers or a suitable puller, prise up the reluctor and withdraw it from the shaft, taking

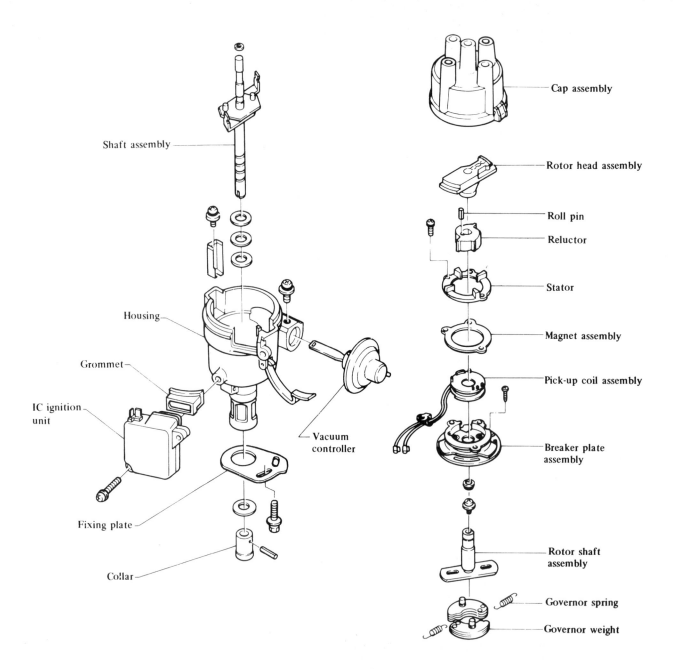

Fig. 4.8 Exploded view of the breakerless distributor (Sec 8)

9.2 Pulley notch and timing cover marks (A10 engine)

9.5 Distributor clamp plate, retaining bolt to cylinder block and alignment marks (A12 engine)

special care not to distort or damage the projecting teeth.
6   Extract the roll pin.
7   Lift out the pick-up coil unit.
8   Remove the retaining screws and lift out the breaker plate unit.
9   Support the distributor and using a suitable punch drift out the pinion (or collar) retaining pin. Remove the pinion (or collar) and washer, noting their relative positions.
10   Withdraw the rotor shaft and driveshaft unit upwards from the distributor body.
11   Before dismantling the centrifugal advance mechanism components, examine them for signs of damage and wear. If they are found to be in good condition then further dismantling is not necessary or advised. Should any of the components be defective, dismantle the assembly as follows.
12   Mark the relative positions of the drive and rotor shafts. Extract the packing from the top of the rotor and then remove the retaining screw which secures the rotor shaft to the driveshaft and separate the two.
13   Mark for positional identification a governor spring and its bracket, also a governor weight and its pivot. The respective governor springs and weights can now be unhooked and removed. Take care not to stretch and distort the springs as they are unhooked.
14   Clean all parts and inspect for wear and damage. If wear in the shaft, bushes, governor weight pivots or holes is excessive, then the distributor should be renewed on an exchange basis. Check the distributor cap for tracking, indicated by a thin black line between the segments. Renew the cap if any sign of tracking is apparent. If the vacuum advance unit or IC ignition unit is suspected of malfunction they cannot be repaired and should therefore be renewed.
15   Reassembly is the reverse of dismantling. Align the match marks so that parts are reassembled in their original positions and note the following special points.
16   Smear the governor weights and springs with grease before assembly. Also lubricate the top of the rotor shaft with grease as it is assembled.
17   When refitting the pinion or collar it should be set at its original position on the shaft.
18   Check that the reluctor is correctly repositioned on the shaft as shown in Fig. 4.9.
19   Centralise the stator and reluctor before tightening the retaining screws.
20   Readjust the air gap as given in Section 7.
21   When refitting the IC ignition unit, ensure that its mating surfaces with the distributor are perfectly clean and dry.
22   Before refitting the distributor into the engine, check that the governor action is satisfactory by supporting the drive pinion and twisting the rotor a fraction against the spring tension. When released it should return to its original position. Check that the rotor and driveshaft rotate freely without binding or excessive slackness.
23   When the distributor is refitted to the engine, retime the ignition as described in Section 9.

9   Ignition – timing adjustment

1   When timing the ignition on breakerless distributor type systems (A14 and A15 engines), a stroboscopic timing light must be used. Static timing is not possible. Timing checking and adjustment should only be required if the distributor has been removed for overhaul or the ignition timing has been otherwise disturbed.

Ignition timing – static method

2   A static ignition timing check is the basic method employed on contact breaker systems if a stroboscopic timing light is not available. To do this, first remove the number 1 spark plug. Turn the engine (with a spanner on the crankshaft pulley bolt) in its normal direction of rotation until on the compression stroke (felt by placing finger over No 1 plug hole) the timing cover mark and the notch on the pulley are aligned (see Specifications for correct timing) (photo).
3   Rotate the engine in an anticlockwise direction just past the mark, then clockwise so that the timing marks are aligned. The foregoing procedure ensures that all backlash is removed from the timing assembly.
4   Remove the distributor cap and check that the rotor arm points towards No 1 cylinder firing position. Reference to the No 1 HT lead connection in the cap will determine this position.
5   Slacken the distributor clamp plate pinch-bolt (photo) and rotate the distributor body until the points are just opening.
6   Difficulty is sometimes experienced in determining exactly when the contact breaker points open. This can be ascertained most accurately by connection of a 12 volt bulb in parallel with the contact breaker points (one lead to earth and the other from the distributor low tension terminal). Switch on the ignition and with the distributor adjusting plate securing screw slack, turn the distributor until the bulb just lights up, indicating that the points have just opened. Retighten the securing screw.
7   When using this method, it should be noted that to get the very best setting the final adjustment must be made on the road. The distributor can be moved slightly until the best setting is obtained. The amount of wear in the engine, quality of petrol used, and amount of carbon in the combustion chambers, all contribute to make the recommended settings no more than nominal ones. To obtain the best setting under running conditions start the engine and allow to warm up to normal temperature, and then accelerate in top gear from 30-50 mph, listening for heavy pinking. If this occurs, the ignition needs to be retarded slightly until just the faintest trace of pinking can be heard under these operating conditions.
8   Since the ignition advance adjustment enables the firing point to be related correctly in relation to the grade of fuel used, the fullest advantage of any change of fuel will be obtained only be readjustment of the ignition settings.
9   Finally, tighten the distributor body-to-clamp plate bolt.

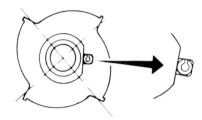

Fig. 4.9 Reluctor position and roll pin fitting to be as shown (Sec 8)

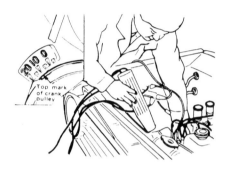

Fig. 4.10 Checking the ignition timing using a stroboscope (Sec 9)

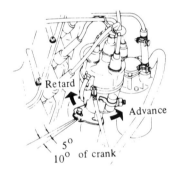

Fig. 4.11 Adjustment positions for distributor (Sec 9)

Ignition timing using a stroboscopic lamp

10 This method of ignition timing is essential for the transistorized ignition system. It is also generally accepted as being a more accurate method of setting the timing where the mechanical type contact breaker distributor is fitted.

11 Initially check the contact breaker points gap (Section 2) or the air gap (Section 7) and set to the specified clearance if necessary.

12 Connect a timing light (stroboscope) between number one spark plug and number one HT lead terminal, or as directed by the manufacturers.

13 Mark the indicator on the timing cover at the specified BTDC mark (see the Specifications) and the mark on the crankshaft pulley with white paint or chalk. Loosen the distributor clamp plate bolt.

14 Warm up the engine to the normal operating temperature and run it at the specified idling speed.

15 By directing the timing light onto the chalked marks, the mark on the crankshaft pulley will appear to be stationary. Having previously loosened the distributor body clamp plate bolt, the distributor may be rotated slightly until the timing marks are in alignment, then the clamp plate bolt is retightened to set the timing (Figs. 4.10 and 4.11). Where insufficient adjustment is provided by the plate-to-cylinder block slotted hole, a further adjustment may be possible by loosening the plate-to-distributor retaining screw and moving the plate accordingly. Retighten the screw on completion. Switch off the ignition and detach the timing light.

10 Spark plugs and HT leads

1 The correct functioning of the spark plugs is vital for the correct running and efficiency of the engine. The plugs fitted as standard are listed in the Specifications.

2 At intervals of 6000 miles (10 000 km) the plugs should be removed, examined, cleaned and, if worn excessively, renewed. The condition of the spark plug will also tell much about the overall condition of the engine.

3 If the insulator nose of the spark plug is clean and white, with no deposits, this is indicative of a weak mixture, or too hot a plug (a hot plug transfers heat away from the electrode slowly – a cold plug transfers it away quickly).

4 If the top and insulator nose are covered with hard black looking deposits, then this is indicative that the mixture is too rich. Should the plug be black and oily, then it is likely that the engine is fairly worn, as well as the mixture being too rich.

5 If the insulator nose is covered with light tan to greyish brown deposits, then the mixture is correct and it is likely that the engine is in good condition.

6 If there are any traces of long brown tapering stains on the outside of the white portion of the plug, then the plug will have to be renewed, as this shows that there is a faulty joint between the plug body and the insulator, and compression is being allowed to leak away.

7 Plugs should be cleaned by a sand blasting machine, which will free them from carbon more thoroughly than cleaning by hand. The machine will also test the condition of the plugs under compression. Any plug that fails to spark at the recommended pressure should be renewed.

8 The spark plug gap is of considerable importance, as, if it is too large or too small the size of the spark and its efficiency will be seriously impaired. The spark plug gap should be set to the specified dimension (refer to the Specifications) for the best results.

9 To set it, measure the gap with a feeler gauge, and then bend open, or close, the outer plug electrode until the correct gap is achieved. The centre electrode should never be bent as this may crack the insulation and cause plug failure, if nothing worse.

10 When refitting the plugs, remember to use new plug washers and refit the leads from the distributor in the correct firing order 1, 3, 4, 2; No 1 cylinder being the one nearest the left side of the vehicle, looking forward.

11 The plug leads require no routine attention other than being kept clean and wiped over regularly. If they are cracked or broken they must be renewed.

11 Ignition system – fault diagnosis (general)

Failure of the ignition system will either be due to faults in the HT or LT circuits. Initial checks should be made by observing the security of spark plug terminals, and distributor, coil and battery connection. More detailed investigation and the explanation and remedial action in respect of symptoms of ignition malfunction are described in the next Sections.

12 Ignition system (mechanical contact breaker type) – fault diagnosis

Engine fails to start

1 If the engine fails to start and the car was running normally when it was last used, first check there is fuel in the fuel tank. If the engine turns over normally on the starter motor and the battery is evidently well charged, then the fault may be in either the high or low tension circuits. First check the HT circuit.

2 One of the commonest reasons for bad starting is wet or damp spark plug leads and distributor. Remove the distributor cap. If condensation is visible internally, dry the cap with a rag and also wipe over the leads. Refit the cap.

3 If the engine still fails to start, check that current is reaching the plugs, by disconnecting a plug lead at the spark plug end, and hold the end of the cable (with a pair of insulated handle pliers) about $\frac{3}{16}$ in (5 mm) away from the cylinder block. Spin the engine on the starter motor.

4 Sparking between the end of the cable and the block should be fairly strong with a regular blue spark. If current is reaching the plugs, then remove them and clean and regap them. The engine should now start.

5 If there is no spark at the plug leads take off the HT lead from the centre of the distributor cap and hold it to the block as before. Spin the engine on the starter once more. A rapid succession of blue sparks between the end of the lead and the block indicates that the coil is in order and that the distributor cap is cracked, the rotor arm faulty, or the carbon brush in the top of the distributor cap is not making good contact with the spring on the rotor arm. Possibly the points are in bad condition. Clean and reset them as described in this Chapter.

6 If there are no sparks from the end of the lead from the coil, check the connections at the coil end of the lead. If it is in order start checking the low tension circuit.

7 Use a 12V voltmeter or a 12V bulb and two lengths of wire. With the ignition switch on and the points open test between the low tension wire to the coil (it is marked +) and earth. No reading indicates a break in the supply from the ignition switch. Check the connections at the switch to see if any are loose. Refit them and the engine should run. A reading shows a faulty coil or condenser, or broken lead between the coil and the distributor.

8 Take the condenser wire off the points and earth. Test between the moving point and earth (points open). If there now is a reading, then the fault is in the condenser. Fit a new one and the fault is cleared.

9 With no reading from the moving point to earth, take a reading between earth and the contact breaker (–) terminal of the coil. A reading here shows a broken wire which will need to be renewed between the coil and distributor. No reading confirms that the coil has failed and must be replaced, after which the engine will run once more. Remember to refit the condenser wire to the points assembly. For these tests it is sufficient to separate the points with a piece of dry paper while testing with the points open.

Engine misfires

10 If the engine misfires regularly run it at a fast idling speed. Pull off each of the plug caps in turn and listen to the note of the engine. Hold the plug cap in a dry cloth or with a rubber glove as additional protection against a shock from the HT supply.

11 No difference in engine running will be noticed when the lead from the defective circuit is removed. Removing the lead from one of the good cylinders will accentuate the misfire.

12 Remove the plug lead from the end of the defective plug and hold it about $\frac{3}{16}$ in (4.7 mm) away from the block. Restart the engine. If the sparking is fairly strong and regular the fault must lie in the spark plug.

13 The plug may be loose, the insulation may be cracked, or the points may have burnt away giving too wide a gap for the spark to jump. Worse still, one of the points may have broken off. Either renew the plug, or clean it, reset the gap, and then test it.

14 If there is no spark at the end of the plug lead, or if it is weak annd intermittent, check the ignition lead from the distributor to the plug. If the insulation is cracked or perished, renew the lead. Check the connections at the distributor cap.

15 If there is still no spark, examine the distributor cap carefully for tracking – black lines running between two or more electrodes, or between an electrode and some other part of the distributor. These lines are paths which now conduct electricity across the cap thus letting it run to earth. The only answer is a new distributor cap.

16 Apart from the ignition timing being incorrect, other causes of misfiring have already been dealt with under the section dealing with the failure of engine to start. To recap – these are that:

(a) The coil may be faulty giving an intermittent misfire
(b) There may be a damaged wire or loose connection in the low tension circuit
(c) The condenser may be short-circuiting
(d) There may be a mechanical fault in the distributor (broken driving spindle or contact breaker spring)

17 If the ignition timing is too far retarded, it should be noted that the engine will tend to overheat, and there will be a quite noticeable drop in power. If the engine is overheating and the power is down, and the ignition timing is correct, then the carburettor should be checked, as it is likely that this is where the fault lies.

Engine fires but will not run

18 If the resistor wire from the ignition switch to the coil is broken or disconnected, the engine will still fire when the starter motor is operated since the resistor wire is then bypassed. Do not substitute ordinary wire for the resistor wire as this may overload the coil.

13 Ignition system (breakerless) – fault diagnosis

Diagnosing faults in the HT circuit of the breakerless ignition system is the same as described in Section 12. For checking the LT circuit special test equipment is required and this job should be entrusted to your local Datsun dealer.

Basic tasks which can be undertaken include an inspection of all wiring and its connections for condition and security, and checking the air gap between the reluctor and pick-up coil as given in Section 7.

Chapter 5 Clutch

For modifications, and information applicable to later models, see Supplement at end of manual

Contents

Specifications

General
Clutch type .... Single dry plate, diaphragm spring
Actuation:
    RHD models .... Cable
    LHD models .... Hydraulic

Clutch disc
Type:
    A10 engine .... 160 CBL
    A12, A14 and A15 engines .... 190 CBL

Lining dimensions:	160 CBL	190 CBL
Outer diameter	160 mm (6.30 in)	190 mm (7.48 in)
Inner diameter	110 mm (4.33 in)	132 mm (5.20 in)
Thickness	3.2 mm (0.126 in)	3.2 mm (0.126 in)

Disc installed thickness (all models) .... 7.3 to 7.7 mm (0.287 to 0.303 in)
Number of damper springs 6

Clutch cover (pressure plate)
Type:
    A10 engine .... FC 160S
    A12, A14 and A15 engines .... FC 190S

Clutch pedal
Pedal height:
    LHD models .... 179 to 185 mm (7.05 to 7.28 in)
    RHD models .... 177 to 183 mm (6.97 to 7.20 in)
Pedal free play (LHD) .... 1 to 5 mm (0.04 to 0.20 in)
Pedal free travel (RHD) .... 31 mm (1.22 in)
Withdrawal lever clearance (RHD) .... 12 mm (0.47 in)

Hydraulic system
Master and slave cylinder piston-to-cylinder bore clearance .... Less than 0.15 mm (0.0059 in)

Torque wrench settings

	lbf ft	kgf m
Clutch cover-to-pressure plate bolts	7 to 9	1.0 to 1.3
Clutch unit-to-flywheel bolts	5.1 to 7.2	0.7 to 1.0
Clutch hose-to-operating cylinder (LHD)	12 to 14	1.7 to 2.0
Operating cylinder retaining bolts (LHD)	22 to 30	3.1 to 4.1
Master cylinder-to-dash panel (LHD)	5.8 to 8.0	0.8 to 1.1
Pushrod locknut (LHD)	5.8 to 8.0	0.8 to 1.1
Pedal stopper locknut (RHD)	5.8 to 8.0	0.8 to 1.1
Pedal stopper locknut (LHD)	12 to 16	1.6 to 2.2

1 General description

All vehicles are fitted with a diaphragm spring, single plate clutch. The unit comprises a pressed steel cover, pressure plate and diaphragm spring.

The clutch disc is free to slide along the splined primary drive gear assembly, and is held in position between the cover and the pressure plate by the pressure of the pressure plate spring. Friction lining material is riveted to the clutch disc and it has a spring cushioned hub to absorb transmission shocks and to help ensure a smooth take-off.

The clutch disc and cover can be removed or replaced without the need to dismantle any other components. The clutch has one or two features that distinguish it from more conventional clutches. These are: the relative assembled location of clutch cover and disc, the selection of a pushrod that operates the clutch through the primary gear drive, and finally, the unusual type of release bearing mechanism.

The clutch is actuated either hydraulically (LHD vehicles) or mechanically by a cable (RHD vehicles). Where the clutch is actuated hydraulically, the pendant clutch pedal is connected to the clutch master cylinder and hydraulic fluid reservoir by a short pushrod. The master cylinder and hydraulic reservoir are mounted on the engine side of the bulkhead in front of the driver.

Depressing the clutch pedal moves the piston in the master cylinder forwards, so forcing hydraulic fluid through the clutch hydraulic pipe to the slave cylinder.

The piston in the slave cylinder moves forward on the entry of the fluid and actuates the clutch release arm by means of a short pushrod.

The release arm pushes the release bearing forwards to bear against the pressure plate through a pushrod that runs through the centre of the primary drive gear assembly, so moving the centre of the diaphragm spring inwards, and disengaging the pressure plate from the clutch disc.

When the clutch pedal is released the diaphragm spring forces the pressure plate into contact with the friction linings on the clutch disc. The clutch disc is now firmly sandwiched between the pressure plate and the covers so the drive is taken up.

As the friction linings on the clutch disc wear, the pressure plate automatically moves closer to the disc to compensate. There is then no need to periodically adjust the clutch.

Where a cable type clutch actuating mechanism is fitted, the principle of operation is similar to that already described for the hydraulic type, but correct adjustment must at all times be maintained, as described in Section 3.

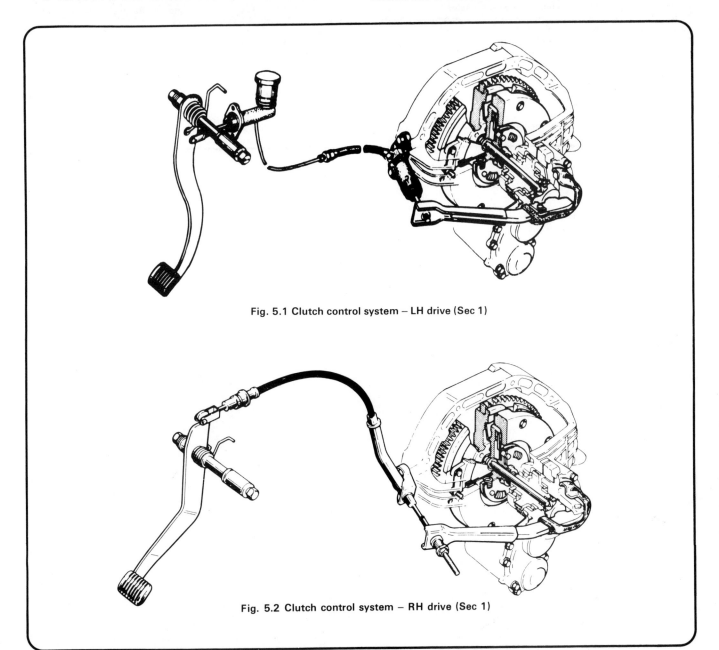

Fig. 5.1 Clutch control system – LH drive (Sec 1)

Fig. 5.2 Clutch control system – RH drive (Sec 1)

2   Hydraulically operated clutch – pedal height and free play checking and adjustment

1   The clutch pedal height and free play must be checked and if necessary adjusted at the specified routine maintenance intervals. Refer to Fig. 5.4 and measure the clutch pedal top surface-to-floor dimension (H).
2   If necessary, adjust the clutch pedal height to the specified amount by loosening the pedal stop locknut and moving the stop adjuster nut accordingly. Retighten the locknut to secure the adjustment.
3   Check and if necessary adjust the pedal free play (A) to the specified amount by loosening the master cylinder pushrod locknut and turning the rod in the desired direction to give the correct free play. Retighten the locknut to secure.

3   Cable operated clutch – pedal height and free play checking and adjustment

1   The clutch pedal height must be checked and if necessary adjusted at the specified routine maintenance intervals. Refer to Fig. 5.5.
2   Check the fully released clutch pedal-to-floor clearance (measuring from the top surface of the pedal).
3   To adjust the pedal height (H), loosen the pedal stop adjuster locknut and then turn the adjuster nut as required to obtain the specified clearance. Retighten the locknut to secure.
4   The clutch pedal free travel is checked by measuring the clearance at the withdrawal lever between the adjuster nut and ball seat (B in Fig. 5.6). The correct clearance is shown in the illustration.
5   Adjustment is made as follows. Tighten the adjuster nut at the withdrawal lever to take up the pedal free play completely and then depress the pedal several times. Now loosen off the adjuster nut to provide the specified nut-to-ball seat clearance. Tighten the locknut to secure.
6   When adjustment is complete, the pedal free travel measured at the centre of the pedal pad should be as given in the Specifications.

4   Clutch pedal (hydraulic) – removal and refitting

1   Prise free the clevis pin retaining clip and withdraw the clevis pin from the pushrod clevis and pedal.
2   Prise free the E-ring from the pedal pivot pin, disengage the return spring and withdraw the pedal and spring.
3   Inspect and renew any parts as required.
4   Refit in the reverse order of removal, applying a multi-purpose grease to the pedal bushes and pivot pin. Check that the retaining clips and return spring are fully engaged and then adjust the pedal height and free play as given in Section 2.

5   Clutch pedal and cable – removal and refitting

1   Remove the locknut and adjusting nut and then detach the clutch cable from the withdrawal lever.
2   Detach the control cable from the clutch pedal by removing the clevis pin.
3   Unscrew and remove the pedal pivot pin retaining nut and washers, disconnect the return spring and remove the pedal and spring (Fig. 5.9).
4   Refitting is the reverse of the removal procedure. Apply grease to the clutch pedal shaft and pivot bushes. Check the clutch adjustment as described in Section 3. When fitted, ensure that the cable has no excessive bends in it.

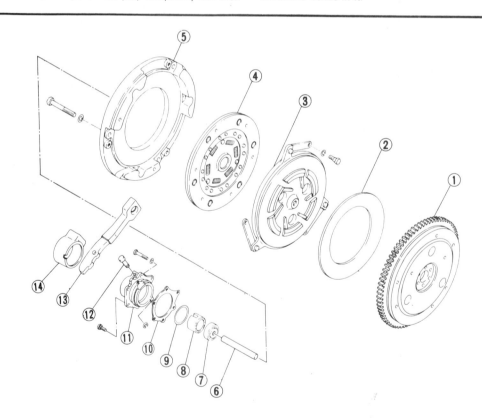

Fig. 5.3 Exploded view of the clutch unit and release bearing assembly (Sec 1)

1 Flywheel	5 Clutch cover	9 O-ring	12 Withdrawal lever pin
2 Diaphragm spring	6 Pushrod	10 Bearing housing packing	13 Withdrawal lever
3 Pressure plate	7 Release bearing	11 Bearing housing	14 Dust cover
4 Clutch disc	8 Pushrod A piece		

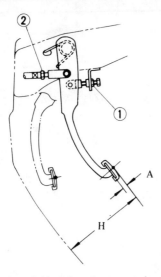

Fig. 5.4 Clutch pedal height adjustment check (hydraulic operation) (Sec 2)

1   Pedal stop locknut   2   Pushrod locknut

H = 7.05 to 7.28 in (179 to 185 mm)
A = 0.04 to 0.2 in (1 to 5 mm)

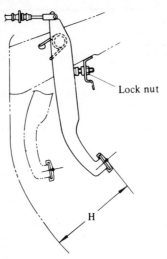

Fig. 5.5 Clutch pedal height adjustment check (cable operation) (Sec 3)

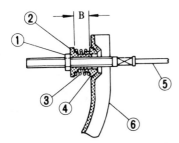

Fig. 5.6 Clutch pedal free travel adjustment (Cable operation) (Sec 3)

B = 0.47 in (12 mm)

1   Locknut   4   Ball seat
2   Adjusting nut   5   Clutch cable
3   Preload spring   6   Withdrawal lever

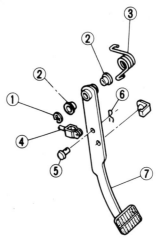

Fig. 5.7 Clutch pedal components (hydraulic operation) (Sec 4)

1   E-ring   5   Clevis pin
2   Bushing   6   Retaining clip
3   Return spring   7   Pedal
4   Master cylinder push rod

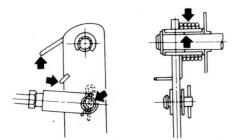

Fig. 5.8 Pedal lubricating points (hydraulic operation) (Sec 4)

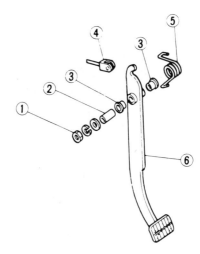

Fig. 5.9 Clutch pedal components (cable operation) (Sec 5)

1   Nut   4   Clutch control cable
2   Pedal shaft   5   Return spring
3   Bushings   6   Pedal

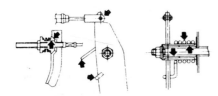

Fig. 5.10 Pedal lubricating points (cable operation) (Sec 5)

6 Hydraulic system – bleeding

1 The need for bleeding the cylinders and fluid line arises when air gets into the system, because of a joint or seal leaking or when any part of the system is being dismantled. Air also gets into the system if the level of the fluid reservoir becomes too low. Bleeding is the process of excluding air from the system.

2 When bleeding the system, do not allow the hydraulic fluid level in the reservoir to drop below the minimum level. Top up using only clean hydraulic fluid which has been stored in an air-tight container and has remained unshaken for the preceding 24 hours.

3 Start by topping up the reservoir fluid level, then obtain a piece of $\frac{3}{16}$ in (4.76 mm) bore diameter rubber tube of about 2 to 3 feet long and a clean glass jar. A small quantity of fresh, clean hydraulic fluid is also necessary. The services of an assistant will be required.

4 Detach the cap (if fitted) on the bleed nipple at the clutch slave cylinder and clean up the nipple and surrounding area. Unscrew the nipple $\frac{3}{4}$ turn and fit the tube over it. Put about $\frac{1}{2}$ in (13 mm) of fluid in the jar and put the other end of the pipe in it. The jar can be placed on the ground under the car.

5 The clutch pedal should then be depressed quickly and released slowly until no more air bubbles come from the pipe. Quick pedal action carries the air along rather than leaving it behind. Keep the reservoir topped-up.

6 When the air bubbles stop, tighten the nipple with the pedal held at the end of a down stroke.

7 Check that the operation of the clutch is satisfactory. Even though there may be no exterior leaks it is possible that the movement of the pushrod from the clutch cylinder is inadequate because fluid is leaking internally past the seals in the master cylinder. If this is the case, it is best to renew all seals in both cylinders.

7 Master cylinder – removal, servicing and refitting

Note: *Two makes of master cylinder are available. Nabco and Tokico. The repair kits or component parts are not interchangeable, so be sure to use the correct replacement parts.*

1 The master cylinder and fluid reservoir are a single unit. Indication of something wrong with it is if the pedal travels down without operating the clutch efficiently (assuming of course, that the system has been bled and there are no leaks).

2 To remove the unit from the car first seal the cap with a piece of film to reduce fluid spillage whilst dismantling the pipes. Alternatively, the fluid may be pumped out from the clutch cylinder bleed nipple by opening the nipple and depressing the pedal several times.

3 From inside the car remove the locknut which attaches the pushrod assembly to the clevis, and disconnect the pushrod.

4 Disconnect the fluid line which runs between the master cylinder and the slave (operating) cylinder.

5 Unscrew and remove the two bolts which secure the master cylinder to the engine rear bulkhead.

6 Withdraw the master cylinder from the bulkhead.

7 Peel back the rubber dust cover from the end of the master cylinder and then remove the retaining ring, stopper and pushrod.

8 From underneath the cylinder unscrew and remove the supply valve stopper and washers.

9 The internal components may then be ejected, either by tapping the end of the cylinder on a piece of wood or by applying air pressure from a tyre pump at the fluid outlet pipe.

10 Clean all components in clean hydraulic fluid or methylated spirit. Examine the internal surfaces of the master cylinder for scoring or bright areas; also the surface of the piston. Where these are apparent, renew the complete master cylinder assembly.

11 Discard all rubber seals, making sketches if necessary before removing them from the piston so that the new seals will be fitted with their lips and chamfers the correct way round.

12 Obtain a repair kit and examine all the items supplied for damage, particularly the seals for cuts or deterioration in storage.

13 Commence reassembling by dipping the new seals in clean hydraulic fluid and fitting them to the piston, using only the fingers to manipulate them into their grooves. Ensure that they are correctly located with regard to the contour as originally fitted.

14 Use all the new items supplied in the repair kit and reassemble in the reverse order to dismantling, lubricating each component in clean

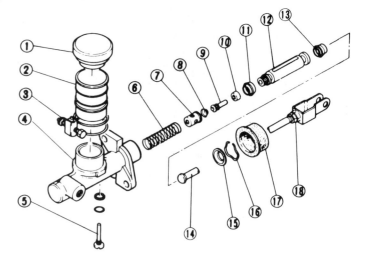

Fig. 5.11 Clutch master cylinder components (Sec 7)

1	Reservoir cap	7	Spring seat	13	Secondary cup
2	Reservoir	8	Valve spring	14	Pushrod
3	Reservoir band	9	Supply valve rod	15	Stopper
4	Cylinder body	10	Supply valve	16	Stopper ring
5	Supply valve stopper	11	Primary cup	17	Dust cover
6	Return spring	12	Piston	18	Locknut

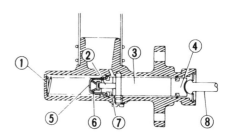

Fig. 5.12 Sectional view of the master cylinder showing piston assembly (Sec 7)

1	Return spring	5	Spring seat
2	Supply valve rod	6	Valve spring
3	Piston	7	Primary cup
4	Secondary cup	8	Pushrod

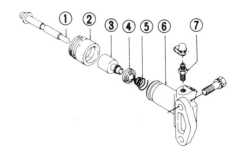

Fig. 5.13 The clutch operating (slave) cylinder components (Sec 8)

1	Pushrod	5	Piston spring
2	Dust cover	6	Cylinder body
3	Piston	7	Bleeder screw
4	Piston cup		

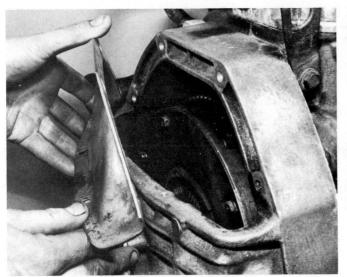

9.6a Remove the clutch housing inspection cover ...

9.6b ... and unscrew the clutch cover bolts

9.7 Remove the access cover

9.8a Prise back the rubber dust cover

9.8b Withdraw the E-ring

9.11 Remove the plate and disc

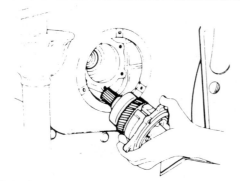

Fig. 5.14 Removing the primary drive gear unit (Sec 9)

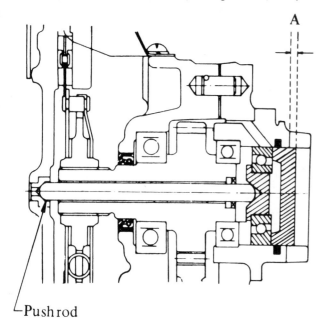

Fig. 5.15 Selecting the correct pushrod length. For A see text (Sec 12)

Fig. 5.16 Identification mark for length of pushrod (Sec 12)

hydraulic fluid before it is fitted into the master cylinder.
15 Bolt the master cylinder to the engine rear bulkhead.
16 Reconnect the fluid pipe between the master and slave cylinders, fill the reservoir with clean hydraulic fluid and bleed the system. Probe the reservoir vent hole in the cap to ensure that it is not clogged.
17 Adjust the clutch pedal height and free play if necessary as described in Section 2.

8 Slave (operating) cylinder – removal, servicing and refitting

Note: *Two makes of operating cylinder are available. Nabco and Tokico. The repair kits or component parts are not interchangeable, so be sure to use the correct replacement parts.*
1 Disconnect the fluid pipe from the slave cylinder. To do this, uncouple the union at the master cylinder and plug the union outlet to prevent loss of fluid. Now unscrew the flexible pipe from the slave cylinder, taking care not to twist the pipe, and retaining the sealing washer.
2 Unscrew and remove the slave cylinder to clutch housing securing

bolts and lift the cylinder away. Remove the operating rod.
3 Peel back the dust cover and remove the circlip.
4 Eject the internal components of the slave cylinder either by tapping the end of the unit on a piece of wood or by applying air pressure from a tyre pump at the fluid hose connection.
5 Wash all components in clean hydraulic fluid or methylated spirit. Discard the seals and examine the piston and cylinder bore surfaces for scoring or bright areas. Where these are evident, renew the complete assembly.
6 Obtain a repair kit and examine all the items supplied for damage, particularly the seal for cuts or deterioration in storage.
7 Commence reassembling by dipping the new seal in clean hydraulic fluid and fitting it to the piston, using the fingers only to manipulate it.
8 Use all the new items supplied in the repair kit and reassemble in reverse order of dismantling, lubricating each component in clean hydraulic fluid before it is fitted into the cylinder bore.
9 When all the internal components have been installed, fit a new circlip and the new rubber dust cover supplied with the repair kit.
10 Refit the slave cylinder to the clutch housing, reconnect the fluid supply pipe and the operating pushrod to the clutch release lever.
11 Bleed the hydraulic system, as described in Section 6.

9 Clutch unit – removal

The clutch unit complete can be removed with the engine and transmission left in position in the car. The photographs have been taken with the engine removed for the sake of clarity.
1 Disconnect the battery earth (ground) cable.
2 Detach the fresh air duct.
3 Disconnect the ignition coil-to-distributor HT lead.
4 Remove the fuel filter from its bracket.
5 Detach the clutch control cable, or slave cylinder operating rod from the clutch withdrawal lever. This will depend on whether it is a LHD or RHD model.
6 Remove the inspection cover from the clutch housing. Remove the six bolts which secure the clutch cover. These bolts should be slackened off gradually and evenly, after first marking the relative positions of the clutch and flywheel (photos). Note: Removal of the spark plugs will enable the engine to be turned more easily to gain access to each of the clutch cover bolts.
7 Unscrew and remove the three access cover retaining screws and remove the cover from within the right-hand wheel housing (photo). This is made easier by removing the front wheel on that side.
8 Reaching through the access hole, prise back the rubber dust cover (photo) and remove the E-ring securing the withdrawal lever pin (photo). Remove the pin and withdrawal lever.
9 Remove the six bolts on the bearing housing, and withdraw the primary drive gear assembly through the opening on the right-hand side wheel housing.
10 Lift the clutch cover and disc out through the inspection opening in the upper part of the clutch housing.
11 Remove the strap bolts which secure the pressure plate to the cover and take off the plate and clutch disc (photo). Note that the relative position of pressure plate and cover are indicated on the edge of the assembly either by white paint spots or by an arrow and raised pointer.

10 Clutch unit – inspection and renovation

1 Since the clutch on this vehicle is so easily removed, there is no reason to delay when renewal becomes necessary. The only positive indication that something needs doing is when the clutch starts to slip or when squealing noises on engagement indicate that the friction lining has worn down to the rivets. In such instances it can only be hoped that the friction surfaces on the cover and pressure plate have not been badly worn or scored. A clutch will wear according to the way in which it is used. Much intentional slipping of the clutch while driving – rather than the correct selection of gears – will accelerate wear.
2 Examine the surfaces of the pressure plate and cover for signs of scoring. If this is only light it may be left, but if very deep the pressure plate and cover assembly will have to be renewed as a unit because they are a balanced assembly.
3 The friction plate lining surfaces should be at least 0.012 in (0.3

13.2 Locate the diaphragm spring

13.4 Alignment arrow on cover edge to raised lug

13.5 Refit the clutch unit to the flywheel

mm) above the rivets, otherwise the disc is not worth putting back. If the lining material shows signs of breaking up or black areas where oil contamination has occurred it should also be renewed. If facilities are readily available for obtaining and fitting new friction pads to the existing disc, this may be done, but the saving is relatively small compared with obtaining a complete new disc assembly, which ensures that the shock absorbing springs and the splined hub are renewed also. An allowance is usually given for exchange units.
4   The maximum disc plate run-out should not exceed 0.020 in (0.50 mm), measured 3.54 in (90 mm) from the hub centre on all engines except the A10, on which it should be measured 2.95 in (75 mm) from the hub centre.
5   The disc hub-to-primary drive gear splines backlash must not exceed 0.016 in (0.4 mm).
6   Where the driven plate and/or pressure plate and cover have been renewed, the pushrod length must be calculated and a new pushrod fitted if necessary as described in Section 12.

11 Pushrod and release bearing unit – removal and refitting

1   Detach the clutch control cable on right-hand drive models, or the clutch slave (operating) cylinder on left-hand drive models.
2   Remove the pushrod and release bearing assembly as given in Section 9, paragraphs 7 to 9 inclusive.
3   Place the primary drive gear on end, splines uppermost, with the two outer flanges supported. Using a hammer and a piece of wood on the pushrod, lightly tap the assembly out of the end of the drive gear. A drift may be required to completely remove the pushrod.
4   Prise out the O-ring in the bearing housing.
5   Reassembly is the reverse of the removal procedure. Apply a light coating of multi-purpose grease to the sliding part of the withdrawal lever and the primary gear splines.
6   Where the release bearing components have been renewed, a pushrod of suitable length must be refitted. Three pushrod lengths are available. Refer to the next Section for selection procedures.

12 Pushrod – selection

1   If any parts of the clutch or release mechanism are renewed, it will be necessary to check the pushrod clearance and renew the pushrod if necessary.
2   With the primary drive gear, and the release mechanism, in

position and bolted up, gently press the release bearing, and thus the pushrod, until movement is arrested by the pressure plate. Then measure the depth 'A' as shown in Fig. 5.15. Select a pushrod from the table below to keep the clearance at 'A' to the specified value of 0.020 to 0.098 in (0.5 to 2.5 mm) on A14 and A15 engines and 0.055 to 0.063 in (1.4 to 1.6 mm) on A10 and A12 engines.

Length of notch on rod	Length of pushrod A14 and A15 engine	Length of pushrod A10 and A12 engine
6.0 mm (0.236 in)	115 mm (4.53 in)	130 mm (5.118 in)
None	114 mm (4.49 in)	129 mm (5.078 in)
3.5 mm (0.138 in)	113 mm (4.45 in)	128 mm (5.039 in)

3   As shown in Fig. 5.16 the presence or absence of a notch of a specified length indicates the pushrod overall length.

13 Clutch unit – refitting

1   Before starting to reassemble the clutch unit, ensure that all components are clean and free of oil and grease. Both the clutch cover and pressure plate are dynamically balanced and they must therefore be correctly positioned during assembly in order to maintain this balance.
2   Locate the diaphragm spring into its flanged recess in the flywheel, with its concave side towards the flywheel (photo).
3   Locate the clutch disc between the clutch cover and the pressure plate with its raised centre facing towards the clutch cover (away from the flywheel).
4   Position the clutch cover and the pressure plate so that the alignment arrow mark on the cover outer edge aligns with the raised lug of the pressure plate (photo), then insert and tighten the retaining bolts (with washers). Tighten bolts in a progressive and even manner to the specified torque setting.
5   Offer up the clutch assembly to the flywheel aligning the marks made prior to dismantling and insert the retaining bolts finger tight. Where a new clutch assembly is being fitted, locate it to the flywheel in a similar relative position to the original by reference to the index marking and dowel positions (photo).
6   Now refit the primary gear unit to the clutch housing to align the clutch disc hub with the primary gear splines. The clutch cover retaining bolts can now be tightened to the specified torque.
7   The remainder of the reassembly procedure is a reversal of the removal process. On completion recheck the clutch pedal adjustment as given in Section 2 or 3 as applicable.

14 Fault diagnosis – clutch

Symptom	Reason(s)
Judder when taking up drive	Loose engine or gearbox mountings Badly worn friction surface or contaminated with oil Worn splines on primary drive gear input shaft or driven plate hub
Clutch spin (failure to disengage) so that gears cannot be meshed	Incorrect release bearing clearance Incorrect pushrod length Driven plate sticking on input shaft splines due to rust. May occur after vehicle standing idle for long period Damage or misaligned pressure plate assembly
Clutch slip (increase in engine speed does not result in increase in vehicle road speed – particularly on gradients)	Incorrect release bearing clearance Friction surfaces worn out or oil contaminated Incorrect pushrod length
Noise evident on depressing clutch pedal	Dry, worn or damaged release bearing Insufficient pedal free travel Weak or broken pedal return spring Weak or broken clutch release lever return
Noise evident as clutch pedal released	Distorted driven plate Broken or weak driven plate damper springs Insufficient pedal free travel Weak or broken clutch pedal return spring Weak or broken release lever return spring Distorted or worn input primary gear shaft splines Release bearing loose on retainer hub

Chapter 6 Transmission

For modifications, and information applicable to later models, see Supplement at end of manual

Contents

Specifications

Manual transmission

General
Maker's identification:

4-speed	F4WF60A
5-speed	F5WF60A
Synchromesh	On all forward gears

Gear ratios

	4-speed	5-speed
A10, A12 and A14 engines:		
1st	3.673 : 1	4.018 : 1
2nd	2.217 : 1	2.475 : 1
3rd	1.433 : 1	1.720 : 1
4th	1.000 : 1	1.254 : 1
5th	-	1.000 : 1
Reverse	4.093 : 1	4.093 : 1
A15 engine:		
1st	3.479 : 1	4.018 : 1
2nd	2.100 : 1	2.475 : 1
3rd	1.375 : 1	1.720 : 1
4th	1.000 : 1	1.254 : 1
5th	-	1.000 : 1
Reverse	4.093 : 1	4.093 : 1
Final drive ratio:		
A10, A12 and 1979 A14 engines	3.471 : 1	3.471 : 1
1980 A14 and A15 engines	3.471 : 1	3.222 : 1

Gear clearances

	4-speed	5-speed
Backlash:		
Primary drive and primary idler gears	0.0024 to 0.0063 in (0.06 to 0.16 mm)	0.0024 to 0.0063 in (0.06 to 0.16 mm)
Main drive gear	0.0012 to 0.0051 in (0.03 to 0.13 mm)	0.0012 to 0.0051 in (0.03 to 0.13 mm)
Main forward gears	0.002 to 0.006 in (0.05 to 0.16 mm)	0.002 to 0.006 in (0.05 to 0.16 mm)
Reverse idler gear	0.002 to 0.006 in (0.05 to 0.16 mm)	0.003 to 0.006 in (0.08 to 0.16 mm)
Mainshaft gear endfloat:		
1st gear	0.0079 to 0.0118 in (0.20 to 0.30 mm)	0.0079 to 0.0118 in (0.20 to 0.30 mm)
2nd and 3rd gears	0.0079 to 0.0118 in (0.20 to 0.30 mm)	0.0079 to 0.0138 in (0.20 to 0.35 mm)
4th gear	-	0.0079 to 0.0118 in (0.20 to 0.30 mm)
Countergear endfloat	Zero	Zero
Reverse idler gear endfloat	-	0 to 0.0146 in (0 to 0.37 mm)
Primary idler sub gear endfloat	Less than 0.0043 in (0.11 mm)	Less than 0.0043 in (0.11 mm)

Synchro hubs
Baulk ring-to-cone gap:
New .... 0.0374 to 0.0591 in (0.95 to 1.50 mm)
Wear limit .... 0.020 in (0.5 mm)

Final drive
Side gear-to-thrust washer clearance .... Less than 0.008 in (0.2 mm)
Adjusting shim thickness .... 0.008 and 0.012 in (0.2 and 0.3 mm)
Pinion-to-ring gear backlash .... 0.0024 to 0.0059 in (0.06 to 0.15 mm)

Gearshift mechanism
Shift rod length .... 4.50 to 4.56 in (114.3 to 115.7 mm)
Shift lever pull-back length:
4-speed .... 0.31 in (8 mm)
5-speed .... 0.453 in (11.5 mm)

Automatic transmission

General
Transmission type .... Semi-automatic, 3-speed, torque converter and automatic choke
Maker's identification F53WF60S

Gear ratio
1st (L) .... 1.603 : 1
2nd (D) .... 1.000 : 1
3rd (OD) .... 0.726 : 1
Reverse (R) .... 1.846 : 1
Final drive .... 4.692 : 1
Speedometer gear ratio 16/14

Transmission fluid capacity .... 5.25 US qt (4.4 Imp qt, 5.0 litres)

Engine stall speed .... 1950 to 2250 rpm

Gear clearances
Backlash:
Primary drive-to-primary idler gear .... 0.0024 to 0.0063 in (0.06 to 0.16 mm)
Primary idler-to-main drive imput gear .... 0.0024 to 0.0063 in (0.06 to 0.16 mm)
Main drive gear .... 0.0012 to 0.0051 in (0.03 to 0.13 mm)
Low gear .... 0.0020 to 0.0059 in (0.05 to 0.15 mm)
OD gear .... 0.0020 to 0.0059 in (0.05 to 0.15 mm)
Main reverse to reverse idler .... 0.0020 to 0.0059 in (0.05 to 0.15 mm)
Reverse idler to counter reverse gear .... 0.0020 to 0.0059 in (0.05 to 0.15 mm)
Endfloats:
Low and OD gears .... 0.0079 to 0.0118 in (0.20 to 0.30 mm)
Reverse gear .... 0.0079 to 0.0138 in (0.20 to 0.35 mm)
Reverse idler gear and countergear .... 0.0039 to 0.0157 in (0.10 to 0.40 mm)

Synchro hubs
Baulk ring-to-cone gap:
New .... 0.047 in (1.2 mm)
Wear limit .... 0.020 in (0.5 mm)

Final drive
Pinion-to-ring gear backlash .... 0.0024 to 0.0063 in (0.06 to 0.16 mm)
Differential side bearing adjusting shims .... 0.008 in (0.2 mm) and 0.012 in (0.3 mm)
Differential side gear thrust washers .... 0.028 in (0.7 mm), 0.032 in (0.8 mm), 0.035 in (0.9 mm), 0.039 in (1.0 mm) and 0.043 in (1.1 mm)

Torque converter
Lever bearing plate thicknesses .... 0.047 in (1.2 mm), 0.055 in (1.4 mm), 0.063 in (1.6 mm), 0.071 in (1.8 mm) and 0.079 in (2.0 mm)

Oil pump
Housing-to-gear clearance:
  New .... 0.0008 to 0.0016 in (0.02 to 0.04 mm)
  Wear limit .... 0.0031 in (0.08 mm)
Control valve spring free lengths:
  Clutch control valve .... 1.004 in (25.5 mm)
  Pressure regulator valve .... 2.240 in (56.9 mm)
  Modulator valve .... 1.240 in (31.5 mm)

Torque wrench settings

	lbf ft	kgf m
Manual transmission		
Clutch housing-to-transmission casing	12 to 17	1.6 to 2.3
Transmission mounting bracket-to-engine	43 to 58	6.0 to 8.0
Bottom cover-to-transmission casing	4.3 to 7.2	0.6 to 1.0
Mainshaft locknut	36 to 43	5.0 to 6.0
Main driveshaft locknut	43 to 58	6.0 to 8.0
Check ball plugs	8 to 22	1.1 to 3.0
Reverse idler gear shaft locknut (double)	72 to 87	10 to 12
Bearing retaining bracket	12 to 17	1.6 to 2.3
Transmission cover	12 to 17	1.6 to 2.3
Main drive gear mounting nut	43 to 58	6.0 to 8.0
Primary gear cover (M6)	4.3 to 7.2	0.6 to 1.0
Primary gear cover (M8)	12 to 17	1.6 to 2.3
Primary gear bearing housing-to-cover	4.3 to 7.2	0.6 to 1.0
Speedometer pinion gear (up to 1979)	4.3 to 7.2	0.6 to 1.0
Speedometer pinion gear (from 1980)	2.2 to 3.6	0.3 to 0.5
Drain and filter plugs	18 to 25	2.5 to 3.5
Mainshaft bearing retainer (4-speed)	12 to 16	1.6 to 2.2
Reverse fork lever bracket (4-speed)	12 to 16	1.6 to 2.2
Countergear shaft retaining plate (5-speed only)	12 to 17	1.6 to 2.3
Final gear side flange nut	87 to 101	12 to 14
Final gear-to-differential casing	43 to 58	6 to 8
Shift rod-to-control lever	5.8 to 8.0	0.8 to 1.1
Support bracket-to-transmission casing:		
10 mm bolts	12 to 16	1.6 to 2.2
8 mm bolts	5.8 to 8.0	0.8 to 1.1
Shift rod-to-lever (control shaft)	5.8 to 8.0	0.8 to 1.1
Selector shaft adjustment nut	12 to 16	1.6 to 2.2
Shift rod locknut	5.8 to 8.0	0.8 to 1.1
Control lever base bracket-to-floor	5.8 to 8.0	0.8 to 1.1
Base bracket-to-mounting bracket	2.4 to 3.2	0.33 to 0.44
Automatic transmission		
Converter housing-to-engine bolts	12 to 15	1.6 to 2.1
Mounting bracket-to-transmission bolts	43 to 58	6.0 to 8.0
Driveplate-to-engine bolts	36 to 43	5.0 to 6.0
Side flange-to-driveshaft	29 to 36	4.0 to 5.0
Converter housing, primary gear cover reaction flange and transmission case cover bolts:		
Size M12 (standard)	12 to 17	1.6 to 2.3
Size M12 (seal bolt)	13 to 18	1.8 to 2.5
Size M10	4.6 to 6.1	0.64 to 0.85
Mainshaft locknut	36 to 43	5.0 to 6.0
Reverse idler shaft mounting nuts	72 to 87	10 to 12
Main drive gear mounting nut	43 to 58	6.0 to 8.0
Converter cover retaining bolts	12 to 17	1.6 to 2.3
Oil pump housing-to-cover (reaction flange) bolts	12 to 17	1.6 to 2.3
Separator plate-to-reaction flange	12 to 17	1.6 to 2.3
Parking pawl bracket	12 to 17	1.6 to 2.3
Final gear mounting bolts	43 to 59	6.0 to 8.1
Flange nuts (final drive)	87 to 101	12 to 14

PART A : MANUAL TRANSMISSION

1 General description

The power from the engine is transmitted through the clutch, primary gear train to the main drive input gear, and subsequently to the mainshaft in the gearbox.

The gearbox is fairly standard having a 4-speed mainshaft and layshaft (countershaft). A 5-speed transmission is fitted to the Coupe model. The mainshaft transmits the drive to the final drive and differential unit which shares the same housing with the gearbox. A common lubrication system is shared by the two assemblies.

The final gear used in the final drive is a helical gear which is of the same design as that used in the transmission, requiring no adjustment for gear contact pattern.

The transmission gearchange is of a remote control floor shift type. It consists essentially of a hand lever, a linkage which connects the hand lever to the transmission, and a radius link assembly which supports the linkage at the location between the control rod and the transmission. The reverse stop mechanism is incorporated in the socket located at the lower end of the hand lever.

2 Manual transmission – removal and refitting

1 The transmission unit can only be removed from the vehicle together with the engine. Details of this and of engine and gearbox separation are given in Chapter 1.

2 Reassembly of the transmission unit to the engine is a reversal of the removal procedure, but if the clutch disc has been disturbed it will have to be centralised as given in Chapter 5.

3 When the two units are mated together, insert each of the respective retaining bolts before tightening them. Tighten all bolts to their specified torque settings, starting with the lower bolts.

4 To refit the engine and transmission refer to Chapter 1, Section 41.

3 Transmission dismantling – general

1 Ensure that an exceptionally clean area is available for the dismantling, and that a good supply of clean fluff-free rags is available together with various jars and containers in which to store items.

2 It is sound policy to refit bolts, after a component has been dismantled, to aid reassembly. Failing this, identify them in some other way.

3 For complete dismantling you will need the following items:

 (a) *Good quality circlip pliers; 2 pairs, 1 expanding and 1 contracting*
 (b) *Copper head mallet, at least 2 lbs*
 (c) *Drifts, steel $\frac{3}{8}$ in and brass $\frac{3}{8}$ in*
 (d) *Small containers for needle rollers*

4 Any attempt to dismantle the gearbox without the foregoing is not necessarily impossible, but will certainly be very difficult and inconvenient resulting in possible injury or damage.

5 Take care not to let the synchromesh hub assemblies come apart before you want them to. It accelerates wear if the splines of hub and sleeve are changed in relation to each other. As a precaution it is advisable to make a line-up mark with a dab of paint.

6 Before finally going ahead with dismantling, first ascertain the availability of spare parts. If several major components need renewing, work out the total cost. It could well be that a reconditioned unit is cheaper in the long run.

4 Transmission (4-speed) – dismantling

1 Support the assembly on a stand or on a bench. The housing is made of aluminium alloy, so great care must be taken, as it is easily damaged. Prior to dismantling the unit clean all dirt and grease from it with a suitable grease solvent. Remove the drain plug, drain the oil into a container and refit the drain plug.

2 Remove the bolts that secure the clutch thrust bearing housing and the primary drive gear. Withdraw the assembly (photo).

3 Remove the bolts that secure the primary gear cover and remove the cover by tapping it with a soft hammer (photo). This might be a little difficult owing to the bearings in the cover. **Do not** prise it off with a screwdriver. It will be noted that some bolts either have a white or green protective resin on the threads, in order to prevent oil leakage. When refitting any bolts of this type a protective coating of non-setting gasket sealer should be applied to the threads.

4 Detach the bottom cover from the transmission case by removing the retaining bolts. Use a screwdriver, mesh the reverse gear and 1st gear (or 2nd) at the same time. Unscrew the main drive gear nut and remove the main drive input gear. Collect the lockwasher and thrust washer under the nut.

5 Remove the primary idler gear, preferably by using a slide hammer type of puller; if this is not available, an ordinary three-legged type of puller will do.

6 Remove the clutch housing bolts and lift away the clutch housing.

7 Drive out the primary drive and primary idler gear bearings with a press. Press out the ball-bearing of the main drive input gear, using the bearing retainer as a support.

8 Remove the nuts securing the driving flanges (one each side) to the differential and tap off the flanges using a block of wood and a hammer. If they do not come off easily it may be necessary to use a puller. When undoing the flange securing nuts it is necessary to restrain the flange from turning (photos); Fig. 6.4 shows the special Datsun tool for this, but two bolts and a suitable bar can be used as shown in the associated photograph.

9 Remove the bolts securing the transmission case cover and remove the cover (photo). It will probably be necessary to separate the cover from the case by using a hammer and a block of wood. Note the bolts with resin on the threads, and also the varying bolt lengths and their respective positions.

10 Remove the speedometer pinion gear (photo).

11 Lift out the differential unit.

12 Remove the detent plugs and take out the locking springs and steel balls.

13 Remove the taper plug from the casing; this provides access to drive out the roll pin on the 1st/2nd gearchange fork (photos).

14 Using a suitable drift, drive out the roll pin that secures the gearchange fork to the fork shaft, then remove the shaft and fork.

15 Remove the bolts that retain the reverse gear fork and bracket. Separate the bracket from the fork by unclipping the pivot pin and lifting out the fork.

16 Remove the bolts and double nuts that secure the mainshaft bearing retainer and remove the retainer (photo).

17 Remove the reverse idler gear and its shaft.

18 The next step can be a little tricky. In order to remove the countershaft (layshaft) it is necessary to drive it out using either a special Datsun tool or a piece of rod of the same diameter as the shaft and the same length as the distance between the two faces of the gearbox casing. One could argue that the tool, or rod, is more important when reinserting the layshaft (in order to retain the needle bearings in position) but it is just as well to use it at this stage to ensure that it fits and no needle bearings are lost.

19 Drive out the countershaft, using the tool described above, then remove the countershaft and gear cluster, and collect the countergear spring and thrust washers.

20 Using a suitable drift, remove the roll pins from each of the remaining selector forks and pull each selector shaft out through the casing, complete with the attached dogs. Collect the selector forks and store in a safe place. Engage 3rd gear before removing the 3rd/4th selector fork roll pin. The interlock plungers can now be removed from their housing in the casing between the selector shafts (Fig. 6.7).

21 Lift the gear mainshaft assembly and the main drive input gear out of the casing through the final drive side. Collect the needle bearing from the mainshaft nose.

22 Measure the endplay present in each gear of the manshaft, as shown in Fig. 6.8. If the specified limit is exceeded, new parts will have to be fitted.

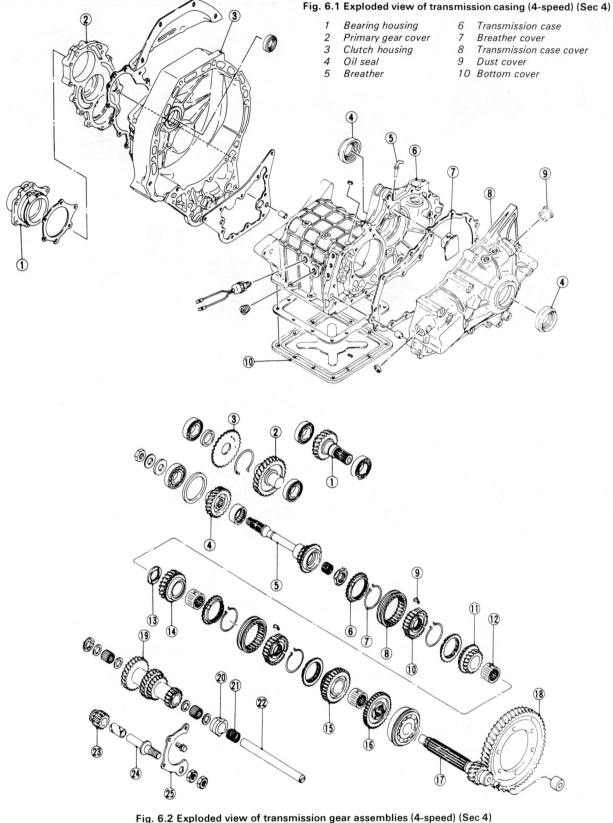

Fig. 6.1 Exploded view of transmission casing (4-speed) (Sec 4)

1	Bearing housing	6	Transmission case
2	Primary gear cover	7	Breather cover
3	Clutch housing	8	Transmission case cover
4	Oil seal	9	Dust cover
5	Breather	10	Bottom cover

Fig. 6.2 Exploded view of transmission gear assemblies (4-speed) (Sec 4)

1	Primary drive gear	8	Coupling sleeve
2	Primary idler gear	9	Shifting insert
3	Sub gear	10	Synchronizer hub
4	Main drive input gear	11	3rd main gear
5	Main drive gear	12	Main gear bushing
6	Baulk ring	13	Main gear spacer
7	Spread spring	14	2nd main gear
		15	1st main gear
		16	Reverse main gear
		17	Mainshaft
		18	Final gear
		19	Countergear
		20	Thrust washer
		21	Thrust spring
		22	Countergear shaft
		23	Reverse idler gear
		24	Reverse idler shaft
		25	Bearing retainer

4.2 Removing the primary drive gear

4.3 Removing the primary gear cover securing bolts

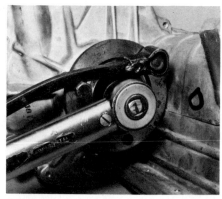

4.8a Prevent the flange from turning with a suitable bar and two bolts

4.8b Remove the flange retaining nut

4.9 Separate the cover from the transmission case

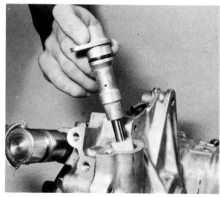

4.10 Removing the speedometer pinion gear

4.13a Remove the taper plug from the casing ...

4.13b ... and drive out the roll pin on the 1st/2nd gearchange fork

4.16 The mainshaft bearing retainer is secured by through-bolts and double nuts

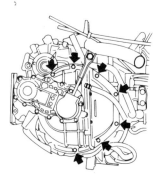

Fig. 6.3 The clutch housing bolt positions (arrowed) (Sec 4)

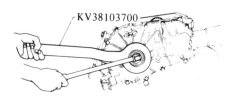

KV38103700

Fig. 6.4 Method of undoing the drive flange nut using Datsun special tool (Sec 4)

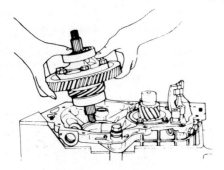

Fig. 6.5 Lift out the differential unit (Sec 4)

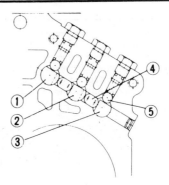

Fig. 6.7 Position of detent balls and interlock plungers (Sec 4)

1	1st/2nd fork	4	Interlock plungers
2	3rd/4th fork shaft	5	Detent balls
3	Reverse fork shaft		

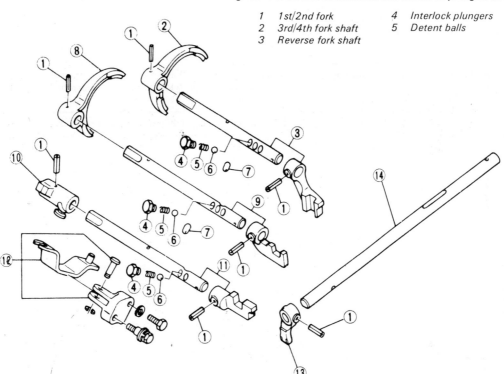

Fig. 6.6 The gearchange shafts and forks (4-speed gearbox)
(Sec 4)

1	Roll pins	7	Interlock pins	11	Reverse shift end and shift rod
2	1st-2nd shift fork	8	3rd-4th shift fork	12	Reverse fork lever assembly
3	1st-2nd end and shift rod	9	3rd-4th shift end and shift rod	13	Shifter
4	Straight thread plugs	10	Reverse shift fork	14	Control shaft
5	Lock springs				
6	Check balls				

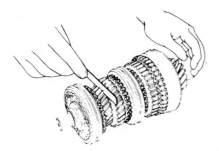

Fig. 6.8 Measure the mainshaft gear endplay (Sec 4)

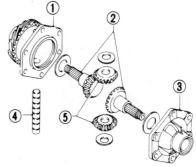

Fig. 6.9 Exploded view of the differential unit (Sec 6)

1	Differential case A	4	Pinion shaft
2	Side gears	5	Pinion mates
3	Differential case B		

5   Mainshaft – dismantling

1   Place the mainshaft in a vice, but ensure that some form of padding is used so as not to damage the gears.
2   Remove the locknut from the end of the mainshaft. **The locknut is staked, so when it is removed be sure to clean the threaded portion of the mainshaft until all the metal chips are removed. The locknut should be discarded and should not be re-used.**
3   Remove the 3rd and 4th synchronizer, 3rd gear, main gear bushing, main gear spacer, 2nd gear, main gear bushing, 1st and 2nd synchronizer, 1st and main gear bushing from mainshaft in order enumerated.
4   Press out the bearing from the mainshaft. This can be done by resting the outer face of the bearing on the vice, and with a piece of wood interposed, lightly tapping the shaft down through the bearing. Leave the circlip on the bearing outer face.
5   The inspection and reassembly details of the synchronizer units are given in Section 9.

6   Final drive and differential – dismantling and inspection

1   Place the final drive assembly in a vice, using padded jaws, and pull off the differential side bearings using a puller.
2   Remove the bolts that secure the final drive gear to the differential.
3   Detach the differential case. Withdraw the differential pinion, by using a drift and hammer, from the mainshaft, and then remove the differential side gears and pinion.
4   If inspection of the differential unit components shows excessive wear or damage to the gears, the unit should be renewed complete.

7   Countershaft – dismantling and reassembly

1   Place the countershaft in a vice with padded jaws. Although the countershaft is out of the gear assembly at this stage, it is now necessary to remove the dummy shaft and then the needle roller bearings and spacers.
2   Reassembly is the reverse of dismantling. Insert the spacers and needle rollers into both sides of the countergear. Apply grease liberally to the bearing needles (this will keep them in position), and fit the dummy shaft, thrust washer and spring (photo).
3   The assembly is now ready for fitting in the gearbox during final assembly of the transmission.

8   Primary drive gear and idler gear – dismantling and reassembly

1   The primary drive gear can be dismantled by first using a piece of bar and tightly tapping the pushrod through the assembly so that the thrust bearing and its two-piece carrier block emerge. Then tap the pushrod right through.
2   The front section of the drive gear can now be removed by using a suitable drift and driving it out.

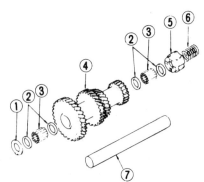

Fig. 6.10 Countershaft and gear assembly (Sec 7)

1	Thrust washer	4	Countergear	6	Spring
2	Spacers	5	Thrust washer	7	Countershaft
3	Needle bearings				

3   The drive gear and idler gear bearings can be removed using a suitable puller.
4   With the bearing removed, the sub gear, spacer and spring ring can be withdrawn from the primary idler gear, but note which holes in the sub gear and primary idler gear the spring ring is engaged in (Fig. 6.11).
5   To reassemble the sub gear and primary idler gear unit, fit the spacer and sub gear onto the idler gear and engage the spring ring into the holes in which it was originally fitted. Press the bearing into position on the primary gear shaft, then check that the sub gear moves smoothly and measure its endfloat (photo) which should not exceed the maximum specified. If necessary, correct the endfloat by removing the bearing and fitting a sub gear spacer of an alternative thickness to suit. Sub gear spacers are available in the following thicknesses:

   0.2677 in (6.80 mm)
   0.2697 in (6.85 mm)
   0.2717 in (6.90 mm)
   0.2736 in (6.95 mm)
   0.2756 in (7.00 mm)

6   If any clutch components have been renewed it is most important that the length of the pushrod is selected as covered in Chapter 5.

9   Transmission components – inspection and checking

1   Thoroughly clean all parts in cleaning solvent, and blow dry with compressed air. Check each part for wear, damage, or other defective conditions.
2   Inspect the primary gear cover, clutch housing, transmission case and transmission case cover. Repair or renew parts if burrs, pitting or damage are apparent on their mating surfaces.
3   Repair or renew a dowel pin if it is distorted or other damage is apparent.
4   Make sure that each bearing is thoroughly cleaned and free from dirt.
5   Check ball-bearings to ensure that they roll freely and are free from cracked, pitted, or worn balls. Also check outer and inner races and balls for indications of bearing creepage. Renew if any of the above conditions are apparent.
6   Renew needle roller bearing, if worn or damaged.
7   Check all the gears for wear, damaged or chipped teeth. Where such damage is evident, the driven and driving gears should be renewed as a set. Where the gearbox has covered a substantial period of service it will be appropriate to test for backlash and endfloat with the gear train assembled on the mainshaft and countershaft and installed in the gearbox. Use a dial gauge to check for backlash, turning each gearwheel as far as it will go whilst holding the mainshaft perfectly still. The permitted backlash tolerance is given in the Specifications. Use a feeler gauge to check for endplay.
8   Where the backlash or endplay is greater than that specified, consideration should be given to purchasing a reconditioned gearbox as the cost of a complete set of gears and other internal components will probably prove uneconomical by comparison.
9   Check baulk rings for evidence of wear, pitting, cracking, or damage. If any of the above conditions are apparent, renew the baulk rings.
10   Measure the clearance between the baulk ring end and cone (Fig. 6.12). If it is less than the minimum specified, renew the baulk ring.
11   Renew the oil seals and O-rings as a matter of course during assembly.
12   When reassembling the synchronizers, insert the hub into the coupling sleeve, fit the shift inserts in the three grooves in the hub and then engage the spread spring protrusion into the groove to secure the insert to the coupling sleeve inner face. Fit the opposing spread spring on the other side of the hub, but be careful not to engage the spring front and rear ends into the same insert. Check the hub-to-sleeve action by hand to ensure that it operates satisfactorily.

10   Transmission reassembly – general

1   Ensure that all parts are thoroughly cleaned and lubricated with oil before reassembly. Do not use any liquid sealants between the casing mating surfaces.
2   Apply a non-setting gasket sealant to the threads of the trans-

123

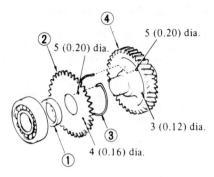

Fig. 6.11 The primary idler and sub gear unit components.
Location hole diameters in mm (in) (Sec 8)

1 Spacer   3 Ring spring
2 Sub gear   4 Primary idler gear

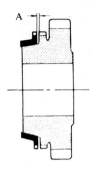

Fig. 6.12 Check the baulk ring-to-cone clearance (A) (Sec 9)

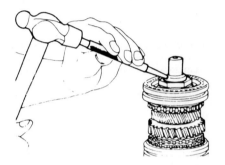

Fig. 6.14 Stake the mainshaft nut (Sec 11)

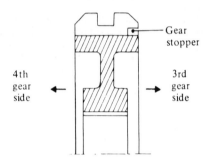

Fig. 6.13 Gear stopper must face 3rd gear (Sec 11)

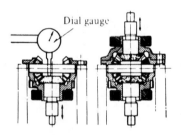

Fig. 6.15 Measure the side gear endplay (Sec 12)

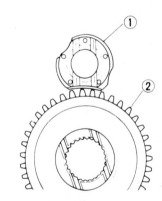

Fig. 6.16 Countershaft thrust washer (1) and reverse gear (2)
(Sec 13)

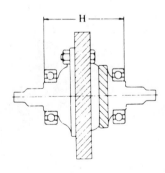

Fig. 6.17 Side bearing height (H) (Sec 13)

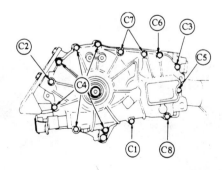

Fig. 6.18 The 4-speed transmission cover bolt positions showing
the bolt lengths. Seal bolts C5 to C8 (Sec 13)

C1   3.27 in (83 mm)   C4   1.77 in (45 mm)   C7   1.77 in (45 mm)
C2   2.76 in (70 mm)   C5   2.36 in (60 mm)   C8   3.27 in (83 in)
C3   1.18 in (30 mm)   C6   1.38 in (35 mm)

mission case seal bolts prior to assembly.
3   Always use new gaskets and oil seals when reassembling.
4   Tighten all fastenings to their specified torque wrench settings.

11 Mainshaft – reassembly

1   Ensure that the sliding surfaces of the mainshaft bushes are lubricated with oil before assembly.
2   Press the ball-bearing onto the mainshaft (photo) and fit the reverse gear (photo). Slide the bush into position on the mainshaft, so that the oil holes are aligned (photo). Fit the first gear, baulk ring and synchronizer hub (photos). Make sure that the insert is correctly seated in the groove of the baulk ring.
3   Fit the second gear bush with its oil hole aligned with the hole in the mainshaft and then fit the second gear (photos).
4   Fit the main gear spacer, followed by the bush and third gear. Fit the baulk ring and synchronizer hub (photos). When assembling 3rd/4th synchromesh hub, ensure that gear stopper faces the 3rd gear side as shown in Fig. 6.13.
5   Mount the mainshaft in a vice equipped with soft-faced jaws, to avoid damage to the gears.
6   Fit the mainshaft locknut (photo) and tighten to the specified torque wrench setting.
7   Recheck the endplay, and if within the specified limit, stake the locknut to the shaft (photo).

12 Final drive and differential – reassembly

1   Press the differential side bearings into the differential case. If a proper press is not available, use a hammer and block of wood to spread the load over the face of the bearing. Tap the bearing home gently.
2   The next stage is slightly more complex and involves the use of a dial gauge. Fit the final drive assembly on a testing tool like that shown in Fig. 6.15. If you cannot obtain the official Datsun tool there should be no problem in making one up locally. Using the dial gauge, adjust each side gear endplay to less than 0.008 in (0.2 mm) by selective thrust washers. Sizes of thrust washers available are given in the Specifications.
3   Fit the final drive gear on the differential assembly. Apply thread locking compound to the bolts and tighten them to the specified torque wrench setting.

13 Transmission (4-speed) – reassembly

1   Lubricate the lip of the differential side flange oil seal with multi-purpose grease, and press it into position using a block of wood between the faces of a vice. Note that the lip should be innermost.
2   Ensure the main drive gear bearing is in position in the casing, then ease the main drive gear through the bearing and into position. Fit the needle bearing in the main drive gear and then fit the mainshaft in the casing (photos).
3   Insert the bottom selector shaft, slide the fork over it and engage the fork with the nearest coupling sleeve on the mainshaft. Secure in

position with a roll pin. Insert the interlock plunger through the bore in centre selector shaft housing (photo).
4   Insert the centre selector shaft, slide the fork over it and engage the fork with the end coupling sleeve on the mainshaft. Secure in position with a roll pin. Insert the interlock plunger (photos).
5   Hold the countergear in position in the transmission case, with the thrust washers and spring correctly located, and then insert the countershaft into the counter gear and drive out the dummy shaft (photos). Make sure that the cut-out part of the countershaft is lined up with the bearing retainer (photo).
6   Fit the reverse idler shaft, reverse idler gear and the bearing retainer. Make sure that the cut-out part of the reverse idler shaft is lined up with the bearing retainer (Fig. 6.16). Tighten the idler shaft retaining nuts (double nuts) and the bearing retainer bolts to their specified torque settings (photos).
7   Insert the reverse fork shaft, slide the reverse fork pivot over the shaft and secure with a roll pin (photo).
8   Fit the reverse fork bracket and secure with two bolts. Fit the reverse fork on the pivot and secure to the bracket with a clevis pin and clip (photos).
9   Fit the detent balls, locking springs and retaining plugs (photos). Manipulate the selector shafts to ensure that all gears can be selected.
10   Before fitting the differential unit, measure the side bearing height, 'H' in Fig. 6.17. After selecting a suitable shim from the following table, fit the differential assembly (photos):

Height 'H'	Shim Thickness
4.720 to 4.730 in (119.91 to 120.10 mm)	Unnecessary
4.715 to 4.719 in (119.76 to 119.90 mm)	0.0078 in (0.2 mm)
4.710 to 4.714 in (119.66 to 119.75 mm)	0.0118 in (0.3 mm)

11   Fit the transmission case cover (photo), applying non-setting gasket sealant to the seal bolts, and tighten all bolts to their specified torque settings. The respective bolt fitting positions are shown in Fig. 6.18.
12   Apply thread locking compound to the threads of the differential side flanges, then fit them and tighten the retaining nuts to the specified torque setting. Restrain the flanges from turning; refer to Section 4, paragraph 8.
13   Fit the reversing lamp switch in its housing in the casing (photo).
14   Fit the clutch housing. Apply non-setting gasket sealant to the threads of the seal bolts (photo).
15   Drive the primary idler gear a short way into the clutch housing with a wooden mallet, making sure that its sub gear side is towards the primary gear cover.
16   Fit the main drive input gear. Fit the primary idler sub gear to the correct position by inserting a rod through the hole in the sub gear and into the hole in the primary idler gear to align them, then fit the main drive input gear and bearing. Next fit the thrust washer, lockwasher and main drive gear nut. The nut for the main drive gear must be fitted with the chamfered side facing the lockwasher (photos).
17   Engage two gears at the same time, to prevent the main drive from turning, then tighten the nut to the specified torque setting. Bend over the lockwasher to lock the nut, then disengage the two gears.
18   Fit the primary gear cover on the clutch housing (photo).

7.2 Apply grease when fitting the needle rollers in the countershaft

8.5 Check the primary idler gear endfloat with a feeler gauge

11.2a Press the ball-bearing onto the mainshaft

11.2b Fit the reverse gear ...

11.2c ... then slide the bush into position with the oil holes aligned with the mainshaft oil holes ...

11.2d ... followed by 1st gear, baulk ring ...

11.2e ... and synchronizer hub

11.3a Fit 2nd gear bush ...

11.3b ... and then 2nd gear

11.4a Fit the main spacer ...

11.4b ... followed by the bush ...

11.4c ... then the 3rd gear, baulk ring ...

11.4d ... and synchronizer hub

11.6 Fitting the mainshaft locknut

11.7 Recheck the gear endplay with a feeler gauge

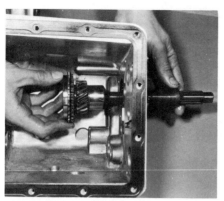

13.2a Position the main drive gear in the casing ...

13.2b ... fit the needle bearing ...

13.2c ... and then fit the mainshaft to engage with the main drive gear

13.3 Fitting the bottom selector shaft and interlock plunger

13.4a Fit the centre selector shaft and fork ...

13.4b ... and secure with a roll pin ...

13.4c ... then fit the interlock plunger

13.5a Fit the countershaft into the countergear

13.5b Countergear thrust washer and spring

13.5c Ensure that the cutout on the countershaft is positioned to line up with the bearing retainer

13.6a Fit the reverse idler shaft and gear ...

13.6b ... and then the bearing retainer and idler shaft nuts

13.7 Insert the reverse fork shaft and pivot

13.8a The reverse fork bracket is retained by two bolts

13.8b Fit the reverse fork on the pivot and secure to the bracket with a clevis pin

13.9a Insert the detent balls and springs ...

13.9b ... and fit the retaining plugs

13.10a Position the selected shim on the casing ...

13.10b ... and fit the differential unit

13.11 The transmission case cover ready for fitting

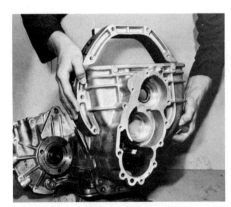
13.14 When refitting the clutch housing, don't forget to apply sealant to the seal bolts

13.16a Position the primary idler sub/gear with a bar, fit the main drive input gear and ...

13.16b ... then the thrust washer, lockwasher and main drive gear nut

13.18 Fitting the primary gear cover

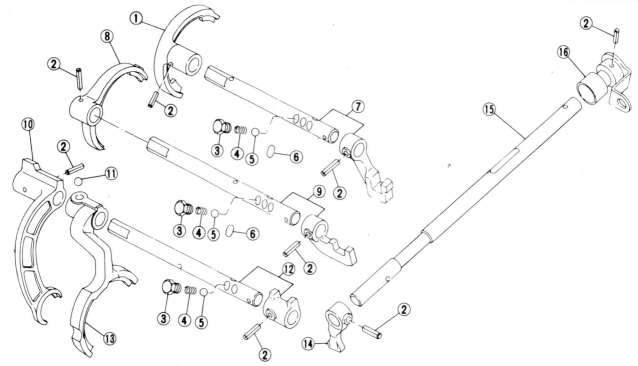

Fig. 6.19 The 5-speed gear selector units (Sec 15)

1	4th/5th gear shift fork	5	Check ball	8	2nd-3rd shift fork	11	Check ball	14	Shifter
2	Roll pins	6	Interlock plungers	9	2nd-3rd shift end and shift rod	12	1st-reverse shift end and shift rod	15	Control shaft
3	Straight thread plugs	7	4th-5th shift end and shift rod	10	Reverse shift fork	13	1st shift fork	16	Shift lever
4	Lock spring						

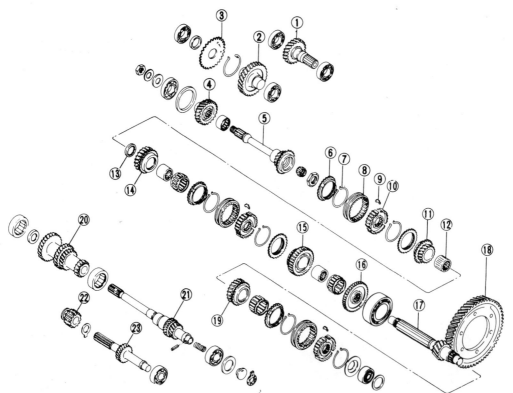

Fig. 6.20 The 5-speed transmission gear assembly components (Sec 15)

1	Primary drive gear	7	Spread spring	13	Main gear spacer	19	1st main gear
2	Primary idler gear	8	Coupling sleeve	14	3rd main gear	20	Countergear
3	Sub gear	9	Shifting insert	15	2nd main gear	21	1st-reverse countergear
4	Main drive input gear	10	Synchronizer hub	16	Reverse main gear	22	Reverse idler gear
5	Main drive gear	11	4th main gear	17	Mainshaft	23	Reverse idler input gear
6	Baulk ring	12	4th gear bushing	18	Final gear		

19 Fit the speedometer pinion gear and the bottom cover.
20 Do not fit the bearing housing assembly and primary drive gear at this stage because of the difficulty of lining up with the flywheel and clutch assembly.
21 Refit the clutch operating lever and secure in position with the pivot pin through the primary drive gear flange. Fit a locking clip over the pin. Fit the protective rubber boot.
22 Reconnect the transmission to the engine, first by the single bolt through the transmission flange and engine stay rod, then by the bolts through the clutch housing to the engine endplate. The clutch should still be in position on the flywheel.
23 Now refit the primary drive gear and bearing assembly. If the clutch has been removed it is most likely that you will have to use some form of centering tool to line up the clutch with the primary drive gear splines. Another way of tackling it is to loosen the clutch bolts, insert the primary drive gear, and adjust the clutch position until the two are mated correctly. Then tighten the bolts.
24 Refit the clutch inspection cover. The assembly is now ready for refitting in the car. Refer to Chapter 1 for these details.

14 Transmission (5-speed) – general

The removal, dismantling and reassembly procedures are similar to those for the 4-speed transmission. Unless otherwise described, refer to the relevant Section for the 4-speed transmission.

15 Transmission (5-speed) – dismantling

1 Remove the differential side flanges and primary gear.
2 Remove the speedometer pinion gear.
3 Remove the bolts securing the transmission case cover and lift off the cover. Take care not to lose the lock ball when removing the cover. Note each bolt length and its fitted position as they are removed.
4 Detach the counter thrust bush from first and reverse countergear (photo).
5 Remove the detent ball plugs and take out the steel balls (photo).
6 Drive the roll pin out of the reverse shift fork, using a parallel pin punch. Drive out the first and reverse fork shaft from the clutch housing side with a suitable drift.
7 To remove the cover side taper roller bearings, apply a suitable puller to the first gear and remove the bearing together with the retainer washer, first synchronizer assembly, first gear needle bearing, first and reverse countergear and reverse idler input gear. Then remove the reverse idler gear and reverse shift fork.
8 Lift out the differential unit.
9 Remove the plug from the service hole, drive the roll pins out of the shift forks and then withdraw the fork shafts. When removing the 4th/5th shift fork roll pin, shift to 5th gear and then drive the pin out (photos).
10 Remove the bearing retainer plate.
11 Remove the mainshaft gear assembly and main drive gear from the transmission case towards the final drive gear side by tapping the main drive gear lightly.
12 Remove the countershaft and gear assembly, the 2nd/3rd shift fork and the 4th/5th shift fork.
13 Remove the mainshaft locknut.
14 From the mainshaft remove the 4th/5th synchronizer, 4th gear, main gear bush, main gear spacer, 3rd gear, main gear needle bearing, main gear bush, 2nd/3rd synchronizer, 2nd gear, main gear needle bearing, main gear bush, reverse gear and bearing housing in that order; see Fig. 6.20.
15 If necessary, remove the mainshaft bearing with a puller. If the bearing is removed it should be discarded and a new bearing fitted at reassembly.

16 Transmission (5-speed) – reassembly

1 Press the mainshaft bearing onto the shaft.
2 Insert the bearing outer race into the bearing housing, then fit the bearing housing and reverse gear on the mainshaft. Ensure that the cutaway section of the reverse gear is aligned with the 2nd main gear bush.

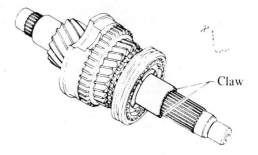
Fig. 6.21 Fit the 3rd gear bush (Sec 16)

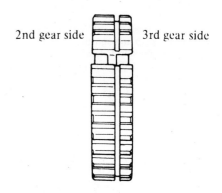
2nd gear side   3rd gear side
Fig. 6.22 Fitting direction of 2nd/3rd synchro hub (Sec 16)

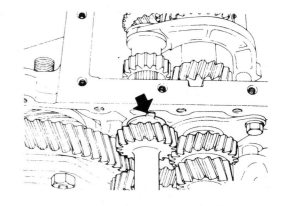
Fig. 6.23 Reverse idler washer fitted in position (Sec 16)

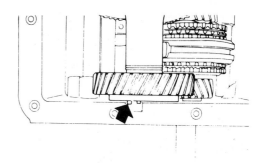
Fig. 6.24 Countergear thrust washer fitted in position (Sec 16)

3   Fit the 2nd gear bush, needle bearing, 2nd main gear, baulk ring, 2nd/3rd synchro hub assembly and the 3rd main gear bush. When fitting the 3rd main gear bush ensure that the claw is lined up with the main gear spacer. When fitting the 2nd/3rd synchro hub, the thinner spline tooth side must be towards the 3rd gear; see Figs. 6.21 and 6.22.

4   Fit the needle bearing, baulk ring, 3rd gear and main gear spacer. When fitting the main gear spacer ensure that the uneven surface side is towards the 4th gear.

5   Fit the 4th gear bush, 4th gear, baulk ring, 4th/5th synchro hub and mainshaft locknut. Tighten and then stake the locknut. Refer to Specifications for the nut torque setting.

6   Fit the differential side flange oil seals.

7   Fit the main drive gear and mainshaft assembly into the transmission case and at the same time insert the 2nd/3rd shift fork, 4th/5th shift fork and countergear with thrust washer into the case.

8   Relocate the countershaft bearing retainer plate and tighten the bolts to the specified torque.

9   Carefully insert the countershaft shaft into position.

10   Slide the 2nd/3rd fork shaft through the casing and the 2nd/3rd shift fork, then secure it to the shift fork with a new roll pin.

11   Fit the 2nd/3rd detent ball, spring and plug. Align the notch in the 2nd/3rd shaft with the ball and place in neutral position. Smear the detent plug with sealant prior to fitting.

12   Locate the interlock plunger between 2nd/3rd and 4th/5th selector rods and then fit the 4th/5th selector rod in a similar manner.

13   Fit the countershaft needle bearing and bearing retainer.

14   With a suitable selected shim fit the differential unit in the casing.

15   Fit the 1st gear needle bearing, 1st gear, baulk ring, synchronizer unit, 1st shift fork, retainer washer, 1st/reverse countergear with ball-bearing, reverse idler input gear with ball-bearing and washer, reverse idler gear and reverse shift fork at the same time and then fit the taper roller bearing using a suitable drift. Ensure that the claw on the reverse idler input gear washer is pointed towards the bottom cover and that the countergear thrust washer is set as shown in Figs. 6.23 and 6.24.

16   Insert the interlock plunger between 2nd/3rd and 1st/reverse fork shafts and fit the 1st/reverse fork shaft.

17   Measure the 1st/reverse countergear bearing height, H in Fig. 6.25, and select the required number of shims from the following table:

Height 'H' in (mm)	Required thickness in (mm)	Number of shims
3.472 to 3.480 (88.20 to 88.40)	0	0
3.465 to 3.471 (88.00 to 88.19)	0.008 (0.2)	1
3.457 to 3.464 (87.80 to 87.99)	0.016 (0.4)	2
3.449 to 3.456 (87.60 to 87.79)	0.024 (0.6)	3

18   Determine the mainshaft bearing shim thickness as follows:

(a)   Fit the bearing outer race on the mainshaft bearing and measure dimension 'B' in Fig. 6.26

(b)   Measure depth of mainshaft bearing outer race housing of case cover, 'A' in Fig. 6.27

(c)   The required thickness of adjusting shim required can be determined by the formula, $T = A - B + 0.5$

T = Required thickness of mainshaft bearing adjusting shim (mm)

A – Measured case cover depth (mm)

B – Measured mainshaft bearing height (mm)

19   Select the required shim from the following:

Shim thickness in (mm)
0.0012 (0.03)
0.0020 (0.05)
0.0028 (0.07)
0.0039 (0.1)
0.0118 (0.3)
0.0197 (0.5)
0.0276 (0.7)
0.0354 (0.9)

20   Fit the selected mainshaft bearing adjusting shim onto the case cover and press the mainshaft bearing outer race completely into the case cover.

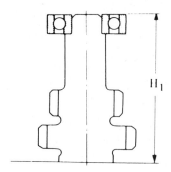

Fig. 6.25 Measure the 1st/reverse countergear bearing height (H1) (Sec 16)

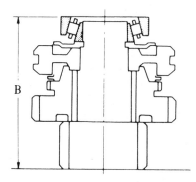

Fig. 6.26 Mainshaft bearing height (B) (Sec 16)

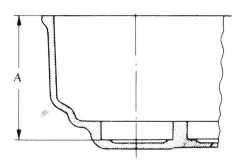

Fig. 6.27 Case cover depth measurement points (A) (Sec 16)

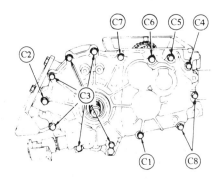

Fig. 6.28 The 5-speed transmission cover bolt positions showing the bolt lengths. Seal bolts C5 to C8 (Sec 16)

C1	3.27 in (83 mm)	C5	2.76 in (70 mm)
C2	2.76 in (70 mm)	C6	3.27 in (83 mm)
C3	1.77 in (45 mm)	C7	1.77 in (45 mm)
C4	1.18 in (30 mm)	C8	3.27 in (83 mm)

15.4 Remove the thrust bush

15.5 Remove the detent ball plugs

15.9a Remove service plug ...

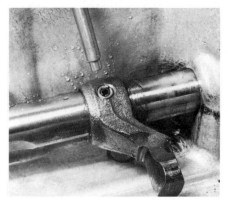
15.9b ... to drive out the shift rod selector roll pin

16.21 Locate the countershaft thrust washer (A) and shims (B) into the case cover

16.22a With the shift forks in neutral position (note detent ball in 1st shift fork) ...

16.22b ... refit the case cover

16.23 Tighten the case cover bolts

16.25a Lubricate the main gear assemblies before ...

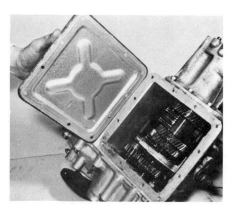
16.25b ... refitting the bottom cover

17.3 The control lever base bracket and selector rod connection

17.4 Do not alter the shift rod length setting

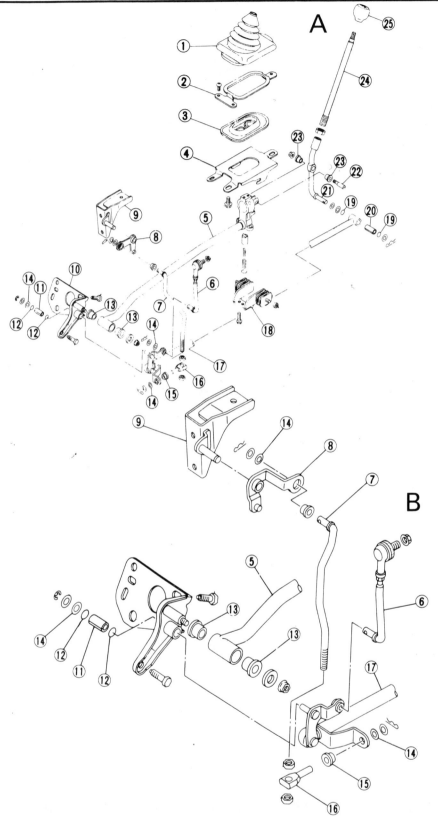

Fig. 6.29 Exploded diagram of the 4-speed (A) and 5-speed (B) gearchange linkage assemblies. (Most of 5-speed assembly is similar to 4-speed) (Sec 17)

1 Rubber boot	7 Selector rod	12 O-rings	17 Control rod	21 Lower control lever
2 Dust cover holder	8 Selector lever	13 Bushings	18 Control rod mounting	22 Control lever pin
3 Dust cover	9 Transmission mounting	14 Spring washers	bracket	23 Bushings
4 Control rod base bracket	bracket	15 Bushing	19 O-rings	24 Upper control lever
5 Support rod	10 Support bracket	16 Trunnion	20 Bushing	25 Control knob
6 Shift rod	11 Bushing			

21 Attach with grease the counter thrust bush to 1st/reverse counter-gear, and the thrust washer and selected shims to the case cover (photo).
22 With the fork shafts in neutral position, fit the case cover on the transmission case. Do not forget to fit the 1st shift fork detent ball (photos).
23 Insert the case cover bolts into their respective locations as given in Fig. 6.28 and smear the seal bolts with a non-setting sealant. Tighten all bolts to the specified torque (photo).
24 Refit the differential side flanges, referring to Section 13, paragraph 12 for details.
25 Lubricate the main gear assemblies (photo), locate the bottom cover gasket and refit the cover (photo).
26 Refit the clutch housing, the primary idler and sub gear unit and the main input gear assembly as given in Section 13, paragraphs 14 to 24 inclusive.
27 Refit the reversing light switch and speedometer drive unit to complete.

17 Gearchange linkage – removal, inspection and refitting

1 From inside the car, detach the gear lever rubber boot from its floor fixing.
2 You now need to work underneath the car, so jack it up and support with axle stands for security. Ensure that the handbrake is secure and chock the wheels.
3 Unscrew and remove the three control lever base bracket retaining bolts and lower the bracket. If you only wish to detach the control rod assembly, remove the spring retaining clip and pull the rod from the lever together with the flat washers (photo).
4 Detach and remove the selector lever and shift rod from the control shaft (Fig. 6.30), but do not alter the shift rod length (photo).
5 Unbolt and detach the exhaust pipe mounting bracket and support plate (photos).
6 The gearchange linkage assembly can now be carefully withdrawn downwards and removed from underneath the car.
7 Each linkage is securely retained with various fasteners such as washers and circlips. Special care should be taken so that they may be reinstalled in exactly the same location when reconnecting the linkage.
8 Inspect all the linkage components for general wear, corrosion or distortion. If general sloppiness is apparent in the linkage it is recommended that all the circlips, springs and clips are renewed as a matter of course.
9 Installation of the linkage is a reversal of the removal procedures, noting the following points.
10 O-rings are fitted between the shift lever and radius link assembly and between gear lever and control rod. The O-rings and radius link bosses should be lubricated with multi-purpose grease.
11 The shift lever and selector lever should also be greased (Fig. 6.33).
12 The shift rod length is critical and if disturbed should be reset at the dimension given in Fig. 6.36.

18 Gearchange linkage – adjustment

1 Set the hand lever to the neutral position and then loosen the control rod lever adjustments nuts.
2 Refer to Fig. 6.34, part A or B as applicable for your particular model, push the shift lever fully forwards as shown by P1 and back it up as shown in Fig. 6.35.

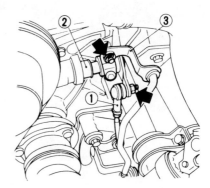

Fig. 6.30 Selector lever and shift rod detachment points (arrowed) (Sec 17)

1 Shift rod 2 Control shaft 3 Selector lever

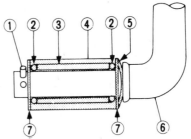

Fig. 6.31 The control lever-to-control rod component locations (Sec 17)

1 Retaining pin   5 Spring washer
2 O-rings   6 Lower control lever
3 Bush   7 Washers
4 Control rod

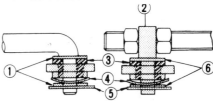

Fig. 6.32 The linkage connection component locations (Sec 17)

1 Washer   3 Bushes   5 Cotter pins
2 Trunnion   4 Spring washers   6 Washers

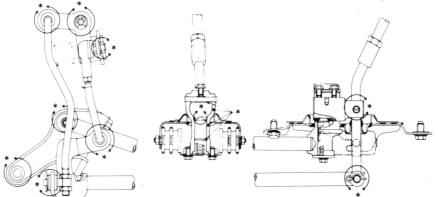

Fig. 6.33 The linkage lubrication points – use a multi-purpose grease (Sec 17)

17.5a Unbolt the exhaust pipe bracket and linkage plate

17.5b Detach the linkage plate

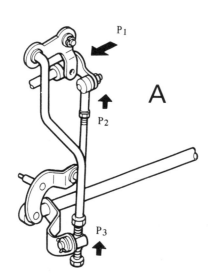

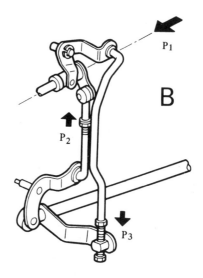

Fig. 6.34 Linkage adjustments for the 4-speed (A) and the 5-speed (B) transmission. For key see text (Sec 18)

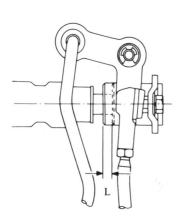

Fig. 6.35 Measure pull-back length of shift lever at L (Sec 18)

4-speed gearbox – L = 0.31 in (8 mm) approx
5-speed gearbox – L = 0.45 in (11.5 mm) approx

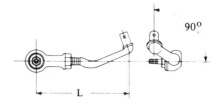

Fig. 6.36 Shift rod lever length (L) should be set at 4.50 to 4.56 in (114.3 to 115.7 mm) (Sec 18)

3   Hold the selector lever in this position and move the shift lever in direction P2 so that on 4-speed models, 3rd gear is engaged, whilst on 5-speed models, 2nd gear is engaged.
4   Push the control rod fully downwards or upwards as shown by P3 according to model, and then turn the adjuster nut until it abuts the trunnion. Rotate the adjuster nut a further 90° ($\frac{1}{4}$ turn) and then lock the lever in this position by tightening the adjuster nut on each side.
5   Actuate the gear lever and check that each gear can be engaged with a smooth and precise action without any feeling of binding or sloppiness.
6   Further minor adjustment may be necessary but do not alter the shift rod length which should be as given in Fig. 6.36.

19 Fault diagnosis – manual transmission

Note: *It is sometimes difficult to decide whether it is worthwhile removing and dismantling the gearbox for a fault which may be nothing more than a minor irritant. Gearboxes which howl, or where the synchromesh can be 'beaten' by a quick gearchange, may continue to perform for a long time in this state. A worn gearbox usually needs a complete rebuild to eliminate noise because the various gears, if re-aligned on new bearings, will continue to howl when different wearing surfaces are presented to each other. The decision to overhaul therefore, must be considered with regard to time and money available, relative to the degree of noise or malfunction that the driver has to suffer.*

Symptom	Reason(s)
Difficulty in changing gear	Control linkage out of adjustment or in need of lubrication Selector mechanism worn or damaged Clutch fault (see Chapter 5)
Jumping out of gear	Control linkage out of adjustment Interlock plunger worn Detent springs or balls worn or damaged Excessive gear endfloat Mainshaft mounting nut loose
Excessive noise	Oil level low or incorrect grade Worn or damaged bearings Worn or damaged gears
Noise on turns only	Final drive fault Wheel bearing defective (see Chapter 11) Driveshaft fault (see Chapter 7)

PART B: AUTOMATIC TRANSMISSION

20 Automatic transmission – general description and precautions

A selective automatic transmission system is fitted to some models. The main component units of this gearbox are the torque converter, an electro-hydraulically operated clutch, and the main gearbox which has similar characteristics to that of the 4-speed manual transmission. Briefly explained, the automatic transmission operation is as follows.

Drive from the engine is transmitted through the hydraulic torque converter, comprising a pump (impeller) which is directly engaged with the engine crankshaft, a turbine and a stator to increase the torque. A clutch unit is attached to the turbine. The clutch hub engages with the splines of the drive gear shaft of the gearbox.

The clutch unit is operated automatically by means of the electro-hydraulic control unit. As the oil pressure in the torque converter increases, the oil pressure on the clutch drops and the piston presses against the clutch cover, engaging the clutch and enabling the fluid power of the turbine to be transmitted to the primary drive gear train. The clutch is automatically disengaged when the torque converter pressure drops and the clutch disc pressure is increased (see Fig. 6.38). The wet type clutch employed is more durable than the normal dry single plate clutch used with manual gearboxes, and should give very little trouble and rarely if ever need renewing.

The clutch operation is controlled by the control valve which in turn is actuated by the solenoid unit. The solenoid is activated in conjunction with the movement of the gear selector lever, its knob switch and the shift stroke switch mounted on the transmission cover.

An involute gear oil pump is integral with the pump impeller of the torque converter and feeds oil to the base of the transmission case, to the oil strainer, pump housing inlet port, the outlet port and the control valve line pressure circuit. Excessive oil pressure is relieved by means of a pressure regulator valve in the line pressure circuit. The pressure regulator valve operates in conjunction with the vacuum modulator valve which regulates the pressure valve opening in accordance with the engine throttle movement (as the inlet manifold vacuum increases so the line pressure drops). The oil pressure circuit diagram is shown in Figs. 6.42 and 6.43.

As previously mentioned, the gearbox itself is of similar construction to that of the 4-speed manual gearbox, although some modifications have been made for adaption to use as a selective type automatic transmission.

The only maintenance normally required is to check the transmission oil level and top up as and when necessary, and to renew the oil at the specified mileage intervals. The details of oil level checking and renewal are given in Section 21.

Should this transmission start to malfunction in any way, refer to Section 32 for a general fault diagnosis and to Section 31 for the fault diagnosis checks which can be made without too much specialised equipment. Do not allow a fault to go unchecked or unrectified – it could prove expensive!

Unlike many other automatic transmissions, the Datsun selective automatic transmission can be dismantled and repaired by a competent DIY mechanic. However, particular care must be taken during overhaul operations and it is advisable therefore to read through the instructions of the task(s) at hand before starting any repairs. Reference should also be made to Section 23.

21 Automatic transmission oil – level checking and renewal

Oil level check

1   The oil level of the automatic transmission is best checked directly after the car has been used, when the oil temperature will have reached 86° to 158°F (30° to 70°C). If the oil is cold, run the engine at its normal idle speed for 10 minutes so that the oil reaches this temperature.

2   The car must be parked on level ground and the shift (gear) lever set in the 'P' position. Leave the engine idling when checking the oil level.

3   Withdraw the oil level dipstick and observe the level reading, which should be between the 'L' and 'H' markings on the stick. Wipe the dipstick clean and reinsert it (with the L and H markings downwards) and recheck the reading. If the oil level is low, top up using only the specified type of automatic transmission fluid. Take care not to overfill; the level must not exceed the 'H' mark.

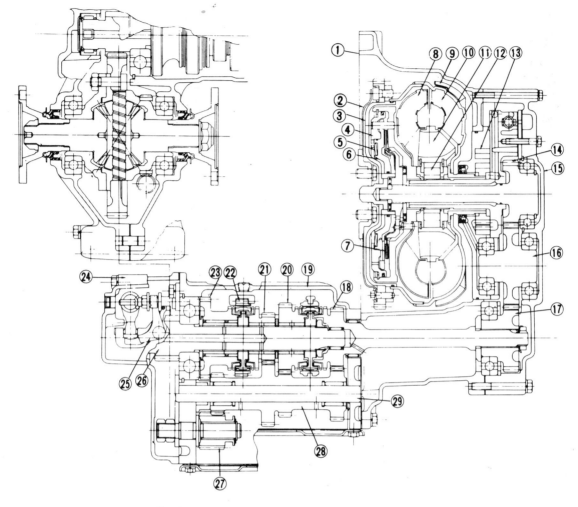

Fig. 6.37 Automatic transmission – sectional view (Sec 20)

1	Converter housing	9	Cooling shroud
2	Driveplate	10	Pump impeller
3	Torque converter cover	11	Stator
4	Outer piston	12	One way clutch
5	Diaphragm spring	13	Oil pump
6	Inner piston	14	Primary drive gear
7	Clutch disc	15	Primary gear cover
8	Turbine runner		

16	Primary idler gear	23	Reverse gear (R)
17	Main drive input gear	24	Transmission case cover
18	Main drive gear (D)	25	Return lever
19	Transmission case	26	Mainshaft
20	Low gear (L)	27	Reverse idler gear
21	Overdrive gear (OD)	28	Countergear
22	Parking gear	29	Countershaft

Oil renewal

4   The automatic transmission oil must be renewed at the specified mileage intervals – see Routine Maintenance.

5   The car must be parked on level ground and the engine switched off.

6   Remove the drain plug and drain the old oil into a suitable container for disposal, then refit the plug.

7   Refill to the correct level, using only the specified type of transmission fluid. Run the engine on completion and recheck the level as given previously.

22 Automatic transmission – removal and refitting

1   The automatic transmission unit can only be removed together with the engine as described in Chapter 1.

2   Once the engine and automatic transmission have been removed from the car, they can then be separated and this is detailed in Chapter 1, Section 6.

3   When refitting the automatic transmission to the engine, first ensure that the converter unit is fully located in its housing. Refer to Fig. 6.45 and check the distance 'A' indicated to ensure that the

specified tolerance exists.

4   When in position, tighten the driveplate-to-torque converter bolts and the transmission-to-engine retaining bolts to their specified torque settings.

23 Automatic transmission overhaul – general

Although no special tools are required to dismantle, overhaul and reassemble the automatic transmission, a good basic engineering tool kit should be at hand. Some special Datsun tools are mentioned in the text since they will be of assistance if available and should be used in preference to alternative or fabricated tools. The basic tool kit should also include a micrometer, a dial gauge and an assortment of tubing and drifts for the removal and fitting of bearings and seals where necessary.

The following general precautions must be taken:

(a)   *If hosing down or steam cleaning the transmission and/or its associated components, ensure that no steam, cleaning fluid or water enter those components which cannot be thoroughly dried and cleaned off. Cleaning fluid must not be allowed to contact any rubber parts*

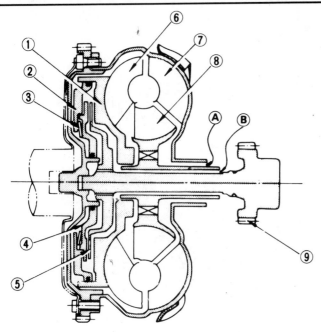

Fig. 6.38 The clutch and torque converter assembly components
(Sec 20)

1	Clutch cover	6	Turbine runner
2	Outer piston	7	Pump impeller
3	Diaphragm spring	8	Stator
4	Inner piston	9	Primary drive gear
5	Clutch disc		

A   torque converter line
B   oil pressure to clutch disc side

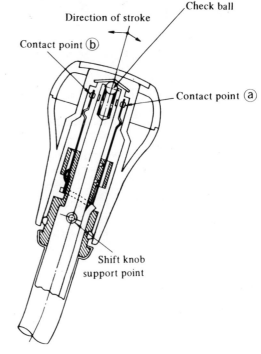

Fig. 6.39 Sectional view of gear lever selector knob switch unit
(Sec 20)

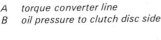

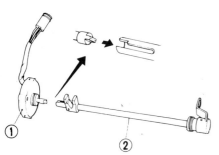

Fig. 6.40 The shift stroke switch (1)
and control shaft (2) (Sec 20)

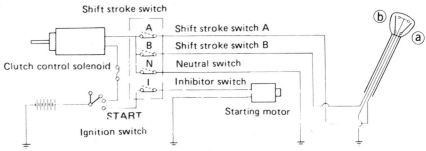

Fig. 6.41 The gear selector, starter and clutch control circuit (Sec 20)

(b)   Always use clean lint-free rags to remove dirt and wipe
components dry
(c)   Always renew the packing seals and gaskets and seals during
reassembly
(d)   During assembly torque tighten all bolts and nuts where
specified and apply a coating of automatic transmission fluid
to the liquid contact components
(e)   Note that the torque converter cannot be removed without
first removing its housing

24 Automatic transmission – dismantling

Converter housing removal

1   Unscrew and remove the reversing light switch.
2   Unscrew and remove the two oil cooler hoses.
3   Unscrew and remove the transmission drain plug and drain the
fluid into a suitable container for disposal.
4   Unscrew and remove the bottom cover retaining bolts and remove
the bottom cover and gasket.
5   Unscrew the oil strainer nut and bolt and remove the strainer unit

from the gearbox (Fig. 6.46).
6   Detach the vacuum diaphragm and rod.
7   Unscrew and remove the primary gear cover bolts. As each is
withdrawn, note its length and position for correct location on
reassembly. The cover will probably require tapping free with a soft-
headed hammer, but do not allow the reaction flange unit to become
dislodged and drop out. The primary gear cover seal bolts (resin
coated) must be renewed once removed.
8   Withdraw the primary drive gear and the primary idler gear.
9   Referring to Fig. 6.47, engage (mesh) L or D gear and push the
park pawl into the park gear using a screwdriver, thus locking the gear
rotation. Now bend straight the main drive input gear locknut washer,
then loosen and remove the locknut. Withdraw the main drive input
gear.
10 The respective bearings of the main drive input gear, primary drive
and primary idler gear can be removed with a suitable puller, but note
that the primary drive gear bearing is retained by a circlip.
11 Loosen and remove the suction tube retaining bolt and lift the
suction tube out of the gearbox.
12 Unbolt and remove the converter housing, together with the
torque converter and oil pump unit. Note the bolt lengths and their

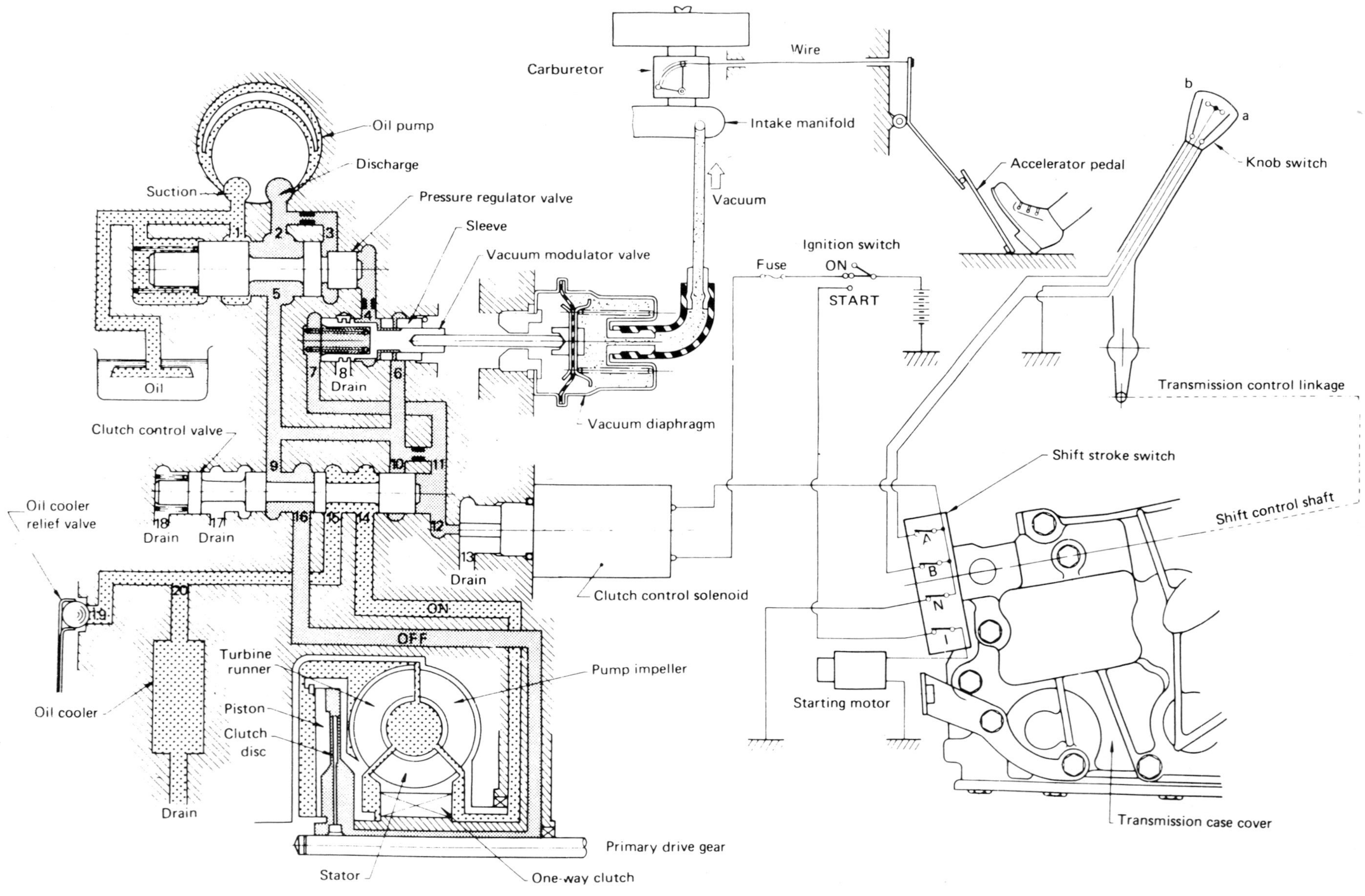

Fig. 6.42 The oil pressure circuit with N or P engaged – clutch is 'off' (disengaged) (Sec 20)

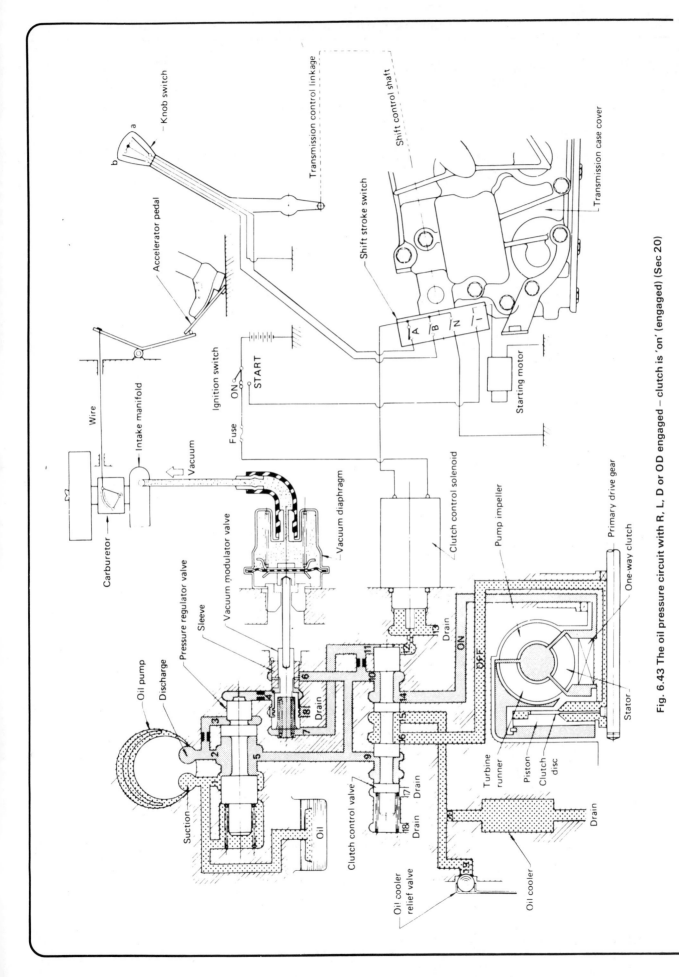

Fig. 6.43 The oil pressure circuit with R, L, D or OD engaged – clutch is 'on' (engaged) (Sec 20)

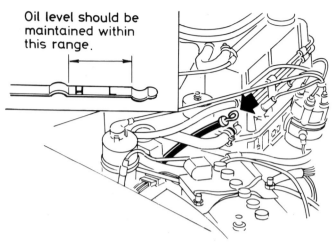

Fig. 6.44 Automatic transmission dipstick location and oil level markings (inset) (Sec 21)

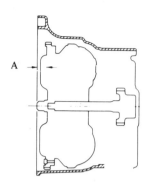

Fig. 6.45 Converter position in housing – distance A must be at least 0.75 in (19 mm) (Sec 22)

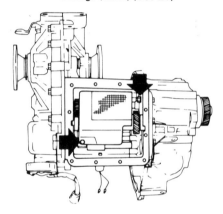

Fig. 6.46 Oil strainer in the gearbox. Securing bolts are arrowed (Sec 24)

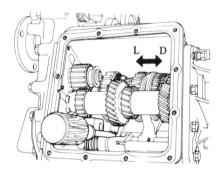

Fig. 6.47 Lock gears by meshing L or D gear and engage park pawl with its gear with a screwdriver as shown (Sec 24)

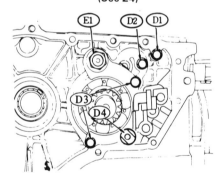

Fig. 6.48 Remove the nuts in the order given in the text (Sec 24)

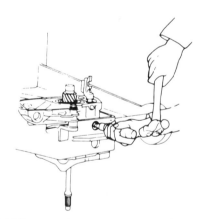

Fig. 6.49 Remove the taper thread plug (Sec 24)

positions as they are removed for correct refitting. Refer to Section 28 for separation of the torque converter and clutch unit.

Final drive unit

13 Refer to Section 4, paragraphs 8 to 11 inclusive, and carry out the operations described.

Gear assemblies

14 Refer to Fig. 6.48. Remove bolts D1 and D2 to remove the parking pawl bracket. Now loosen and remove the double nuts E1, bolts D3 and the return lever guide (D4), and withdraw the bearing retainer plate.
15 Before removing the main gear assembly, measure the main gear backlash and check that the readings are within the specified limits.
16 Remove the reverse idler gear and its shaft (noting the fitted direction of the gear).

17 Use a suitable diameter shaft and drift out the countergear shaft. If available use Datsun special tool number ST23100000 (countershaft guide). Take care not to damage or lose any of the countershaft needle roller bearings during removal as they are not of the caged type. Lift out the countergear and if the needle bearings are still in position, reinsert the shaft to retain them.
18 Unscrew and remove the detent ball plugs and then withdraw the detent springs and balls from their location apertures in the gearcase.
19 Remove the transmission taper thread plug by drifting it out using a suitable punch or drift as shown (Fig. 6.49). This allows access to the R-OD shift fork retaining pin.
20 Use a pin punch and carefully drive out the shift fork retaining pins, then withdraw the respective rods and lift out the forks. The L-D shift fork will have to be positioned in Low for its retaining pin removal. The E-ring will have to be removed before extracting the Park fork rod. The rod interlock plungers must be removed and kept in a safe place

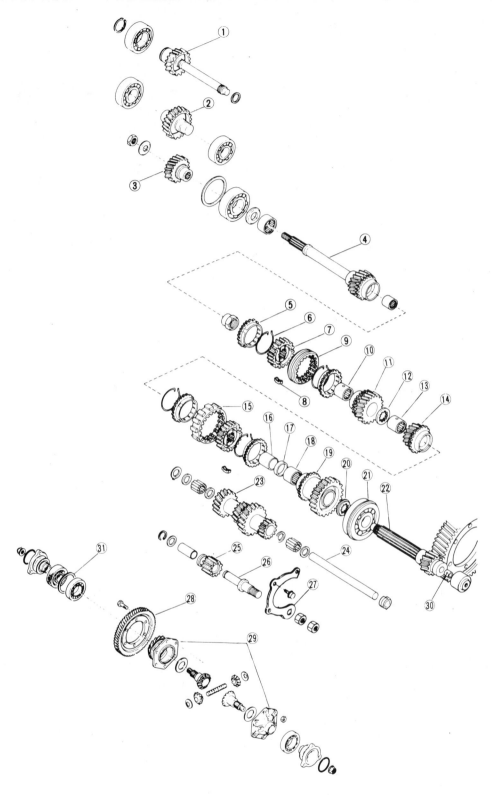

Fig. 6.50 Exploded view of the gear assembly components (Sec 24)

1 Primary drive gear	8 Shifting insert	14 OD gear	20 Mainshaft spacer	26 Reverse idler shaft
2 Primary idler gear	9 Coupling sleeve	15 Parking gear	21 Main bearing	27 Bearing retainer
3 Main drive input gear	10 Low gear bushing	16 Reverse gear bushing	22 Mainshaft	28 Final gear
4 Main drive gear	11 Low gear	17 Distance piece	23 Countergear	29 Differential case
5 Baulk ring	12 Main gear spacer	18 Needle bearing	24 Countershaft	30 Mainshaft plug
6 Spread spring	13 OD gear bushing	19 Reverse gear	25 Reverse idler gear	31 Side bearing shim
7 Synchronizer hub				

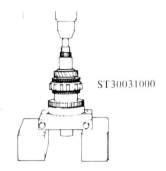

Fig. 6.51 Datsun special tool used to dismantle the mainshaft gears (Sec 24)

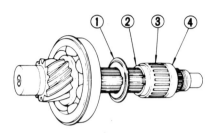

Fig. 6.52 Mainsaft spacer (1), reverse gear bush (2), needle bearing (3) and distance piece (4) (Sec 27)

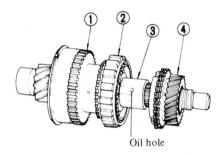

Oil hole

Fig. 6.53 Assemble reverse gear (1), parking gear (2), OD gear bush (3) and OD gear (4) (Sec 27)

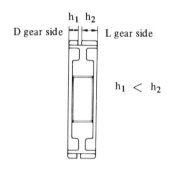

Fig. 6.54 Synchronizer fitting position (Sec 27)

together with the rods and forks.

21 The mainshaft assembly can now be removed from the gearbox, withdrawal being towards the final drive gear side.

22 Before dismantling the mainshaft gear assemblies, the gear endfloats should be checked and compared with the tolerances given in the Specifications. Where the endfloat readings are found to be excessive and/or the gears are noticeably worn, with excessive backlash or are possibly damaged, then the mainshaft should be dismantled for attention. If the gearbox has covered a high mileage then the synchro units will probably need renewing and again, the mainshaft must be dismantled in this instance for their renewal, or renewed complete.

Mainshaft dismantling

23 Place the mainshaft in a vice, but ensure that some form of padding is used so as not to damage the gears.

24 Remove the locknut from the end of the mainshaft. **The locknut is staked, so when it is removed be sure to clean the threaded portion of the mainshaft until all the metal chips are removed. The locknut should be discarded and should not be re-used.**

25 Withdraw the L-D synchronizer and low gear.

26 Support the assembly astride two blocks and then drift or press out the low gear bush, spacer, parking gear and R-OD synchronizer, reverse gear, distance piece, needle roller bearing, reverse gear bush, mainshaft spacer and bearing. If available use the special Datsun tool ST30031000 shown in Fig. 6.51.

27 The synchronizer hub assemblies can be dismantled, inspected and reassembled in the same manner prescribed for the synchro units of the manual gearbox types.

28 The main gearbox is now dismantled. Do not dismantle the torque converter, clutch or oil pump units unless really necessary. Refer to Sections 18 and 29 for details if required.

25 Automatic transmission components – inspection and checking

1 The inspection procedures are in general the same as those given in Section 9 of this Chapter, but reference should be made to the automatic transmission section of the Specifications for the respective component wear limit tolerances.

2 The torque converter, oil pump and clutch inspection procedures are given in Sections 28 and 29 respectively.

3 Renew all oil seals where applicable.

4 Clean all joint faces and check for damage or distortion.

26 Final drive and differential unit – dismantling and reassembly

This assembly is identical to that fitted to manual gearboxes. Refer to Sections 6 and 12 for dismantling and assembly details.

27 Automatic transmission – reassembly

Before reassembling the transmission, ensure that all parts are thoroughly cleaned and lubricated with automatic transmission oil before assembly. Do not use any liquid sealants between the casing mating surfaces.

Apply a non-setting gasket sealant to the threads of the bolts specified as seal bolts prior to assembly.

Always use new gaskets and oil seals.

Mainshaft reassembly

1 If a new mainshaft is being fitted, insert the mainshaft plug so that the mainshaft end is flush with it.

2 Press or drift the ball-bearing into position on the shaft.

3 Fit the mainshaft spacer with its irregular surface towards the bearing, followed by reverse gear bush, the needle bearing and distance piece (Fig. 6.52).

4 Locate reverse gear, OD-R synchronizer (with parking gear), OD gear bush and gear. The parking gear must be fitted with its even side towards reverse gear. The OD gear bush oil hole must align with the mainshaft oil hole (Fig. 6.53).

5 Fit the main gear spacer and then press or drift the low gear bush into position.

6 Now slide low gear and the L-D synchronizer into position. The L-D coupling sleeve must be located with its thick outer shouldered section towards the low gear (Fig. 6.54).

7 Support the mainshaft assembly in a soft jawed vice and then fit and tighten the new locknut to the specified torque setting. Recheck

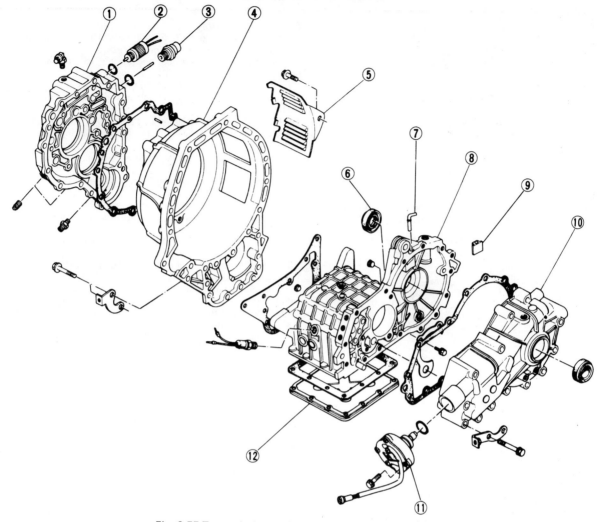

Fig. 6.55 Transmission casings and associated fittings (Sec 27)

1	Primary gear cover	4	Converter housing	7	Breather	10	Transmission case cover
2	Clutch control solenoid	5	Stone guard	8	Transmission case	11	Shift stroke switch
3	Vacuum diaphragm	6	Oil seal	9	Breather cover	12	Bottom cover

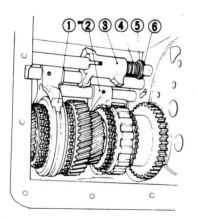

Fig. 6.56 Selector forks and rods (Sec 27)

1 L-D shift fork
2 R-OD shift fork
3 Parking actuator
4 Parking lock spring
5 Washer
6 E-ring

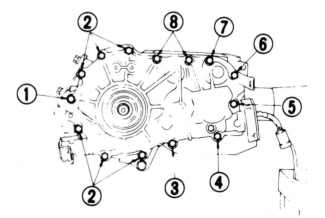

Fig. 6.57 Transmission case bolt positions and lengths. Seal bolts 4, 5, 7 and 8 (Sec 27)

1	2.76 in (70 mm)	4	3.27 in (83 mm)	7	1.38 in (35 mm)
2	1.77 in (45 mm)	5	2.36 in (60 mm)	8	1.77 in (45 mm)
3	3.27 in (83 mm)	6	1.18 in (30 mm)		

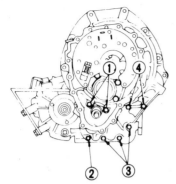

Fig. 6.58 The torque converter housing retaining bolt positions and lengths. Seal bolts 2 and 3 (Sec 27)

1	4.33 in (110 mm)	3	0.98 in (25 mm)
2	1.57 in (40 mm)	4	1.18 in (30 mm)

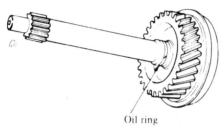

Oil ring

Fig. 6.59 Primary drive gear with oil ring in position (Sec 27)

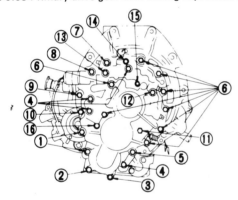

Fig. 6.60 Primary gear cover showing bolt positions and lengths. Seal bolt 2 (Sec 27)

1	7.68 in (195 mm)	10	1.77 in (45 mm)
2	7.68 in (195 mm)	11	0.98 in (25 mm)
3	2.56 in (65 mm)	12*	1.57 in (40 mm)
4	1.38 in (35 mm)	13*	1.38 in (35 mm)
5	2.36 in (60 mm)	14*	2.76 in (70 mm)
6	1.18 in (30 mm)	15	1.18 in (30 mm)
7*	2.95 in (75 mm)	16	0.98 in (25 mm)
8*	2.76 in (70 mm)		*Fit with plain washer
9*	2.56 in (65 mm)		

the gear endfloat, then stake punch its shouldered flange into the indent in the mainshaft to lock it in position.

Countergear

8 Lubricate the needle bearings with grease and insert them together with the spacers into the countergear. If a dummy countershaft is being used, slide it carefully into position (use Datsun special countershaft guide, number ST23100000, if available) to hold the bearings in position whilst fitting the countershaft.

9 Locate the thrust washers the correct way round and hold in position with grease.

Final drive and differential unit

10 Assemble the final drive and differential unit as given in Section 12.

Gearbox assembly

11 Carefully press or drift the differential side flange oil seals into position. Smear the seal lips with grease.

12 Insert the main drive gear and the mainshaft into position in the gearcase.

13 Fit the R-OD shift fork and the L-D shift fork into position and then slide the shift rod into position and secure it with a new roll pin to the R-OD fork.

14 Place the interlock plunger into position in the gearcase, then slide the L-D fork rod into position through the parking actuator and L-D shift fork.

15 Locate the park fork rod, spring washer and parking actuator, then fit the E-ring and roll pin to secure.

16 Fit the detent ball, spring and plug, the threads of which should be smeared with a locking sealer.

17 Lower the countergear assembly into position (ensuring that the thrust washers are located), then push the countershaft into position through the gear, pushing out the dummy shaft (if fitted). When in position ensure that the countershaft cutaway section aligns with the bearing retainer.

18 Insert the reverse idler shaft and engage the reverse idler gear, the bearing retainer and parking pawl bracket. The cutaway section of the reverse idler shaft must also align with the bearing retainer when fitted. Tighten the idler shaft mounting double nut to the specified torque setting, also the parking pawl bracket-to-gearcase bolts.

19 Prior to locating the differential case assembly, the side bearing height must be measured and suitable shims fitted as described in Section 13, paragraph 10.

20 Position the respective selector fork rods so that they are in neutral, then fit the transmission case cover and tighten the retaining bolts to the specified torque settings. Ensure as the cover is fitted that the shifter engages with the fork rod brackets. Any retaining seal bolts with the resin coating removed should be renewed. The respective case cover bolt positions are shown in Fig. 6.57.

21 Apply thread locking compound to the threads of the differential side flanges, then fit them and tighten the retaining nuts to the specified torque settings. Restrain the flanges from turning as given in Secion 4, paragraph 8.

Converter housing assembly

22 Position the torque converter housing onto the gearcase with its new gasket and secure with the retaining bolts. The respective bolt lengths and their positions are shown in Fig. 6.58. Renew the seal bolts.

23 Locate the torque converter into position in its housing and support it with the special holder (Datsun number KV31100600) if available. Ensure that the torque converter is able to move freely.

24 The reaction flange/oil pump unit can now be fitted, altering the torque converter position if necessary. Ensure that the seal ring is securely located around the pump housing.

25 Locate and secure the suction tube into position in the converter housing. Secure with a bolt and lockwasher to the reaction flange. Check that the O-ring is fitted correctly.

26 If removed, press or drift the primary drive bearings into position.

27 Reassemble in order the spacer, main drive input gear, the lockwasher and gear mounting nut. The nut must be tightened to the specified torque setting and secured by bending over a lockwasher tab onto a nut flat. Fit the nut with its chamfered side to the lockwasher. To prevent the main drive gear from rotating as the nut is tightened, mesh two gears simultaneously in a similar manner to that described when dismantling.

28 Refit the primary idler gear and primary drive gear (remembering to locate the oil ring as shown in Fig. 6.59).

29 Locate the reaction flange packing and refit the primary gear cover. The respective bolts and their positions when fitted are shown in Fig. 6.60. Check that the large o-ring is correctly located during assembly. Tighten bolts to the specified torque settings.

30 Refit the oil strainer.

31 Refit the bottom cover with a new gasket.

32 Relocate the speedometer pinion unit.

33 Refit the vacuum diaphragm and its rod, using a new washer.

34 Refit the clutch control solenoid with a new washer.

35 Refit the reversing lamp switch, the shift stroke switch, the oil cooler hoses, drain plug, taper plug and filler plug. Smear the plug threads with sealant.

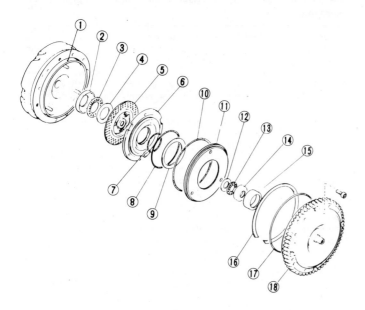

Fig. 6.61 Torque converter/clutch assembly (Sec 28)

1	Clutch cover (with torque converter)	10	Seal ring
2	Bearing case	11	Outer piston
3	Needle thrust bearing	12	Plate
4	Plate	13	Needle thrust bearing
5	Clutch disc	14	Bearing case
6	Inner piston	15	Bushing
7	O-ring	16	Snap-ring
8	O-ring	17	O-ring
9	Diaphragm spring	18	Torque converter cover

Fig. 6.62 Remove the piston (Sec 28)

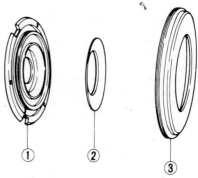

Fig. 6.63 Location and fitting direction of diaphragm spring (Sec 28)

1   Inner piston   2   Diaphragm spring   3   Outer piston

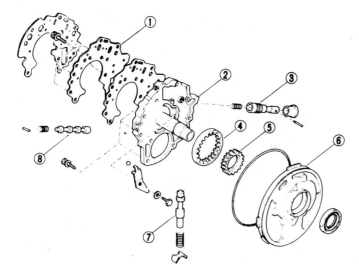

Fig. 6.64 The oil pump and reaction flange assembly components (Sec 29)

1	Separator plate	5	Inner gear
2	Reaction flange	6	Oil pump housing
3	Vacuum modulator valve	7	Pressure regulator valve
4	Outer gear	8	Clutch control valve

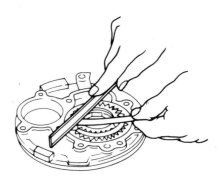

Fig. 6.65 Check the gear-to-body clearance (Sec 29)

28 Clutch and torque converter – dismantling, inspection and reassembly

Refer to Fig. 6.61 for an exploded view showing the various parts of the clutch/torque converter assembly.

1   Check the outer surfaces of the clutch and torque converter units and look for any alignment markings which may have been made. If you cannot find any, scribe or punch (lightly) two alignment marks to ensure correct repositioning on reassembly.

2   Unscrew and remove the four converter cover retaining bolts and then detach the cover, taking care not to drop the clutch hub bearing. As the cover bolts were treated with lock sealant during assembly, you will probably find them quite tight during removal.

3   Extract the snap-ring and then remove the outer and inner piston and diaphragm spring, tapping lightly free with a soft-headed hammer.

4   Withdraw the clutch disc, then remove the cover bearing with its casing and plate washer.

5   The respective components are now dismantled and can be cleaned for inspection. Do not attempt to dismantle the torque converter any further since it is of welded construction and cannot be stripped. Inspect the converter for any signs of damage, distortion or

leakage and renew if defective in any way.

6   Inspect the clutch disc and bearings and if worn, damaged or suspect in any way renew as applicable.

7   Before reassembly the torque converter oil can be renewed and this is essential if the old oil is contaminated. To do this first drain the old oil out of the converter, then wash out the converter with just under a pint (0.5 litre) of non-lead petrol or kerosene (paraffin). Blow through with air and drain out the cleaning fluid. The converter is now refilled with the same quantity (0.5 litre) of transmission fluid, air is again applied and the fluid drained. The converter is now ready for assembly.

8   Reassembly of the torque converter and clutch is a reversal of the removal procedure, but note the following:

(a) As they are assembled, coat all parts with transmission fluid

(b) Ensure that the diaphragm spring is correctly fitted as shown in Fig. 6.63

(c) Do not damage the seal rings during assembly and when the snap-ring is fitted, ensure that it is fully located

(d) The converter cover bolts must be treated with a locking sealant solution before fitting. Do not forget to align the cover/converter marks

(e) If when assembled the clutch disc appears to drag, change the converter cover bearing plate washer for a thicker one. The standard fitted plate thickness is 0.039 in (1.0 mm). The clutch disc must always be checked whenever any converter or clutch components have been renewed

(f) When the torque converter is refitted to the oil pump and reaction flange and to the primary drive gear, check that the converter can rotate freely in both directions

29 Oil pump and control valves – dismantling, inspection and reassembly

Refer to Fig. 6.64 for an exploded view of the various components

1   Unscrew and remove the reaction flange-to-oil pump retaining bolts, then separate the flange from the pump.

2   The pump inner and outer gears can now be removed, but note carefully their fitted positions as they are withdrawn as they must be refitted the correct way round during reassembly (and also during the clearance checks).

3   Clean and inspect the respective components for signs of excessive wear and/or damage.

4   Fit the gears into the pump housing and using a feeler gauge and a straight-edge (rule) as shown in Fig. 6.65, measure the gear-to-housing face clearance. Should the clearance exceed the maximum specified, renew the gears and housing. Renew the oil seal in the oil pump housing as a matter of course.

5   The respective control valves can be removed from the reaction flange, but take special care during removal and assembly as they are precision parts. Keep the respective components of each valve assembly in order of fitting when removed to avoid confusion when reassembling. The valves are removed as follows:

(a) To remove the clutch control valve (refer to Fig. 6.66), remove the stopper and then extract the spring and valve

(b) The pressure regulator valve and spring can be extracted on removal of the retainer

(c) To remove the vacuum modulator valve, carefully drift out the retaining pin using a suitable punch, then extract the sleeve,

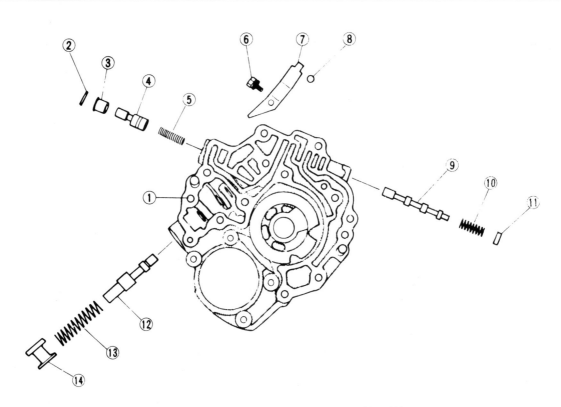

Fig. 6.66 The pump valves and their locations (Sec 29)

1 Reaction flange	5 Spring	9 Clutch control valve	12 Pressure regulator
2 Retaining pin	6 Bolt	10 Spring	valve
3 Sleeve	7 Leaf spring	11 Stopper	13 Spring
4 Vacuum modulator valve	8 Steel ball		14 Retainer

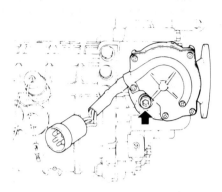

Fig. 6.67 Remove bolt (arrowed) securing shift control switch (Sec 30)

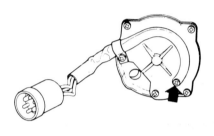

Fig. 6.68 Remove screw (arrowed) and insert locking pin (Sec 30)

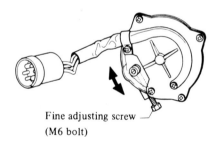

Fine adjusting screw
(M6 bolt)

Fig. 6.69 Shift control switch adjustment (Sec 30)

**Distance A: 22 mm (0.87 in)
(when energized)**

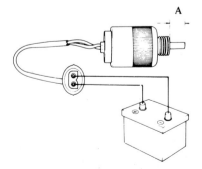

Fig. 6.70 Clutch control solenoid check (Sec 31)

A = 22 mm (0.87 in) (solenoid energized)

the vacuum modulator valve and its spring
(d) The oil cooler relief valve leaf spring is secured by a bolt which when removed allows the spring and steel ball to be withdrawn

6   Clean and inspect the respective components for signs of excessive wear, burning, distortion and damage. If the separate plate or its packings are scored or damaged in any way. renew them. Similarly check the valve ports and renew the reaction flange if scored or damaged. If the valve springs appear weak or distorted, renew them. Check their free lengths against the specified figures.
7   Reassemble the respective valve assemblies into their housings in the reaction flange, having dipped them in clean automatic transmission fluid. Refit in the reverse sequence to removal.
8   Insert the oil pump gears into position in the pump housing. Refit the reaction flange to the pump housing and tighten the retaining bolts to the specified torque.

30 Shift stroke switch – removal and refitting

1   Disconnect the battery earth lead. Set the gear selector to N.
2   The shift stroke switch is located on the side of the transmission casing. Unplug the switch connector and remove the bolt securing the switch (Fig. 6.67), then remove the switch.
3   When refitting the switch, first make sure the gear selector is still at N. Remove the screw (arrowed, Fig. 6.68) and insert a 3 mm (0.12 in) diameter rod to lock the switch rotor.
4   Lubricate the switch O-ring with automatic transmission fluid, then offer the switch to the transmission. Make sure that the cut-out portion of the control shaft engages with the switch pawl. Adjust if necessary using the 6 mm bolt on the side of the switch casing.
5   When adjustment is correct, tighten the mount bolt, remove the alignment rod and insert the screw.
6   Remake the electrical connections and reconnect the battery earth lead.

31 Automatic transmission – fault diagnosis checks

Given below are some of the checks which can be made should problems occur in the automatic transmission. If the checks given do not give a positive indication of the cause of the problem, consult your Datsun dealer who will be able to give further checks to diagnose the trouble and its cause.

Before attempting any checks, first check the transmission oil level to ensure that it is correct. If the oil level is correct, check the engine idle speed which must also be correct.

In checks B and C you will require the use of a circuit tester.

A – clutch control solenoid check
1   Drain the transmission oil, then disconnect the clutch control solenoid wires at the connector end and unscrew and remove the solenoid unit from the transmission.
2   Referring to Fig. 6.70, connect the solenoid wires as shown to a twelve volt battery and note if the pushrod is actuated when the unit is energized. When disconnected it should be possible to press the rod in and return it using finger pressure; if not, renew the unit.
3   Refit the solenoid, connect up the wires and top up the transmission oil as given in Section 21 to complete this check.

B – Shift stroke switch check
4   Detach the connector from the switch and using a circuit tester, test for continuity between the connector terminals whilst moving the shift lever. The circuits and their operational checks are shown in Fig. 6.71 and the accompanying table.
5   If a circuit defect is proved, renew the switch.

C – Hand lever knob switch
6   Detach and remove the central console for access to the switch connector. Detach the connector and then using a circuit tester, check the circuit continuity of the switch in each of its movement positions. Refer to Fig. 6.72 for details.

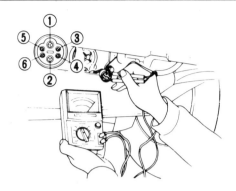

Fig. 6.71 Shift control switch circuit check (Sec 31)

	N	P	R	L	D	OD
1 to 2 (Inhibitor switch)	ON	ON	OFF	OFF	OFF	OFF
3 to 4 (Neutral switch)	ON	ON	OFF	OFF	OFF	OFF
3 to 5 (Shift stroke switch A)	ON	ON	*OFF	*OFF	ON	ON
3 to 6 (Shift stroke switch B)	ON	ON	ON	ON	OFF	OFF
Clutch	OFF	ON	ON	ON	OFF	OFF

* or normally ON if switch is OFF when pushed in direction of overstroke

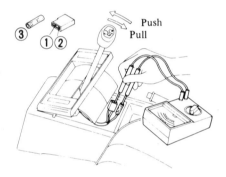

Fig. 6.72 Checking the knob switch with meter connection
(Sec 31)

	Switch pushed	Switch released	Switch pulled
1 to 3 (Knob switch (a)	ON	OFF	OFF
2 to 3 (Knob switch (b)	OFF	OFF	ON

D – Stall test

7   To carry out this test you will need a tachometer (rpm indicator) which should be connected to the engine so that it can be seen from the driver's seat. Before making the test, check that the engine transmission oil levels are up to the specified marks.

8   Select 'P' and then start and run the engine at 1200 rpm for about ten minutes to warm up the torque converter oil. Position wheel chocks to the front and rear wheels and ensure that the handbrake is fully applied. Do not carry out this test in a confined space!

9   With the footbrake fully applied, move the shift lever to the 'D' position and then gradually depress the accelerator pedal until it bottoms. When the engine speed levels off, note the speed (rpm) and release the accelerator pedal immediately.
This test must be completed within five seconds or the oil will overheat and the clutch disc could suffer as a result.

10   As soon as the test is completed, select 'N' and let the engine run for a few minutes at 1200 rpm to allow for cooling off. This is particularly important if a further test is to be made.

11   If the stall speed was found to be higher than specified, the clutch is faulty and is slipping. To inspect and renew this unit the transmission must be removed from the vehicle and the torque converter/clutch unit separated as given in Section 28.

12   If the stall rpm noted was within the specified limit the engine and

torque converter are both operating normally. To check the one-way clutch of the torque converter in this instance, a road test is required as described later.

13   If the stall rpm was lower than the specified figure, the engine or torque converter one-way clutch is at fault, in which case carry out a road test as follows to confirm it.

14   Select 'D' and accelerate the car. If acceleration is poor up to 30 mph (50 kph) but is normal in the higher speed ranges, the torque converter one-way clutch is slipping.

15   If the car speed is limited to 50 mph (80 kph), the torque converter one-way clutch has seized, and this being the case the oil temperature will rise above normal.

16   If either of the above faults is evident, the torque converter one-way clutch must be removed and attended to without delay, or further damage could result caused by overheating oil.

17   If the road test performance is not satisfactory at any speed, then the engine is probably at fault and should be checked together with the carburettor and ignition settings.

18   If the upward gear changes are not very smooth or the gearshift movement feels abnormal, a line pressure check should be made. This check is best entrusted to your Datsun dealer since it requires the use of specialised equipment.

32 Fault diagnosis – automatic transmission

Symptom	Reason(s)
Engine starter fails to operate with selector in 'N' or 'P' position	Faulty starter motor Ignition switch or battery terminals loose Starter inhibitor switch faulty Battery needs recharging Faulty shift stroke switch or wiring
No drive in any shift position	Faulty shift stroke switch or wiring Transmission oil level low Transmission oil pressure incorrect – check pressure circuit
Clutch slip	Transmission oil level low Transmission oil pressure low or too high (lubrication circuit fault) Faulty or worn clutch unit
Gear shifting difficult – vehicle stationary	Transmission oil level low Shift control linkage faulty Faulty clutch control solenoid Synchronizers/gears/bearings worn or damaged Faulty shift stroke switch/wiring Fault in oil circuit valves – incorrect oil pressure
Gears shifting difficult – vehicle moving	Faulty synchronizers Excessive gear endfloat Transmission bearings defective Selector mechanism faulty
Transmission slips out of gear	Remote control linkage fault Worn/defective synchronizer Mainshaft worn/defective Transmission bearing worn/defective Defective check spring Defective engine mountings
Unsmooth shift control	Accelerator pedal depressed when shifting Incorrect engine idle speed Faulty diaphragm or hoses/connections Transmission oil pressure incorrect Faulty clutch
Engine races when driving	Hand resting on shift knob Incorrect transmission oil level Faulty shift stroke switch or wiring/connections Faulty shift knob switch or wiring/connections
Poor acceleration	Clutch slip – carry out stall rpm test

Chapter 7 Driveshafts

For modifications, and information applicable to later models, see Supplement at end of manual

Contents

Specifications

Driveshaft
Inner joint type .... Double offset joint
Outer joint type .... Birfield joint

Maximum swivel movement
Double offset joint .... 20°
Birfield joint .... 42°

Torque wrench settings

	lbf ft	kgf m
Driveshaft attaching bolts	29 to 36	4 to 5
Front hub nut:		
UK models	58 to 116	8 to 16
USA models	87 to 145	12 to 20

1 General description

1   Power is transmitted to the front wheels by two driveshafts which are carried by knuckle arms attached to the lower ends of the struts. Each driveshaft is supported on two ball-bearings mounted back-to-back, and is splined to the wheel hub.

2   Constant velocity (CV) joints are incorporated at each end of the driveshafts. The joint at the wheel end of the shaft provides a forty-two degree swivel movement, while the double offset type of joint at the other end of the shaft allows for a movement of twenty degrees.

3   The outer universal joints are of the Birfield constant velocity type. The driveshaft fits inside the circular outer CV joint which is also the driven shaft. Drive is transmitted from the driveshaft to the driven shaft by six steel balls which are located in curved grooves machined in line with the axis of the shaft on the inside of the driven shaft and on the outside of the driveshaft. This allows the driven shaft to hinge freely on the driveshaft, but at the same time keeps them together. Enclosing the CV joint is a rubber boot.

4   In most instances the driveshaft removal and overhaul procedures can be achieved using normal workshop tools, but it may be found necessary to use Datsun special tool number ST35100000 to remove the driveshaft. Failing this a slide hammer will suffice.

2 Routine maintenance

1   At intervals of 6000 miles (10 000 km), inspect the rubber boots (photo) which protect the constant velocity joints. If they are torn, split or show signs of deterioration they should be renewed as soon as possible. When the boot splits the CV joint becomes contaminated by water, road dust and grit, which soon results in rapid failure of the bearings in the joint.

2   Wear in the joints is detected by a regular knocking when the front wheels are turned on full lock. In very severe cases it is only necessary to turn the wheels slightly for the noise to begin.

3   The CV joints are lubricated and sealed during assembly and therefore require no further lubrication once in service.

3 Driveshaft – removal

1   Remove the wheel trim from the wheel from which the driveshaft is to be removed.

2   Loosen the front roadwheel securing nuts and jack up the car on the same side.

3   As it will be necessary to work underneath the car, supplement the

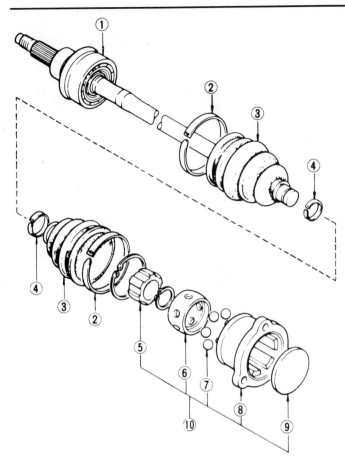

Fig. 7.1 Exploded view of the driveshaft assembly (Sec 1)

1 Outside joint assembly (Birfield joint)	6 Cage
	7 Balls
2 Bands	8 Outer ring
3 Dust covers	9 Plug
4 Bands	10 Inside joint assembly (Double offset joint)
5 Inner ring	

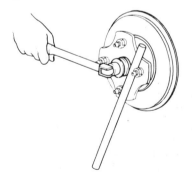

Fig. 7.2 Wheel hub nut removal method, using bar to prevent hub from turning (Sec 3)

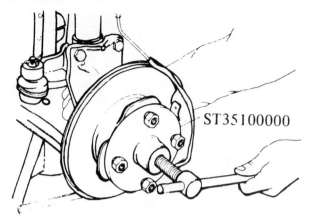

Fig. 7.3 Driveshaft removal using Datsun special tool number ST35100000 (Sec 3)

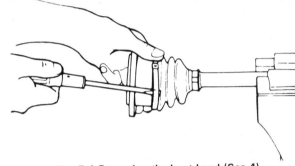

Fig. 7.4 Removing the boot band (Sec 4)

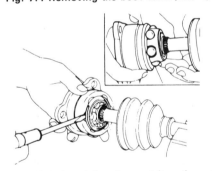

Fig. 7.5 Prising off the retaining ring and (inset) separating joint (Sec 4)

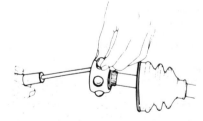

Fig. 7.6 Taking out the ballbearings (Sec 4)

jack with a stand or support blocks. This will minimise the danger should the jack collapse.

4   Remove the roadwheel.

5   Remove the bolts which secure the driveshaft to the final drive assembly, then use the subframe to support the detached driveshaft (photo).

6   Prise free the split pin from the hub nut and then unscrew and remove the hub nut. Engage a suitable bar diagonally across two wheel studs to prevent the hub from turning (Fig. 7.2). The nut is very tight – make sure the car is securely supported.

7   It will now be possible to partially free the end of the driveshaft

from the centre of the hub. With a soft drift and hammer tap the end of the shaft until it is seen to move inwards slightly. Sometimes the shaft can be completely removed this way but great care must be taken or the splines, bearings or oil seals will be damaged. If the resistance to the initial taps is significant it is better to obtain a special tool from your Datsun agent (ST35100000) – see Fig. 7.3.

8   Place the special removal tool ST35100000 on the hub and secure it with the wheel nuts. The driveshaft can now be removed by screwing in the removal tool, but take care not to damage the oil seals.

9   Inspect the driveshaft for distortion, corrosion or cracks. Renew if necessary.

2.1 Check the CV joint protective rubber boots for deterioration and damage (outer joint shown)

3.5 Detaching the driveshaft-to-final drive connection

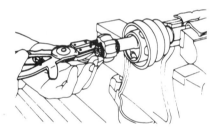

Fig. 7.7 Remove the inner ring circlip using circlip pliers (Sec 4)

4 Constant velocity joint (inner) – dismantling

1   The double offset type of constant velocity joint used at the final drive end of the driveshaft can be dismantled if defective parts are to be renewed. The driveshaft must be removed as given in the previous Section.
2   Place the driveshaft in a vice equipped with soft jaws. Expand and remove the band which secures the rubber boot, and remove the boot from the joint.
3   Use a screwdriver to prise off the retaining ring and withdraw the flanged outer ring of the joint. You will also need to remove the sealing plate from the other end of the joint.
4   Wipe the grease from the ball cage and take out the ball-bearings. Rotate the cage by approximately half a turn, and detach it from the inner ring.
5   Take off the retaining circlip, using a pair of circlip pliers, and withdraw the inner ring of the joint by lightly tapping it with a soft-faced mallet.
6   Finally, withdraw the flanged outer ring and the rubber boot.

5 Constant velocity joint (inner) – inspection and reassembly

1   Thoroughly clean all the component parts of the joint by washing in paraffin.
2   Examine each ball in turn for cracks, flat spots, or signs of surface pitting.
3   The cage which fits between the inner and outer races must be examined for wear in the ball cage windows and for cracks which are especially likely to develop across the narrower portions between the outer rims and the holes for the balls.
4   Wear is most likely to be found in the ball tracks on the inner and outer races. If the tracks have widened the balls will no longer be a

Fig. 7.8 Boot retaining band tightening method (Sec 5)

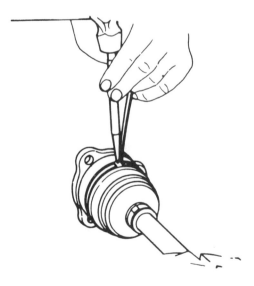

Fig. 7.9 Lock the retaining band with a punch to secure (Sec 5)

tight fit and, together with excessive wear in the ball cage windows, will lead to the characteristic 'knocking' on full lock described previously.

5   If wear is excessive then all the parts must be renewed as a matched set.

6   Examine the rubber boot and renew if there is evidence of splits, wear or deformation. It is sound policy to renew it anyway since it could save another strip later on.

7   Reassembly is a reversal of the dismantling procedure. Lubricate the assembly with a molybdenum disulphide grease, taking care not to allow any dirt to remain on the components. Ensure that the circlip is fully engaged before packing the unit with grease and locating the seal plate.

8   Take care not to damage the rubber dust boot when fitting it and its retaining clips (bands). Use a screwdriver and pliers to fit the bands as shown (Fig. 7.8). The bands must be encircled round the cover twice, bent over and centre-punched to secure (Fig. 7.9).

6   Constant velocity joint (outer) – removal and refitting

1   If the Birfield joint assembly shows any signs of rust or excessive play the joint should be renewed.

2   Remove the driveshaft as described in Section 3.

3   The next task is to remove the joint from the driveshaft. First remove the boot by expanding the clips and then easing it back from the joint. Remove the joint by tapping the outer edge of the CV joint with a hide or plastic-headed hammer. The CV joint is held to the shaft by an internal circular section circlip and tapping the joint in the manner described forces the circlip to contract into a groove, so

allowing the joint to slide off. Remove the boot.

4   When reassembling, it is as well to fit a new boot, since it might well save a major operation later on. Slide the boot over the shaft and do not secure at this stage. Obtain a new CV joint and ensure that it is packed with the correct molybdenum disulphide compound grease.

5   Fit the CV joint onto the shaft the correct way round and with the joint pressing against the circlip. Contract the circlip right into its groove in the shaft with the aid of two screwdrivers, so the inner race of the CV joint will slide over. It may be necessary to tap the outside end of the joint smartly with a soft-faced hammer in order to close the circlip completely. Tap the joint until it is fully home with the inner race resting against the large retaining clip. The circular section circlip should now have expanded inside the joint.

6   Secure the rubber boot, and refit the driveshaft to the car, as described in Section 7.

7   Driveshaft – refitting

1   Refitting the driveshaft is a reversal of the removal procedure.

2   When installing the driveshafts make sure that the lips of the oil seals are lubricated with multi-purpose grease and are not damaged on installation. The driveshaft can be tapped into position with a hammer until the threads are sufficiently exposed, but the flange of the shaft should be protected with a soft pad so that the seal plate does not suffer damage.

3   When fitting the driveshaft attaching bolts ensure that the nuts are to the driveshaft side. Use new self-locking nuts.

4   Tighten the wheel hub nut and the driveshaft attaching bolts to their specified torque settings.

Chapter 8 Steering, wheels and tyres

For modifications, and information applicable to later models, see Supplement at end of manual

Contents

Specifications

General

System type	Rack-and-pinion, manual or power steering system
Steering gear model:	
Manual steering	RP 15L
Power steering	IPRP 15L

Steering gear details

	RP 15L	IPRP 15L
Steering gear ratio	17.7	15.9
Steering wheel turns - lock to lock	3.4	3.0
Steering wheel axial play	0	0
Steering wheel play at rim	0.79 to 1.18 in (20 to 30 mm)	
Pinion axial play (maximum)	0 to 0.012 in (0 to 0.3 mm)	–
Pinion gear rotating torque (max)	17 lbf in (20 kgf cm)	13 lbf in (15 kgf cm)
Tie-rod length	5.24 in (133 mm)	5.33 in (135.5 mm)
Rack stroke (from neutral position)	2.68 in (68 mm)	2.58 in (65.5 mm)
Steering wheel turning force - maximum (power steering) (at wheel circumference)	5.5 lb (2.5 kg)	
Power steering fluid capacity	1.5 Imp pint (1.75 US pints) (0.8 litre)	
Power steering rack starting force	40 lb (18 kg)	
Balljoint (outside) swing torque	13 to 61 lbf in (15 to 70 kgf cm)*	
Balljoint (inside) swing torque	4.3 to 13 lbf in (5 to 15 kgf cm)*	

* Manual and power steering models

Steering geometry

Refer to Chapter 11 Specifications

Wheels and tyres

Wheel size:	
Steel	4½J13
Aluminium	5J13
Tyre pressures (cold) front and rear:	
Speeds below 60 mph (100 kph)	24 lbf/in² (1.7 kgf/cm²)
Speeds above 60 mph (100 kph)	28 lbf/in² (2.0 kgf/cm²)

Torque wrench settings
Steering wheel and column components

	lbf ft	kgf m
Steering wheel nut	22 to 25	3.0 to 3.5
Steering column clamp bolt	6.5 to 10.1	0.9 to 1.4
Steering column bracket bolt	6.5 to 10.1	0.9 to 1.4
Lower steering column joint	17 to 22	2.4 to 3.0
Lower joint-to-steering gear	17 to 22	2.4 to 3.0

	lbf ft	kgf m
Manual steering gear and linkage component fixings		
Tie-rod-to-knuckle arm	40 to 47	5.5 to 6.5
Tie-rod outer socket locknut	27 to 34	3.8 to 4.7
Tie-rod inner socket locknut	58 to 72	8 to 10
Gear housing clamp	16 to 25	2.2 to 3.4
Retainer locknut	29 to 43	4 to 6
Power steering gear and linkage component fixings		
Tie-rod-to-knuckle arm	40 to 47	5.5 to 6.5
Tie-rod outer socket locknut	27 to 34	3.8 to 4.7
Tie-rod inner socket locknut	58 to 72	8 to 10
Gear housing clamp	16 to 25	2.2 to 3.4
Gear housing retaining bolt	16 to 25	2.2 to 3.4
Retainer locknut	29 to 43	4 to 6
Housing plug	36 to 51	5 to 7
Cylinder locknut	43 to 58	6 to 8
Cylinder retaining bolt	16 to 22	2.2 to 3.0
End cover locknut	43 to 58	6 to 8
Cylinder tube flare nut	14 to 22	2 to 3
Self locking nut (pinion)	14 to 19	2 to 2.6
Pump mounting bolt	14 to 19	2 to 2.6
Pump pulley locknut	31 to 46	4.3 to 6.3
High pressure hose-to-pump	22 to 36	3 to 5
High pressure hose-to-gear	14 to 22	2 to 3
Low pressure hose-to-gear	14 to 22	2 to 3
Wheels		
Wheel nuts (steel and aluminium wheels)	58 to 72	8 to 10

1 General description

The steering system comprises the steering wheel, column with flexible joint and lower column-to-pinion assembly. The steering gear itself is of the rack-and-pinion type, the rack being connected to the steering tie-rods, the balljoints of which connect to the steering knuckle on each side.

On some later models power steering is fitted and this is also of the rack-and-pinion type, with the hydraulic piston assembly integral with the rack and pinion unit, the hydraulic fluid of the system being pressurized by a belt-driven pump.

2 Steering wheel – removal and refitting

1 Disconnect the battery earth (ground) lead.
2 Pull free the central horn pad. On some models it will be necessary to unscrew the two setscrews on the underside of the steering wheel to release the pad.
3 Carefully remove the pad return spring using a screwdriver. Do not distort the spring.
4 Remove the steering wheel nut and then remove the steering wheel by striking it with the heel of your hand. Do not use a hammer; if it is difficult to remove, a puller should be used, located in the threaded holes provided on the steering wheel.
5 Refitting is the reverse of the removal procedure. Tighten the steering wheel nut to the specified torque.
6 When the wheel and horn pad are fully fitted, rotate the wheel in each direction to ensure that it does not drag or have any tight spots in its movement. Ensure that the horn operates in a satisfactory manner.

3 Steering column – removal and refitting

1 Referring to the previous Section, remove the steering wheel.
2 Remove the steering column cover retaining screws and detach the covers (photo).
3 Remove the two screws attaching the multi-switch assembly to the steering column and remove the switch.
4 Support the steering column at the top and remove the bolts securing the upper and lower steering column clamps.
5 Remove the screws securing the column hole cover assembly to the bulkhead.
6 Unscrew and remove the lower column universal joint-to-pinion gear shaft clamp bolt (photo).
7 The steering column assembly can now be withdrawn through the interior of the car.

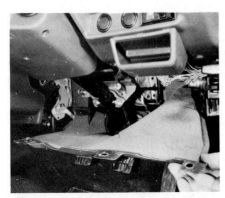
3.2 Removing the column lower cover

3.6 Remove the lower column-to-pinion shaft bolt (arrowed) (manual steering shown)

3.8 Lower clamp retaining bolts

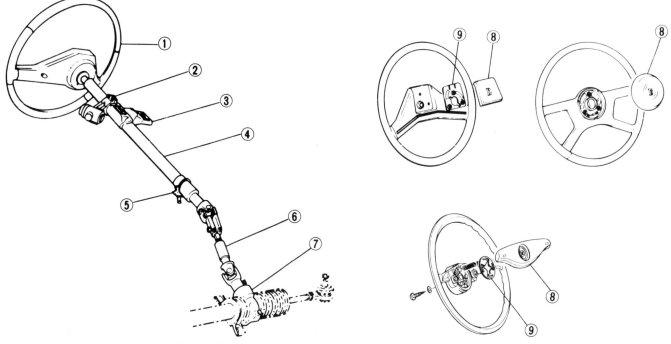

Fig. 8.1 Manual steering – wheel and column components (Sec 2)

1	Steering wheel	4	Steering column assembly	7	Pinion gear housing
2	Steering lock	5	Lower bracket	8	Horn pad
3	Column clamp	6	Lower joint	9	Return spring

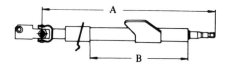

Fig. 8.2 Check the collapsible column dimensions (Sec 4)

Manual steering:
A = 24.04 to 24.16 in (610.7 to 613.7 mm)
B = 16.56 to 16.27 in (420.5 to 423.5 mm)
Power steering:
A = 24.48 to 24.60 in (621.9 to 624.9 mm)
B = 15.06 to 15.18 in (382.5 to 385.5 mm)

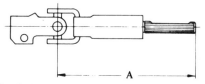

Fig. 8.3 Check the lower column joint length at points shown (Sec 4)

A = 5.77 to 5.85 in (146.5 to 148.5 mm)

8   Refitting is the reverse of the removal procedure, but note the following points:

(a) Set the roadwheels in the straight-ahead position
(b) Tighten the lower clamp first (photo), then the upper clamp bolts and the column hole cover screws in that order. Make sure that the seal of the column hole cover is not twisted or turned over and that the lip makes correct contact with the lower joint shaft
(c) Refit the steering wheel as described in Section 2

---

4   Steering column – dismantling, inspection and reassembly

1   Before dismantling the component parts of the steering column unit, refer to Fig. 8.2 and 8.3 and check the column dimensions as shown. If the vehicle has been involved in a front end collision and the dimensions measured are not as specified then the column unit complete must be renewed.
2   Remove the circlip and washer from the top of the column and then extract the shaft assembly from the column tube.
3   Clean and inspect the respective components.
4   Check the column bearings for wear or damage; if necessary renew them and lubricate them with multi-purpose grease.
5   Inspect the column shaft and casing for evidence of distortion, corrosion or cracks.
6   Inspect the universal joints for excessive play or damage and renew as necessary.
7   To remove the ignition switch/steering lock unit, refer to Section 5.

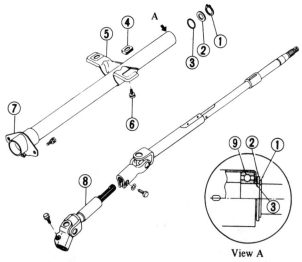

View A

Fig. 8.4 Steering column components (Sec 4)

1	Circlip	4	Coating plate	7	Lower bracket
2	Washer	5	Column clamp	8	Lower joint
3	O-ring	6	Bolt	9	Bearing

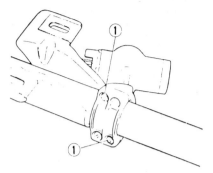

Fig. 8.5 Steering lock retaining screws (1) (shear type) (Sec 5)

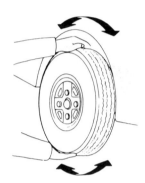

Fig. 8.6 Wheel bearing check method (Sec 6)

8   Reassembly is a reversal of the removal procedure. The lower joint-to-steering column retaining bolts must be hand tightened initially until the unit is refitted, when they must be tightened to the specified torque. When refitting the spring clamp, ensure that its claw faces upwards.

5   Steering lock/ignition switch – removal and refitting

1   Disconnect the battery earth (ground) cable.
2   Remove the screws retaining the upper steering column cover and withdraw the cover.

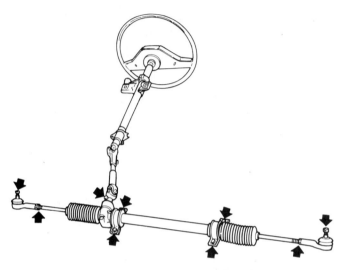

Fig. 8.7 Check steering gear components indicated for security and signs of wear (Sec 6)

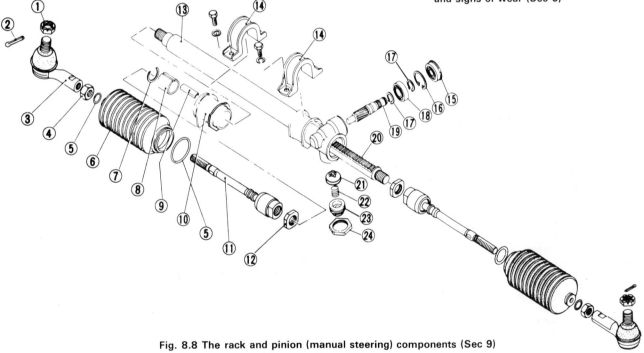

Fig. 8.8 The rack and pinion (manual steering) components (Sec 9)

1 Nut	9 Plate	15 Oil seal	19 Steering gear pinion
2 Split pin	10 Steering gear mounting	16 Pinion bearing outer circlip	20 Steering rack gear
3 Tie-rod outer socket assembly	11 Tie-rod inner socket assembly	17 Pinion bearing inner circlip	21 Steering gear retainer
4 Nut	12 Locknut	18 Steering pinion bearing	22 Retainer spring
5 Boot clamp	13 Steering gear housing assembly		23 Retainer adjusting screw
6 Steering gear boot	14 Mounting clamp		24 Locknut
7 Circlip			
8 Steering rack bushing			

3   Drill out the shear head screws from the unit clamp (Fig. 8.5).
4   Remove the clamp screws, detach the unit wires and withdraw the unit.
5   To refit the unit, align the steering lock hole of the column tube with its mating section of the steering lock unit.
6   Insert the shear head screws. Check the lock for correct operation, then tighten to shear off the heads.
7   The remainder of the reassembly procedure is a reversal of the removal process.

6   Steering components – inspection for wear

1   Wear in the steering gear and linkage is indicated when there is considerable movement in the steering wheel without corresponding movement at the roadwheels. Wear is also indicated when the vehicle tends to wander off the line one is trying to steer. There are three main steering groups to examine in such circumstances. These are the wheel bearings, the linkage joints and bushes, and the steering gear itself.
2   First jack up the front of the vehicle and support it on stands under the side frame members so that both wheels are clear of the ground.
3   Grip the top and bottom of the wheel and try to rock it. It will not take any great effort to be able to feel any play in the wheel bearing. If this play is very noticeable it would be as well to adjust it straight away as it could confuse further examinations. It is also possible that during this check play may be found in the transverse link balljoint which must be rectified accordingly. Refer to Chapter 11 for details of both procedures.
4   Next grip each side of the wheel and try rocking it laterally. Steady pressure will, of course, turn the steering but an alternated back and forth pressure will reveal any loose joint. If some play is felt it would be easier to get assistance from someone so that while one person rocks the wheel from side to side, the other can look at the joints and bushes on the track rods and connections.
5   On the steering gear itself, check the column universal joints for wear and the column mountings for security.
6   Check the steering rack mountings for security and the rubber boots for signs of leaks.
7   If all the above items are in order, check the steering rack and pinion for wear by agitating the steering wheel and looking for excessive 'lost movement' between the column shaft action and that of the steering rods.
8   On power steering equipped models, check for signs of leaks from the system hoses and connections.
9   If after the above inspections are carried out no apparent defects exist in the steering components and connections but the steering is unsatisfactory, a check should be made on the steering geometry as discussed in Section 17.

7   Steering tie-rod outer balljoint – removal and refitting

1   The removal of the balljoints is necessary if they are to be renewed, or if the rubber boots on the steering gear are being renewed.
2   It is not necessary to jack up the car, but the increase in height above ground level may make it more convenient to do so.
3   Slacken the joint nut after removing the split pin; completely remove it to clear the threads, and refit it after oiling them until the head of the nut is level with the end of the stud. This will protect the threads in subsequent operations if the same joint is being refitted.
4   If a claw clamp is being used to break the taper of the joint pin from the steering arm, the joint may be disconnected without further ado (photo).
5   If no clamp claw is available and it is necessary to strike the pin out, it is essential to provide a really firm support under the steering arm first. A firm tap with a normal weight hammer is all that is then necessary to move the pin out of the steering arm. Another way is to strike one side of the arm whilst holding the head of another hammer against the opposite side. This tends to 'jump' the taper pin out.
6   If the nut turns the pin when trying to remove it (despite the precaution taken in paragraph 3) jam the pin back into the arm with a jack to hold it whilst the nut is removed. If difficulty is experienced with a joint being renewed then cut it off.

7   Once the balljoint is clear, slacken the locknut on the rod but leave it at its original position. The joint may then be removed and a new one fitted by screwing it up as far as the locknut, keeping the track setting at its correct adjustment position. The pin should point upwards and then be fitted into the steering arm.
8   Refit the castellated locknut and secure with a split pin. See Specifications for the correct torque. Tighten the locknut on the tie-rod.
9   It is advisable to have the front wheel alignment checked as soon as possible to ensure that the setting is correct.

8   Rack-and-pinion unit (manual steering) – removal and refitting

1   Jack up the front of the car, chock the rear wheels and support the front end on axle stands or wooden blocks.
2   Remove the front wheels.
3   Remove the split pins and castellated nuts from the ends of each tie-rod balljoint. Separate the tie-rods from the steering arms as described in Section 7.
4   From inside the car, remove the lower steering column cover and then loosen off the steering column-to-lower joint clamp bolt.
5   Remove the bolt securing the bottom universal joint assembly to the steering gear pinion (photo 3.6).
6   Remove the bolts that secure the steering gear clamps to the subframe (photo) and pull the steering gear assembly out to the side.
7   Before refitting the steering gear make sure that the wheels are in the straight-ahead position, also that the rack is in the middle of its travel. This can be done by ensuring that the distance between the ends of the tie-rods and the steering gear housing on both sides is the same.
8   Position the steering gear in its location on the subframe and at the same time mate the splines on the pinion with the splines of the lower universal joint of the steering column.
9   Make sure that the subframe bracket is aligned with the mount on the side of the steering gear housing by turning and/or moving the mounting as necessary.
10 Fit and tighten the securing clamps and bolts. The black clamp fits to the pinion side and the white clamp on the steering gear mount (rubber) side.
11 Check wheel alignment and steering action on completion.

9   Rack-and-pinion unit (manual steering) – dismantling and inspection

Dismantling
1   Clean the outside of the steering gear housing and tie-rods with a grease solvent and wipe dry.
2   Clamp the rack-and-pinion assembly in a vice, taking care not to damage the housing.
3   Remove the boot clamps from the steering gear boots (Fig. 8.8).
4   Loosen the tie-rod locknuts and inner socket assemblies.
5   Unscrew and remove the tie-rods. Do not dismantle the inner socket assemblies.
6   Loosen the adjusting screw locknut and remove the retainer adjusting screw, then take out the retainer spring and steering gear retainer.
7   Remove the pinion oil seal from its housing.
8   Using circlip pliers, remove the circlip from the pinion housing and withdraw the pinion.
9   Pull the rack out of the gear housing.
10 Remove the circlip securing the pinion bearing and press the bearing off the pinion shaft.
11 Remove the circlip retaining the rack bushing in the steering gear housing and take out the rack bushing.

Inspection
12 Clean all parts in paraffin, thoroughly, and then either let dry naturally or, if available, use compressed air. Check each part for evidence of deterioration, (ie burrs, cracks, chipped rack or pinion). If damaged, the rack-and-pinion must be replaced as a matching pair.
13 Check the tie-rod inner and outer balljoints for excess axial play. Use an ordinary spring balance to check the torque necessary to move the balljoints axially. Limits are detailed in the Specifications.

7.4 Using a clamp claw balljoint separator to detach the tie-rod end from the steering arm

8.6 Remove the steering clamp bolts on each side

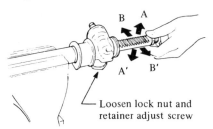

Loosen lock nut and retainer adjust screw

Fig. 8.9 Check the pinion housing bush (Sec 9)

A to A' wear limit = 0.028 in (0.7 mm)
B to B' wear limit = 0.020 in (0.5 mm)

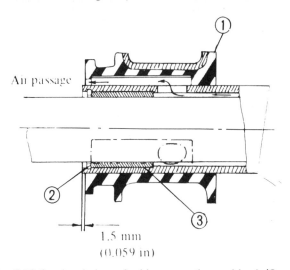

Fig. 8.10 Sectional view of rubber mounting and bush (Sec 10)

1 Steering gear mounting   2 Circlip   3 Rack bush

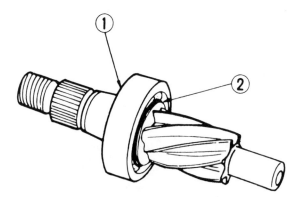

Fig. 8.11 Pinion bearing and circlips. For 1 and 2 see text (Sec 10)

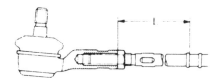

Fig. 8.12 Adjust tie-rod length (L) to 5.24 in (133 mm)

14 Visually inspect the bearing for cracked, pitted or worn balls and races. Ensure that it runs freely. Renew if at all doubtful. The oil seal should be renewed as a matter of policy.
15 Renew the retainer spring if it is worn or distorted.
16 Renew the rack bushing if it is scored, cracked or excessively worn. Check this by loosening the locknut and retainer adjuster screw, then set the rack in its central position and measure the bush wear in the housing (Fig. 8.9). If worn beyond the specified limits, renew the gear housing assembly.

10 Rack-and-pinion unit (manual steering) – reassembly and adjustment

1 Using a suitable drift and hammer, drive the bushing into the rack and secure with a circlip.

2 Fit the rubber mounting on the end of the tube, ensuring that the cut-out in the mounting is lined up with the hole in the tube. Ensure that the ventilation hole is free from grease.
3 Press the bearing over the pinion and secure it with circlips, ensuring that the circlips are located in the correct grooves. Circlip sizes are selected from the table below. Item (2) in Fig. 8.11 will always be (d) in the table, while item (1) must be chosen to give an axial play of less than 0.0039 in (0.1 mm).

Circlip thickness in (mm)
a   0.041 to 0.043 (1.04 to 1.09)
b   0.043 to 0.045 (1.09 to 1.14)
c   0.045 to 0.047 (1.14 to 1.19)
d   0.047 to 0.049 (1.19 to 1.24)
e   0.049 to 0.051 (1.24 to 1.29)

4 Place the housing in a vice; then lightly grease all the mating surfaces and teeth. Insert the rack from the housing side, mesh the pinion with the rack and secure with a circlip selected from the following table. Use the thickest circlip that will fit.

Circlip thickness in (mm)
- a   0.067 to 0.069 (1.70 to 1.75)
- b   0.065 to 0.067 (1.65 to 1.70)
- c   0.063 to 0.065 (1.60 to 1.65)
- d   0.061 to 0.063 (1.55 to 1.60)

5 Insert the oil seal with the lip face towards the outside, over the pinion stem and onto the circlip. Pack the seal with grease. Check that the pinion assembly rotates smoothly.
6 Measure the axial play of the pinion; it should be within the specified limits.
7 Fit the gear retainer and retainer spring into the housing.
8 Screw in the adjusting screw until the retainer is tight and then back-off the screw approximately 20 to 25 degrees. Apply a coat of thread-locking compound round the adjusting screw and tighten the locknut to the specified torque.
9 When assembly is completed, check the torque required to keep the rack-and-pinion in motion:

(a) Using a spring balance check that the pinion rotary torque is less than 17 lbf in (20 kgf cm)
(b) Check that the force required to pull the rack is between 33 and 66 lb (15 and 30 kg)

Screw the adjusting screw in or out as necessary to obtain these figures. Check that the rack moves smoothly over its full travel distance.
10 Connect the outer sockets to the tie-rods. Adjust the exposed length of each tie-rod to 5.24 in (133 mm) and tighten the locknuts temporarily (Fig. 8.12).
11 Fit the rubber boots, first greasing the groove in the tie-rods where the boots are secured. This will facilitate rotation of the boots if they twist in subsequent adjustment of the tie-rods.

Pinion side

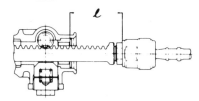

Steering gear mount side

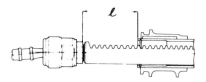

Fig. 8.13 Rack stroke (I) each side to be 2.68 in (68 mm) (Sec 10)

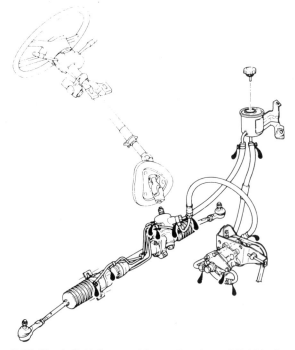

Fig. 8.15 Check fluid lines and hoses for signs of fluid leakage (Sec 11)

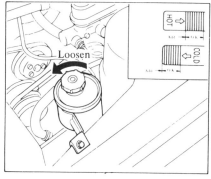

Fig. 8.14 Fluid reservoir and (inset) level indicator markings (Sec 11)

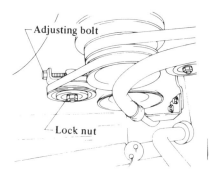

Fig. 8.16 Pump drivebelt adjuster bolt and locknut (Sec 11)

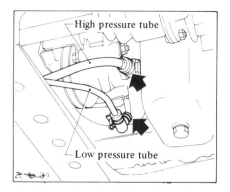

Fig. 8.17 Detach high and low pressure tube-to-pump connections to drain the system (Sec 12)

12 Connect the tie-rods to the inner sockets, after fitting the inner socket springs. Screw in the inner sockets, as far as they will go, then apply thread-locking compound to the threads of the locknuts and tighten them to the specified torque. The smaller locknut goes on the pinion side.

13 Mate the boot with the groove in the gear housing and ensure that the boot is not distorted when securing it.

14 Recheck that the exposed length of the tie-rods is as given above and tighten the outer balljoint locknuts to the specified torque.

11 Power steering system – maintenance and checking

The following service checks must be carried out at the specified intervals given in the Routine Maintenance Section at the front of this manual.

1 With the engine switched off, unscrew and remove the power steering fluid reservoir cap and check the fluid level on the dipstick. Depending on whether the fluid is hot or cold, the level should be up to the appropriate mark on the dipstick as shown in Fig. 8.14. If the fluid level is shown to be below the applicable level marking, top up (but do not overfill) using only the specified fluid. During this operation take particular care not to let any dirt enter the system and use only new fluid. Wipe clean and refit the cap, then recheck the level to ensure that it is correct.

2 Referring to Fig. 8.15, check the respective fluid lines and their connections for security and signs of leaks at the points indicated. Any defective lines or connections must be made secure or renewed as applicable.

3 If a fluid leak is suspected but cannot be readily seen, apply the handbrake and start the engine and allow it to idle at 1000 rpm with the fluid at its normal operating temperature. If the fluid is cold, warm it up by driving the car or by turning the steering wheel from lock to lock continuously until the fluid reaches operating temperature (about two minutes should be sufficient). The tyres must of course be inflated to their correct specified pressure. To make the leak check, turn the steering wheel from lock to lock several times, holding at full lock position each turn for five seconds, and recheck the respective components in the system whilst holding on lock. An assistant will obviously be required here to turn the steering wheel or to check the steering lines and components for leaks.

4 Check the power steering pump drivebelt for condition and adjustment. If necessary adjust the belt tension by loosening the adjuster locknut and turning the adjuster bolt as required to obtain the necessary deflection of 0.24 to 0.31 in (6 to 8 mm) under thumb pressure.

12 Power steering system fluid – draining, refilling and bleeding

1 It should not normally be necessary to drain the power steering fluid for replacement, but if it is known to have overheated, has air in it or worse still dirt, the system must be drained and new fluid inserted.

2 To drain the system, refer to Fig. 8.17 and place a suitable container under the high and low pressure hose-to-pump connections.

Detach the hoses at the pump and allow the system to drain.

3 Before reconnecting the hoses, ensure that they and their pump connections are perfectly clean. The drained fluid must be disposed of – never reuse it!

4 Top up the system through the reservoir filler neck in the following manner to bleed the system.

5 Jack up and support the car so that the front wheels are clear of the ground. Check that the handbrake is fully applied.

6 Add fluid to the top of the reservoir filler neck and then turn the steering wheel from lock to lock about ten times (with the engine off) and add fluid accordingly so that the level is not allowed to drop below the low level mark.

7 As soon as the fluid level remains unchanged, start up the engine and allow it to idle. Again rotate the steering wheel from lock to lock until no air bubbles exist in the fluid. Maintain the fluid at its correct level during this operation and do not hold the steering on full lock for longer than fifteen seconds at a time.

8 On completion switch off the engine. Ensure that the reservoir cap is clean before refitting it and fluid level is correct (not overfull). Check the hose connections for signs of leaks and if satisfactory, lower the car and give it a test drive to ensure that the steering feels correct.

13 Rack-and-pinion unit (power steering) – removal and refitting

1 For better accessibility and to prevent damaging it, unbolt and remove the bonnet (hood).

2 Apply the handbrake, chock the rear wheels and then raise the car at the front end to allow sufficient room for working underneath it. Support with safety stands and remove the front wheels.

3 Unbolt and remove the engine buffer rod and then fit an engine lifting eye in its place (see Chapter 1, Section 5). Attach an engine lifting sling and arrange a hoist so that the engine can be raised just enough to remove the following items:

(a) *The transmission shifter and selector rods from the transmission*
(b) *The exhaust downpipe from the manifold and the exhaust pipe-to-transmission retaining bracket*
(c) *The lower buffer rod*
(d) *The front and rear engine mounting insulators*

Refer to Chapters 1 and 6 as applicable for further details regarding disconnecting these items.

4 Remove the retaining screws and withdraw the lower steering column cover from within the car. Loosen, but do not remove, the steering column-to-lower joint bolt.

5 Unscrew and remove the lower column joint-to-steering pinion gear shaft retaining bolt. Detach this joint from the shaft by pulling it upwards.

6 Refer to Section 7 and disconnect the steering tie-rod balljoints on each side.

7 Drain the power steering fluid as given in the previous Section.

8 Unscrew and remove the steering rack-to-subframe mounting bolts.

9 Move the engine forwards just enough to enable the steering unit to be withdrawn sideways through the wheel arch together with its linkages (Fig. 8.18).

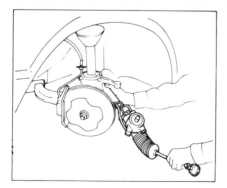

Fig. 8.18 Withdrawing the steering gear (Sec 13)

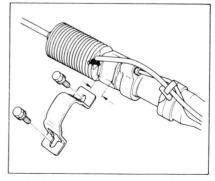

Fig. 8.19 Steering clamp position (Sec 13)

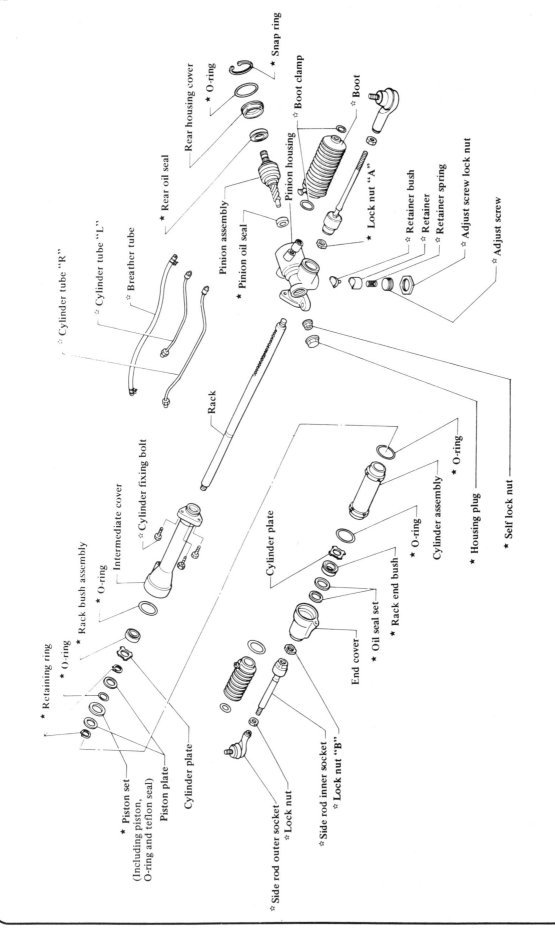

Fig. 8.20 The power steering gear components (Sec 15)

10 Refitting is a reversal of the removal procedure, but note the following points:

(a) When refitting the steering column shaft to the pinion, centralise the steering wheel and the front wheels before engaging

(b) Do not fully tighten the steering rack unit and column retaining bolts until the complete assembly is in position

(c) Ensure that the steering clamp is correctly positioned as shown in Fig. 8.19

(d) Tighten all bolts to their specified torque wrench settings

(e) When the hoses and lines are reconnected and the engine/transmission components reattached, top up and bleed the power steering system as given in Section 12

(f) Check for leaks from the power steering system components (see Section 11)

(g) Have the steering and wheel alignment checked by your Datsun dealer at the earliest opportunity

(h) Test drive the vehicle to ensure that the steering is functioning correctly

14 Rack-and-pinion unit (power steering) overhaul – general precautions

1 It is not generally recommended that the rack and pinion unit on power steering models be dismantled by the DIY mechanic for the following reasons:

(a) The power steering actuating cylinder is integral with the rack-and-pinion and the only items which can be removed are the unit seals. If any of the mechanical parts are worn or defective they cannot be repaired and only the complete assembly can be renewed

(b) Special Datsun tools are required for certain operations and unless these are available no attempt should be made to overhaul the unit. The special tools required are: Mounting bracket number KV48102200, torque wrench adaptor tool number ST31275000, and special torque wrench KV48102300. In addition, an ordinary torque wrench and a spring balance will be required

2 In addition to the above items, you will need a perfectly clean working area as cleanliness during dismantling and assembly is of utmost importance.
3 If the above listed tools are available and you decide to dismantle the unit, first check that all components likely to be required are readily available from your Datsun dealer.

15 Rack-and-pinion unit (power steering) – dismantling, inspection and reassembly

If you have not already done so, read the previous Section concerning special precautions on overhauling the power steering rack-and-pinion unit.
1 Refer to Fig. 8.20 for an exploded view of the steering gear components.
2 Attach mounting bracket KV48102200 to the pinion housing flange as shown (Fig. 8.21) and mount the unit in a vice. Clean its external parts.
3 Disconnect the cylinder tube and drain out any remaining fluid from the unit, then using special tool ST31275000 engaged with the steering pinion, measure the pinion rotational torque. The maximum permitted torque is listed in the Specifications.
4 If adjustment is necessary to correct the rotational torque and bring it within this figure, loosen the locknut on the base of the pinion housing and turn the adjuster screw accordingly. If it is found that adjustment is not possible, do not bother with further dismantling as the unit is mechanically defective and must be renewed.
5 Now test the steering rack starting force with a spring balance as shown (Fig. 8.23). This should not exceed 40 lb (18 kg). Again, renew the complete unit if the starting force is not within this figure.
6 Unclip and remove the breather tube and the rack protective rubber boots. Prise the boots free with a flat screwdriver blade.
7 Unscrew the inner socket locking nuts and withdraw the tie-rods from the steering unit.

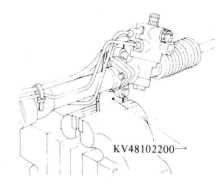
Fig. 8.21 Use special mounting bracket KV48102200 if available (Sec 15)

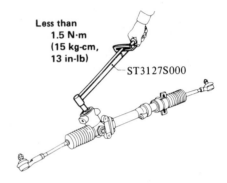
Fig. 8.22 Check the pinion rotating torque with special tool ST31275000 (Sec 15)

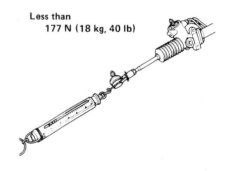
Fig. 8.23 Check the rack starting force (Sec 15)

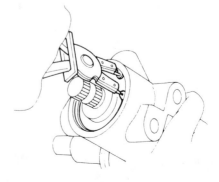
Fig. 8.24 Remove the circlip (Sec 15)

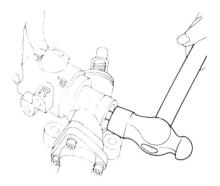

Fig. 8.25 Drive out the pinion (Sec 15)

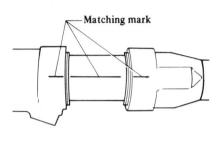

Matching mark

Fig. 8.26 Scribe some alignment marks (Sec 15)

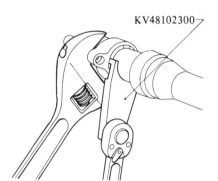

KV48102300

Fig. 8.27 Remove end cover locknut with special tool KV48102300 if available (Sec 15)

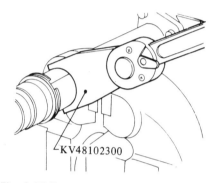

KV48102300

Fig. 8.28 Remove the cover locknut (Sec 15)

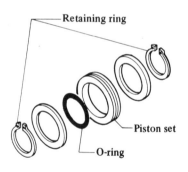

Retaining ring

Piston set

O-ring

Fig. 8.29 Piston assembly components (Sec 15)

Fig. 8.30 Insert the rack bush (Sec 15)

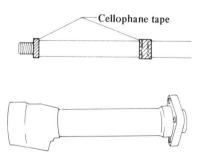

Cellophane tape

Fig. 8.31 Protect the shaft piston areas (Sec 15)

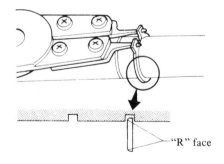

"R" face

Fig. 8.32 Refit the circlip (Sec 15)

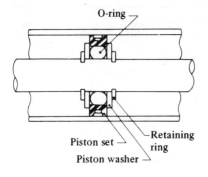

Fig. 8.33 Insert the piston assembly components (Sec 15)

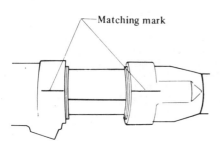

Fig. 8.35 Align the respective cover marks (Sec 15)

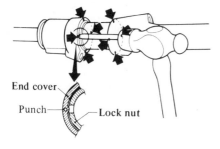

Fig. 8.37 Stake the intermediate cover and end cover where arrowed (Sec 15)

Pinion housing side:

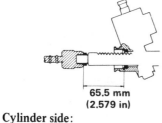

65.5 mm (2.579 in)

Cylinder side:

65.5 mm (2.579 in)

Fig. 8.40 Rack stroke to be as shown (Sec 15)

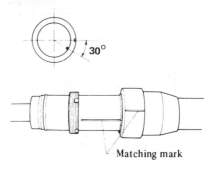

Fig. 8.34 Alignment marks to be 30° apart (Sec 15)

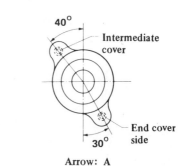

Arrow: A

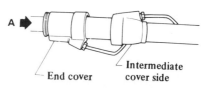

Fig. 8.36 Align covers as shown if no alignment marks are visible (Sec 15)

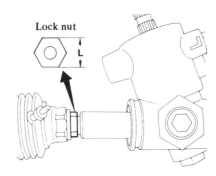

Fig. 8.38 Locknut identification – measure dimension L (Sec 15)
Pinion housing side nut L = 0.87 in (22 mm)
Cylinder side nut L = 1.18 in (30 mm)

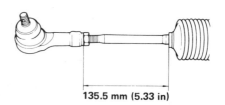

135.5 mm (5.33 in)

Fig. 8.39 Adjust tie-rod and balljoint to give dimension shown (Sec 15)

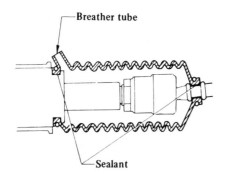

Fig. 8.41 Location of breather tube (Sec 15)

Fig. 8.42 Check the steering wheel turning force (Sec 15)

8   Unscrew the outer socket locking nut and detach the outer socket from the inner socket. Do not dismantle the balljoint assemblies, if worn renew them complete.

9   Remove the cylinder tube 'R' (Fig. 8.20) disconnecting the cylinder side flare nut first, then the pinion side. Take care not to damage the flare nut.

10   Remove the cylinder tube 'L' in similar fashion.

11   Loosen the adjuster screw locknut and unscrew to remove the adjuster screw and retainer from the pinion housing.

12   Remove the circlip from its location groove in the pinion housing (Fig. 8.24), then remove and discard the housing plug.

13   Remove and discard the self-locking nut and then lightly tap the pinion shaft with a soft-headed mallet to remove it from the housing (Fig. 8.25).

14   Withdraw the rear housing cover from the pinion and then prise free the rear oil seal, using a screwdriver or similar tool to lever it out. Remove the O-ring.

15   Remove the pinion oil seal.

16   To remove the end cover oil seals, make alignment marks on the end cover, the intermediate cover and cylinder and using tool KV48102300 and an open-jawed wrench remove the end cover (see Figs. 8.26 and 8.27).

17   Remove the plate and rack end bush from the cylinder, followed by the oil seals and O-ring.

18   To remove the intermediate cover oil seal, use special tool KV48102300 and remove the cover locking nut as shown (Fig. 8.28), then remove the cylinder and O-ring.

19   Remove the circlip, taking care not to score the rack and then remove the respective piston set components (Fig. 8.29).

20   Using an Allen key, unscrew the cylinder retaining bolts and detach the intermediate cover from the pinion housing, tapping it lightly with a soft-headed mallet to free it.

21   Remove the cylinder plate from the intermediate cover, followed by the rack bush assembly and O-ring.

22   No further dismantling is permissible. Wash all parts thoroughly in a solvent or automatic transmission fluid. Blow dry with compressed air or wipe dry with a nylon or paper cloth.

23   Examine all components carefully. If any of the mechanical components of the steering gear are badly worn or damaged, renew the complete unit.

24   Renew all oil seals and O-rings as a matter of course, and also renew the locknuts.

25   During reassembly keep all parts perfectly clean and lubricate with grease or automatic transmission fluid as given. Take care when fitting the new seals not to damage or distort them.

26   Reassembly is a reversal of the removal procedure, but the following special points must be adhered to, therefore reassemble as follows.

27   Smear the intermediate cover O-ring with automatic transmission fluid (ATF) and fit it into position in the cover.

28   Smear the rack bush with ATF and carefully drive this into position using a suitable tube drift (Fig. 8.30).

29   Wrap some insulation tape or Cellophane round the rack and edges and piston areas on the shaft (Fig. 8.31) to protect the intermediate cover oil seal and then carefully fit the cover. Fit the cover retaining bolts and tighten to the specified torque. Remove the tape.

30   Fit the cylinder plate followed by the retaining circlip onto the rack, taking care not to score the rack surfaces. Position the circlip as shown in Fig. 8.32.

31   Locate the piston components as shown in Fig. 8.33, these being the piston plate, the O-ring, the piston set and the second piston plate (washer). The piston set comprises the O-ring and Teflon seal. Secure the assembly with the circlip.

32   Fit the cylinder O-rings, smeared with ATF, and then insert the cylinder, turning it 30° from its original fitted position as noted by the alignment marks (Fig. 8.34).

33   Using tool KV48102300, tighten the cylinder locknut to the specified torque.

34   Fit the new oil seal into the end cover (having smeared it with ATF), driving it into position with a tube drift.

35   Insert the rack end bush (vertically) in a similar fashion, followed by the cylinder plate. Refit the end cover, aligning the mark with that of the intermediate cover (Fig. 8.35). Where alignment marks are not visible, position the end cover as shown in Fig. 8.36.

36   Tighten the end cover locknut, using special tool KV48102300, to the specified torque. Using a suitable centre punch, stake the intermediate cover and the end cover in four places each to prevent the locknut coming loose (Fig. 8.37).

37   Using a suitable diameter drift, carefully drive the new pinion oil seal into its housing.

38   Smear the O-ring with ATF and locate it in the housing cover.

39   Smear the rear oil seal with ATF and fit this into position in the cover. Wrap some insulating tape around the pinion shaft splines to protect the seal when fitting the cover, refit the cover and remove the tape.

40   Coat the pinion and rack teeth with grease and then fit the pinion assembly into its housing, taking care not to damage the Teflon ring. With the rack-and-pinion gear teeth engaged, drive the pinion fully home using a drift and then locate the circlip in the housing groove to secure.

41   Fit the pinion self-locking nut and tighten to the specified torque, gripping the pinion shaft in suitable hand grips or a soft-jawed vice with cloth wrapped around the shaft to prevent it turning when tightening the nut.

42   Smear some grease onto the rack side of the retainer bush and fit it together with the retainer into the pinion housing, followed by its spring and adjuster screw, the threads of which must be smeared with sealant.

43   Fully tighten the retainer adjustment screw, then unscrew it 20° to 25° and retaining in this position, fit and tighten the locknut to secure the adjuster screw in the set position. Check the pinion rotating force (see paragraph 3) and if correct fit the pinion housing plug (coat the threads with sealant) and stake punch to secure.

44   Fit the respective tubes L and R, taking care not to overtighten or damage the flare nuts.

45   Screw the left and right-hand tie-rods (inner sockets) into position so that they butt against the rack end each side, then tighten the locknuts to secure. Make sure that you use the correct locknut on each side, the differences being shown in Fig. 8.38. If the balljoints (outer sockets) are already fitted, the rubber protector boots (gaiters) will have to be located onto the rods first.

46   Fit the protector boots loosely over the rods, then fit the tie-rod balljoints, screwing them into position to achieve the dimension shown in Fig. 8.39, then tighten the locknut to secure in position.

47   Measure the rack stroke on each side at the points shown in Fig. 8.40 to ensure movement is correct.

48   Smear the rubber boot-to-tie-rod and pinion housing contact areas with sealant, locate the boots and secure with clips. Note that the

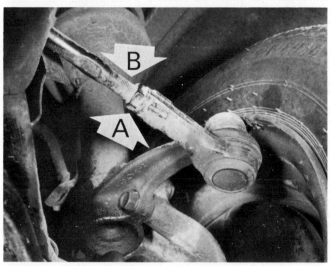

17.9 Loosen locknut (A) and rotate tie-rod (B) to adjust toe-in

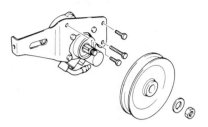

Fig. 8.43 Remove pulley and pump retaining bolts (Sec 16)

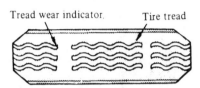

Fig. 8.44 Tread wear indicators are present on original tyres (Sec 18)

breather tube must be positioned as shown in Fig. 8.41.
49 Check the pinion rotating force and the rack starting force as given in paragraphs 3 and 5 respectively. Adjust further if necessary to comply with the respective torque and force requirements.
50 After refitting, turn the steering wheel 360° from its central position and using a spring balance as shown (Fig. 8.42), check the wheel turning force which should be about 5.5 lb (2.5 kg) measured at its circumference.

16 Power steering pump, hoses and reservoir – removal and refitting

Pump unit
1 Disconnect the high and low pressure hoses at their pump unit connections and drain the fluid into a suitable container. Plug the hoses whilst disconnected to prevent the ingress of dirt into the system.
2 Unscrew and remove the two high pressure hose bracket bolts and remove the bracket.
3 Use a screwdriver or chisel and bend straight the pump pulley nut lockwasher, then applying extra belt tension to prevent the pulley from turning, unscrew and remove the retaining bolt and washer. Remove the belt and pulley.
4 Unscrew and remove the pump retaining bolts and remove the pump unit.
5 If the pump unit shows signs of leaking, is damaged, excessively worn or known to malfunction, then it must be renewed as a unit.
6 Refit the pump in the reverse sequence to removal. Retension the drive belt (see Section 11), top up the fluid level and bleed the system as given in Section 12.

Hydraulic hoses
7 Whenever the hydraulic hoses are removed, care must be taken not to damage the connecction flare nuts. Always plug disconnected hoses and their connections to prevent the ingress of dirt. Do not attempt to repair damaged hoses, always renew. When refitting hoses ensure that their connections are correct, the flare nuts not over-tightened and of course do not forget to remove the plugs!
8 Top up the fluid level and bleed the system (Section 12) on completion, and check for leaks.

Reservoir tank
9 Should the reservoir tank show any signs of leakage, or be damaged in any way, it must be renewed. To remove it, disconnect the low pressure lines, drain out the fluid from the tank and unbolt and remove it.
10 Refit in the reverse order to removal, top up the fluid level and bleed the system (Section 12) to complete.

17 Front wheel alignment and steering geometry

1 Accurate front wheel alignment is essential for good steering and satisfactory tyre wear. Before considering the steering geometry, check that the tyres are correctly inflated, that the front wheels are not buckled, the hub bearings are not worn or incorrectly adjusted, and that the steering linkage is in good order, without slackness or wear at the joints (see Section 6).
2 The following factors affect the wheel alignment setting:
Camber is the angle at which the front wheels are set from the vertical when viewed from the front of the vehicle. Positive camber is the amount (in degrees) that the wheels are tilted outwards at the top from the vertical.
Castor is the angle between the steering axis and a vertical line when viewed from each side of the vehicle. Positive castor is when the steering axis is inclined rearward. Both the camber and castor angles are preset during manufacture and cannot be adjusted.
Toe-in is the amount by which the distance between the front inside edges of the roadwheels (measured at hub height) is less than the diametrically opposite distance measured between the rear inside edges of the front roadwheels.
3 The toe-in is adjustable by altering the tie-rod settings each side as required. For truly accurate setting checks and adjustment, special-ised alignment equipment is required and this task is best entrusted to your local Datsun dealer. The toe-in should always be checked, and if necessary adjusted, if the vehicle has been involved in an accident or the front steering and suspension has been subjected to harsh treatment such as hitting a high kerb or travel over poor road conditions, also after steering unit repair work.
4 A reasonably accurate alternative adjustment and check procedure may be carried out by the DIY mechanic as follows.
5 Position the vehicle on level ground with the front wheels in the straight-ahead position. Check that the tyres are inflated to the correct pressures and if possible make the check with a full fuel tank.
6 Obtain or make a toe-in gauge. One may be easily made from tubing, having an adjustable nut and setscrew at one end.
7 Using the gauge, measure the distance between the two inner wheel rims at hub height at the rear of the wheels.
8 Rotate the wheels (by pushing the car forwards) through 180° (half a turn) and again using the gauge, measure the distance of hub height between the two inner wheel rims at the front of the wheels. This measurement should be less than that previously taken at the rear of the wheel by the amount given in the Specifi-cations in Chapter 11, and represents the correct toe-in.
9 Where the toe-in is found to be incorrect, slacken the locknuts on the steering tie-rod balljoints each side and rotate the rods accordingly to give the correct toe-in, then retighten the locknuts (photo). Make equal adjustment on each side, otherwise the straight-ahead position of the steering wheel will be altered.

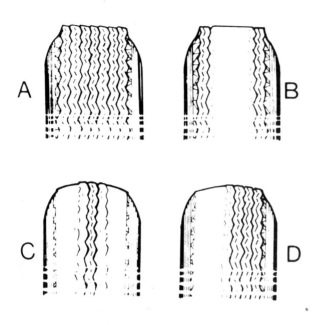

Fig. 8.45 Tyre wear patterns and causes (Sec 18)

A 'Feathering' due to incorrect toe-in
B Over-inflation
C Under-inflation
D Wear due to incorrect camber, worn wheel bearings or fast cornering, or grossly incorrect toe-in

18 Wheels and tyres – general

1 Whenever the roadwheels are removed it is a good idea to clean the insides to remove accumulations of mud.
2 Check the condition of the wheel for rust, and repaint if necessary.
3 Examine the wheel stud holes. If these are tending to become elongated, or the dished recesses in which the nuts seat have worn or become overcompressed, then the wheel will have to be renewed. Where aluminium wheels are fitted a different pattern of wheel nut is used. Never lubricate the wheel nuts or stud threads, but keep them clean and free or rust.
4 With a roadwheel removed, pick out any embedded flints from the tyre tread, and check for splits in the sidewalls or damage to the tyre carcass generally.
5 Where the depth of tread pattern is 1 mm or less, the tyre must be renewed. The tyres fitted as original equipment have tread wear markers at six points around the circumference. These markings give warning of 1.6 mm of tread remaining (Fig. 8.44).
6 Rotation of the roadwheels to even out wear may be a worthwhile idea if the wheels have been balanced off the car. Do not move radial tyres from side to side, only front to rear.
7 If the wheels have been balanced on the car then they cannot be moved round as the balance of the wheel, tyre and hub will be upset.
8 It is recommended that wheels are balanced whenever new tyres are fitted, and rebalanced halfway through the life of the tyre to compensate for the loss of tread rubber due to wear.
9 Finally, always keep the tyres (including the spare) inflated to the recommended pressures, and always refit the dust caps on the tyre valves. Tyre pressures are best checked first thing in the morning when the tyres are cold.

19 Fault diagnosis – steering

Fault diagnosis of the steering system is included in the fault diagnosis for the suspension; refer to Chapter 11.

Chapter 9 Braking system

Contents

Specifications

System type .... Four wheel, dual circuit, hydraulic actuation with servo assistance

Front brakes

Type	Single cylinder disc brake
Disc pad dimensions – in (mm):	
Width	1.654 (42.0)
Thickness (new)	0.406 (10.3)
Length	2.236 (56.8)
Disc pad wear limit – in (mm)	0.079 (2.0)
Disc repair limit – in (mm):	
Thickness	0.339 (8.6)
Run out (at circumference)	0.0047 (0.12)
Parallelism	0.0012 (0.03)

Rear brakes

Type	Drum with internal expanding shoes and self-adjusting mechanism
Shoe lining dimensions – in (mm):	
Width	1.328 (35.0)
Thickness (new)	0.189 (4.8)
Length	7.68 (195.0)
Lining wear limit – in (mm)	0.059 (1.5)
Drum repair limits – in (mm):	
Maximum inside diameter	8.05 (204.5)
Ovality – maximum allowable	0.0008 (0.02)
Radial run-out	0.004 (0.1)
Taper	0.0008 (0.02)

Hydraulic system

Brake pedal adjustments settings – in (mm):	
Free height – LH drive models	7.09 to 7.32 (180 to 186)
Free height – RH drive models	6.97 to 7.20 (177 to 183)
Free play at pedal pad	0.04 to 0.20 (1 to 5)
Full stroke at pedal pad	5.08 (129)
Depressed height (minimum)	2.76 (70)
Master cylinder inner diameter – in (mm)	0.812 (20.64)
Wheel cylinder inner diameter – in (mm):	
Front	1.894 (48.1)
Rear	0.687 (17.46)

Brake booster (servo)
Type M60
Diaphragm diameter – in (mm) 6.0 (152.4)
Pushrod length – in (mm) .... 0.3839 to 0.3937 (9.75 to 10.00)
Operating rod length – in (mm) 5.12 (130)

Handbrake
Stroke – in (mm) .... 3.66 to 4.17 (93 to 106)
Number of notches .... 7 to 8

Torque wrench settings

	lbf ft	kgf m
Disc caliper bolt	40 to 47	5.5 to 6.5
Disc backplate bolts	2.4 to 3.2	0.33 to 0.44
Disc-to-wheel hub	18 to 25	2.5 to 3.4
Rear wheel cylinder bolts	4.3 to 5.8	0.6 to 0.8
Rear brake backplate bolts	18 to 25	2.5 to 3.4
Brake servo unit-to-body	5.8 to 8.0	0.8 to 1.1
Handbrake lever bolt	6.7 to 8.7	0.93 to 1.20
Handbrake adjustment locknut	2.2 to 2.9	0.3 to 0.4
Front cable bracket bolt	2.2 to 2.9	0.3 to 0.4
Cable clamp bolt	2.7 to 3.7	0.38 to 0.51
Brake master cylinder-to-booster	5.8 to 8.0	0.8 to 1.1
Master cylinder check valve plug:		
Nabco	18 to 25	2.5 to 3.5
Tokico	58 to 65	8.0 to 9.0
Master cylinder stopper screw:		
Nabco	1.1 to 2.2	0.15 to 0.30
Tokico	5.1 to 6.5	0.7 to 0.9
Three-way connector bolt	5.8 to 8.0	0.8 to 1.1
Dual proportioning valve bolt	4.3 to 5.1	0.6 to 0.7
Operating rod locknut	12 to 16	1.6 to 2.2
Bleed nipples	5.1 to 6.5	0.7 to 0.9
Brake pipe flare nuts	11 to 13	1.5 to 1.8
Brake lamp switch locknut	12 to 16	1.6 to 2.2
Brake fulcrum pin nut	12 to 19	1.6 to 2.6

1 General description

The braking system is hydraulically operated on all four wheels with discs on the front and drum on the rear.

The hydraulic system is of the dual line type, whereby the front brakes and the rear brakes are operated by separate hydraulic circuits from the tandem type master cylinder, so that should one circuit fail, braking action will still be effective on two wheels.

A servo booster, brake fluid leakage warning device and a pressure regulating valve are fitted in the system. The servo increases braking force and the pressure regulator ensures greater safety by preventing the rear wheels locking before the front wheels.

The handbrake lever is mounted between the front seats and operates on the rear wheels by a system of cables, equalizer and adjuster. When the handbrake is applied a warning light on the instrument panel illuminates.

The rear drum brakes are a leading-trailing type, expanded by a wheel cylinder to move outwards into contact with the rotating brake drum. An automatic adjuster unit is fitted to each rear brake unit.

The front brake is a single cylinder type disc brake. It has two pistons on one side of the brake disc. With the aid of the yoke, the pads grip the disc equally from both sides. Brake adjustment is not necessary as pad clearance is automatically adjusted due to the elasticity of the piston seal.

2 Routine maintenance

1   Every 250 miles (400 km) or weekly, whichever occurs first, check the fluid level in both the master cylinder reservoirs (photo). If necessary, top up with fluid of the specified type which has been stored in an airtight container and has remained unshaken for the previous 24 hours.
2   Check that the reservoir cap breather holes are clear.
3   If topping up is required frequently in one reservoir, inspect the hydraulic pipes of that particular circuit for leaks.
4   At 6000-mile intervals, remove the rear brake drums and inspect

the brake linings for excessive wear – see Specifications for wear limits – and renew if necessary.
5   At the same interval, examine the thickness of the friction lining material of the front disc brake pads. If any one is worn down to the minimum allowable (see Specifications) then all the disc pads should be renewed as a set on both front wheels. No adjustment is required to disc brakes.
6   Every 12 000 miles (20 000 km), bleed the hydraulic system of old fluid and refill with fresh. Check the operation of the handbrake.
7   Every 48 000 miles (80 000 km) renew all flexible hoses, and all rubber seals within the hydraulic components.

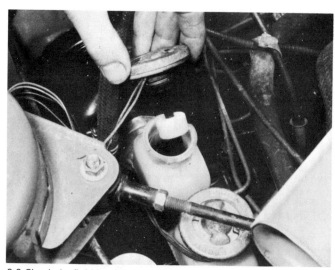

2.2 Check the fluid levels in the master cylinder

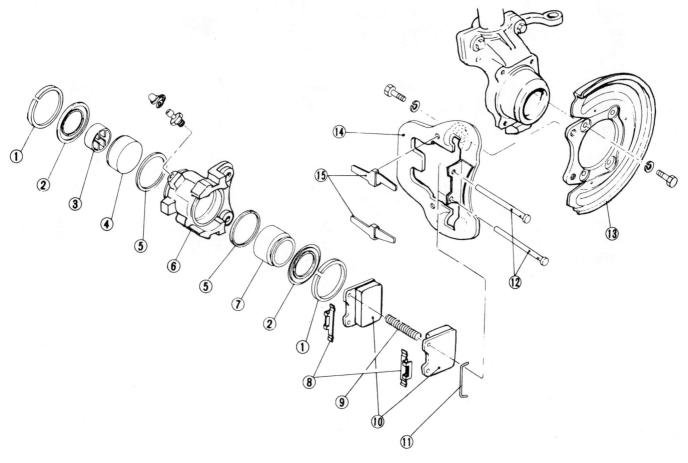

Fig. 9.1 Exploded view of front disc brake (Sec 3)

1	Retaining rings	4	Piston A (inner piston)	7	Piston B (outer piston)	10	Pads	13	Baffle plate
2	Boots	5	Piston seals	8	Hanger springs	11	Clip	14	Yoke
3	Bias ring	6	Cylinder body	9	Spring	12	Clevis pins	15	Yoke springs

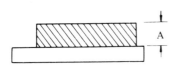

Fig. 9.2 Measure pad lining thickness (A) (Sec 3)

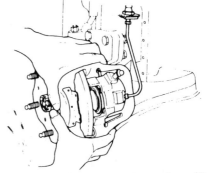

Fig. 9.4 Pull the yoke to depress the inner piston (Sec 3)

3 Front brake pads – inspection and renewal

1   Raise the front of the vehicle, support securely and remove the roadwheels.
2   Remove the spring clips from the retaining pins and then extract the retaining pins, coil springs and pad springs (photos). Check that the pad springs rebound easily.
3   Using pliers, withdraw the pads from the caliper, together with the anti-squeal shims (if fitted) (photos).
4   With the pads removed, on no account depress the brake pedal.
5   Brush out any dust from within the caliper body. Take care not to inhale the dust – it is asbestos-based and a health hazard.
6   Check the pads for wear. If any one is worn down to or beyond the specified limit, they must all be renewed as a set. A pad set kit

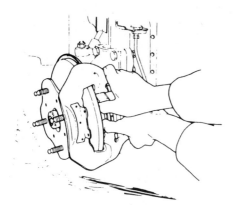

Fig. 9.3 Depressing the outer piston to accept a new pad (Sec 3)

3.2a Remove the spring clips from the retaining pins ...

3.2b ... and then withdraw the retaining pins

3.3a Withdraw the disc pads

3.3b A front disc pad and spring

comprises four pads, two clips and four pad pins and springs.

7   Whilst the pads are removed also check the disc for excessive wear, referring to Section 6, and if necessary have the disc reground or renew it as applicable.

8   Before reassembling the pads, clean and lubricate the yoke guide groove of the cylinder body, the yoke sliding surface sections and the end face of the piston with PBC grease. Do not use any other type of grease or lubricant and take care not to allow the grease to get onto the pads or rotor.

9   Unscrew the caliper bleed nipple so that by using the fingers, held square to the face of the outer piston, the piston can be depressed into the cylinder far enough to accommodate the new, thicker, inner pad. Only depress the piston the minimum amount needed to provide a wide enough gap for the pad; if it is pushed in too far, the piston seal will be damaged by the piston groove.

10   Now depress the inner piston into its cylinder by pulling the yoke of the caliper until sufficient gap is made to enable the new thicker outer pad to be installed. Install the anti-squeal shims (where fitted) with the arrow pointing forwards, ie in the direction of disc rotation.

11   Tighten the bleed nipple, fit the pad pins and clips and then depress the brake pedal several times to settle the new pads.

12   Refit the roadwheel and lower the vehicle to the ground.

13   Check the reservoir fluid level for the front hydraulic circuit.

4   Caliper unit – removal and refitting

1   Remove the disc pads as described in Section 3.

2   Disconnect the brake hose from the caliper. To do this, first disconnect the rigid pipe from the flexible hose at the support bracket union and then unscrew the flexible hose. Plug the open ends of the pipes.

3   Remove the bolts securing the caliper to the steering knuckle and lift the caliper assembly away from the disc.

4   Refitting is the reverse of the removal procedure. Tighten the caliper securing bolts to the specified torque. Bleed the hydraulic system as described in Section 14.

5   Caliper unit – dismantling, servicing and reassembly

1   Drain the brake fluid from the caliper through the flexible hose connection.

2   Unscrew and remove the bleed nipple.

3   Depress each piston in turn as described in Section 3.

4   Secure the longer edge of the caliper yoke in a vice and tap the top

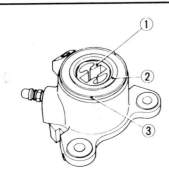

Fig. 9.5 The cylinder body and piston components (Sec 5)

1 *Bias ring*   2 *Boot*   3 *Retaining ring*

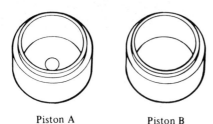

Piston A   Piston B

Fig. 9.6 The inner (A) and outer (B) pistons must be correctly located (Sec 5)

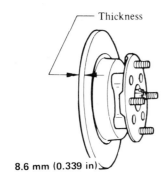

← Thickness

8.6 mm (0.339 in)

Fig. 9.7 Check the disc thickness (Sec 6)

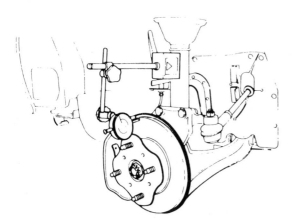

Fig. 9.8 Check the disc run-out using a dial gauge (Sec 6)

of the yoke lightly with a hammer. This action will disconnect the caliper body from the yoke.

5   Remove the bias ring from the inner piston (Fig. 9.5).

6   Remove the retaining rings and boots from the ends of both pistons.

7   Eject both pistons. This may be achieved by blocking the fluid inlet hole and applying air pressure at the bleed nipple hole. Note the location of each piston as they are ejected. They differ in that the inner piston is indented in its inner bottom face (see Fig. 9.6).

8   Carefully extract the piston seals from their grooves in the cylinders.

9   Detach the spring from the yoke.

10 Clean all components in methylated spirit or clean hydraulic fluid. Inspect the cylinder walls for scoring, bright spots or corrosion. Where these are evident, renew the complete caliper assembly.

11 Obtain a repair kit which will contain all the necessary seals and new parts. Check that the rubber seals have not deteriorated or become deformed in storage.

12 Dip the new seals in hydraulic fluid and locate them in their grooves in the cylinder bores. Use only the fingers to manipulate them into position. Note the correct fitting of the seal chamfer.

13 Insert the bias ring into the inner piston so that radiused corner of the ring is to the bottom. Make sure that the inner and outer pistons are correctly identified.

14 Dip each of the pistons in clean hydraulic fluid and insert them into their respective cylinders. Do not push the pistons too far into their cylinders or the seal will be damaged by the piston groove. Position the inner piston so that the yoke groove of the bias ring coincides with the yoke groove of the cylinder.

15 Install the boots and retaining rings.

16 Install the yoke spring.

17 Fit the bias ring to the yoke.

18 Apply a smear of PBC grease to the yoke sliding surface of the cylinder body, then reposition the bias ring so that groove of the bias ring coincides with the yoke.

19 With the yoke spring located in the groove in the cylinder, connect the cylinder body and yoke by applying pressure with the thumbs.

20 Screw in the bleed nipple.

6 Brake disc – inspection, removal and refitting

1   Raise the front of the car, supporting it with safety stands and remove the front wheels.

2   To check the disc run-out you will need the use of a dial gauge and this can be mounted as shown in Fig. 9.8 Make sure that excessive run-out is not due to worn or maladjusted hub bearings.

3   The appearance of the front disc will show even light scoring which is normal. Any deep grooves will indicate the need for renewal or grinding, as will excessive run-out.

4   Always check the tolerances in the Specifications Section before having an original disc ground or refaced. A disc can be removed together with the wheel hub as given in Chapter 11 and then detached from the hub on removal of the retaining bolts, but mark the relative position of the disc to the hub for correct refitting (unless renewing).

5   When refitting the disc and hub, tighten the retaining bolts to the specified torque and check the hub bearing preload during assembly as given in Chapter 11.

6   Bleed the hydraulic system (Section 14) to complete.

7 Handbrake – adjustment

1   As the rear drum brake units are fitted with an automatic adjustment mechanism, the handbrake will not normally require adjustment.

2   There are occasions however when the handbrake may require separate adjustment such as to take up cable stretch, where a new cable has been fitted, or when new brake linings have been fitted to the rear brakes.

3   To check the adjustment of the handbrake, chock the front wheels, then support the rear of the vehicle so that the rear wheels are both clear of the ground. Fully release the handbrake and ensure that both rear wheels rotate freely, then apply the handbrake, pulling it on 7 to 8 notches. Now try turning each wheel in turn by hand. If handbrake adjustment is correct it should not be possible to turn either wheel.

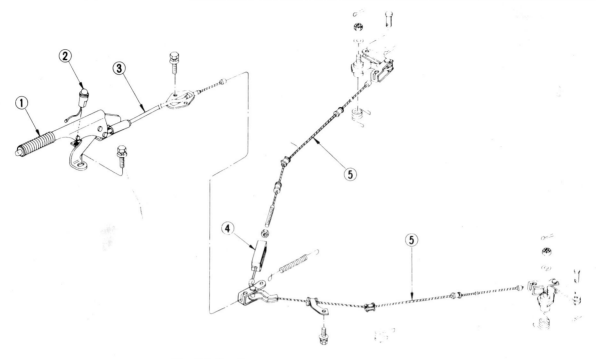

Fig. 9.9 Handbrake assembly components (Sec 8)

1	Handbrake lever	3	Front cable	5	Rear cables
2	Handbrake warning switch	4	Adjuster		

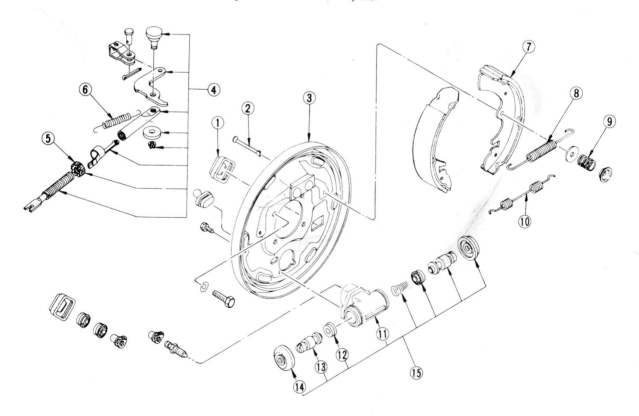

Fig. 9.10 Rear drum brake components (Sec 10)

1	Dust cover	6	Spring	11	Wheel cylinder body
2	Shoe fixing pin	7	Shoe	12	Piston cup
3	Backplate	8	Return spring	13	Piston
4	Adjuster assembly and handbrake lever	9	Shoe fixing spring	14	Dust cover
5	Adjusting nut	10	Return spring	15	Wheel cylinder assembly

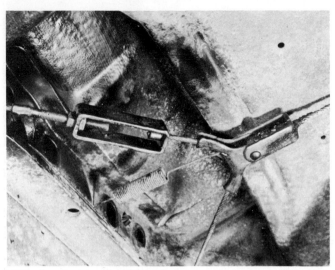

7.5 The handbrake cable adjuster

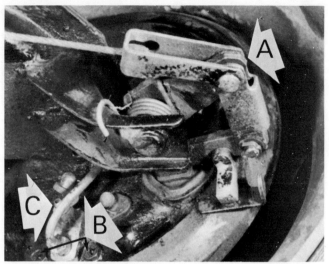

8.11 Cable and clevis connection (A). Note also the wheel cylinder retaining bolts (B), the bleed nipple (C) and its dust cap (removed)

4   If further application of the handbrake lever is needed to lock the rear wheels, release the handbrake and adjust the cable as follows.
5   Working underneath the vehicle clean off any dirt from the threads of the cable adjuster, loosen the locknut, then tighten the adjuster nut (photo) and take up the slack to the point where the wheels are locked at the specified number of notches on applying the handbrake lever. Check when the handbrake lever is released that the rear wheels are free to rotate without binding.
6   Retighten the adjuster locknut to secure in the set position.
7   Finally check that the handbrake warning light operates when the handbrake lever is applied one notch from the off position. If necessary bend the warning switch plate as required, ensuring that the light goes out when the lever is fully released.

8   Handbrake cable and lever – removal and refitting

The handbrake lever and cable assembly components are shown in Fig. 9.9. The front cable and lever are removed separately from the rear cable assembly and they are therefore dealt with individually.

Handbrake lever and front cable

1   Detach the wire from its terminal on the handbrake warning switch.
2   Unscrew and remove the bolts securing the handbrake lever to the floor.
3   Remove the cable lockplate and then from under the car, disconnect the cable from the rear cable pivot bracket. The lever and cable can now be removed from within the car.
4   The front cable can be disconnected from the lever by detaching the pin, but take care not to damage the lever unit.
5   Inspect and renew any worn or defective components as necessary. Check when the lever is in the up position that the pawl disengages from the ratchet teeth when the button is depressed by 0.20 to 0.24 in (5 to 6 mm).
6   Refit in the reverse order to removal, greasing the moving parts. Reconnect the front and rear cables before tightening the retaining bolts.
7   If necessary adjust the cable as given in Section 7, also the warning light switch.

Rear cable

8   Chock the front wheels. Raise the rear of the vehicle and support with safety stands.
9   Working underneath the vehicle, clean the adjuster threads, loosen the adjuster locknut and remove the adjuster.
10 Detach the cable guide.
11 Remove the cable clevis pins (photo) on each side and detach the cable from the actuating levers at the rear, then from the front cable

at the forward end by disengaging the cable nipple.
12 Clean and inspect the cable and renew any defective or excessively worn components. Check the clevis pins in particular and always renew their split pins.
13 Refit in the reverse order to removal, greasing the sliding contact parts. Readjust the cable on completion as given in Section 7.

9   Handbrake warning switch – removal and refitting

1   The handbrake warning switch is mounted on a bracket on the handbrake operating lever mountings. It is actuated when the handbrake is applied, and a warning light on the instrument panel lights up when the ignition is switched on.
2   Apart from checking the electrical connections, any fault will necessitate renewal of the switch.
3   To remove the switch, disconnect the lead wire at the connector, remove the switch bracket securing screw and separate the switch from the bracket.
4   Refitting is the reverse of the removal procedure.

10   Rear brake shoes and drums – inspection, removal and refitting

1   Chock the front wheels. Slacken the rear wheel nuts, jack up the rear of the car and support with safety stands. Remove the rear wheels.
2   Remove the rear brake drum(s), referring to Chapter 11.
3   The brake linings must be renewed if they ae worn to less than the specified minimum. If the shoes are being removed to give access to the wheel cylinders, then protect the linings to prevent any possibility of their becoming contaminated with grease or oil.
4   Before removing the shoe, note the location of the shoes and the position of the shoe return springs (photos).
5   Using a pair of pliers, unhook the return springs from the elongated holes in the shoe webs, then remove the shoe fixing spring and pin (photo).
6   Remove the brake shoes and use rubber bands to retain the wheel cylinder pistons in their cylinders. On no account depress the brake pedal while the drum and brake shoes are removed.
7   Fit the new shoes, making sure they are the right way round and that the return springs are correctly located.
8   Check the condition of the drum. If the friction surface is scored, it must be skimmed on a lathe or renewed.
9   After a considerable mileage the internal diameter of the rear drums may become out-of-round, worn beyond the permissible limit, or tapered.
10 The drums may require renewal or regrinding if deep scoring is visible.

10.4a Note how the shoe return spring and the adjuster spring are located at the bottom ...

10.4b ... and the shoe return spring at the top

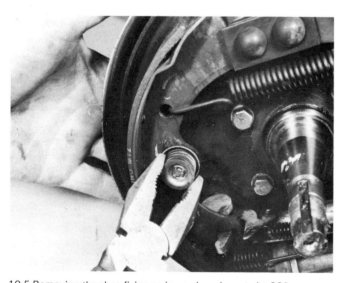

10.5 Removing the shoe fixing spring and washer – twist 90°

10.13 The reassembled brake shoes and springs ready for refitment of the drum

11 Where any of the foregoing conditions are evident, either renew the drums or have them professionally ground, always provided that the new dimensions do not exceed the tolerances given in the Specifications Section.

12 Refitting is a reversal of the removal procedure. Lubricate with PBC grease the wheel cylinder/anchor block and shoe contact areas, the brake shoe-to-backplate contact surfaces, the brake adjuster-to-brake shoe contact points and the anti-rattle spring retainer. Do not let grease get onto the lining or drum contact surfaces.

13 Ensure that the shoe return springs are correctly located and securely fitted (photo). Back off the adjuster to its original setting.

14 Refit the brake drum and adjust the rear hub as given in Chapter 11. Operate the handbrake a number of times so that the automatic adjuster mechanism can move the shoes into their correct position. Check the handbrake adjustment as given in Section 7 and if necessary readjust.

11 Wheel cylinder – removal, overhaul and refitting

1 Chock the front wheels. Raise and support the rear of the car using safety stands amd remove the rear wheels.
2 Refer to Chapter 11 and remove the brake drum.
3 Unscrew the union and disconnect the brake pipe from the wheel cylinder. Plug the pipe to prevent fluid leakage and the ingress of dirt.

4 Detach the handbrake return spring and remove the handbrake cable clevis pin to disconnect the cable.
5 Refer to Section 10 and remove the brake shoes.
6 Prise free the dust cover and then remove the toggle lever and adjuster unit.
7 Unscrew and remove the two retaining bolts and remove the wheel cylinder.
8 Clean the cylinder unit external surfaces before dismantling; cleanliness is of utmost importance when overhauling the unit.
9 Remove the dust cover from each end of the cylinder and then extract the pistons, the piston cups and centre return spring, keeping them in order of fitting. Should they prove difficult to remove, apply low pressure compressed air (eg from a foot pump) into the brake pipe connection hole with the hole wrapped in a clean cloth in which to catch the components as they are ejected.
10 Inspect the cylinder bore for score marks caused by impurities in the hydraulic fluid. If they are found the cylinder and piston will require renewal. If the cylinder bore is sound, thoroughly clean it out with fresh hydraulic fluid.
11 The piston cups and dust covers must always be renewed irrespective of condition. It should be noted that two types of wheel cylinder are fitted, being either of Nabco or Tokico manufacture. As the component parts of each are not interchangeable, be sure to specify

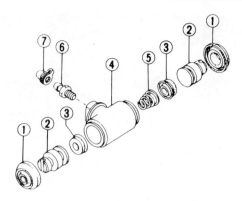

Fig. 9.11 The wheel cylinder components (Sec 11)

1 Dust covers	*4 Wheel cylinder body*	*6 Bleed nipple*
2 Pistons	*5 Spring*	*7 Dust cap*
3 Piston cups		

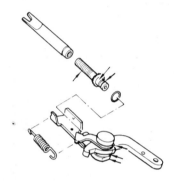

Fig. 9.12 Adjuster unit lubrication points (arrowed) (Sec 11)

which type you require when ordering spare parts or a cylinder kit.
12 Reassembly of the cylinder is a reversal of the removal procedure. Smear the pistons, cylinder and piston cups with hydraulic fluid prior to assembly and take care not to distort or damage any of the components when fitting.
13 When refitting the wheel cylinder, tighten the retaining bolts to the specified torque.
14 When refitting the adjuster nuts be sure to fit them on their correct sides – the right side adjuster has a right-hand thread, the left-hand side a left-hand thread. Lubricate the adjuster and toggle assembly at the points shown in Fig. 9.12 with PBC grease. Also lubricate those items specified in Section 10 when reassembling the brake shoes.
15 Smear the backplate mounting surfaces of the shoe retaining pins and the wheel cylinder with a sealant to prevent the ingress of wear.
16 Top up and bleed the hydraulic system on completion as given in Section 14.
17 Check the handbrake adjustment on completion as given in Section 7.
18 Finally test drive and check the brake operation.

12 Flexible brake hoses – inspection, removal and refitting

1 Periodically, inspect the condition of the flexible brake hoses. If they appear swollen, chafed or when bent double with the fingers tiny cracks are visible, then they must be renewed.
2 Always uncouple the rigid pipe from the flexible hose first, then release the end of the flexible hose from the support bracket. Now unscrew the flexible hose from the caliper or connector. If this method is followed, no kinking of the hose will occur (photo).
3 When fitting the hose, always use a new copper sealing washer.
4 When fitting is complete, check that the flexible hose does not rub against the tyre or other adjacent components. Its attitude may be altered to overcome this by releasing its bracket support locknut and

twisting the hose in the required direction by not more than one quarter turn.
5 Bleed the hydraulic system (Section 14).

13 Rigid brake lines – inspection, removal and refitting

1 At regular intervals wipe the steel brake pipes clean and examine them for signs of rust or denting caused by flying stones.
2 Examine the fit of the pipes in their insulated securing clips and bend the tongues of the clips if necessary to ensure a positive fit.
3 Check that the pipes are not touching any adjacent components or rubbing against any part of the vehicle. Where this is observed, bend the pipe gently away to clear.
4 Any section of pipe which is rusty or chafed should be renewed. Brake pipes are available to the correct length and fitted with end unions from most Datsun dealers and can be made to pattern by many accessory suppliers. When refitting the new pipes use the old pipes as a guide to bending and do not make any bends sharper than is necessary.
5 The system will of course have to be bled when the circuit has been reconnected (Section 14).

14 Hydraulic system – bleeding

1 If any of the hydraulic components in the braking system have been removed or disconnected, or if the fluid level in the master cylinder has been allowed to fall appreciably, it is inevitable that air will have been introduced into the system. The removal of air from the hydraulic system is essential if the brakes are to function correctly, and the process of removing it is known as bleeding.
2 There are a number of one-man, do-it-yourself, brake bleeding kits currently available from motor accessory shops. It is recommended that one of these kits should be used wherever possible as they greatly simplify the bleeding operation and also reduce the risk of expelled air and fluid being drawn back into the system.
3 If one of these kits is not available then it will be necessary to gather together a clean jar and a suitable length of clear plastic tubing which is a tight fit over the bleed screw, and also to engage the help of an assistant.
4 Before commencing the bleeding operation, check that all rigid pipes and flexible hoses are in good condition and that all hydraulic unions are tight. Take great care not to allow hydraulic fluid to come into contact with the vehicle paintwork, otherwise the finish will be seriously damaged. Wash off any spilled fluid immediately with cold water.
5 If hydraulic fluid has been lost from the master cylinder, due to a leak in the system ensure that the cause is traced and rectified before proceeding further or a serious malfunction of the braking system may occur.
6 To bleed the system, clean the area around the bleed screw at the master cylinder or the wheel cylinder to be bled (photo). If the hydraulic system has only been partially disconnected and suitable precautions were taken to prevent further loss of fluid, it should only be necessary to bleed that part of the system. However, if the entire system is to be bled, start at the wheel furthest away from the master cylinder.
7 Remove the master cylinder filler cap and top up the reservoir. Periodically check the fluid level during the bleeding operation and top up as necessary, using only new brake fluid of the specified type. Bleed the air from the system in the following sequence:

> *(a) Master cylinder (where applicable)*
> *(b) Rear brake – left-hand*
> *(c) Front brake – right-hand*
> *(d) Rear brake – right-hand*
> *(e) Front brake – left-hand*

8 If a one-man brake bleeding kit is being used, connect the outlet tube to the bleed screw and then open the screw half a turn. If possible position the unit so that it can be viewed from the car, then depress the brake pedal to the floor and slowly release it. The one-way valve in the kit will prevent dispelled air from returning to the system at the end of each stroke. Repeat this operation until clean hydraulic fluid, free from air bubbles, can be seen coming through the tube. Now tighten the bleed screw and remove the outlet tube (photo).

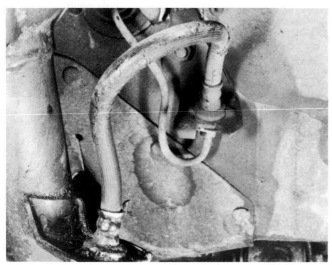

12.2 Typical flexible/rigid pipe connection and retaining bracket

14.6 Wheel cylinder bleed nipple with dust cap removed

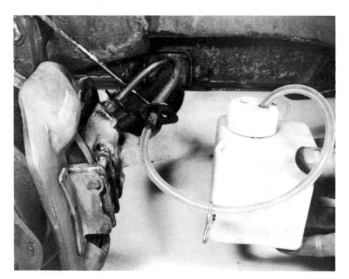

14.8 Connecting the one-man bleed kit to the front brake caliper bleed nipple

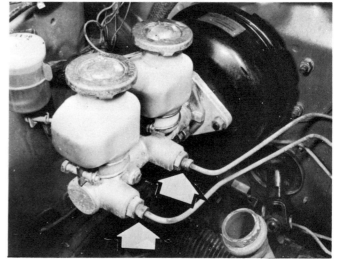

15.1 The master cylinder and servo unit, showing pipes to be disconnected (arrowed)

9   If a one-man brake bleeding kit is not available, connect one end of the plastic tubing to the bleed screw and immerse the other end in the jar containing sufficient clean hydraulic fluid to keep the end of the tube submerged. Open the bleed screw half a turn and have your assistant depress the brake pedal to the floor and then slowly release it. Tighten the bleed screw at the end of each downstroke to prevent expelled air and fluid from being drawn back into the system. Repeat this operation until clean hydraulic fluid, free from air bubbles, can be seen coming through the tube. Now tighten the bleed scew and remove the plastic tube.

10 If the entire system is being bled the procedures described above should now be repeated at each wheel, finishing at the wheel nearest to the master cylinder. Do not forget to recheck the fluid level in the master cylinder at regular intervals and top up as necessary. If the level is allowed to fall so that air is drawn in, the entire process will have to be started again.

11 When completed, recheck the fluid level in the master cylinder, top up if necessary and refit the cap. Check the feel of the brake pedal which should be firm and free fron any sponginess which would indicate air still present in the system.

15 Master cylinder – removal and refitting

1   Disconnect both fluid pipes from the master cylinder body and

push a cap over the open ends of the pipes to prevent dirt entering the system (photo). Be prepared for some loss of hydraulic fluid.

2   Disconnect the fluid level gauge wiring.

3   Unscrew and remove the two master cylinder flange securing nuts and withdraw the unit from the front of the brake vacuum servo unit. Take care not to spill any hydraulic fluid onto the car bodywork.

4   Refitting is the reverse of the removal procedure. After fitting, bleed the hydraulic system as described in Section 14.

16 Master cylinder – dismantling, servicing and reassembly

1   Clean all dirt from the external surfaces of the master cylinder body, taking care that none enters the fluid outlet holes.

2   Remove the reservoir caps and filters and tip out the brake fluid.

3   Extract the circlip from the end of the cylinder body.

4   Unscrew and remove the stop bolt (or screw, as applicable), and then extract the stop ring, the primary piston assembly, the spring and the secondary piston assembly.

5   At this stage examine the surfaces of the pistons and cylinder bore. If there is evidence of scoring or 'bright' wear areas, the complete master cylinder must be renewed as an assembly.

6   Where the components are in good condition, discard all rubber seals and obtain a repair kit which will contain all the necessary items for renewal.

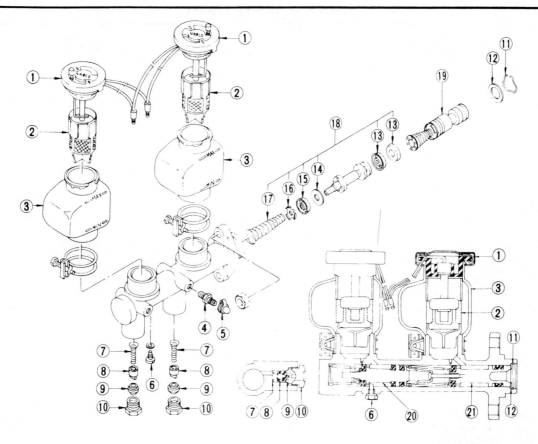

Fig. 9.13 The master cylinder components (Sec 16)

1 Reservoir caps
2 Filters
3 Reservoir tanks
4 Bleed nipple
5 Dust cap
6 Stop screw
7 Valve springs
8 Check valves
9 Valve seats
10 Check valve plugs
11 Stop ring
12 Piston stop
13 Piston cups
14 Spacer
15 Piston cup
16 Spring seat
17 Return spring
18 Secondary piston assembly
19 Primary piston assembly
20 Secondary piston
21 Primary piston

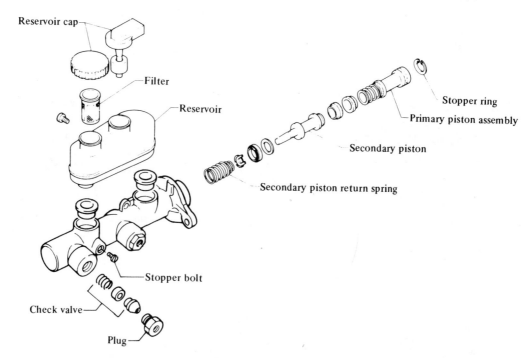

Reservoir cap
Filter
Reservoir
Stopper ring
Primary piston assembly
Secondary piston
Secondary piston return spring
Stopper bolt
Check valve
Plug

Fig. 9.14 The master cylinder and components fitted to later 1981 USA models (Sec 16)

7   Do not detach the reservoirs from the master cylinder body. Should this be necessary for any reason, new reservoirs must be fitted.
8   If the non-return valve requires attention, secure the master cylinder body in the jaws of a vice and unscrew the plugs.
9   Do not dismantle the brake fluid level switch(s), if known to be defective, renew. On 1981 models, do not dismantle the primary piston unit.
10 Note when ordering new components and/or cylinder seal kits that two types of master cylinder have been fitted, these being of Tokico or Nabco manufacture. The component parts of each are not interchangeable.
11 Clean all components in methylated spirit or clean hydraulic fluid.
12 Manipulate the new seals into position using the fingers only.
13 Dip the internal components in clean hydraulic fluid and insert them into the master cylinder body in the reverse sequence to dismantling.

17 Brake fluid level switch – description and testing

1   Brake fluid level switches are fitted into the reservoir(s) on all models and are designed to light the brake warning light on the instrument panel when the level of fluid falls below a certain level in the reservoir(s).
2   The float rides on the surface of the hydraulic fluid and if the level drops to the danger point, a magnet in the float operates a switch, so completing the circuit.
3   To check the operation of the switch: with the ignition switched on, but the engine not running, slowly raise the cap and have an assistant ascertain that the brake warning light is extinguished when the float is raised up to the cap.

18 Proportioning valve – general

This valve is fitted between the front and rear brake lines (photo) and enables the front brakes to operate normally even if the rear brake line has developed a serious leak. Also should there be a leak in the front brake line the rear brake will still function.

It is recommended that every 24 000 miles (40 000 km), valve operation be checked for correct operation. Remove all luggage and then drive the car to a dry road. When the car is travelling at 30 mph (50 km/h) apply the brakes suddenly.

The valve is functioning normally when the rear wheels lock simultaneously with the front wheels or when the front wheels lock before the rear wheels. Examine the skid marks for evidence of this.

Should the rear wheels lock before the front wheels then it is probably that the valve has developed an internal fault and it should be renewed – it cannot be repaired.

18.1 The dual proportioning valve showing port connections
1   From master cylinder   4   To rear wheel cylinder
2   To front wheel cylinder   5   To front wheel cylinder
3   To rear wheel cylinder   6   From master cylinder

19 Vacuum servo unit – description

A vacuum servo unit is fitted and operates in series with the master cylinder to provide assistance to the driver when the brake pedal is depressed. This reduces the effort required by the driver to operate the brake under all braking conditions.

The unit operates by vacuum obtained from the intake manifold and comprises basically a booster diaphragm and control valve assembly.

The servo unit and hydraulic master cylinder are connected together so that the servo unit piston rod (valve rod) acts as the master cylinder pushrod. The driver's braking effort is transmitted through another pushrod to servo unit piston and its built-in control system. The servo unit piston is attached to a rolling diaphragm which ensures an airtight seal between the two major parts of the servo unit casing. The forward chamber is held under vacuum conditions created in the intake manifold of the engine and, during periods when the brake pedal is not in use, the controls open a passage to the rear chamber so placing it under vacuum conditions as well. When the brake pedal is depressed, the vacuum passage to the rear chamber is cut off and the chamber opened to atmospheric pressure. The consequent pressure difference across the servo piston pushes the piston forward in the vacuum chamber and operates the main pushrod to the master cylinder.

The controls are designed so that assistance is given under all conditions and, when the brakes are not required, vacuum in the rear chamber is again established when the brake pedal is released.

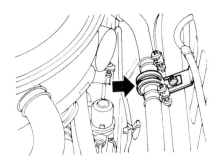

Fig. 9.15 Servo check valve location (Sec 19)

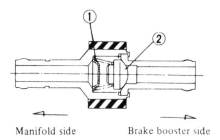

Manifold side   Brake booster side

Fig. 9.16 Sectional view of check valve showing spring (1) and valve (2) (Sec 19)

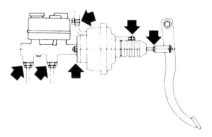

Fig. 9.17 Servo unit removal – disconnect at points indicated (Sec 20)

Length "A"
9.75 - 10.00 mm
(0.3839 - 0.3937 in)

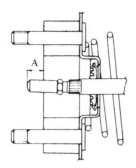

Fig. 9.18 Adjust the pushrod projection length (A) (Sec 20)

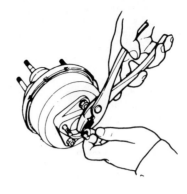

Fig. 9.19 Adjusting the servo pushrod (Sec 20)

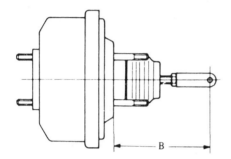

Fig. 9.20 Adjust operating rod length (Sec 20)

B = 5.12 in (130 mm)

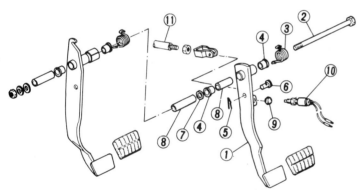

Fig. 9.22 Pedal assembly components (Sec 21)

1	Brake pedal	5	Snap-ring	9	Brake lamp switch pad
2	Fulcrum pin	6	Clevis pin	10	Brake lamp switch
3	Return spring	7	Plain washer	11	Brake pushrod (operating
4	Pedal bushing	8	Pedal shaft		rod)

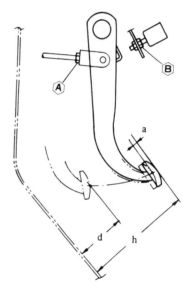

Fig. 9.21 Brake pedal adjustments: A and B are locknuts (Sec 21)

a   Free play   h   Free height (see text)   d   Depressed height

Under normal operating conditions the vacuum servo unit is very reliable and requires no maintenance. Should the unit be suspected of malfunction it will have to be vacuum tested to find the cause of the problem and this is therefore a task for your Datsun dealer.

Before suspecting the servo unit itself, the vacuum lines and pipe joint connections should be checked for condition and security and renewed if necessary.

A check valve is fitted into the vacuum hose lines as shown in Fig. 9.15 and this can be removed for renewal by simply disconnecting the hoses and pulling the valve free. When fitting the new valve be sure to locate it correctly as shown in Fig. 9.16.

If a problem exists within the servo unit itself, remove it and renew it or get your Datsun dealer to overhaul it for you if possible.

It is emphasised that even if the servo unit fails completely, normal brake operation is not affected, the only difference being the need for greater effort at the pedal by the driver. The same applies if the car is being towed with the engine not running.

20 Vacuum servo unit – removal and refitting

1   Remove the master cylinder as described in Section 15.
2   Disconnect the vacuum hose from the servo unit.
3   Release the locknut on the pushrod and unscrew the pushrod from the clevis.
4   Remove the four servo unit securing nuts and withdraw the servo unit from the engine compartment bulkhead.

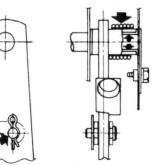

Fig. 9.23 Pedal lubrication points (arrowed) (Sec 21)

5   When refitting the servo unit, check and if necessary adjust the projection of the pushrod, as indicated in Fig. 9.18. To do this, grip the serrated portion of the pushrod and release the locknut. Tighten the locknut after adjustment.

6   Adjust the operating rod length (see Fig. 9.20) to 5.12 in (130 mm).

7   Refitting is otherwise the reverse of the removal procedure. Check the brake pedal position as described in Section 21 after bleeding the hydraulic system as described in Section 14.

21 Brake pedal and stop-lamp switch – adjustment, removal and refitting

1   The pedal height, 'h' in Fig. 9.21, must be adjusted to the following dimension:

Left-hand drive – 7.09 to 7.32 in (180 to 186 mm)
Right-hand drive – 6.97 to 7.20 in (177 to 183 mm)

2   Adjust, if necessary, by slackening the pushrod locknut and adjusting the length of the pushrod. Tighten the locknut.

3   Adjust the stop-lamp switch so that the pedal lightly touches the stopper rubber on the end of the stop-lamp switch. Tighten the stop-lamp switch locknut.

4   To remove the brake pedal, remove the snap pin fitted at the end of the clevis pin. Pull out the clevis pin and separate the pushrod from the brake pedal. Remove the nut securing the fulcrum pin and pull out the fulcrum pin. The brake pedal can now be removed along with the return spring and clutch pedal.

5   Refitting is the reverse of the removal sequence. Apply a coating of multi-purpose grease to the sliding parts and return spring.

22 Fault diagnosis – Braking system

Symptom	Reason(s)
Brake grab	Out-of-round drums Excessive run-out of discs Rust on drums or discs Oil-stained linings or pads
Brake drag	Faulty master cylinder Foot pedal return impeded Reservoir breather blocked Seized caliper or wheel cylinder piston Incorrect adjustment of handbrake Weak or broken shoe return springs Crushed, blocked or swollen pipe lines
Excessive pedal effort required	Linings or pads not yet bedded-in Drum, disc or linings contaminated with oil or grease Scored drums or discs Faulty vacuum servo unit
Brake pedal feels hard	Glazed surfaces of friction material Rust on disc surfaces Seized caliper or wheel cylinder piston
Excessive pedal travel	Low reservoir fluid level Disc run-out excessive Worn front wheel bearings Air in system Worn pad or linings
Pedal creep during sustained application	Fluid leak Internal fault in master cylinder Faulty servo unit non-return valve
Pedal 'spongy'	Air in system Perished flexible hose Loose master cylinder mounting nuts Cracked brake drum Faulty master cylinder Reservoir breather blocked Linings not bedded-in
Fall in reservoir fluid level	Normal due to pad or lining wear (slow fall) Leak in hydraulic system
Rear wheels lock before front wheels during heavy braking	Proportioning valve faulty

Chapter 10 Electrical system

For modifications, and information applicable to later models, see Supplement at end of manual

Contents

Specifications

System type .... 12V, negative earth

Battery
Type .... Lead acid
Capacity .... 60 or 65 Ah depending on model and territory
Electrolyte specific gravity – fully charged at 68°F (20°C):
    All except NS70 battery 1.260
    Type NS70 battery 1.280

Alternator
Make .... Hitachi
Type:
    A10 and A12 engines LT135-13B
    A14 engine .... LR150-53 or LR160-46
    A15 engine .... LR160-125 or LR150-99
Nominal output:
    LT135-13B 35A
    LR150 series 50A
    LR160 series 60A
Regulated output voltage .... 14.4 to 15.0
Minimum brush length:
    LR160-25 and LR150-99 .... 0.276 in (7.0 mm)
    All other models .... 0.295 in (7.5 mm)
Brush spring pressure .... 8.9 to 12.1 oz (255 to 345 g)
Minimum allowable slip ring diameter .... 1.18 in (30.0 mm)

Voltage regulator – mechanical (A10 and A12 engines)

	Hitachi TL12-57	Mitsubishi RQB2220B
Type		
Voltage regulator:		
Core gap	0.0236 to 0.0394 in (0.6 to 1.0 mm)	0.0276 to 0.0512 in (0.7 to 1.3 mm)
Point gap	0.0118 to 0.0157 in (0.3 to 0.4 mm)	0.0118 to 0.0177 in (0.3 to 0.45 mm)
Regulating voltage	14.3 to 15.3 at 68°F (20°C)	14.3 to 15.3 at 68°F (20°C)
Charge relay:		
Core gap	0.0315 to 0.0394 in (0.8 to 1.0 mm)	0.0354 to 0.0551 in (0.9 to 1.4 mm)
Point gap	0.0157 to 0.0236 in (0.4 to 0.6 mm)	0.0275 to 0.0433 in (0.7 to 1.1 mm)
Voltage coil resistance	37.8 ohms at 68°F (20°C)	23.6 ohms at 68°F (20°C)

Starter motor

A10 and A12 engines

Make and type	Hitachi S114-161
System voltage	12V
No load:	
Current	Less than 60A
Revolution	More than 7000 rpm
Terminal voltage	12V
Commutator outer diameter	More than 1.22 in (31 mm)
Brush length	More than 0.47 in (12 mm)
Brush spring tension	3.1 to 4.0 lb (1.4 to 1.8 kg)
Gap between pinion and pinion stopper	0.012 to 0.059 in (0.3 to 1.5 mm)

A14 and A15 engines

Make and type:	
A14 engine	Hitachi S114-161E or S114-208E
A15 engine	Hitachi S114-161F

Details as for S114-161 starter motor but with the following differences:

Commutator outer diameter	More than 1.26 in (32 mm)
Gap between pinion and pinion stopper	0.012 to 0.098 in (0.3 to 2.5 mm)

Fuses

Type	Cartridge
Rating	13 x 10 A
Circuits protected	See wiring diagram

Fusible links

Circuits protected:	Colour	Size
Headlight	Green	0.0008 in² (0.5 mm²)
Rear window defogger and fan motor	Green	0.0008 in² (0.5 mm²)
Ignition switch power supply	Green	0.0008 in² (0.5 mm²)
Fuse block power supply 'B'	Red	0.0013 in² (0.85 mm²)

Bulbs

	Watts
Headlights (sealed beam)	50/40
Headlights (semi-sealed beam)	45/40
Headlights (semi-sealed beam – Halogen)	60/55
Headlights – USA 1981 models (A15 engines)	65/55
Front turn signal lamp (A10 and A12 engine)	21
Front turn/clearance lamp (A14 and A15 engines)	23/8
Side marker/clearance lamp – front and rear	5
Interior light (A10 and A12 engine)	10
Interior light (A14 and A15 engines)	8
Rear turn signal lamp	23
Reverse (back-up) light	23
Stop/tail light	23/8
Number plate light (A10 and A12 engine)	10
Licence plate light (A14 and A15 engines)	8
Luggage compartment light	5
Instrument panel light	3.4
Warning lights	3.4
Heater control panel light	1.4
Radio illumination light	2.5
Ashtray illumination light	1.2
Rear window defogger warning light	1.4

Torque wrench settings

	lbf ft	kgf m
Alternator pulley nut	33 to 43	4.5 to 6.0

1 General description

The electrical system is of the 12 volt negative earth type and the major components comprise a 12 volt battery of which the negative terminal is earthed, an alternator which is driven from the crankshaft pulley and a starter motor.

The battery supplies a steady amount of current for the ignition, lighting, and other electrical circuits and provides a reserve of electricity when the current consumed by the electrical equipment exceeds that being produced by the alternator.

The alternator, depending on type is either fitted with its own integrated circuit (IC) regulator or has a separate electro-mechanical regulator. This ensures a high output if the battery is in a low state of charge or the demand from the electrical equipment is high, and a low output if the battery is fully charged and there is little demand from the electrical equipment.

When fitting electrical accessories to cars with a negative earth system it is important, if they contain silicon diodes or transistors, that they are connected correctly, otherwise serious damage may result to the components concerned. Items such as radios, tape players, electronic ignition systems, automatic headlight dipping etc, should all be checked for correct polarity.

It is important that the battery positive lead is always disconnected if the battery is to be boost charged. Also if body repairs are to be carried out using electric arc welding equipment, the alternator must be disconnected otherwise serious damage can be caused to the more delicate components. Whenever the battery has to be disconnected it must always be reconnected with the negative terminal earthed.

2 Battery – maintenance and inspection

1 Normal weekly battery maintenance consists of checking the electrolyte level of each cell to ensure that the separators are covered by $\frac{1}{2}$ inch (12 mm) of electrolyte. Some batteries have a translucent case through which the electrolyte level can be seen; on other types the cell caps must be removed. If the level has fallen, top up the battery using distilled water only (photo). Do not overfill. If a battery is over-filled or any electrolyte spilled, immediately wipe away the excess as electrolyte attacks and corrodes very rapidly any metal it comes into contact with.

2 As well as keeping the terminals clean and covered with petroleum jelly, the top of the battery, and especially the top of the cells, should be kept clean and dry. This helps to prevent corrosion and ensures that the battery does not become partially discharged by leakage through dampness and dirt.

3 Once every few months remove the battery and inspect the clamp nuts, clamps, tray and battery leads for corrosion (white fluffy deposits on the metal which are brittle to the touch). If any corrosion is found clean off the deposits with ammonia and paint over the clean metal with an anti-rust/anti-acid paint.

4 At the same time inspect the battery case for cracks. If a crack is found, clean and plug it with one of the proprietary compounds marketed. If leakage through the crack has been excessive it will be necessary to refill the appropriate cell with fresh electrolyte as detailed later. Cracks are frequently caused to the top of a battery case by pouring in distilled water in the middle of winter *after* instead of *before* a run. This gives the water no chance to mix with the electrolyte and so the former freezes and splits the battery case.

5 If topping-up the battery becomes excessive and the case has been inspected for cracks that could cause leakage, but none are found, the battery is being overcharged and the alternator control unit will have to be checked and (if possible) reset.

6 With the battery on the bench measure its specific gravity with a hydrometer to determine the state of the charge and condition of the electrolyte. There should be very little variation between the different cells and, if variation in excess of 0.025 is present, it will be due to either:

(a) *Loss of electrolyte from the battery caused by spillage or a leak resulting in a drop in the specific gravity of the electrolyte, when the deficiency was replaced with distilled water instead of fresh electrolyte*

(b) *An internal short circuit caused by a buckled plate or similar malady pointing to the likelihood of total battery failure in the near future*

3 Electrolyte – replenishment

1 If the battery is in a fully charged state but one of the cells maintains a specific gravity reading which is 0.025 or lower than the others, and each cell has been tested with a voltage meter to check for short circuits (a four to seven second test should give a steady reading of between 1.2 and 1.8 volts), then it is likely that electrolyte has been lost from the cell with the low reading at some time.

2 Top up the cell with a solution of 1 part sulphuric acid to 2.5 parts of water. If the cell is already fully topped up, draw some electrolyte out of it with a pipette.

3 When mixing the sulphuric acid and water **never add water to sulphuric acid** – always pour the acid slowly onto the water in a glass container. **If water is added to sulphuric acid it will explode.**

4 Continue to top up the cell with the freshly made electrolyte and to recharge the battery and check the hydrometer readings.

4 Battery – removal and refitting

1 The battery is mounted on a carrier at the front right-hand side of the engine compartment. It should be removed every six months for cleaning and testing.

2 Disconnect the negative and the positive leads from the battery terminals by slackening the clamp bolts and lifting off the clamps.

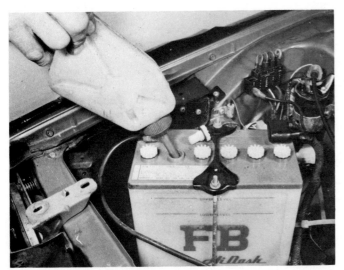

2.1 Topping up the battery electrolyte

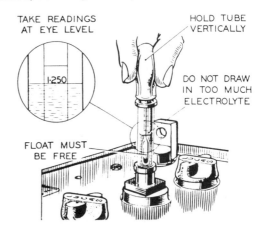

Fig. 10.1 Using a hydrometer to check the battery specific gravity
(Sec 3)

TAKE READINGS AT EYE LEVEL

HOLD TUBE VERTICALLY

1·250

DO NOT DRAW IN TOO MUCH ELECTROLYTE

FLOAT MUST BE FREE

3   Remove the nuts securing the battery securing clamp and take off the clamp. Carefully lift the battery from its carrier and hold it vertically to ensure that none of the electrolyte is spilled.

4   Refitting is the reverse of the removal procedure. Smear the terminals and clamps with petroleum jelly to prevent corrosion. Never use a mineral base grease.

5   Battery – charging

1   In winter time when a heavy demand is placed on the battery, such as when starting from cold, and much electrical equipment is continually in use, it is a good idea to occasionally have the battery fully charged from an external source at a rate of 3.5 to 4 amps.

2   Continue to charge the battery at this rate until no further rise in specific gravity is noted over a four hour period.

3   Alternatively, a trickle charger, charging at the rate of 1.5 amps, can be safely used overnight.

4   Special rapid 'boost' charges which are claimed to restore the power of the battery in 1 to 2 hours are most dangerous unless they are thermostatically controlled as they can cause serious damage to the battery plates through overheating.

5   While charging the battery note that the temperature of the electrolyte should never exceed 113°F (45°C).

6   Take extreme care when making circuit connections to any vehicle fitted with an alternator and observe the precautions given in Section 7.

7   Once the battery has been fully charged, switch off and disconnect the charger. Do not leave the battery on charge indefinitely.

8   When fully charged the specific gravity at 68°F (20°C) should be as given in the Specifications. Note that the temperature given is that of the electrolyte.

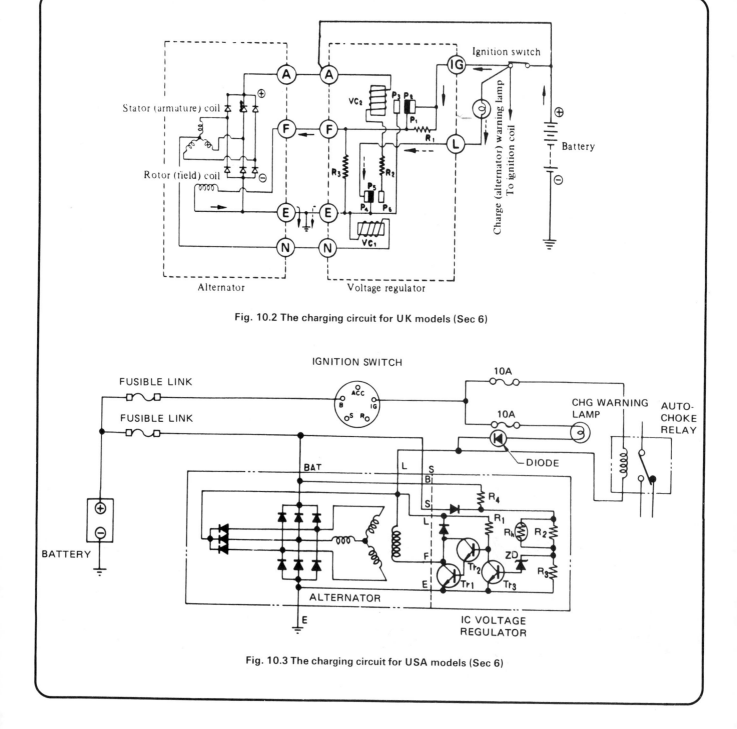

Fig. 10.2 The charging circuit for UK models (Sec 6)

Fig. 10.3 The charging circuit for USA models (Sec 6)

6 Alternator – general description

The main advantage of the alternator over a dynamo lies in its ability to provide a high charge at low revolutions.

The alternator is of the rotating field, ventilated design. It comprises principally, a laminated stator on which is wound a 3-phase output, and a rotor carrying the field windings. The front and rear ends of the rotor shaft run in ball races each of which is lubricated for life, and natural finish die cast end brackets incorporating the mounting lugs.

The rotor is belt-driven from the engine through a pulley keyed to the rotor shaft and a pressed steel fan adjacent to the pulley draws cooling air through the alternator. This fan forms an integral part of the alternator specifications. It has been designed to provide adequate air flow with a minimum of noise and to withstand the high stress associated with maximum speed.

The brush gear of the field system is mounted in the slip ring end brackets. Two carbon brushes bear against a pair of concentric brass slip rings carried on a moulded disc attached to the end of the rotor. Also attached to the slip ring end bracket are six silicon diodes connected in a three-phase bridge to rectify the generated alternating current for use in charging the battery and supplying power to the electrical system.

The alternator output is controlled by an integral electronic or separate electro-mechanical voltage regulator unit and warning light control unit to indicate to the driver when there is a fault in the system.

7 Alternator – special precautions and maintenance

Special precautions

Whenever the electrical system of the car is being attended to or an external means of starting the engine is used there are certain precautions that must be taken, otherwise serious and expensive damage can result.

1 Always make sure that the negative terminal of the battery is earthed. If the terminal connections are accidentally reversed or if the battery has been reverse charged the alternator will burn out.

2 The output terminal of the alternator must never be earthed but should always be connected directly to the positive terminal of the battery.

3 Whenever the alternator is to be removed, or when disconnecting the terminals of the alternator circuit, always disconnect the battery first.

4 The alternator must never be operated without the battery-to-alternator cable connected.

5 If the battery is to be charged by external means, always disconnect both battery cables before the external charger is connected. Never start the car with a battery charger connected.

6 Should it be necessary to use a booster charger or booster battery to start the engine, always double check that the negative cables are connected to negative terminals and positive cables to positive terminals.

7 Before using electric-arc welding equipment to repair any part of the vehicle, disconnect the connector from the alternator and disconnect the positive battery terminal.

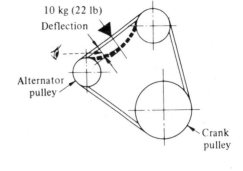

Fig. 10.4 Check the drivebelt tension (Sec 7)

Maintenance

8 The equipment has been designed for the minimum amount of maintenance in service; the only items subject to wear are the brushes and bearings.

9 Brushes should be examined after about 75 000 miles (120 000 km) and renewed if necessary. The bearings are pre-packed with grease for life and should not require further attention.

10 Check the V-belt drive regularly for corrrect adjustment. Deflection should be 0.47 to 0.63 in (12 to 16 mm). Depress the belt with the finger and thumb between the alternator and water pump pulleys.

11 If adjustment is required, loosen the alternator pivot and adjusting link bolts, and reposition the alternator as necessary. Tighten the bolts again afterwards. Do not lever against the body of the alternator or damage may result.

12 If a new belt is fitted, recheck the tension after about 200 miles (300 km) of driving.

8 Alternator – testing in the vehicle

1 Where a faulty alternator is suspected, first ensure that the battery is fully charged; if necessary charge from an outside source.

2 Obtain a 0 to 30 voltmeter.

3 Connect the voltmeter across the battery terminals and check that the voltmeter indicates battery voltage (12 volts).

4 Switch the headlights to main beam.

5 Start the engine and gradually increase its speed to approximately 1100rpm and check the reading on the voltmeter. If it registers over 12.5 volts then the alternator is probably in good condition; if it registers below 12.5 volts then the alternator is faulty, and must be removed and repaired. Do not exceed 1100rpm during the test.

6 The above is only a rough test and should not be regarded as conclusive. Full testing requires skills and equipment unlikely to be possessed by the home mechanic and should be entrusted to an auto-electrician.

9.2 Alternator rear face showing wiring connections (A10 engine)

9.3a Alternator location (A10 engine) showing upper fixing/adjuster strap and bolt

9.3b Alternator location – A12 engine

9 Alternator – removal and refitting

1   Detach the battery earth cable.
2   Disconnect the lead wires and connector, from the rear of the alternator (photo).
3   Slacken the alternator pivot mounting bolts and also the adjustment link bolt sufficiently to allow the alternator to be hinged inwards towards the engine (photos).
4   Disconnect the fan belt from the alternator pulley and then remove the pivot and adjusting link bolts whilst supporting the alternator, and lift it clear.
5   Refitting is a reversal of the removal procedure, but ensure that the fan belt tension is correctly adjusted as described in Section 7.

10 Alternator – brush renewal

1   These are the most likely components to require renewal, and their wear should be checked whenever the alternator is suspected of being faulty (indicated by a discharged battery).
2   On those alternators where the brushes are renewed externally, proceed as follows.
3   Remove the brush holder securing screws and withdraw the cover (Fig. 10.5).
4   Remove the brush holder complete with brushes. Do not disconnect the 'N' terminal from the stator coil lead.
5   If the brushes have worn down to the limit marked on them, renew the brush assembly.

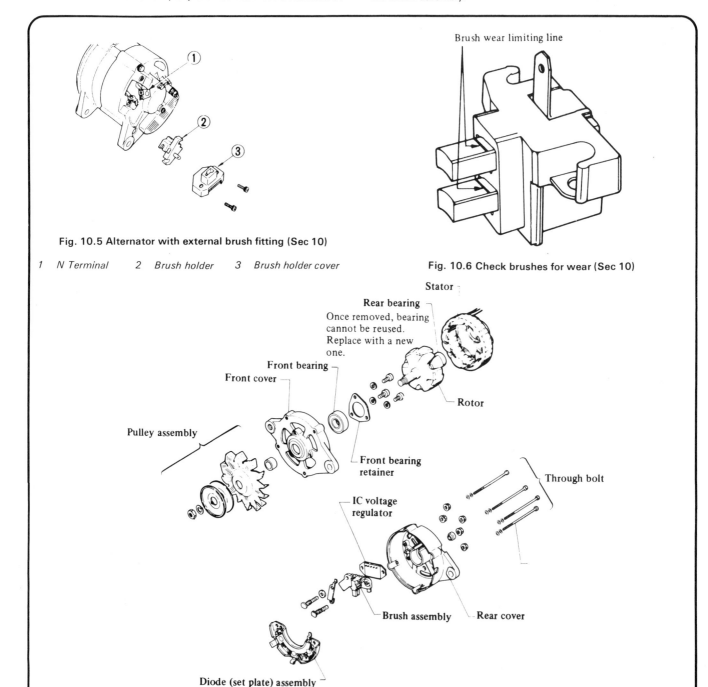

Fig. 10.5 Alternator with external brush fitting (Sec 10)

1   N Terminal   2   Brush holder   3   Brush holder cover

Fig. 10.6 Check brushes for wear (Sec 10)

Fig. 10.7 The alternator components – IC regulator model (Sec 10)

6   Check that the brushes move smoothly in their holders; otherwise clean the holders free from any dust or dirt.
7   Refitting of the brushes is the reverse of the removal procedure.
8   On USA models, the alternator brush holder unit is enclosed within the rear cover and access is only obtainable on removal of the cover. To do this, unscrew and remove the three through bolts and then carefully separate the front cover together with the rotor from the rear cover by tapping it lightly with a small soft-headed mallet.
9   The exposed brushes can now be inspected for excessive wear. If the brushes have worn down to the wear limit mark line, then the brush assembly must be renewed.
10 Since the removal of the brush and IC voltage regulator unit from the rear cover necessitates their disconnection from the stator wiring, also from the diode set plate and the terminal connections, this task is best entrusted to your Datsun dealer or local automotive electrician. If you are doing the work yourself, note that the diodes and the regulator can be damaged by heat from a soldering iron. Grip the leads being soldered with pliers to avoid heat transfer to sensitive components.

11 Alternator – fault finding and repair

Due to the specialist knowledge and equipment required to test and service an alternator it is recommended that if the performance is suspect, the car be taken to an automobile electrician who will have the facilities for such work. Because of this recommendation no further detailed service information is given.

12 Voltage regulator – general description and testing

1   On UK market models, the voltage regulator is fitted separately from the alternator and is of the electro-mechanical type.
2   The electro-mechanical regulator basically comprises a voltage regulator and a charge relay. The voltage regulator has two sets of contact points, lower and upper sets to control the alternator voltage. An armature plate placed between the two sets of contacts, moves upward, downward or vibrates. When closed the lower contacts complete the field circuit direct to earth, and the upper contacts when closed, complete the field circuit to earth through a field coil resistance, thereby producing the alternator output.
3   The charge relay is similar to the voltage regulator. When the upper contacts are closed the ignition warning light extinguishes. The construction of the voltage regulator is basically identical to the charge relay.
4   If the voltage regulator is suspected of malfunction, it should be tested by an auto electrician to diagnose any faults. Before taking this action however first check that the alternator drivebelt is not broken or slack and that the electrical leads are secure.
5   The core gap and points gap clearances can also be checked by removing the regulator unit cover (two screws) and using a feeler gauge, checking the respective clearances as shown in Figs. 10.9 and 10.10. The ignition must be off when making these checks.
6   If the surfaces of the contacts are rough or pitted, clean them by drawing a strip of fine emery cloth between them.
7   If necessary adjust the respective contact gap clearances as shown to the specified amount.
8   The regulating voltage can be adjusted but this must be entrusted to an auto electrician as its setting is critical and depends on the ambient temperature at the time of adjustment.
9   On USA models the regulator is fitted integrally in the alternator and comprises integrated circuits (IC) which incorporate transistors to regulate the current flow through the alternator.
10 An electronic relay is used and this too has transistors.
11 This type of unit is not adjustable and if suspected of malfunction it should be tested and if necessary renewed by an auto electrician.

13 Starter motor – general description

The starter motor comprises a solenoid, a lever, starter drive gear and the motor. The solenoid is fitted to the top of the motor. The plunger inside the solenoid is connected to a centre pivoting lever, the other end of which is in contact with the drive sleeve and drive gear.
When the ignition switch is operated, current from the battery flows through the series and shunt solenoid coils thereby magnetizing

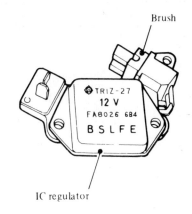

Fig. 10.8 The IC regulator and brush unit (Sec 10)

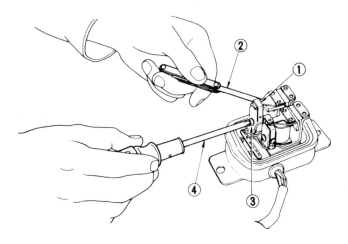

Fig. 10.9 Adjusting the regulator core gap (Sec 12)

1	Armature	3	Adjusting screw
2	Feeler gauge	4	Screwdriver

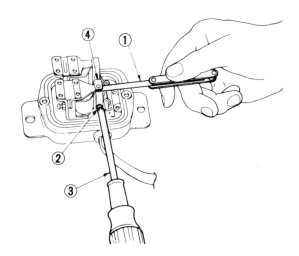

Fig. 10.10 Adjusting the regulator points gap (Sec 12)

1	Feeler gauge	3	Screwdriver
2	Adjusting screw	4	Contact point

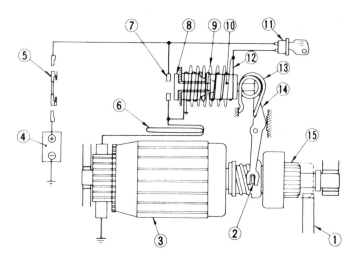

Fig. 10.11 Starting circuit (Sec 13)

1	Ring gear	9	Shunt coil
2	Shift lever guide	10	Plunger
3	Armature	11	Ignition switch
4	Battery	12	Series coil
5	Fusible link	13	Torsion spring
6	Field coil	14	Shift lever
7	Stationary contact	15	Pinion
8	Movable contact		

the solenoid. The plunger is drawn into the solenoid so that it operates the lever and moves the drive pinion int the starter ring gear. The solenoid switch contacts close after the drive pinion is partially engaged with the ring gear.

Both reduction and non-reduction type starter motors are fitted, according to the model and market. The reduction gear reduces the armature speed and increases the rotational torque.

14 Starter motor – testing on engine

1   If the starter motor fails to operate, check the condition of the battery by turning on the headlights. If they glow brightly for several seconds and then gradually dim, the battery is in an undercharged condition.

2   If the headlights continue to glow brightly and it is obvious that the battery is in good condition, check the tightness of the earth lead from the battery terminal to its connection on the body frame. Also check the positive battery lead connections. Check the tightness of the connections at the rear of the solenoid. If available, check the wiring with a voltmeter or test light for breaks or short circuits.

3   If the wiring is in order check the starter motor for continuity using a voltmeter.

4   If the battery is fully charged, the wiring is in order and the motor electrical circuit continuous and it still fails to operate, then it will have to be removed from the engine for examination. Before this is done, however, make sure that the pinion has not jammed in mesh with the ring gear due either to a broken solenoid spring or dirty pinion gear splines. To release the pinion, engage a low gear and with the ignition switch off rock the car backwards and forwards which should release the pinion from mesh with the ring gear; if the pinion still remains jammed the starter motor must be removed.

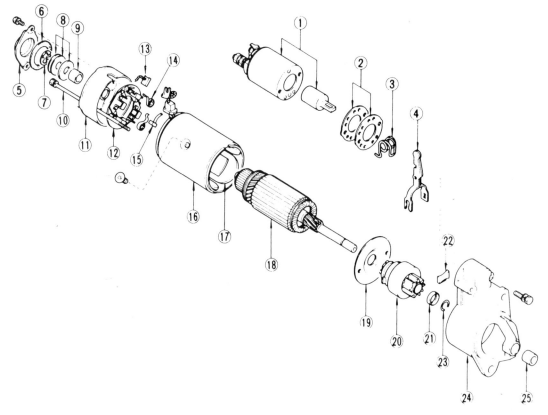

Fig. 10.12 Starter motor components – non-reduction gear type (Sec 16)

1	Solenoid unit	8	Thrust washer	14	Brush spring	20	Pinion assembly
2	Dust cover	9	Rear cover bush	15	Brush (+)	21	Pinion stopper
3	Torsion spring	10	Through bolt	16	Yoke	22	Dust cover
4	Shift lever	11	Rear cover	17	Field coil	23	Stopper clip
5	Dust cover	12	Brush holder assembly	18	Armature	24	Gearcase
6	Dust cover	13	Brush (−)	19	Centre plate	25	Gearcase bush
7	E-ring						

15 Starter motor – removal and refitting

1 Disconnect the battery earth lead.
2 Disconnect the black and yellow wire from the 'S' terminal on the solenoid, and the black cable from the 'B' terminal (also on the end cover of the solenoid).
3 Unscrew and remove the two starter motor securing bolts, pull the starter forward, tilt it slightly to clear the motor shaft support from the flywheel ring gear and withdraw it.
4 Refitting is the reverse of the removal procedure.

16 Starter motor (non-reduction gear type) – dismantling, servicing and reassembly

1 Disconnect the lead from the 'M' terminal of the solenoid.
2 Remove the solenoid securing screws and withdraw the solenoid from the starter motor.
3 Remove the dust cover, the E-ring and the thrust washer(s) from the rear cover as applicable.
4 Unscrew and remove the two screws which secure the brush holder.
5 Unscrew and remove the two tie-bolts and the rear cover.
6 Using a length of wire with a hook at its end, remove the brushes by pulling the brush springs aside.
7 Remove the brush holder.
8 Withdraw the yoke assembly and extract the armature assembly and shift lever. Push the pinion stop towards the pinion to expose the circlip. Extract the circlip and then withdraw the stop and clutch assembly.
9 Check the brushes for wear. If their length is less than that specified, renew them.
10 If an ohmmeter is available, test the field coil for continuity. To do this, connect one probe of the meter to the field coil positive terminal and the other to the positive brush holder. If no reading is indicated then the field coil circuit has a break in it.
11 Connect one probe of the meter to the field coil positive lead and the other one to the yoke. If there is a low resistance, then the field coil is earthed due to a breakdown in insulation. When this fault is discovered, the field coils should be renewed by an automotive electrician as it is very difficult to remove the field coil securing screws without special equipment. In any event, it will probably be more economical to exchange the complete starter motor for a reconditioned unit.
12 Undercut the separators of the commutator using an old hacksaw blade ground to suit a depth of 0.02 to 0.03 in (0.5 to 0.8 mm). The commutator may be polished with a piece of very fine glass paper – never use emery cloth as the carborundum particles will become embedded in the copper surfaces.
13 The armature may be tested for insulation breakdown, again using the ohmmeter. To do this, place one probe on the armature shaft and the other on each of the commutator segments in turn. If there is a reading indicated at any time during the test then the armature must be renewed.
14 Wash the components of the drivegear in paraffin, inspect for wear

or damage, particularly to the pinion teeth, and renew as appropriate. Refitting is a reversal of dismantling but stake a new stop washer in position and lubricate the sliding surfaces of the pinion assembly with a light oil, applied sparingly.
15 Reassembly of the remaining components of the starter motor is the reverse of the dismantling procedure.
16 When the starter motor has been fully reassembled, actuate the solenoid which will throw the drivegear forward into its normal flywheel engagement position. Do this by connecting jumper leads between the battery negative terminal and the solenoid 'M' terminal and between the battery positive terminal and the solenoid 'S' terminal. Now check the gap between the endface of the drive pinion and the mating face of the thrust washer (Fig. 10.15). Adjusting washers are available in different thicknesses.

17 Starter motor (reduction gear type) – dismantling, servicing and reassembly

1 Detach the connection plate from the 'M' terminal on the solenoid unit.
2 Unscrew and remove the solenoid retaining screws and withdraw the solenoid unit. The torsion spring can be removed at this stage, but note how it is located.
3 Unscrew the through bolts and carefully remove the rear cover, by prising it free using a screwdriver or similar but take care not to damage the packing.
4 Withdraw the yoke assembly and extract the armature unit.
5 The brushes and holders can now be removed but note that the positive brush differs in that the brush is isolated from its holder and the connecting wire is attached to the field coil.
6 To extract the brushes hook back the retaining spring and pull the brushes from their respective holders but keep them in order noting their positions in case they do not require renewal.
7 To detach the centre housing from the gearcase simple unscrew and remove the retaining bolts. The reduction/pinion gears can then be removed for examination.
8 The examination and reassembly of the respective components closely follows that of the non-reduction gear type in Section 16 paragraphs 9 to 16, but in addition check the condition of the pinion and reduction gear with overrun clutch components.
9 Any damage or signs of excessive wear in these parts will necessitate renewal. Check also that the sleeve slides freely on the shaft.
10 Check the assembled unit for satisfactory operation before fitting and with the solenoid actuated, check the pinion height difference as shown in Fig. 10.18. If necessary adjust to suit by changing the washer thickness.

18 Fuses and fusible links – general

1 The fuse box is located on the side panel beneath the dashboard. All the fuses are of 10 amp rating and should renewal be necessary, only a fuse of this rating must be used (photo).

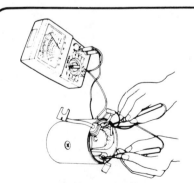

Fig. 10.13 Checking the starter motor field coils for continuity (Sec 16)

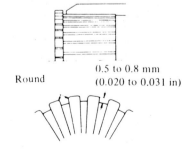

Round
0.5 to 0.8 mm
(0.020 to 0.031 in)

Fig. 10.14 Commutator separators should be undercut as shown (Sec 16)

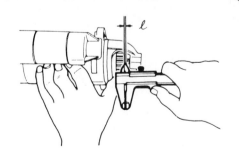

Fig. 10.15 Check the pinion endface-to-thrust washer clearance (Sec 16)

l = 0.3 to 2.5 mm   (0.012 to 0.098 in)

2   If an electrical failure occur and the fuses are in order, check the fusible links situated beside the battery (photo). When a link is found to have overheated, trace the cause and renew the link with one of equal rating.

3   In the event of a fuse or fusible link blowing, always establish the cause before fitting a new one. This is most likely to be due to faulty insulation somewhere in the wiring circuit, or a component fault.

4   Do not be tempted to bypass persistently blowing fuses with silver foil or wire. Serious wiring damage or even fire may result.

19 Headlights – bulb and unit removal and refitting

Semi-sealed beam bulb renewal

1   On this unit the bulb(s) can be removed without removing the complete headlight unit.

2   Raise and support the bonnet and from inside the front panel, peel back the rubber cover and detach the headlight wire connector and rubber surround (photos).

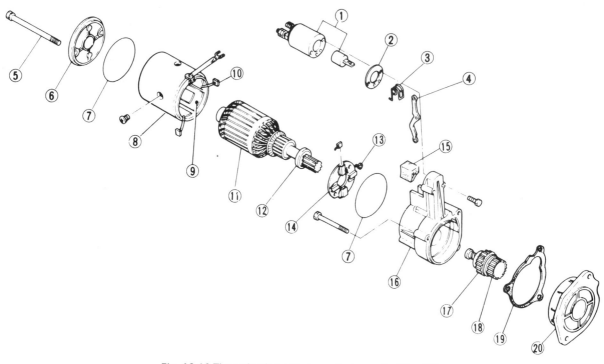

Fig. 10.16 The reduction gear type starter motor (Sec 17)

1 Solenoid unit	6 Rear cover	11 Armature	16 Centre housing
2 Dust cover (Adjusting washer)	7 O-ring	12 Centre bearing	17 Reduction gear
3 Torsion spring	8 Yoke	13 Brush spring	18 Pinion gear
4 Shift lever	9 Field coil	14 Brush holder	19 Packing
5 Through bolt	10 Brush	15 Dust cover	20 Gearcase

18.1 The main fuses shown with the cover removed

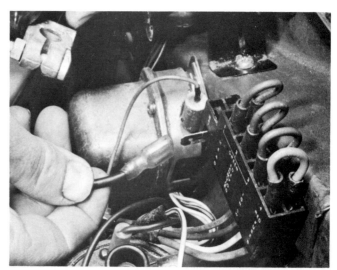

18.2 The fusible link

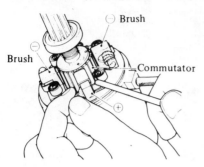

Fig. 10.17 Removing the brushes (Sec 17)

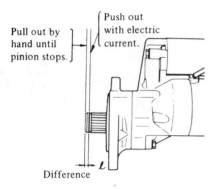

Fig. 10.18 Check the pinion height distance (Sec 17)

l = 0.3 to 1.5 mm (0.012 to 0.059 in)

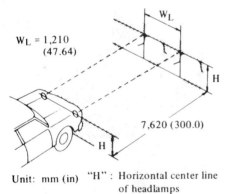

$W_L = 1,210$ (47.64)

7,620 (300.0)

Unit: mm (in) "H" : Horizontal center line of headlamps

Fig. 10.19 Headlight beam alignment – sealed beam types (Sec 20)

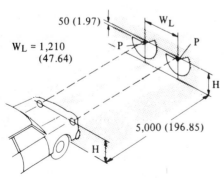

50 (1.97)

$W_L = 1,210$ (47.64)

5,000 (196.85)

"H" : Horizontal center line of headlamps

Unit: mm (in)

Fig. 10.20 Headlight beam alignment – semi-sealed beam types (Sec 20)

3 Rotate the retaining ring to remove it and withdraw the bulb and holder (photos).
4 Refitting of the bulb is a direct reversal of the removal procedure, but check operation on completion.

Sealed beam unit
5 If the bulb blows on this type the complete unit must be renewed.

Headlight unit removal
6 Remove the radiator grille, referring to Chapter 12 if necessary.
7 On the semi-sealed unit, detach the chrome surround ring (photo).
8 Unscrew and remove the headlight unit retaining screws. Do not disturb the beam alignment screws or the lights will have to be readjusted.
9 Withdraw the headlight unit and disconnect the lead wire connectors and rubber cover to remove it completely (photo).
10 Refit in the reverse order but ensure that the headlight unit is the correct way up and if necessary, realign the beam adjustment before refitting the grille.

20 Headlamp aiming (beam alignment)

1 The only entirely satisfactory way of checking headlamp beam alignment is by the use of special optical testers.
2 However, where this equipment is not available, the following beam aiming procedure may be used.
3 Ensure that the tyres are correctly inflated and that the vehicle is on a flat level surface facing a flat wall. Ensure that the fuel tank, radiator and oil sump are full or topped-up to the recommended levels.
4 Referring to Fig. 10.19 or 10.20 position the vehicle at the prescribed distance from a wall and mark the wall to show the corresponding alignment indicator marks for your model. Low beam adjustment settings are shown but check whether you have sealed or bulb type headlight units before marking for alignment. Note that the illustrations shown are for right-hand drive vehicles. For left-hand drive models the aiming pattern is simply reversed.
5 With the car positioned correctly, adjust the beam alignment screws to obtain the correct adjustment.

21 Front combination light – bulb and unit removal and refitting

Bulb renewal
1 Remove the retaining screws and take off the lens (photo).
2 Press in the bulb and rotate it anti-clockwise to remove it from its socket.
3 Fit the new bulb, ensuring that it is locked in the socket and check operation.
4 Position the gasket to the lamp body and fit the lens (and lamp body) using the two screws.

Lamp removal and refitting
5 Disconnect the lamp wires at the connector, and remove the grommet from the body panel.
6 Remove the lens as described in paragraph 1 then withdraw the lamp body (photo).
7 Refitting is the reverse of the removal procedure.

22 Side marker lights (front and rear) – removal and refitting

Bulb renewal
1 Remove the retaining screws and take off the lens (photo).
2 According to the particular type, either press in the bulb and rotate it anti-clockwise to remove it, or pull the bulb and socket forward and take the bulb out.
3 Fit the new bulb (and socket where applicable).
4 Position the gasket to the lamp body and refit the lens and rim.

Lamp removal and refitting
5 With the lens removed, withdraw the unit from the wing panel and detach the wires.

19.2a Detach the headlight wire connector ...

19.2b ... and rubber cover

19.3a Rotate the retaining ring ...

19.3b ... and withdraw the bulb and holder

19.7 Remove the chrome rim

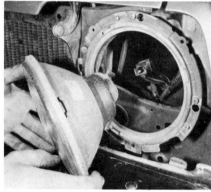
19.8 Withdraw the headlight unit

21.1 Remove the lens retaining screws

21.6 The combination light lens and unit

22.1 Side marker light unit and lens removal

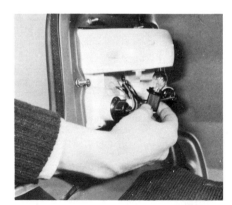
23.1 Rear combination light bulb removal (4-door Saloon)

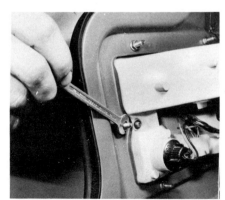
23.2 Removing the unit retaining nuts

23.3 Withdrawing the rear combination light unit – Saloon

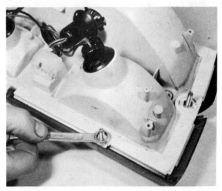

23.4a Remove securing nuts and ...

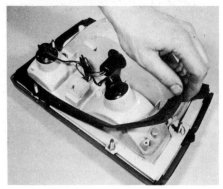

23.4b ... the rubber seal

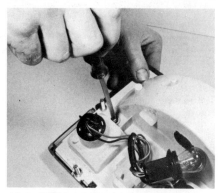

23.4c Remove the central retaining screws

23.5a Remove the dividing seal

23.5b Remove the lenses

24.1 Remove the two retaining screws, then ...

24.2 ... withdraw the number plate light unit

24.3a Detach the lens ...

24.3b ... for access to bulb

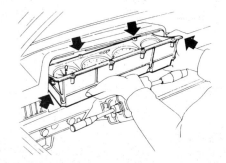

Fig. 10.21 Withdrawing the instrument panel. Retaining screws are arrowed (Sec 26)

6   Refit in reverse order to removal, ensuring that the seal is in good condition and correctly seated. Check the light for satisfactory operation to complete.

23 Rear combination lights – bulb and unit removal and refitting

Saloon, Coupe and Hatchback

1   Unclip the rear panel cover in the boot (luggage compartment). Access to the respective bulbs is then obtainable by unscrewing their holders from the unit (photo).
2   To remove the combination light unit complete, disconnect the wiring connector and then unscrew and remove the unit-to-rear body panel retaining nuts (photo).
3   Withdraw the lens and light unit from the outside (photo).
4   To dismantle the unit remove the securing nuts, carefully prise free the rubber surround seal and remove the central retaining screws (photos).

5   Withdraw the seal from between the lenses and lift the lenses clear (photo).
6   Reassemble in the reverse order to dismantling. Fit new seals where the old ones are worn, perished or damaged. Check the light for satisfactory operation on completion.

Estate

7   Remove the two lens retaining screws and loosen off the lens bracket bolt within the drain channel. The light unit can now be removed from the rear corner panel sufficiently enough to enable any of the bulbs to be removed and if necessary renewed.
8   This unit can be further dismantled by detaching the wire connections to remove the unit completely. Remove the lenses by unscrewing the inner retaining screws.
9   Refit in the reverse order to removal and check all rear lights on completion for satisfactory operation.

24 Number plate light – removal and refitting

Saloon, Coupe and Hatchback

1   This light is housed within the rear bumper channel and is removed by working from underneath. Unscrew and remove the two unit retaining screws (photo).
2   Remove the light unit from the bumper (photo).
3   Unscrew the two lens retaining screws and extract the lens for access to the bulb (photo).
4   Refit in the reverse order and check operation on completion.

Estate

5   The number plate light is located in the tailgate. To remove either of the two bulbs, remove the lens retaining screws and lower the lens.
6   Refit in the reverse order and check light operation on completion.

25 Interior lights – unit and switch removal and refitting

1   To remove the lens, rotate it anti-clockwise. The festoon bulb can then be prised from the holder for renewal (photo).
2   To remove the light unit, first disconnect the battery earth lead, detach the lens, unscrew the securing screws and then carefully pulling the light unit downwards, disconnect the wires.
3   Refit in the reverse order and check operation.
4   The interior light switches housed in the door pillars are easily removed by unscrewing the retaining screw(s), withdrawing the unit and disconnecting the wire connector (photo).
5   Refit in the reverse order.

Luggage compartment light

6   Prise free the lens and extract the festoon bulb from the holder.
7   Refit in the reverse order to removal.

26 Instrument panel – removal and refitting

1   Disconnect the battery earth (ground) cable.
2   Refer to Chapter 8 and remove the steering wheel.
3   Remove the retaining screws and withdraw the steering column covers and the lower cover on the driver's side.
4   Unscrew and remove the instrument panel surround retaining screws (from the upper face), then pivot and withdraw the surround panel.
5   Detach the speedometer cable from the rear of the instrument.
6   Unscrew and remove the instrument panel retaining screws and partially withdraw the panel sufficiently to disconnect the respective wire connectors from the unit (noting their locations).
7   The instrument panel can now be fully withdrawn from its aperture in the dash panel.
8   To check and renew any of the panel illumination or warning light bulbs, withdraw the holder concerned from the rear face of the unit and remove its bulb. The respective light positions are shown in Fig. 10.22.
9   If the unit is to be dismantled for any reason, for example to renew an instrument, remove the respective securing screws and carefully separate the assembly components as required. Take great care in handling as the instruments are delicate and can easily be damaged. The respective assembly components are shown in Fig. 10.23.
10 Both the reassembly of the panel and its refitting are a reversal of the removal procedure. Take care to ensure that all connections are securely made and on completion check the operation of all components concerned.

27 Illumination control rheostat – removal and refitting

1   Disconnect the battery earth lead.
2   Disconnect the wiring harness connector from the rear of the unit.
3   Remove the control knob and then unscrew the retaining bezel nut. Withdraw the unit from underneath.
4   A test circuit for the rheostat is shown in Fig. 10.24.
5   Refit in reverse sequence and check operation.

28 Combination light and indicator switch – removal and refitting

1   Disconnect the battery earth lead.

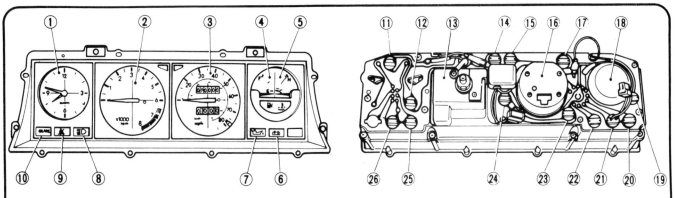

Fig. 10.22 The instrument panel (typical) (Sec 26)

1 Clock	8 High beam pilot lamp	15 Turn signal indicator lamp (LH)	21 Fasten belts warning lamp
2 Tachometer	9 Fasten belts warning lamp	16 Tachometer	22 High beam pilot lamp
3 Speedometer	10 Brake waning lamp	17 Illumination lamp	23 Illumination lamp
4 Fuel level gauge	11 Illumination lamp	18 Clock	24 Illumination lamp
5 Coolant temperature gauge	12 Illumination lamp	19 Illumination lamp	25 Oil pressure warning lamp
6 Charge warning lamp	13 Speedometer	20 Brake warning lamp	26 Charge warning lamp
7 Oil pressure warning lamp	14 Turn signal indicator lamp (RH)		

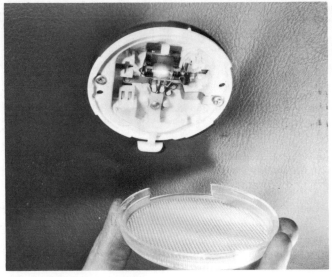

25.1 Interior light lens removal

25.4 Courtesy light door switch

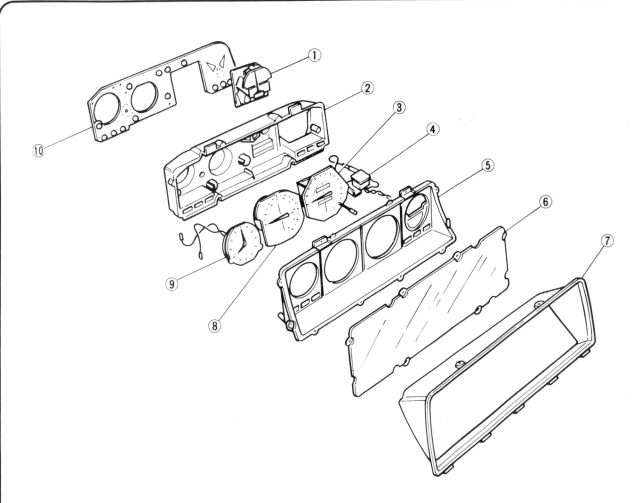

Fig. 10.23 The instrument panel assembly components (Sec 26)

1	Coolant temperature and fuel level gauges	4	Speed switch amplifier (Except Canadian model)	7	Cluster lid
2	Lower cover	5	Upper housing	8	Tachometer
3	Speedometer	6	Front cover	9	Clock
				10	Printed circuit board

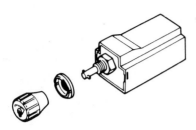

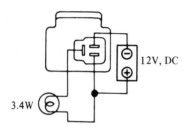

Fig. 10.24 The illumination control rheostat and test circuit (Sec 27)

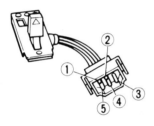

	1	2	3	4	5
OFF				o—o	
ON	o—o—o				

Fig. 10.25 The hazard warning switch and wiring connector showing terminal continuity functions (Sec 29)

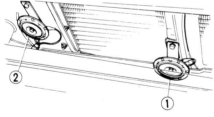

Fig. 10.26 Horn locations (Sec 32)

1   High sound horn   *2   Low sound horn*

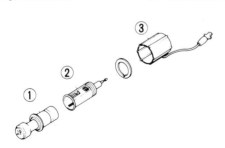

Fig. 10.27 The cigarette lighter components (Sec 33)

1   Lighter   *3   Cover*
2   Housing

2   Refer to Chapter 8 and remove the steering wheel.
3   Remove the retaining screws and withdraw the steering column covers.
4   Detach the wire connectors to the combination switch, then loosen the switch retaining screw and withdraw the switch unit up the column.
5   Refit in the reverse order to removal, but before assembling the column covers, check the various switch functions to ensure that they operate in a satisfactory manner.

29 Hazard warning switch – removal and refitting

1   Disconnect the battery earth lead.
2   Remove the retaining screws and remove the steering column upper cover.
3   Detach the wiring harness connector to the switch, then unscrew and remove its retaining screw to withdraw the switch unit.
4   Refit in the reverse order to removal, but check the switch operation before refitting the upper column cover.

30 Stoplight switch – removal and refitting

1   Disconnect the battery earth cable.
2   Remove the retaining screws and remove the lower column cover.
3   The switch is located on the column bracket (photo).
4   Detach the wire connector, loosen off the switch locknut and then unscrew the switch unit to remove it.
5   Refit in the reverse order to removal but check that the switch and brake pedal are correctly adjusted as given in Chapter 9, Section 21, before retightening the switch locknut.

31 Handbrake warning switch – removal and refitting

Refer to Chapter 9, Section 9 for details.

32 Horn – removal and refitting

1   The horns are located between the front grille panel and the radiator.
2   Disconnect the battery earth lead, then the horn lead(s).
3   Unbolt and remove the horn(s).
4   Refit in the reverse order to removal and check the horns for satisfactory operation.

33 Cigarette lighter – removal and refitting

1   Disconnect the battery earth lead.
2   Remove the central bezel and withdraw the housing cover and housing, disconnecting the lead wire at its connector.
3   Refit in the reverse order to removal.

34 Rear window demister – general

1   The demister switch unit, which includes a warning light, is removed from its location by compressing the securing clips using a small screwdriver or similar implement.
2   Withdraw the switch and disconnect the wires (photo).
3   The bulb and holder can be removed by pulling free from the rear of the unit.
4   If a problem exists in the demister itself, such as a broken filament, a repair can only be made using a special conductive paint and applicator and this should therefore be entrusted to your Datsun dealer.
5   To refit the switch unit, reverse the removal procedure.

35 Rear window wiper motor and switch – removal and refitting

1   Disconnect the battery earth lead.

30.3 The stop-light switch location

34.2 Withdraw the rear screen demister switch to detach the wires

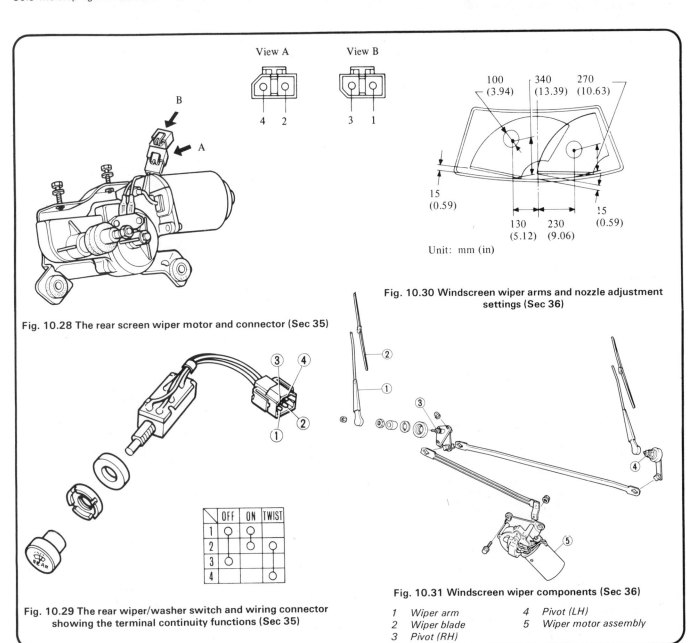

Fig. 10.28 The rear screen wiper motor and connector (Sec 35)

View A

4   2

View B

3   1

100   340   270
(3.94)   (13.39)   (10.63)

15
(0.59)

15
(0.59)

130   230
(5.12)   (9.06)

Unit: mm (in)

Fig. 10.30 Windscreen wiper arms and nozzle adjustment settings (Sec 36)

	OFF	ON	TWIST
1	O	O	
2		O	O
3	O		
4			O

Fig. 10.29 The rear wiper/washer switch and wiring connector showing the terminal continuity functions (Sec 35)

Fig. 10.31 Windscreen wiper components (Sec 36)

1   Wiper arm   4   Pivot (LH)
2   Wiper blade   5   Wiper motor assembly
3   Pivot (RH)

2   Remove the rear trim panel and disconnect the wiring to the wiper motor.
3   Remove the rear wiper arm from the motor drive spindle.
4   Unbolt and withdraw the wiper motor unit.
5   Refit in the reverse order to removal, ensuring that the wiper arm is correctly aligned when fitted.
6   The rear wiper/washer switch can be removed by pulling free the knob, unscrewing the retaining bezel nut and spacer and withdrawing the switch unit from underneath. Disconnect the wiring connector to remove the switch completely.
7   Refit in the reverse order to removal.

36 Windscreen wiper and washer – removal and refitting

Wiper arms and blades

1   To remove a windscreen wiper blade from its arm, pull up the blade, push the lever and disengage the arm (photo).
2   To remove the wiper arm, pivot back the cover, unscrew and remove the retaining nut and pull the arm from its spindle (photo).
3   Refit the blade and arm in the reverse order to removal, ensuring that the arm is positioned on the pivot splines so as to give the correct sweep when operated (Fig. 10.30).

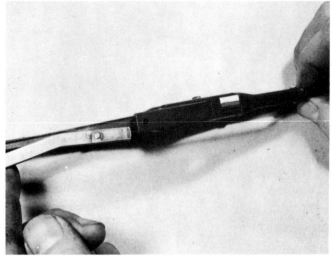

36.1 Removing the wiper blade

36.2 Removing the wiper arm

36.5 Removing the grille for access to the wiper motor linkages

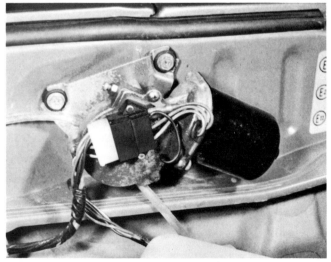

36.8 The wiper motor location on the bulkhead

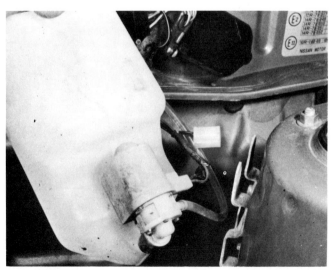

36.10 Windscreen washer unit removal

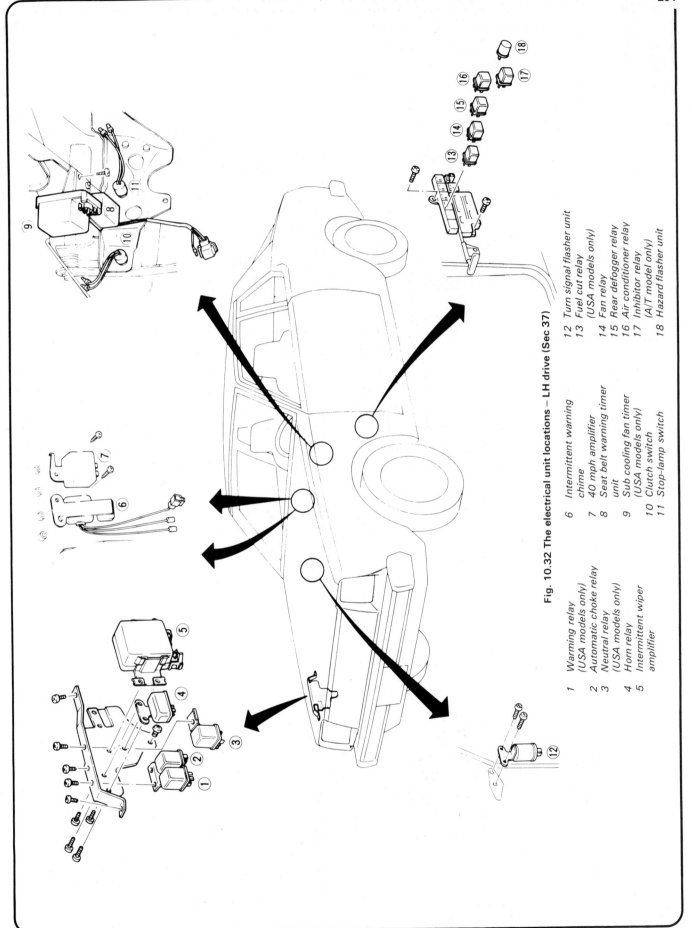

Fig. 10.32 The electrical unit locations – LH drive (Sec 37)

1   Warning relay
    (USA models only)
2   Automatic choke relay
3   Neutral relay
    (USA models only)
4   Horn relay
5   Intermittent wiper
    amplifier
6   Intermittent warning
    chime
7   40 mph amplifier
8   Seat belt warning timer
    unit
9   Sub cooling fan timer
    (USA models only)
10 Clutch switch
11 Stop-lamp switch
12 Turn signal flasher unit
13 Fuel cut relay
    (USA models only)
14 Fan relay
15 Rear defogger relay
16 Air conditioner relay
17 Inhibitor relay
    (A/T model only)
18 Hazard flasher unit

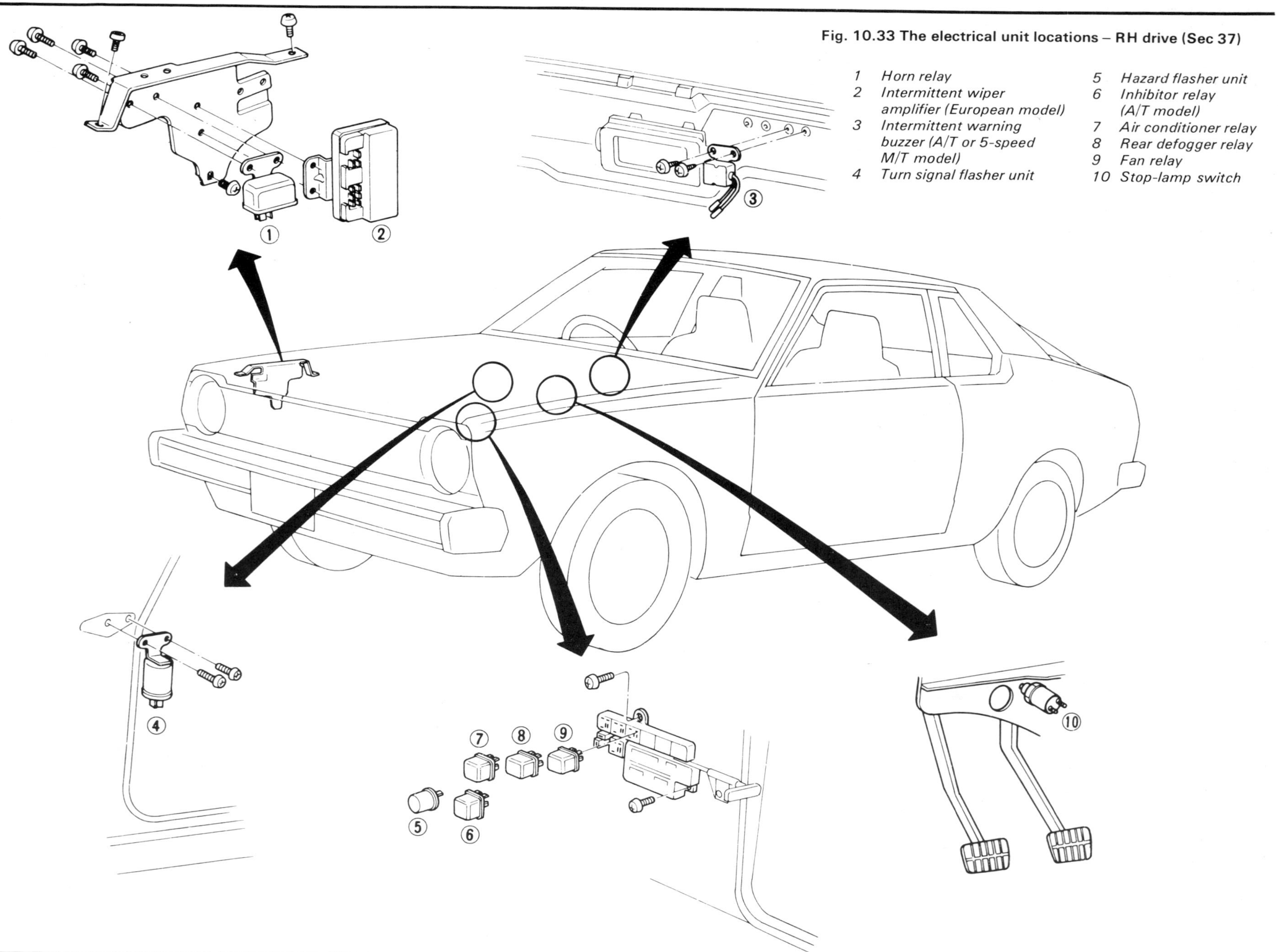

Fig. 10.33 The electrical unit locations – RH drive (Sec 37)

1 Horn relay
2 Intermittent wiper amplifier (European model)
3 Intermittent warning buzzer (A/T or 5-speed M/T model)
4 Turn signal flasher unit
5 Hazard flasher unit
6 Inhibitor relay (A/T model)
7 Air conditioner relay
8 Rear defogger relay
9 Fan relay
10 Stop-lamp switch

Wiper motor

4   Remove the wiper arms.
5   Prise free the grille panel between the windscreen and bonnet and remove it (photo).
6   Disconnect the wiring connector to the motor.
7   Unscrew and remove the wiper motor spindle-to-crankarm retaining nut and disengage the arm.
8   Unbolt and remove the wiper motor (photo).
9   Refit in the reverse order to removal.

Windscreen washer unit

10   To remove the windscreen washer reservoir and pump unit, simply pull the reservoir upwards to disengage it from its retaining brackets on the inner wing panel (photo).
11   Refit in the reverse order to removal and refill the reservoir with water or a windscreen cleaner solution. Do not operate the pump unit when it is dry.

37 Relays – general

1   Relays are fitted to certain switched circuits and their respective locations are shown in Figs. 10.32 and 10.33.
2   If suspected of malfunction, a relay can be checked out using a continuity tester. Repair is not possible; a faulty relay must be renewed.
3   To remove a relay unit, either simply pull it from its connection or remove its retaining screws and detach the lead connections (according to type).
4   Refit in the reverse order to removal and check operation.

38 Ignition switch – removal and refitting

To remove and refit the ignition switch see Chapter 8, Section 5.

39 Seat belt warning system (USA models) – description and testing

1   The seat belt warning system circuit diagram is shown in Fig. 10.34. It is designed to operate when the ignition switch is turned to the 'On' position, when the warning light is activated and remains on for a period of 4 to 8 seconds. Should the driver's seat belt not be fastened, the warning chime is also activated for the same period.
2   Should a fault in the system occur, the individual system components can be removed as follows for checking and, if necessary, renewal.

Warning chime unit

3   Detach the battery earth lead.
4   Refer to Chapter 12 and remove the dashboard.
5   Disconnect the wiring from the chime unit (at the connectors in the leads) and then remove the unit retaining screws and withdraw the unit from the bulkhead. The chime unit location is shown in Fig. 10.35.
6   To check the unit for operation, connect a 12V direct current supply to terminals 1 and 3 or 2 and 3 (see Fig. 10.36), with the power circuit negative terminal attached to the number 3 terminal. If the warning chimes fail to operate then the unit is defective and it must be

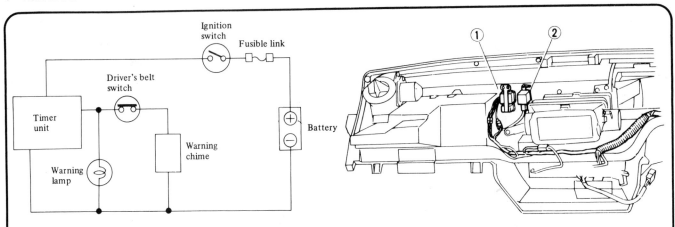

Fig. 10.34 The seat belt warning circuit (Sec 39)

Fig. 10.35 The intermittent warning chime (1) and 40 mph amplifier (2) locations (Sec 39)

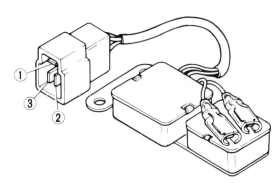

Fig. 10.36 The warning chime unit and wiring connector terminals. For 1, 2 and 3 see text (Sec 39)

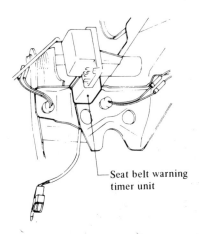

Fig. 10.37 The warning timer unit (Sec 39)

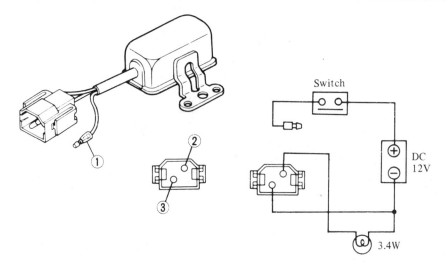

Fig. 10.38 The warning timer unit circuit. For 1, 2 and 3 see text (Sec 39)

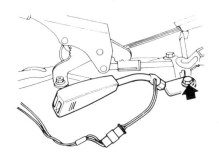

Fig. 10.39 The inner seat belt connection. Belt retaining bolt is arrowed (Sec 39)

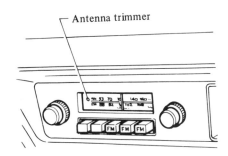

Fig. 10.41 Adjust the trimmer screw for maximum reception (Sec 40)

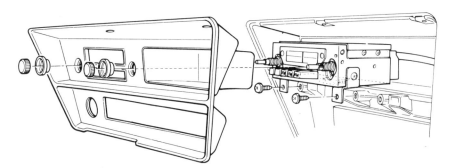

Fig. 10.40 Central panel and radio location (Sec 40)

renewed.

7   Refitting of the chime unit is a reversal of the removal procedure.

Seat belt warning timer

8   Disconnect the battery earth lead.

9   Detach the dashboard lower cover.

10 Disconnect the wire from the timer connection and then remove the timer unit retaining screw (under the pedal bracket) and withdraw the timer.

11 To test the warning timer unit, connect a 12V direct current to the number 1 and 3 terminals shown in Fig. 10.38, with the negative connection to the number 3 terminal. Check that a test light attached to number 2 and number 3 terminals remains on for a period of 4 to 8 seconds only.

12 If the unit is proved to be defective it must be renewed.

13 Refit in the reverse order to removal.

Seat belt switch

14 Disconnect the battery earth lead.

15 Slide the driver's seat fully forward and disconnect the wiring at the connector (Fig. 10.39).

16 Unscrew the retaining bolt and remove the inner seat belt which contains the switch.

17 Refitting is a reversal of the removal procedure.

40 Radio – removal and refitting

1   Disconnect the battery earth lead.

2   Unscrew and remove the central panel retaining screws (photo).

3   Pull free the radio tuner and volume control knobs.

4   Refer to Section 33 and remove the cigarette lighter.

40.2 Remove the central panel screws

40.8 The radio speaker unit (standard)

5   Withdraw the central panel (Fig. 10.40).
6   Remove the two retaining screws and withdraw the radio sufficiently to detach the leads, then remove the unit completely.
7   Refitting is the reversal of the removal procedure. If a new radio or
aerial have been fitted, extend the aerial and tune in to the station with
the poorest reception between 12 and 16 (1200 and 1600 kHZ), then
adjust the trimmer (Fig. 10.41) to get the best possible reception.
8   The speaker unit can be removed by detaching the lower
dashboard panel on the passenger side. Disconnect the speaker wiring
and unscrew and remove the speaker securing screws. Remove the
speaker (photo), handling with care.
9   Refit in the reverse order to removal.

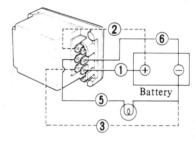

Fig. 10.42 Carburettor fan motor timer unit check diagram. For
key see text (Sec 41)

41 Auxiliary fan (carburettor fuel cooling) timer unit – testing

*The auxiliary fan motor timer unit is mounted on the clutch pedal
bracket (A14 and A15 engine models only). If the fan and its sensor
switch are known to be operational when tested separately (see
Chapter 2), but a fault in this circuit persists, then the timer unit can
be tested as follows.*

1   You will need a 12V 3W test light and leads and a 12 volt battery.
Disconnect the battery leads if using the one on the car.
2   Referring to Fig. 10.42, connect terminal 6 to the battery negative
terminal and then connect the number 5 terminal to the test lamp lead.
The remaining test lamp lead must also be connected to the battery
negative terminal.
3   Connect the number 1 terminal to the battery positive terminal. If
the test light comes on then a fault exists. Otherwise, leave the
terminal connected for the subsequent tests.
4   Connect the number 2 terminal to the battery positive terminal
and then disconnect it. This activates the timer.
5   Connect terminal 3 of the unit to the battery negative terminal. If
the test light comes on then this is correct.
6   The test light should remain on for about 17 minutes and then go
out.
7   With the test light still on, interconnect the number 2 terminal
with the battery positive terminal and check that the test light goes
out. If not, a fault exists.
8   If any of the above tests have shown the timer unit to be faulty
then it should be removed and renewed.

42 Headlight cleaner unit – removal and refitting

1   Disconnect the battery earth lead.
2   Detach the main feed pipe to the T-piece connection (from the
pump unit).
3   Remove the T-piece bracket and pump unit retaining bolts and lift
the pump clear together with the washer reservoir bag.

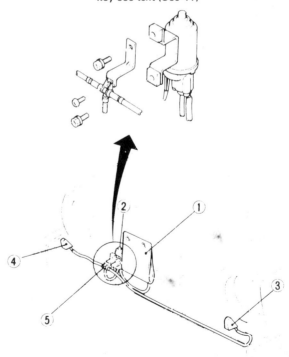

Fig. 10.43 The headlight cleaner assembly (Sec 42)

1	Headlamp cleaner washer bag	3	Nozzle (LH)
2	Headlamp cleaner pump	4	Nozzle (RH)
		5	T-piece

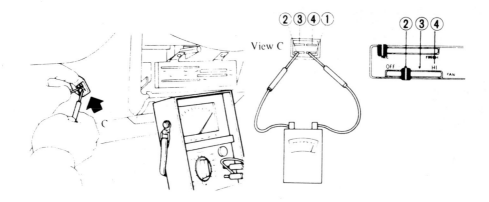

Fig. 10.44 Fan switch check (Sec 43)

1   Ground (Harness colour B)
2   Fan switch 1st position
    (Harness colour YR)

3   Fan switch 2nd position
    (Harness colour Y)

4   Fan switch HI position
    (Harness colour LW)

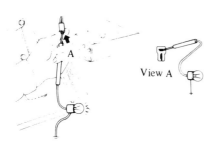

Fig. 10.45 Checking the power supply of blower motor (Sec 43)

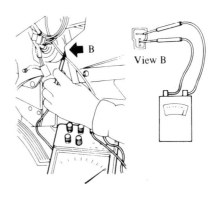

Fig. 10.46 Checking the blower motor (Sec 43)

4   Pump unit refitting is a reversal of the removal procedure.
5   The pump unit switch can be removed by pulling free the switch knob, unscrewing the retaining nut and withdrawing the switch from underneath. Detach the wiring to remove completely.
6   Refitting the switch is a reversal of the removal process.

43 Heater unit – fault diagnosis

1   The heater unit is normally totally reliable and apart from occasionally checking the inlet and outlet hoses for condition and security, requires little or no maintenance.
2   Should the heater become inefficient, first check that the engine is running at its normal operating temperature. If not, then a check should be made of the engine cooling system as given in Chapter 2 (and the thermostat in particular).
3   Other possible causes of an inefficient heater are incorrectly adjusted controls. These can be checked and adjusted as given in Section 44.
4   If the blower unit fails to operate, first check that the switch is satisfactory by checking for continuity at each switch position – see Fig. 10.44.
5   If the switch is working, check the blower motor power supply by detaching the supply wire harness connector and with a test light attached to earth and the lead wire (see Fig. 10.45), turn the ignition switch to the 'ACC' position. The test light should operate; if not, a fault exists in the power supply.
6   To check the blower motor itself, disconnect the wiring 2-pole connector and check for continuity between the terminals as shown (Fig. 10.46). If continuity does not exist, the blower motor will have to be removed for repair or renewal as given in Section 44.

44 Heater unit and controls (non air-conditioned models) – removal and refitting

Heater control unit – removal, refitting and adjustment

1   Disconnect the battery earth lead.
2   Detach and remove the lower facia panels. See Chapter 12 for details.
3   Remove the central panel as given in Section 40, paragraph 2.
4   Detach the heater door control cable and rod shown in Fig. 10.49.
5   Detach the blower unit door control cable (Fig. 10.50).
6   Unscrew and remove the two heater control retaining screws and withdraw the control unit (Fig. 10.51).
7   Refitting is a reversal of the removal process, but before fitting the panels, adjust the control cables and rod as follows.
8   With the temperature control lever set at maximum cold setting, push the air mix door lever in the direction shown in Fig. 10.52 and set the temperature control rod.
9   Position the temperature control lever in the maximum hot setting, pull the air mix door control as shown in Fig. 10.53 and tighten its locking screw.
10 Pull the water cock control rod as directed in Fig. 10.54 and tighten its lock screw.
11 To adjust the inlet door control cable, locate the inlet lever in the 'REC' position and then pushing the inlet door lever as shown (Fig. 10.55), set the control rod.
12 To adjust the mode control rod and cable set the lever in the 'DEF' position, then with the control arm pushed in direction shown (Fig. 10.56), locate the cable with the clip.
13 Push the door control rod in the direction shown (Fig. 10.57) and locate the control rod.

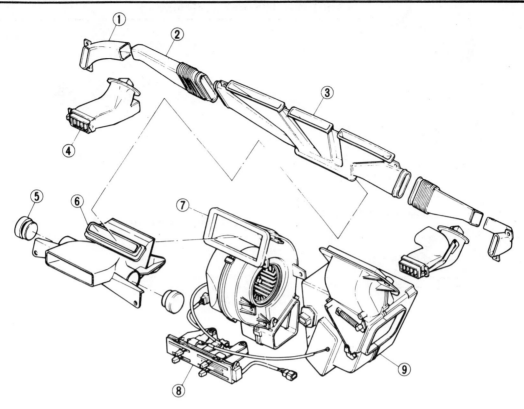

Fig. 10.47 The heater unit components (Sec 44)

1	Side defroster nozzle	4	Side ventilator nozzle	6	Centre ventilator duct	8	Heater control
2	Side defroster duct	5	Cap	7	Blower unit	9	Heater unit
3	Defroster nozzle						

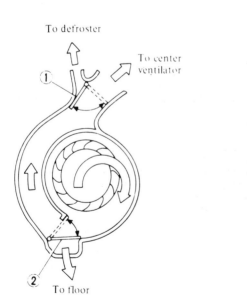

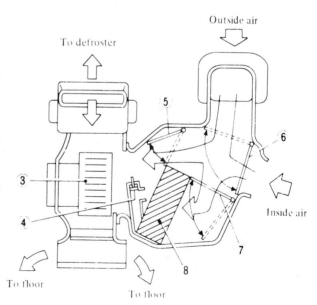

Fig. 10.48 Heater air flow circuits (Sec 44)

1	Face door	3	Fan	5	Air mix door	7	Air mix door
2	Floor door	4	Water cock	6	Intake door	8	Heater core

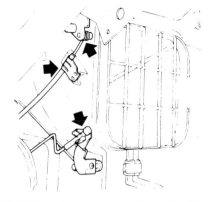

Fig. 10.49 Detach the control cable and rod (Sec 4)

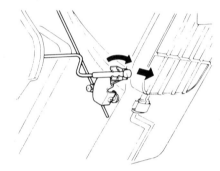

Fig. 10.50 Detach the blower door control cable (Sec 44)

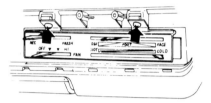

Fig. 10.51 Control panel retaining screws (Sec 44)

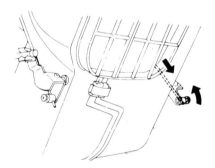

Fig. 10.52 Adjust the temperature control rod (Sec 44)

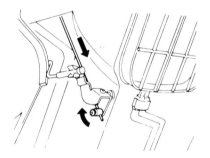

Fig. 10.53 Adjust the air mix door control rod (Sec 44)

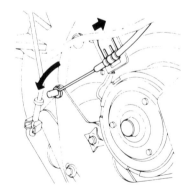

Fig. 10.54 Adjust the water cock control (Sec 44)

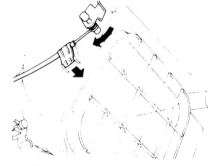

Fig. 10.55 Adjust the inlet door control valve (Sec 44)

Fig. 10.56 Adjust the mode control (Sec 44)

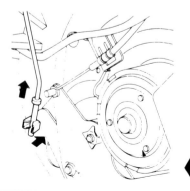

Fig. 10.57 Adjust the face door control rod (Sec 44)

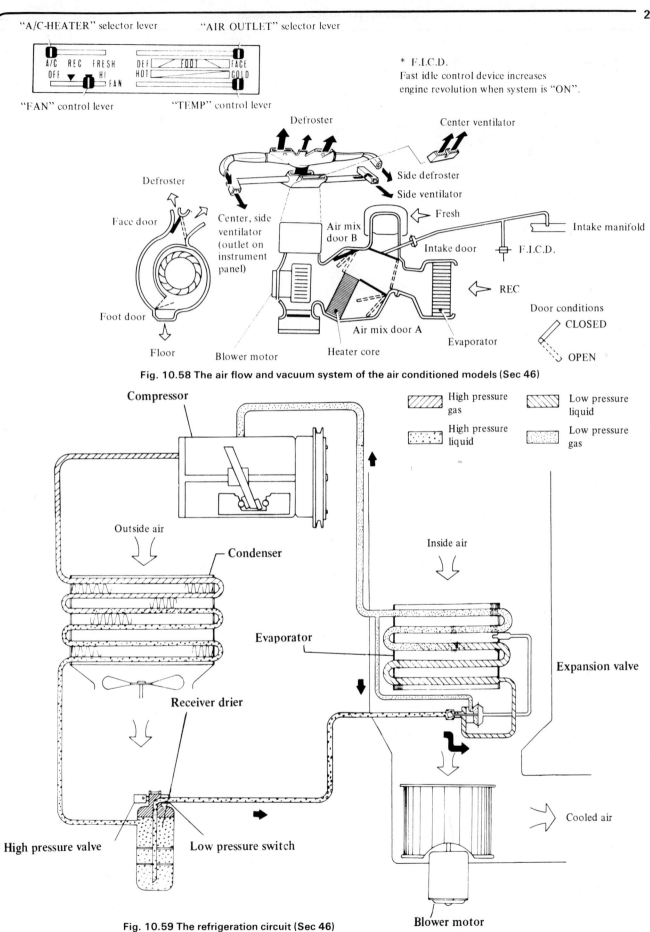

"A/C-HEATER" selector lever   "AIR OUTLET" selector lever

A/C   REC   FRESH   DEF   FOOT   FACE
OFF   ▼   HI   HOT   COLD
      FAN

"FAN" control lever   "TEMP" control lever

* F.I.C.D.
Fast idle control device increases
engine revolution when system is "ON".

Defroster

Center ventilator

Defroster

Side defroster

Side ventilator

Face door

Center, side
ventilator
(outlet on
instrument
panel)

Fresh

Air mix
door B

Intake manifold

Intake door

F.I.C.D.

Foot door

REC

Floor

Air mix door A

Door conditions

CLOSED

Blower motor

Heater core

Evaporator

OPEN

Fig. 10.58 The air flow and vacuum system of the air conditioned models (Sec 46)

Compressor

High pressure
gas

Low pressure
liquid

High pressure
liquid

Low pressure
gas

Outside air

Inside air

Condenser

Evaporator

Expansion valve

Receiver drier

High pressure valve

Low pressure switch

Cooled air

Blower motor

Fig. 10.59 The refrigeration circuit (Sec 46)

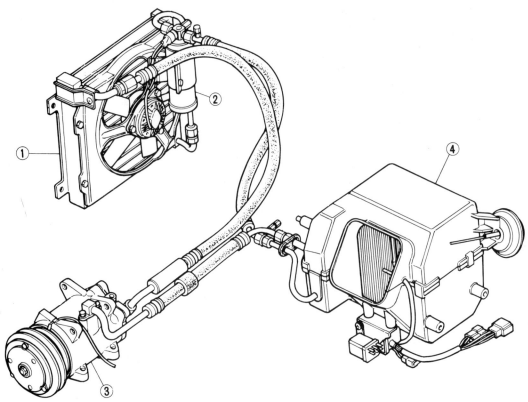

Fig. 10.60 The air conditioning system refrigerant lines (Sec 46)

1 Condenser	*3 Compressor*
2 Receiver dryer	*4 Cooling unit*

Heater/blower unit – removal and refitting

14 Disconnect the battery earth lead.

15 Referring to Chapter 2, drain the engine and heater coolant with the temperature lever set in the maximum heat position.

16 Refer to Chapter 12 and remove the facia/instrument panel assembly. Disconnect the blower unit wires.

17 Detach the heater control cables and rod from the heater.

18 On the engine compartment side of the bulkhead, detach the heater inlet and outlet hoses.

19 Unscrew and remove the five heater unit retaining bolts and carefully remove the heater assembly. Take care not to spill any remaining coolant over the floor coverings or upholstery when withdrawing the unit.

20 To dismantle the heater unit refer to the following Section.

21 Refitting the heater unit is a reversal of the removal procedure. Prior to refitting the lower facia panels, adjust the heater control cables and rod as given above. Check for signs of leaks from the heater hoses on completion.

45 Heater unit – dismantling and reassembly

1 Loosen the heater unit-to-blower unit retaining screws and separate the two assemblies.

2 Remove the water cock.

3 Unclip and separate the front and rear heater unit casings, and then extract the heater core.

4 Clean the respective components and inspect for signs of damage or defects and renew as necessary.

5 Reassemble the heater in the reverse order of dismantling.

46 Air conditioning system – description and maintenance

1 An air conditioning system is available as an optional extra on the 310 range. The system combines heater, refrigeration and blower unit

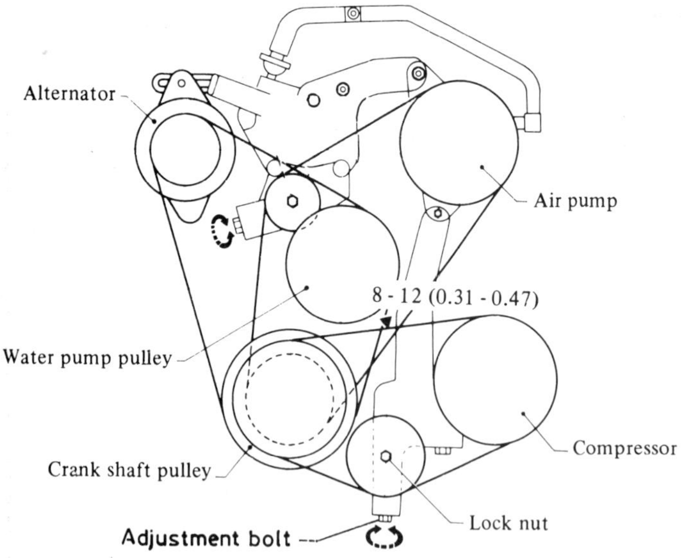

Fig. 10.61 The compressor drivebelt tension must be maintained. Deflection in mm (in) (Sec 46)

Alternator

Air pump

8 - 12 (0.31 - 0.47)

Water pump pulley

Compressor

Crank shaft pulley

Lock nut

Adjustment bolt

211

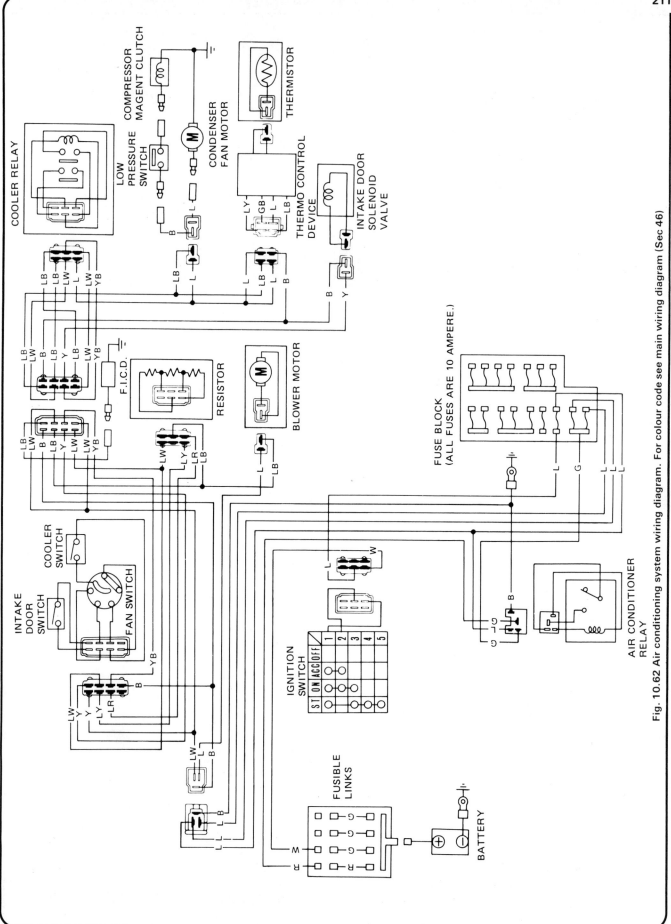

Fig. 10.62 Air conditioning system wiring diagram. For colour code see main wiring diagram (Sec 46)

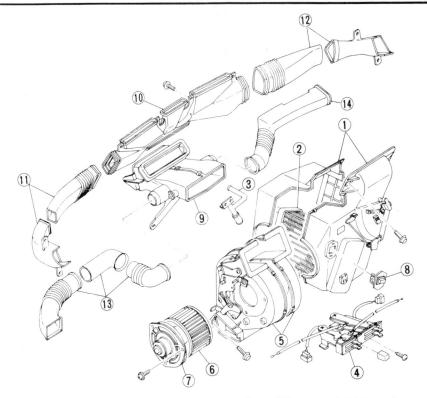

Fig. 10.64 Heater unit components – air conditioned models (Sec 47)

1	Heater case	5	Blower case	9	Air distributor	13	Side ventilation ducts LH
2	Heater core	6	Blower fan	10	Defroster nozzle		
3	Water cock	7	Blower motor	11	Side defroster ducts LH	14	Side ventilation duct RH
4	Heater control	8	Resistor	12	Side defroster ducts RH		

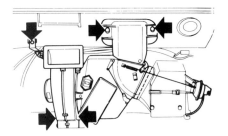

Fig. 10.63 Heater unit retaining bolt positions (Sec 47)

Fig. 10.65 Control levers to be set as shown (Sec 47)

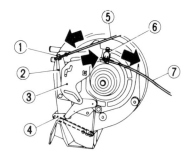

Fig. 10.66 Heater control adjustments (Sec 47)

1	Clip B	5	Rod
2	Link B	6	Clip A
3	Link A	7	Wire casing
4	Link C		

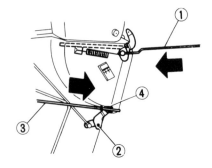

Fig. 10.67 Control cable adjustment

1	Actuator shaft	3	Rod
2	Air mix door lever	4	Clip C

assemblies.

2   The heater system works on the normal principle in conjunction with the engine cooling system and incorporating its own booster (blower) motor.

3   The refrigeration system is shown in Fig. 10.59 and comprises five principal components, these being an evaporator, a compressor, a condenser, a receiver drier and an expansion valve.

4   Due to the nature of the refrigeration gases used in the system, no servicing other than a few basic maintenance tasks can be undertaken by the home mechanic.

5   If it is necessary to disconnect any part of the refrigeration system in order to undertake work on other components, it is most important that the circuit be discharged prior to commencing work by a Datsun dealer or refrigeration engineer having the necessary knowledge and equipment. On completion of the particular service or overhaul the refrigeration system must be recharged again requiring specialised equipment and knowledge.

6   The maintenance tasks which can be carried out safely include checking the compressor belt tension. The driving belt layout is shown in Fig. 10.61 and the tension check points are arrowed. There should be a total deflection of 0.31 to 0.47 in (8 to 12 mm) under average finger pressure.

7   The tension may be adjusted by slackening the idler pulley locknut and moving the idler pulley adjusting bolt in the desired direction.

8   Examine the system hoses and their connections for signs of leakage or deterioration. If evident the connection clips must be tightened, or if necessary, have the hose renewed by your Datsun agent or refrigeration mechanic.

9   Should the vehicle not be used regularly, the air conditioner must be run for a period of about ten minutes once monthly to keep it in good condition.

10 If it is suspected that the amount of refrigerant in the system is incorrect, start the engine and hold it at a steady speed of 1500 rpm. Set the AIR lever in the A/C position and switch on the blower to maximum speed. Check the sight glass after an interval of about five minutes. The sight glass is located on the receiver drier. If a continuous stream of bubbles or mist is observed, then there is very little refrigerant left in the system. Do not operate the air conditioner in this condition. Where some bubbles are seen at intervals of 1 or 2 seconds then there is insufficient refrigerant in the system. The system is correctly charged when conditions within the sight glass are almost transparent, with a few bubbles appearing if the engine speed is raised or lowered. If the system requires recharging, this must be carried out professionally.

11 The air conditioning electrical circuit is shown in the accompanying diagram (Fig. 10.62). No maintenance is required for this part of the system apart from the occasional check to ensure that the wiring and connections are in good condition and securely located.

47 Heater unit (air-conditioned models) – removal and refitting

1   Disconnect the battery earth lead.

2   Set the temperature control lever to 'HOT' and then drain the engine coolant (refer to Chapter 2).

3   Refer to Chapter 12 and remove the dashboard face finishers and the dashboard.

4   Disconnect the inlet and outlet heater hoses.

5   Detach the heater control rod and cables.

6   Disconnect the wiring connector from the blower motor, resistor and cooling unit.

7   Detach the actuator rod from the air intake door shaft.

8   Loosen the band seal at the joint of the cooling and heater unit.

9   Unscrew and remove the heater unit retaining bolts and carefully withdraw the unit (Fig. 10.63).

10 Dismantling of the heater and blower unit is similar too that described for non air-conditioned models (Section 45).

11 Reassembly and refitting of the heater unit is a reversal of the removal procedure. Prior to refitting the facia/dash panels, adjust the controls by first setting the control levers at the positions shown in (Fig. 10.65), then refer to Fig. 10.66.

12 Pull link A and outer case in the direction arrowed and fit the clip. Check that link C is at the position shown.

13 Push link B in the direction indicated by its arrow and fit the rod into its clip.

14 Set the temperature control lever at the cold position, then pushing the air mix door lever in direction shown (Fig. 10.67), locate the rod into its clip.

15 Shut off the inlet door and pull the actuator shaft in direction shown then connect the shaft to the inlet door lever. When assembly is complete, check that outside air is sucked in when the actuator is operated.

Wiring diagrams commence overleaf

Wiring diagram colour code

B	Black
W	White
R	Red
G	Green
Y	Yellow
L	Blue
Br	Brown
Lg	Light green

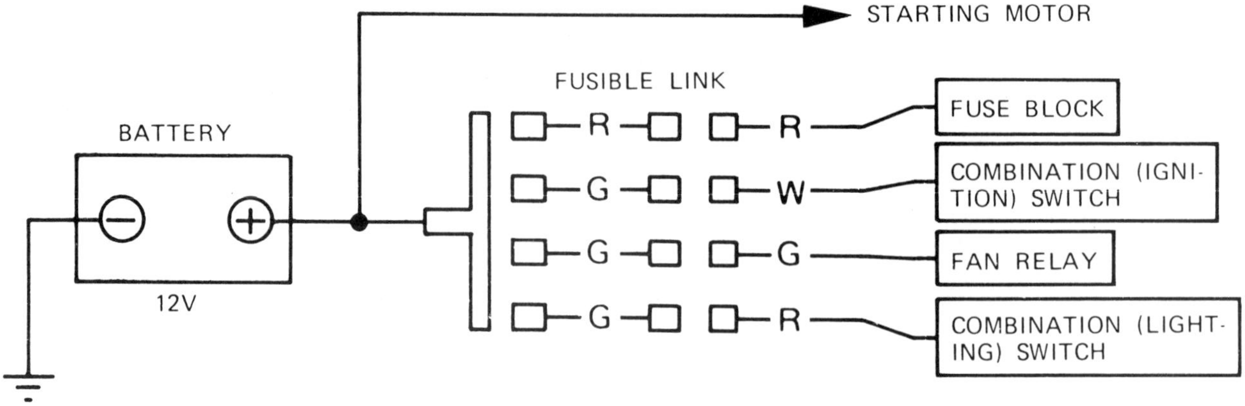

STARTING MOTOR

BATTERY

12V

FUSIBLE LINK

☐—R—☐ ☐—R—— FUSE BLOCK

☐—G—☐ ☐—W—— COMBINATION (IGNI-TION) SWITCH

☐—G—☐ ☐—G—— FAN RELAY

☐—G—☐ ☐—R—— COMBINATION (LIGHT-ING) SWITCH

Fig. 10.68 The electrical system block diagram – all models

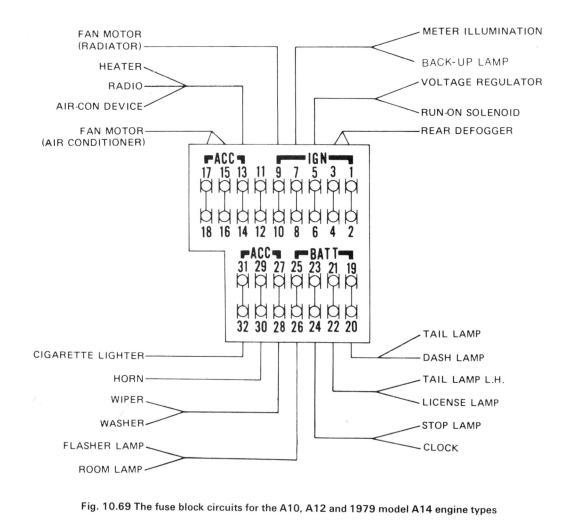

Fig. 10.69 The fuse block circuits for the A10, A12 and 1979 model A14 engine types

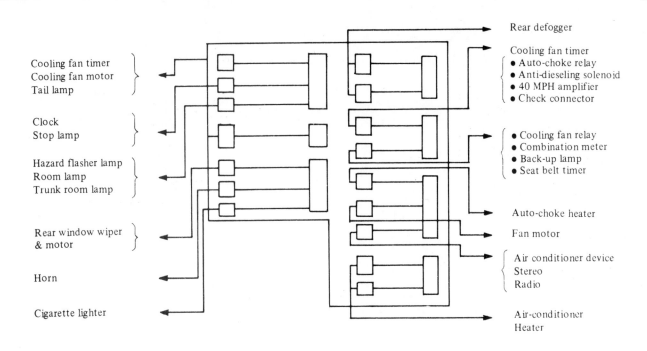

Cooling fan timer
Cooling fan motor
Tail lamp

Clock
Stop lamp

Hazard flasher lamp
Room lamp
Trunk room lamp

Rear window wiper
& motor

Horn

Cigarette lighter

Rear defogger

Cooling fan timer
• Auto-choke relay
• Anti-dieseling solenoid
• 40 MPH amplifier
• Check connector

• Cooling fan relay
• Combination meter
• Back-up lamp
• Seat belt timer

Auto-choke heater

Fan motor

Air conditioner device
Stereo
Radio

Air-conditioner
Heater

Fig. 10.70 Fuse block circuits for the 1980 A14 engine models

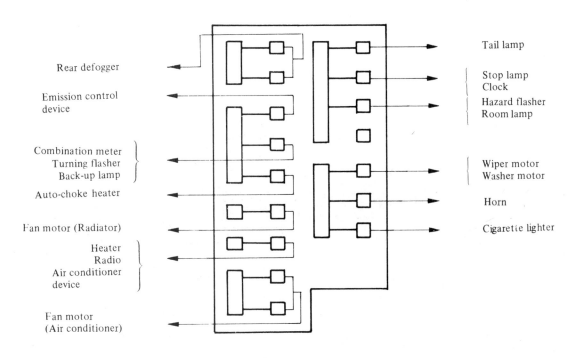

Rear defogger

Emission control
device

Combination meter
Turning flasher
Back-up lamp

Auto-choke heater

Fan motor (Radiator)

Heater
Radio
Air conditioner
device

Fan motor
(Air conditioner)

Tail lamp

Stop lamp
Clock

Hazard flasher
Room lamp

Wiper motor
Washer motor

Horn

Cigarette lighter

Fig. 10.71 Fuse block circuits for the 1981 A 15 engine models

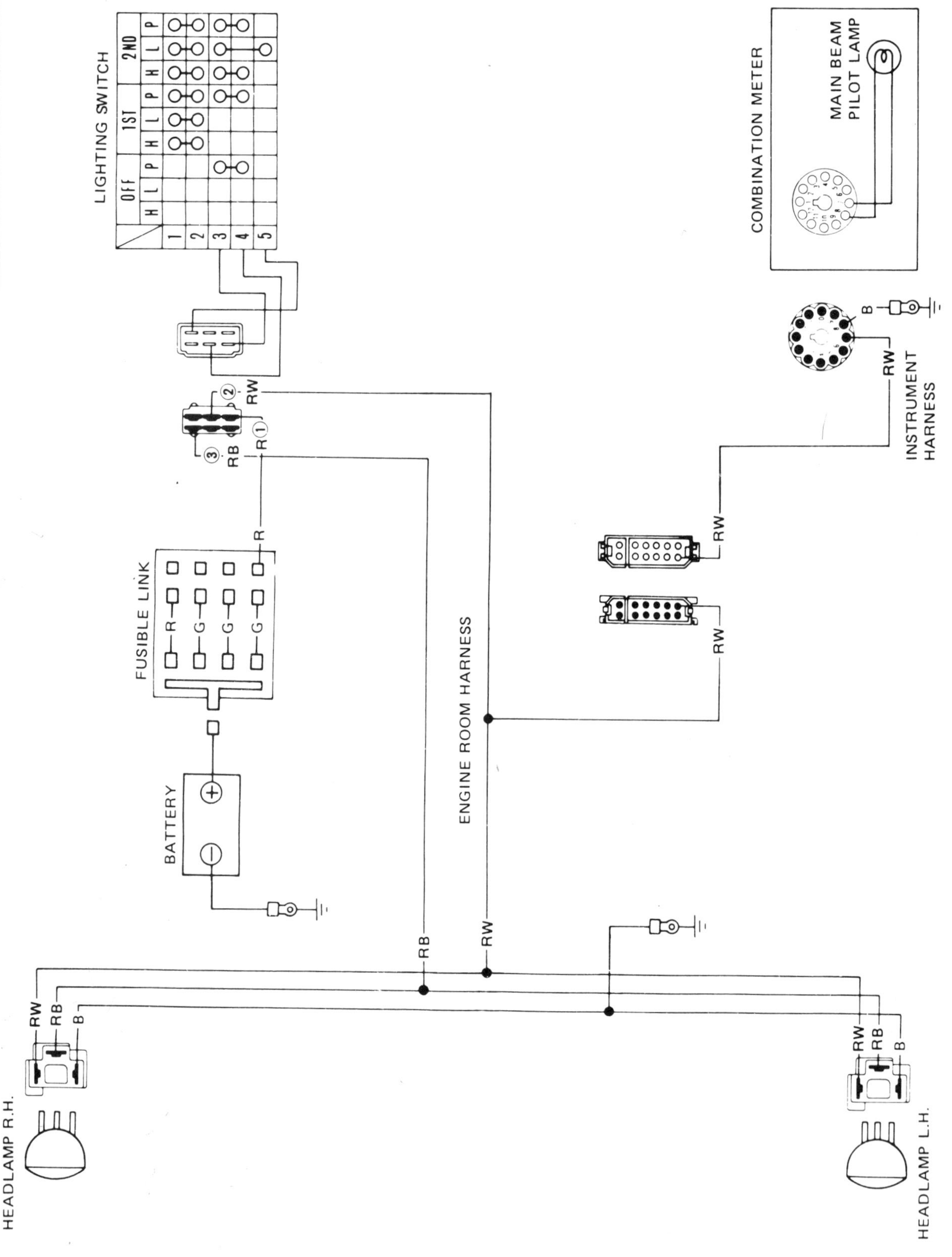

LIGHTING SWITCH

	OFF		1ST		2ND	
	H	L	P	H	L	P
1						
2						
3						
4						
5						

COMBINATION METER

MAIN BEAM PILOT LAMP

B

RW

INSTRUMENT HARNESS

RW

RW

RW

② RW

③ RB R ①

FUSIBLE LINK

R
R—
G—
G—
G—
R

BATTERY
+
−

ENGINE ROOM HARNESS

RB

RW

RW RB B

RW RB B

HEADLAMP R.H.

HEADLAMP L.H.

Fig. 10.72 Headlight circuit diagram – all models

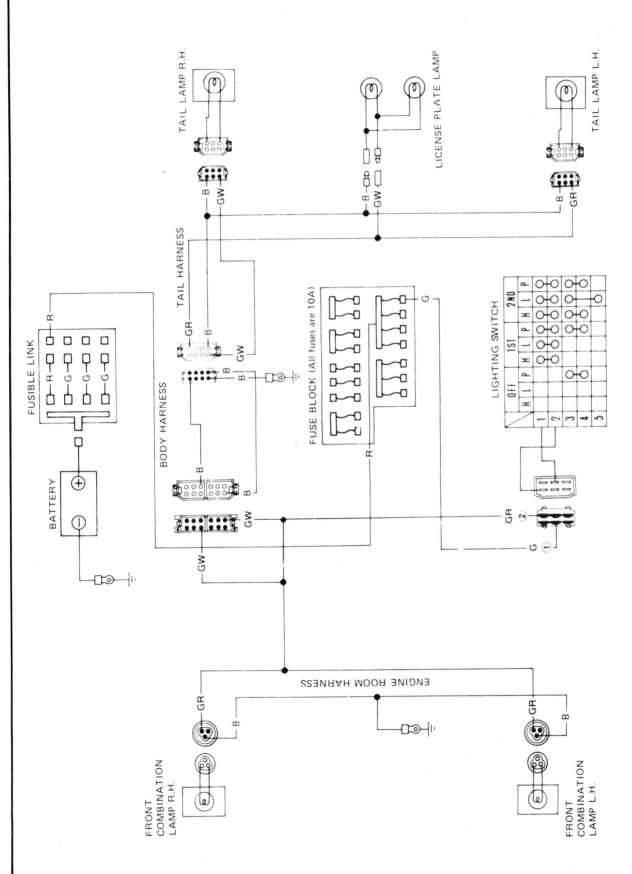

Fig. 10.73 Front/rear combination lights and number plate light circuits – A10 and A 12 engine models

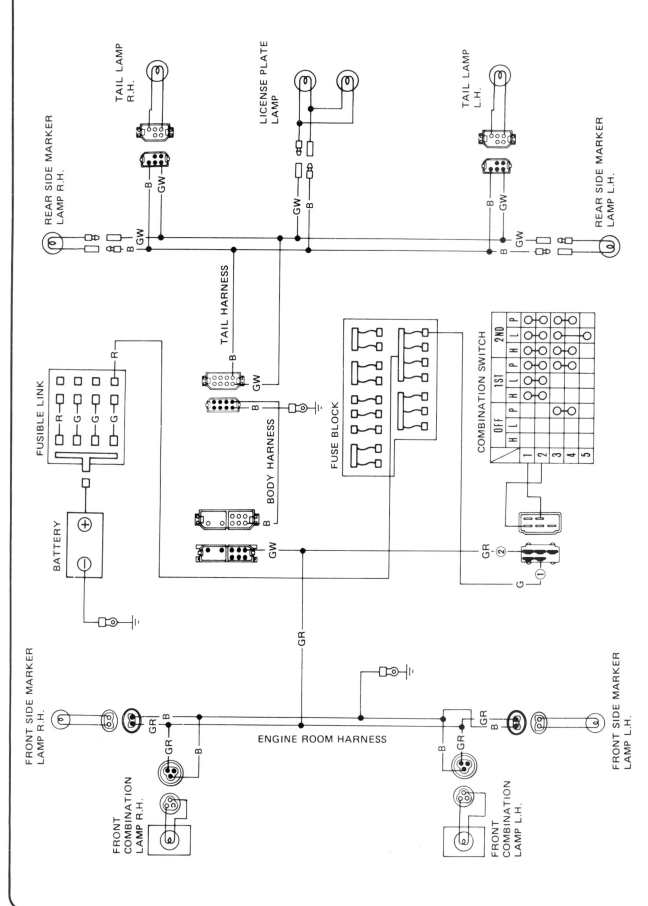

Fig. 10.74 Front/rear combination lights, side marker lights and licence plate light circuits – A14 and A15 engine models

219

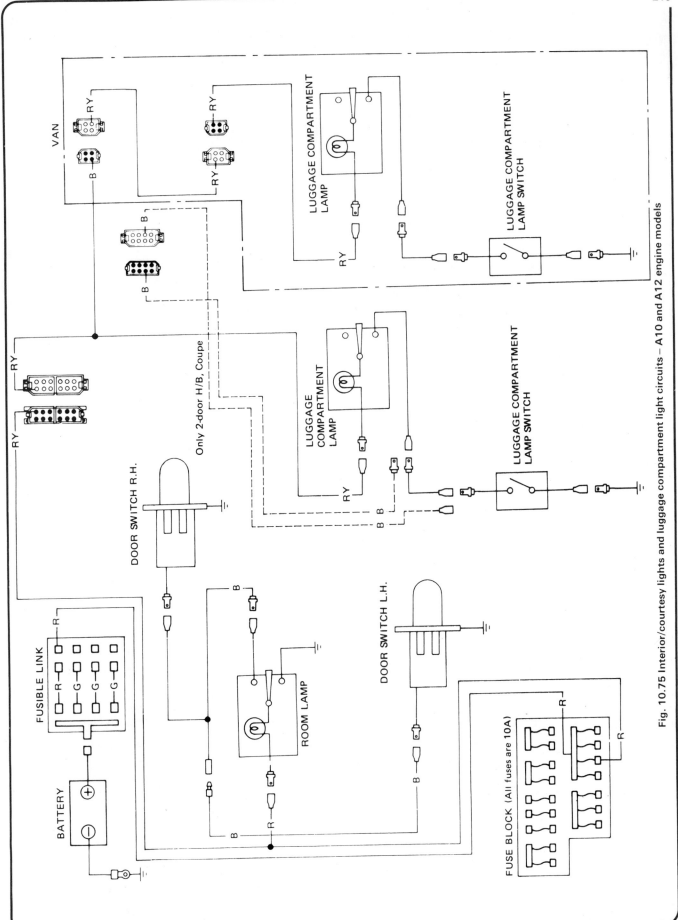

Fig. 10.75 Interior/courtesy lights and luggage compartment light circuits – A10 and A12 engine models

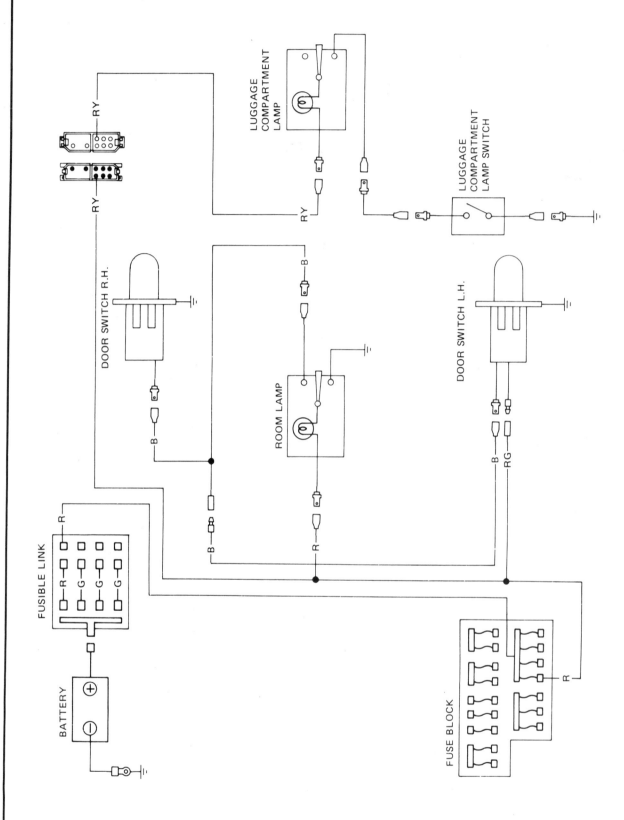

Fig. 10.76 Interior/courtesy lights and luggage compartment light circuits – 1979 A14 engine models

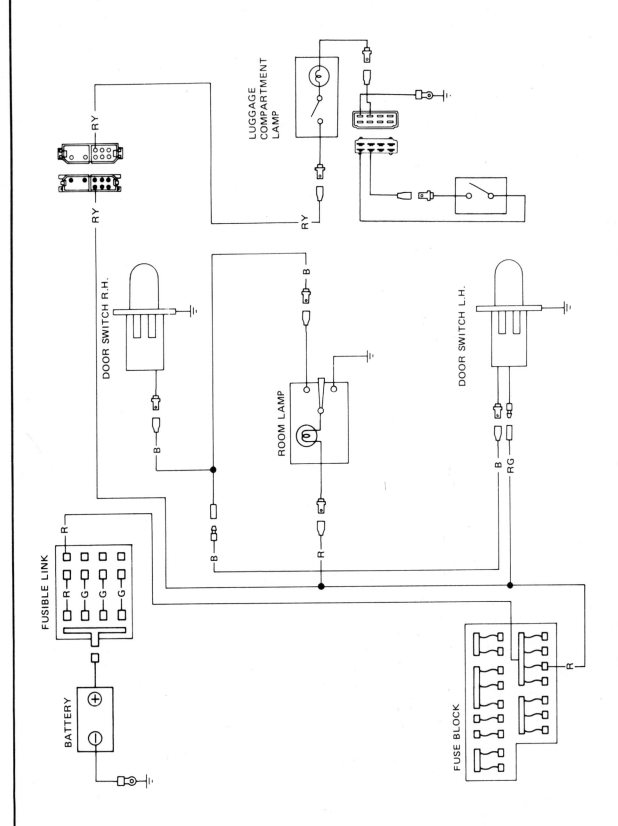

Fig. 10.77 Interior/courtesy lights and luggage compartment light circuits – 1980 and 1981 A14 and A15 engine models

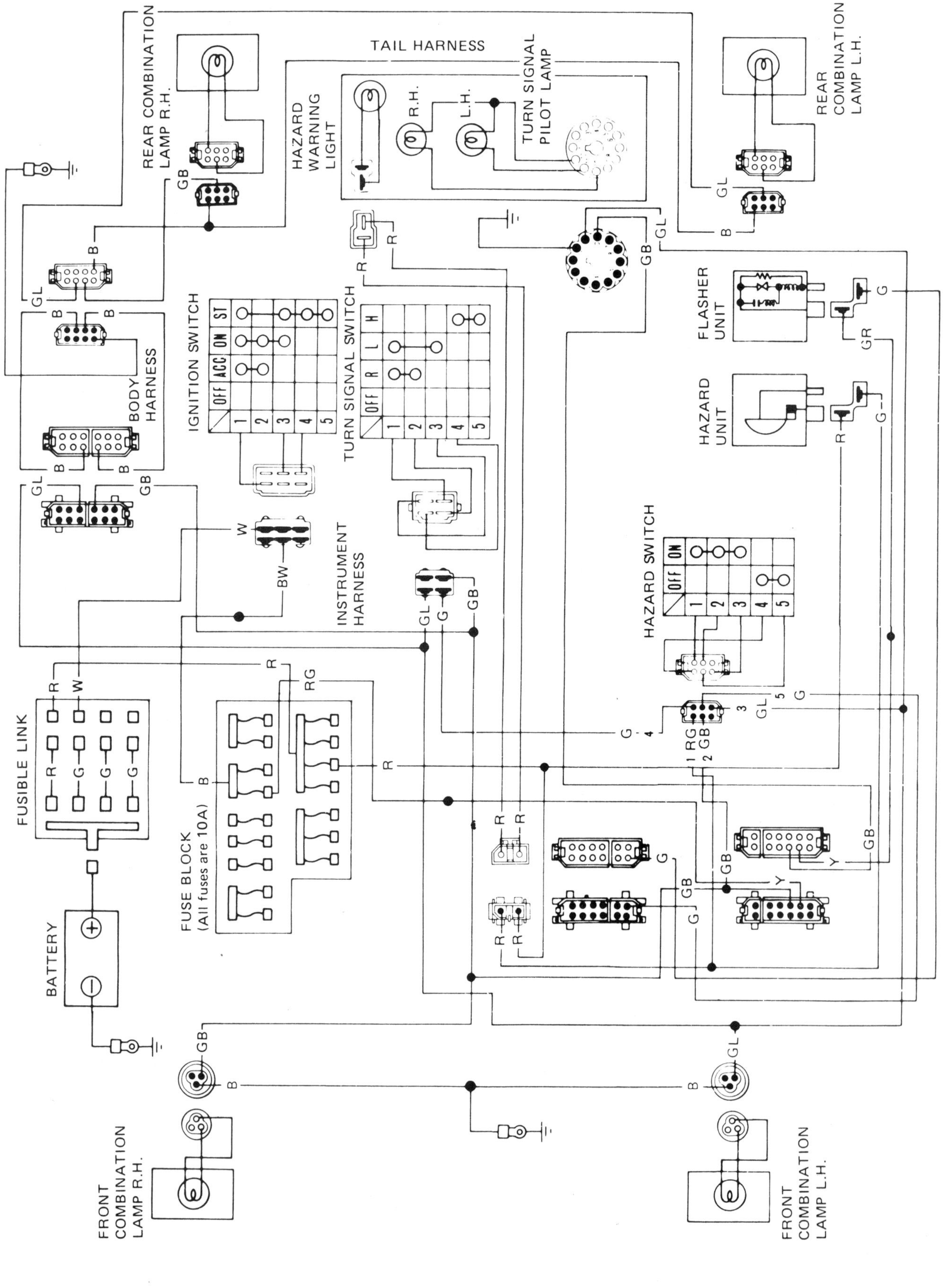

REAR COMBINATION LAMP R.H.

TAIL HARNESS

HAZARD WARNING LIGHT

R.H. L.H.

TURN SIGNAL PILOT LAMP

REAR COMBINATION LAMP L.H.

GB

GL

B

FLASHER UNIT

G

GR

HAZARD UNIT

G

R

GB

GL

B

B

BODY HARNESS

GL

B

GB

IGNITION SWITCH

	OFF	ACC	ON	ST
1				
2				
3				
4				
5				

TURN SIGNAL SWITCH

	OFF	R	L	H
1				
2				
3				
4				
5				

HAZARD SWITCH

	OFF	ON
1		
2		
3		
4		
5		

W

BW

INSTRUMENT HARNESS

GL

G

GB

GL G GB

3

1 RG

2 GB

5

G

4

G

RG

GL

FUSIBLE LINK

R

W

R

R G G G G

BATTERY

FUSE BLOCK
(All fuses are 10A)

B

R

RG

R

R R

R R

G

GB

G

GB

Y

Y

GB

GB

GL

FRONT COMBINATION LAMP R.H.

GB

B

B

GL

FRONT COMBINATION LAMP L.H.

Fig. 10.78 Indicators and hazard warning circuits – A10 and A12 engine models

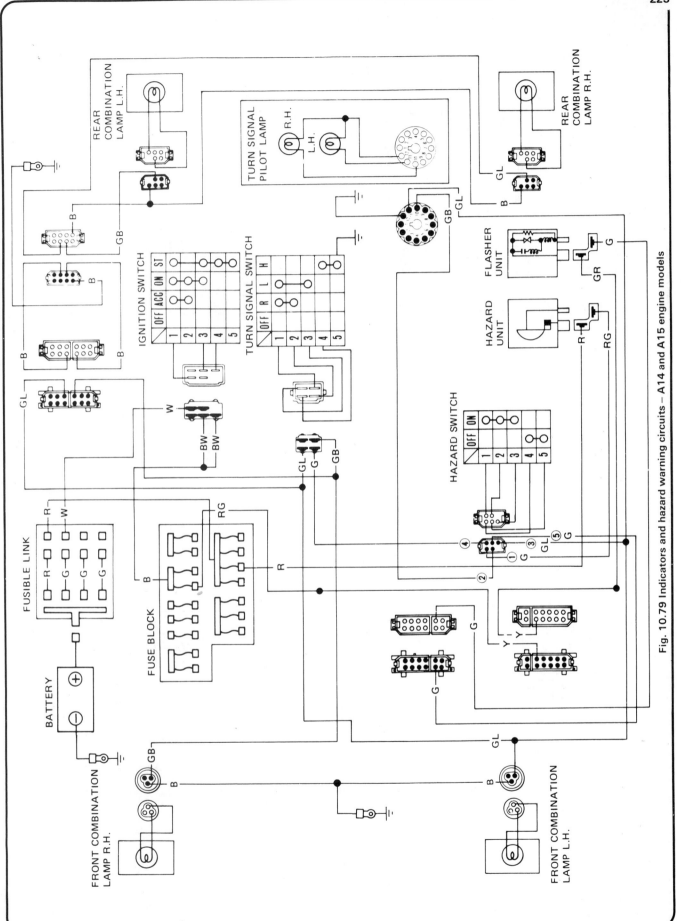

Fig. 10.79 Indicators and hazard warning circuits — A14 and A15 engine models

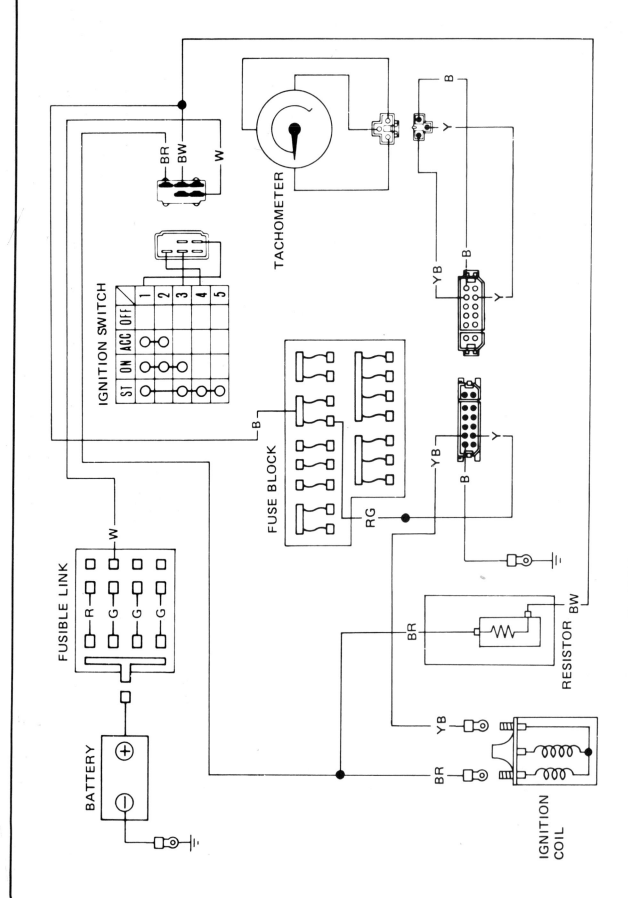

Fig. 10.80 Tachometer wiring diagram — A10 and A12 engine models

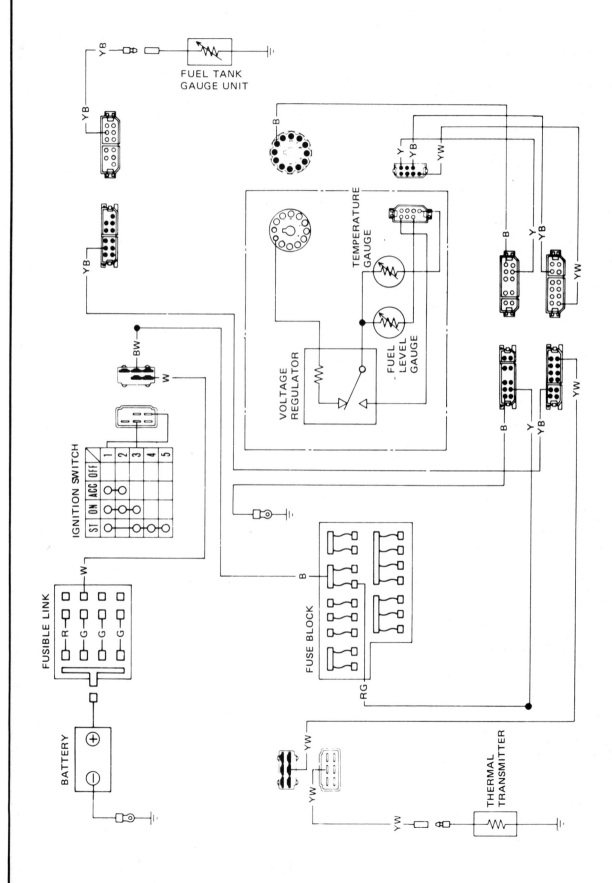

Fig. 10.81 Water temperature/fuel level gauge circuits — A10 and A12 engine models

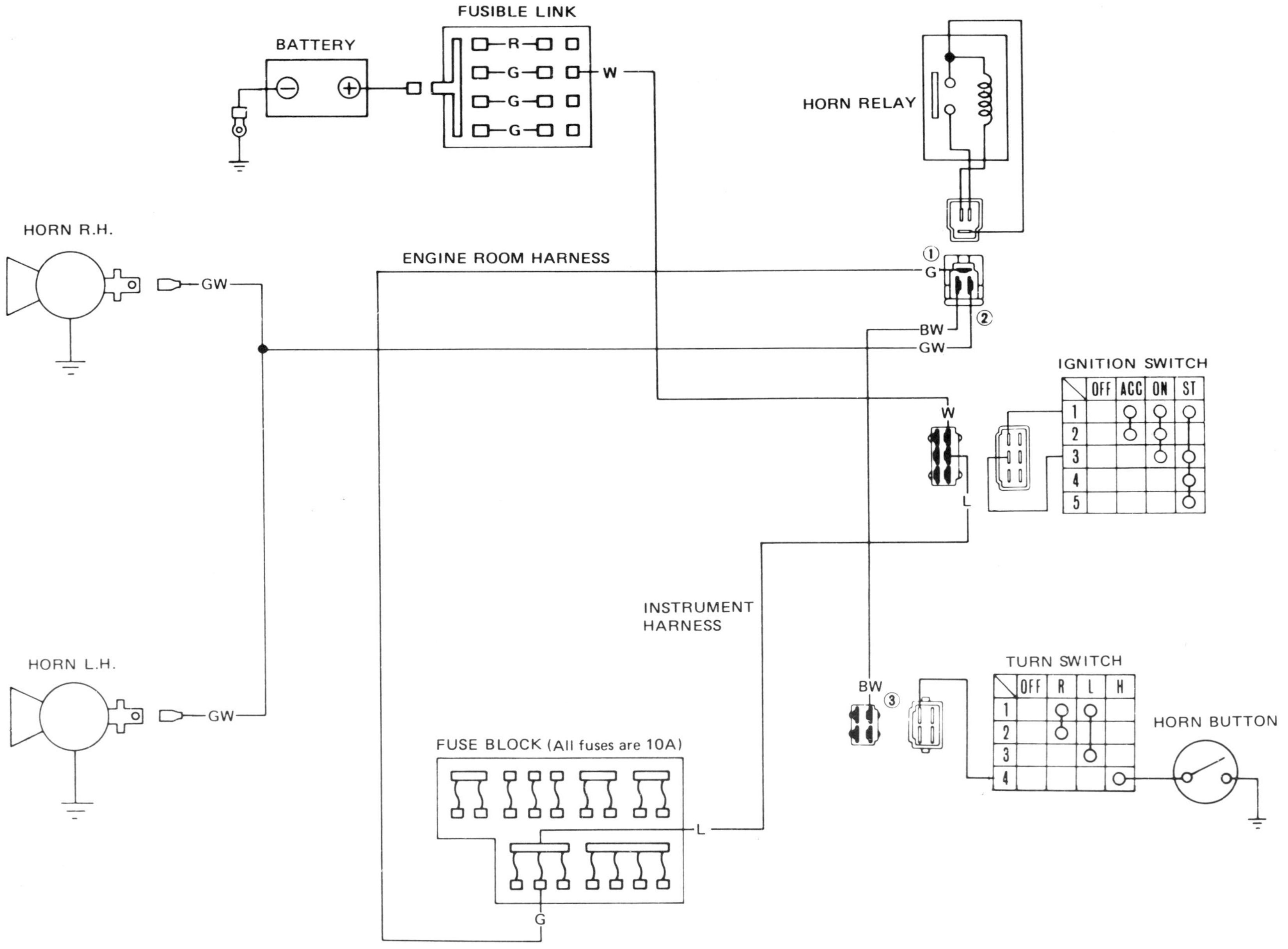

Fig. 10.82 Horn wiring circuit – all models (typical)

227

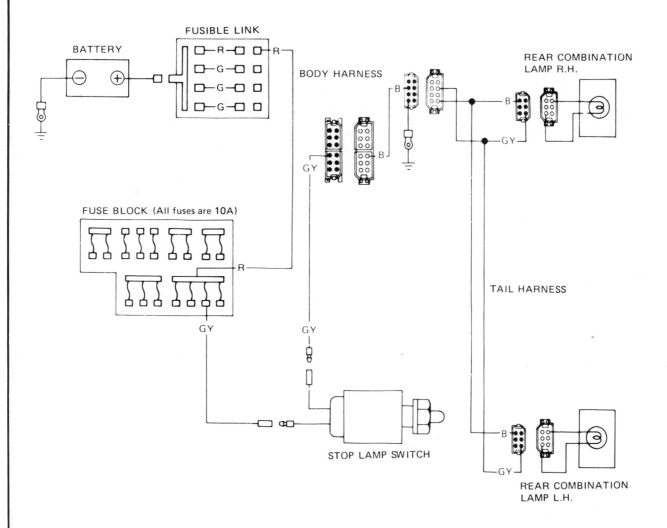

Fig. 10.83 Stop-lights wiring diagram – all models (typical)

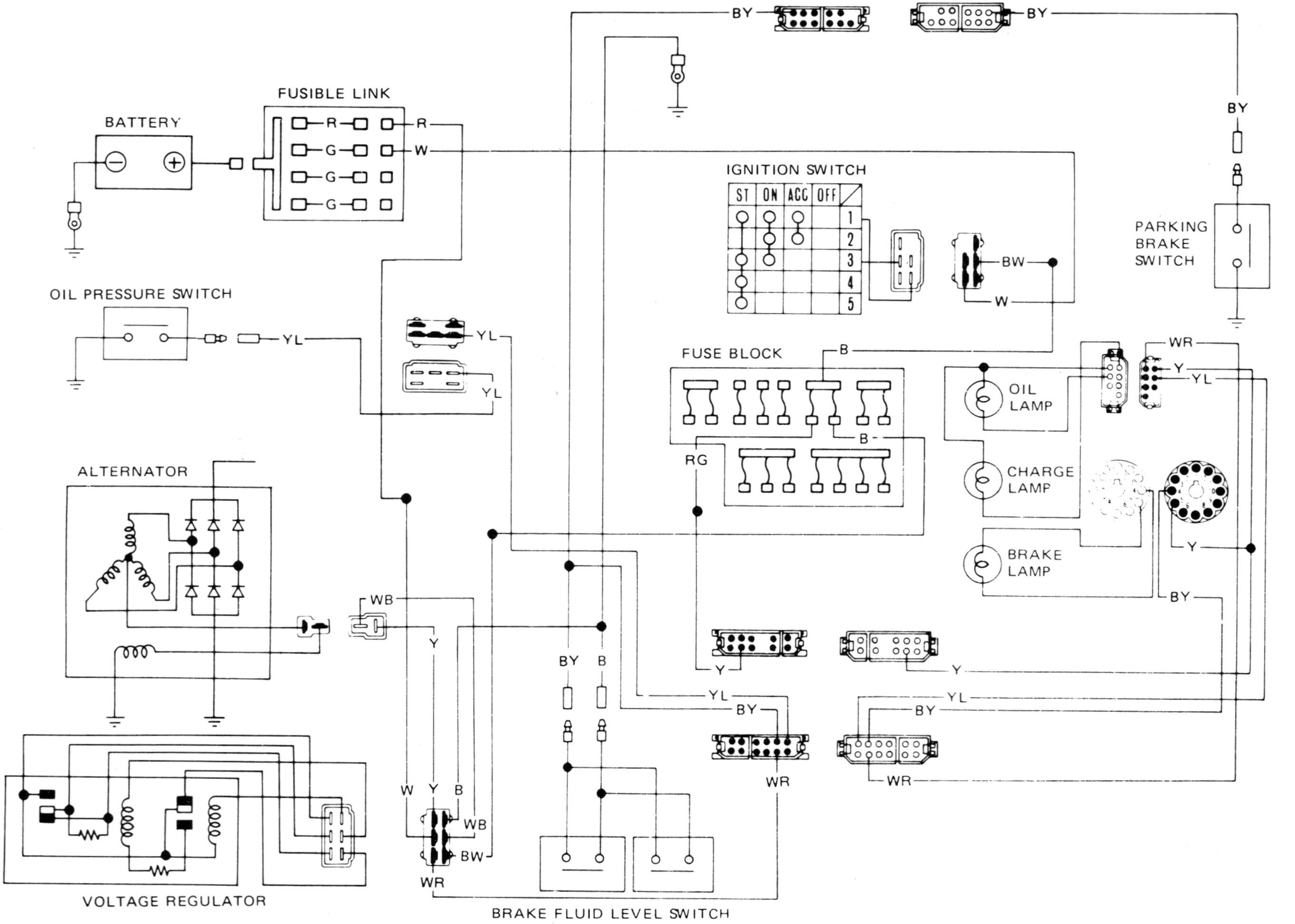

Fig. 10.84 Warning system diagram – A10 and A12 engine models

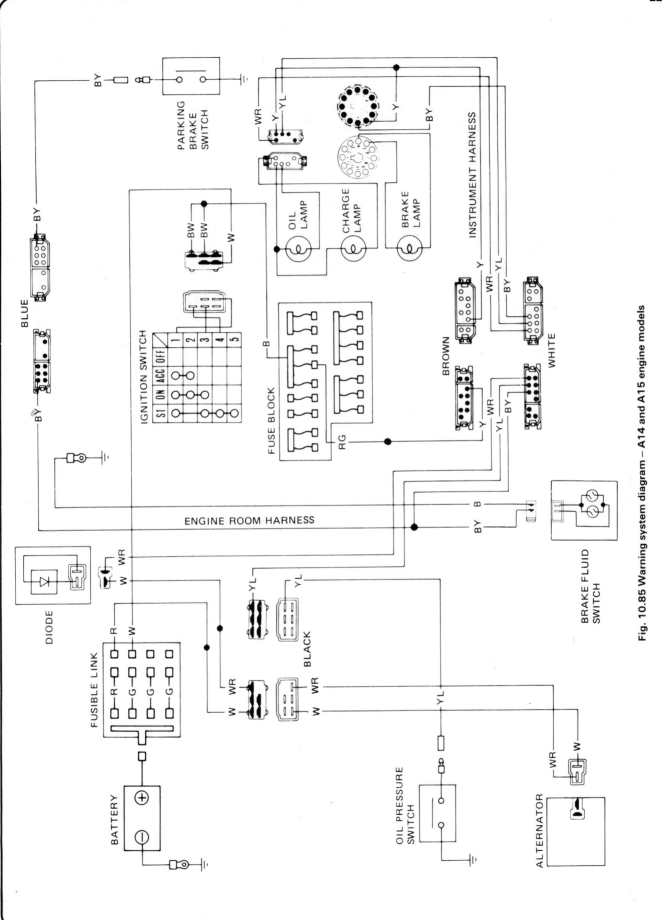

Fig. 10.85 Warning system diagram — A14 and A15 engine models

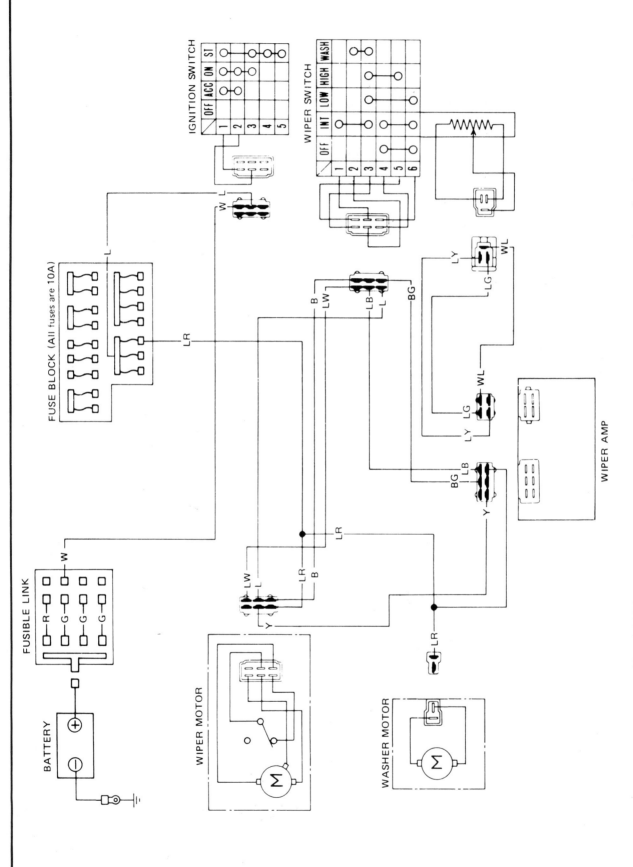

Fig. 10.86 Windscreen wiper and washer circuits – all models up to 1980 with intermittent function

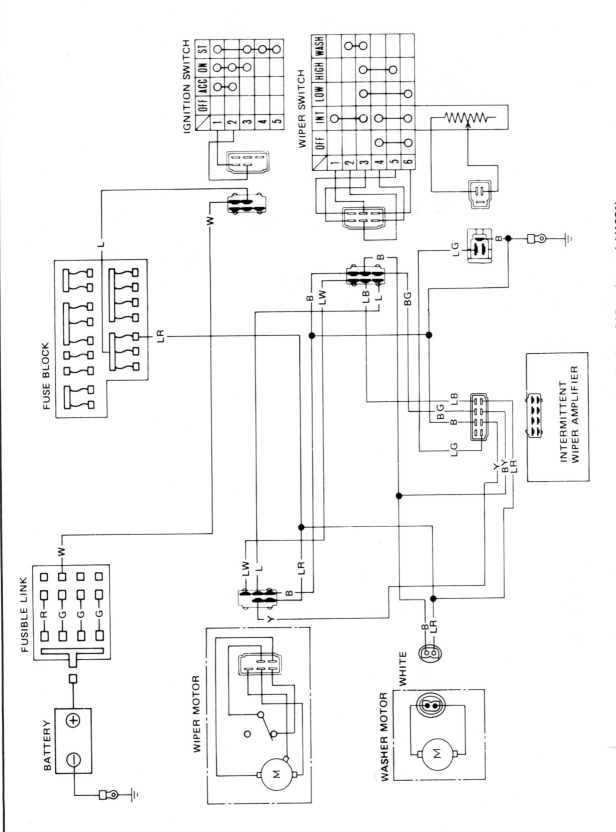

Fig. 10.87 Windscreen wiper and washer circuits – A15 engine model (1981)

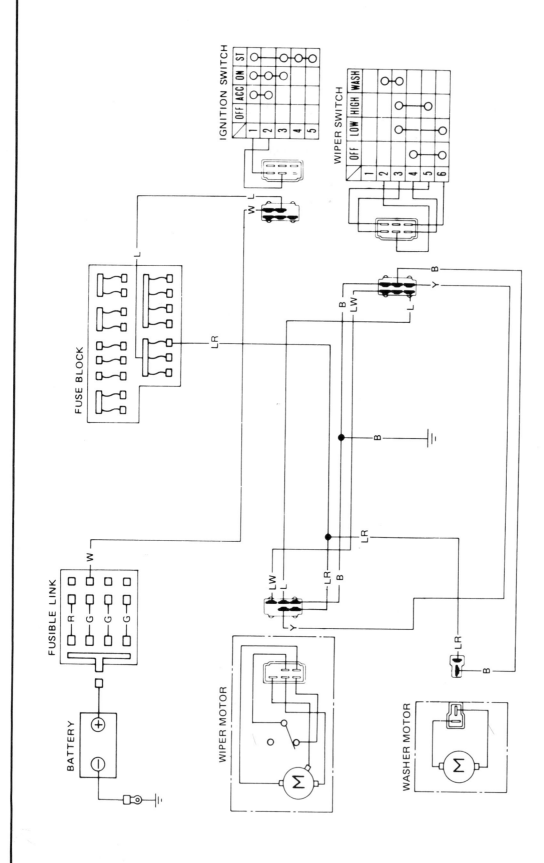

Fig. 10.88 Windscreen wiper and washer circuits without intermittent wiper function

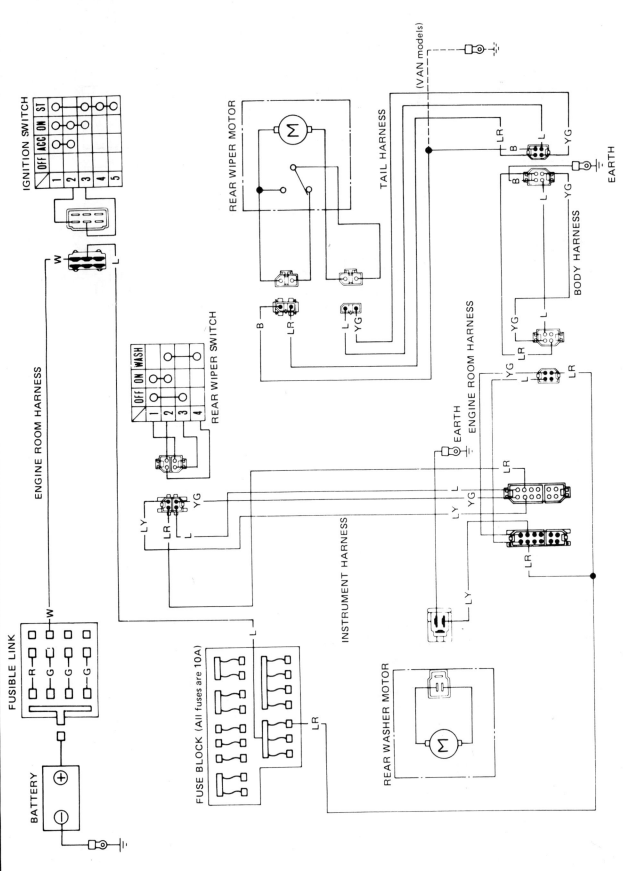

Fig. 10.89 Rear screen wiper and washer circuits — A10 and A12 engine models

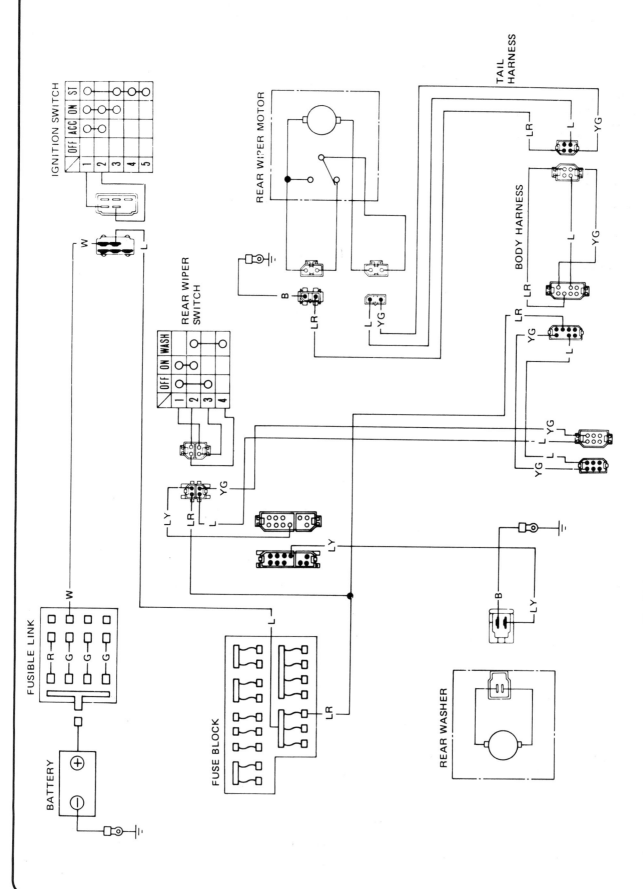

Fig. 10.90 Rear screen wiper and washer circuits – A14 engine – 1979 models

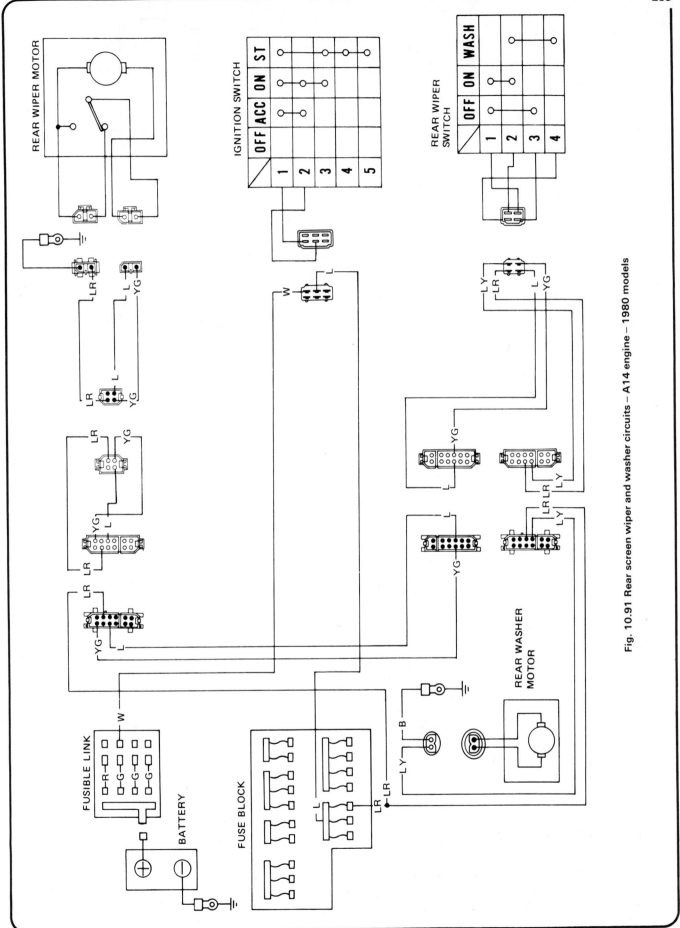

Fig. 10.91 Rear screen wiper and washer circuits – A14 engine – 1980 models

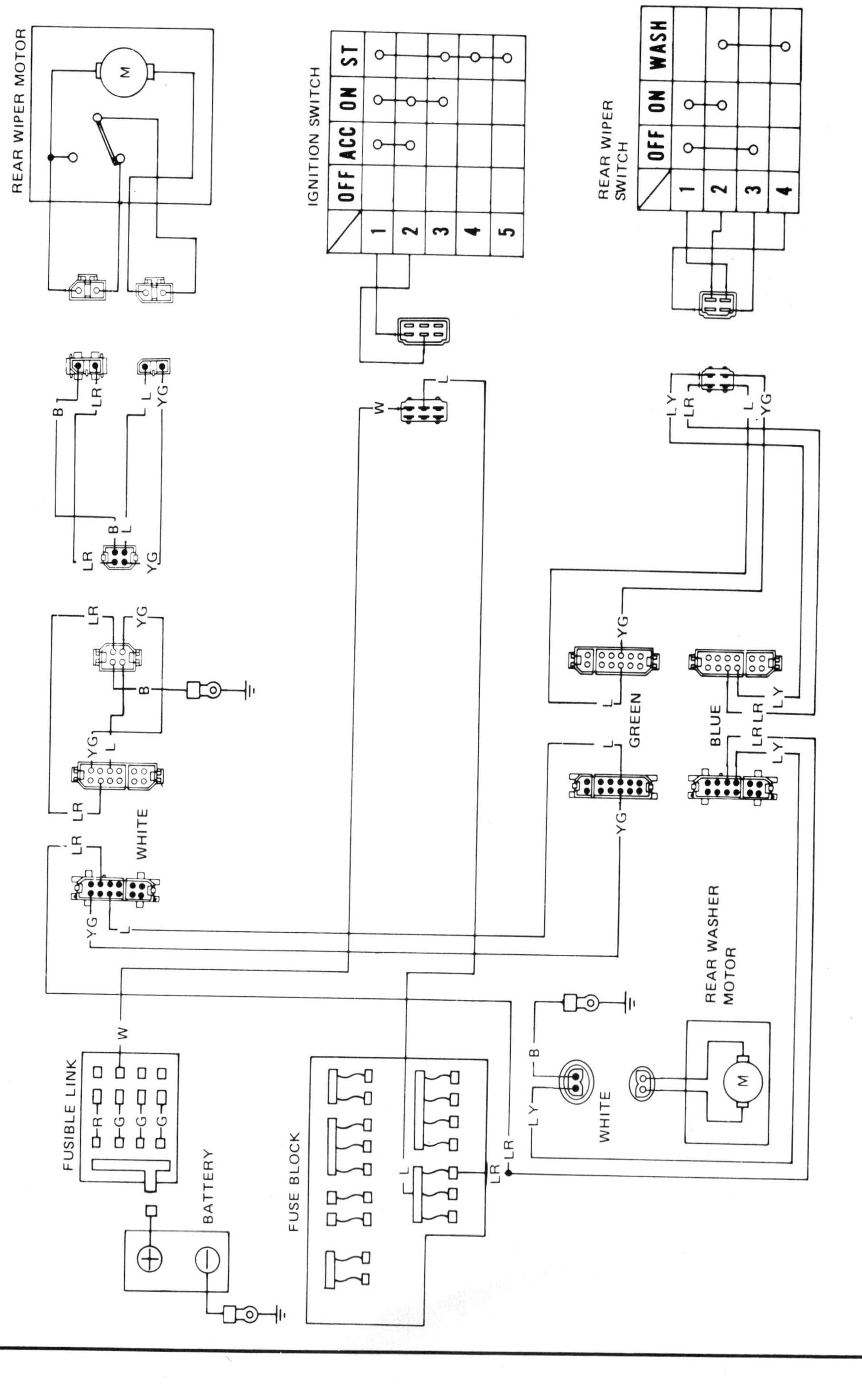

Fig. 10.92 Rear screen wiper and washer circuits – A15 engine – 1981 models

RADIO

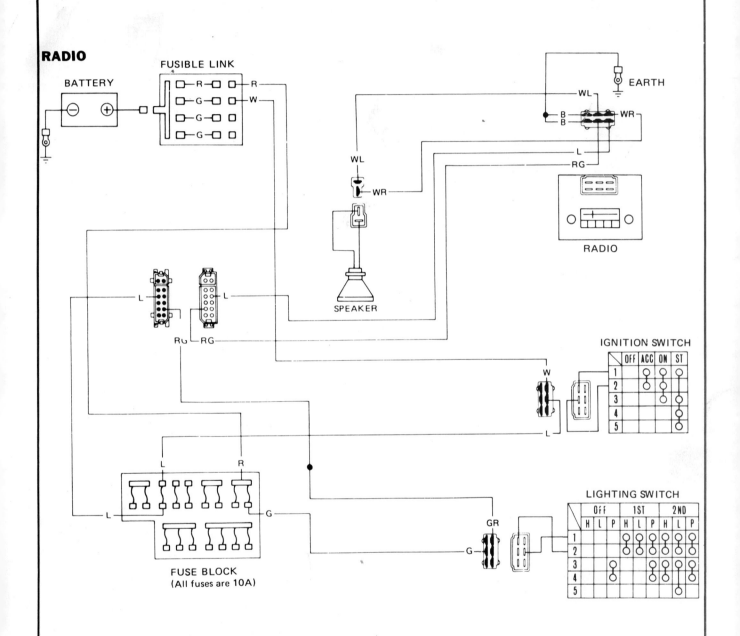

Fig. 10.93 Radio wiring diagram – A10 and A12 engine models

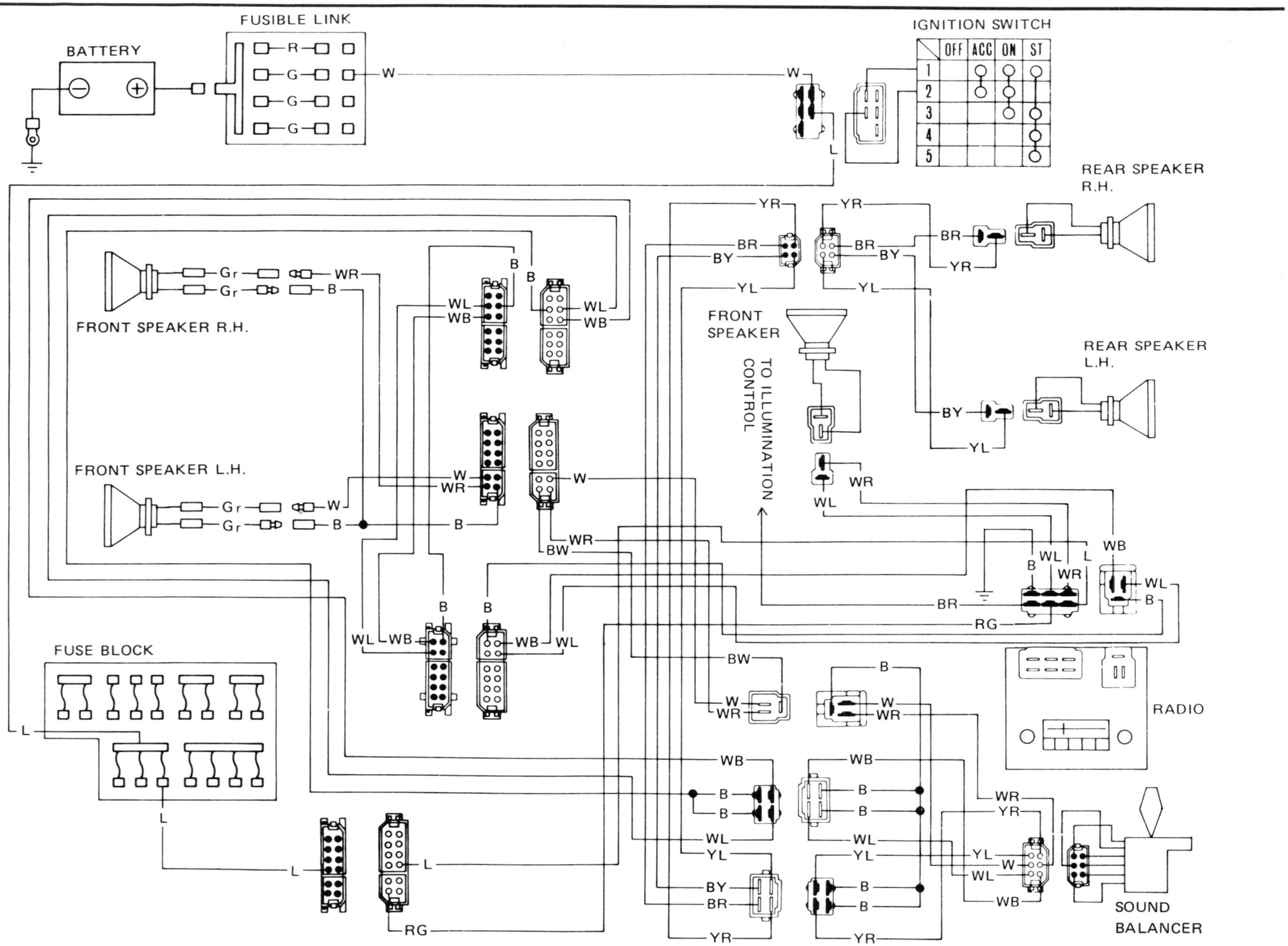

Fig. 10.94 Radio wiring diagram – A14 engine models – 1979

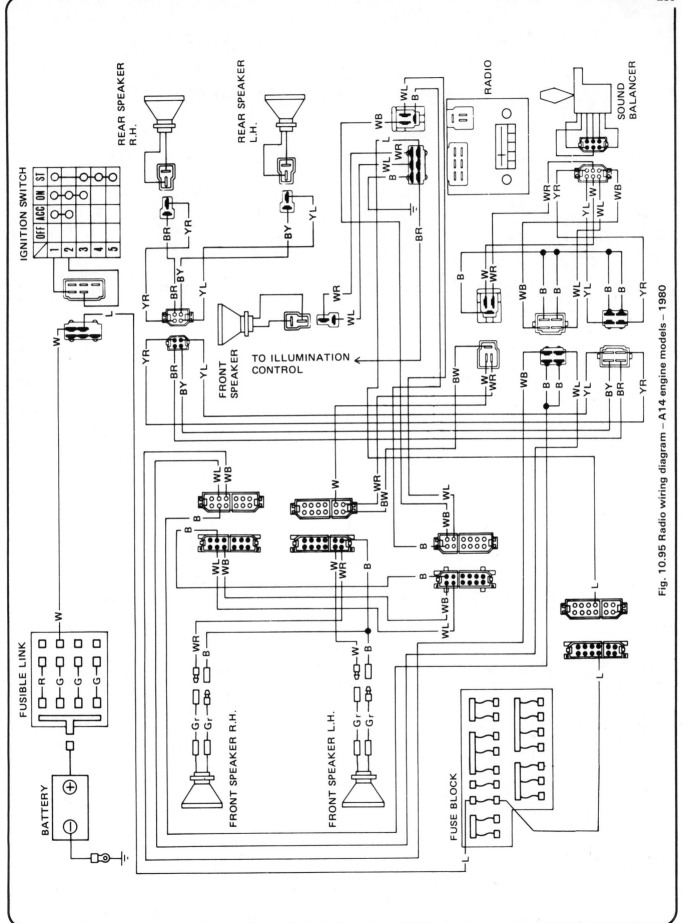

Fig. 10.95 Radio wiring diagram – A14 engine models – 1980

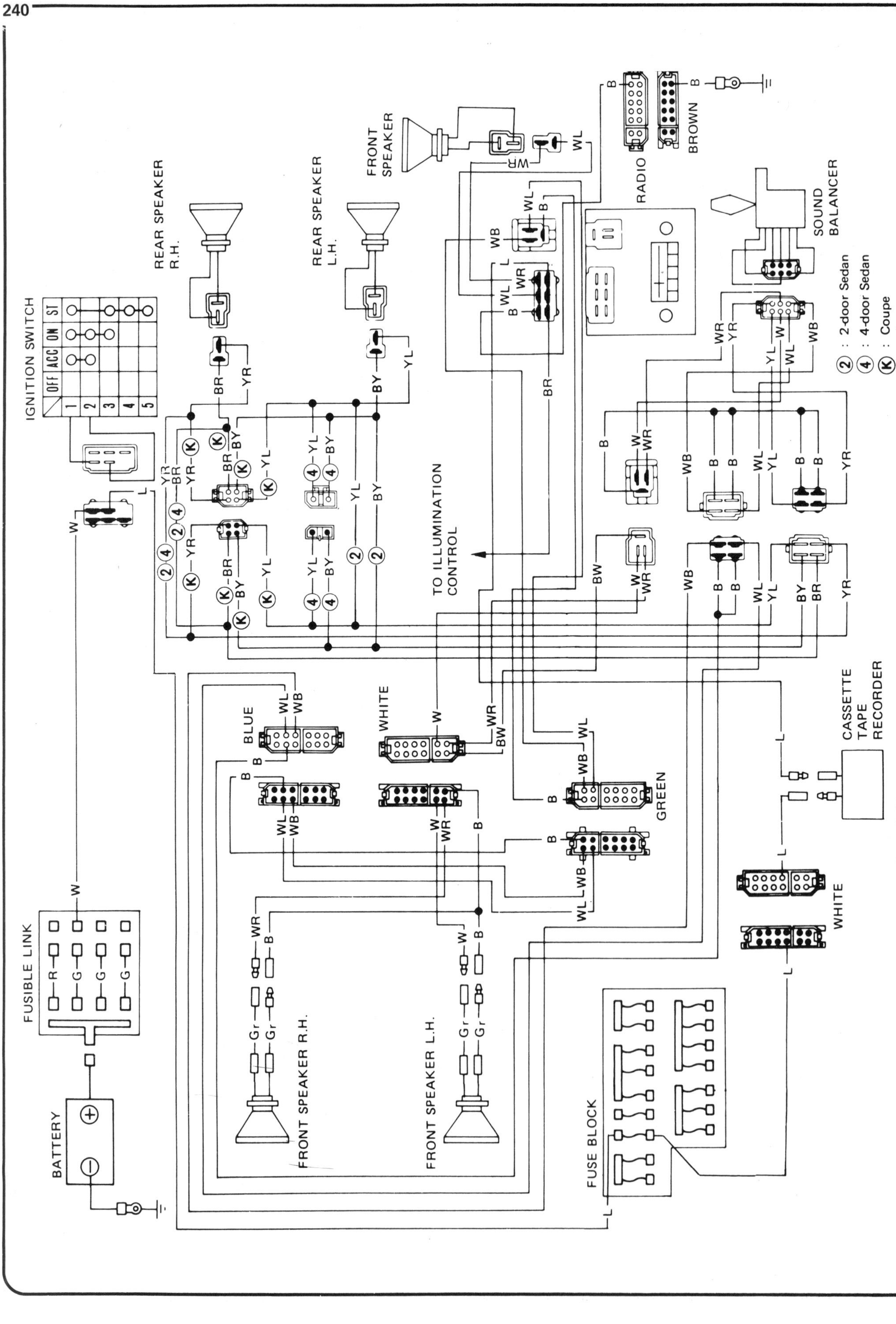

REAR SPEAKER R.H.

REAR SPEAKER L.H.

FRONT SPEAKER

RADIO

BROWN

SOUND BALANCER

IGNITION SWITCH

	OFF	ACC	ON	ST
1				
2				
3				
4				
5				

② : 2-door Sedan
④ : 4-door Sedan
Ⓚ : Coupe

TO ILLUMINATION CONTROL

FUSIBLE LINK

R
G
G
G

BATTERY

+
−

BLUE

WHITE

GREEN

WHITE

FRONT SPEAKER R.H.

FRONT SPEAKER L.H.

FUSE BLOCK

CASSETTE TAPE RECORDER

Fig. 10.96 Radio wiring diagram – A15 engine models – 1981

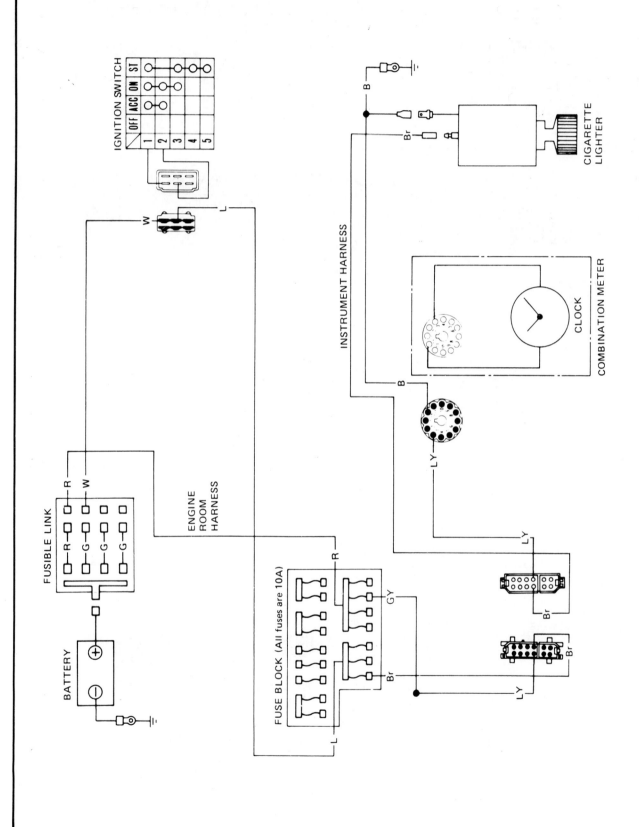

Fig. 10.97 Cigarette lighter and clock wiring diagram – all models (typical)

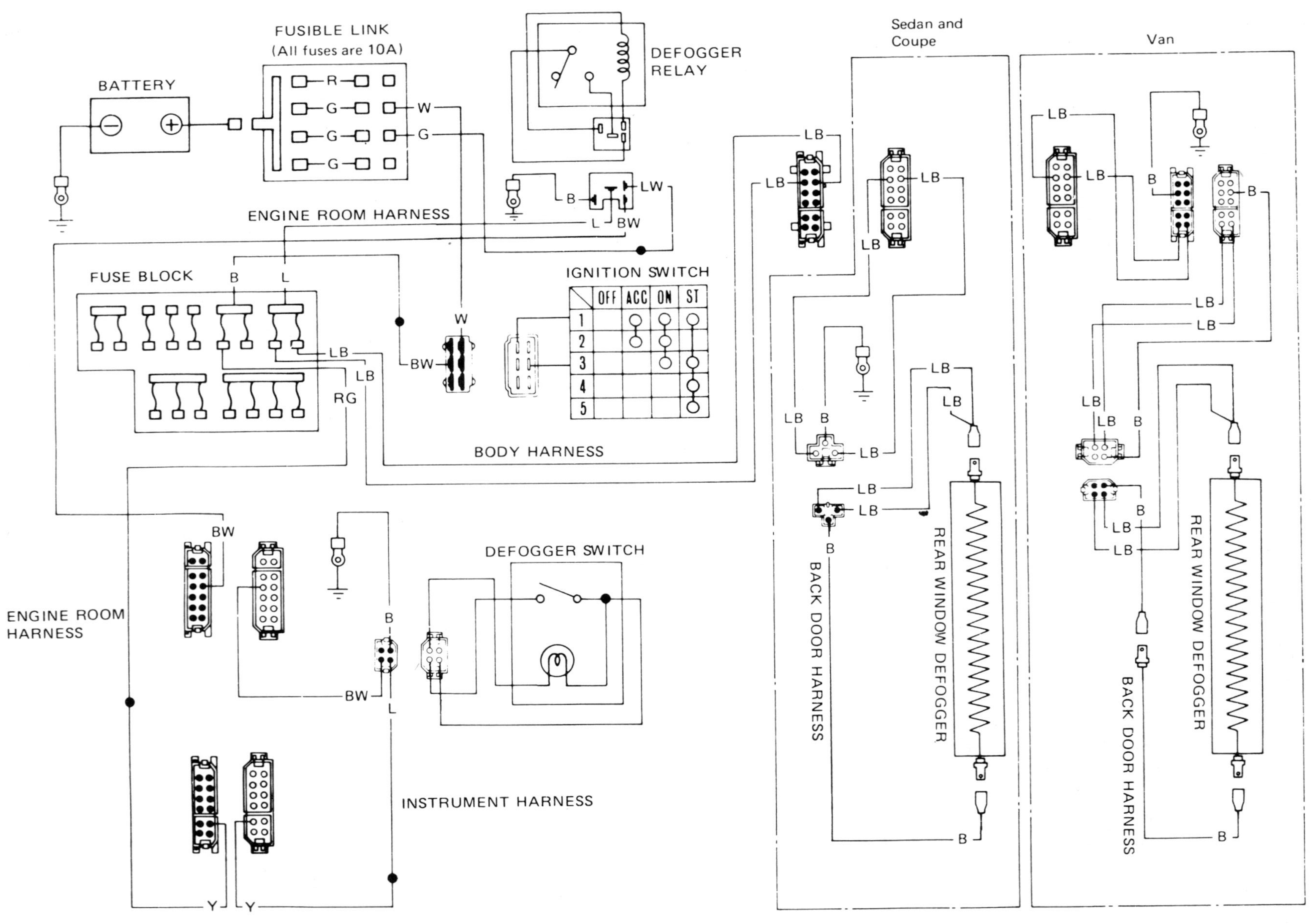

Fig. 10.98 Rear screen demister circuit — A10 and A12 engine models

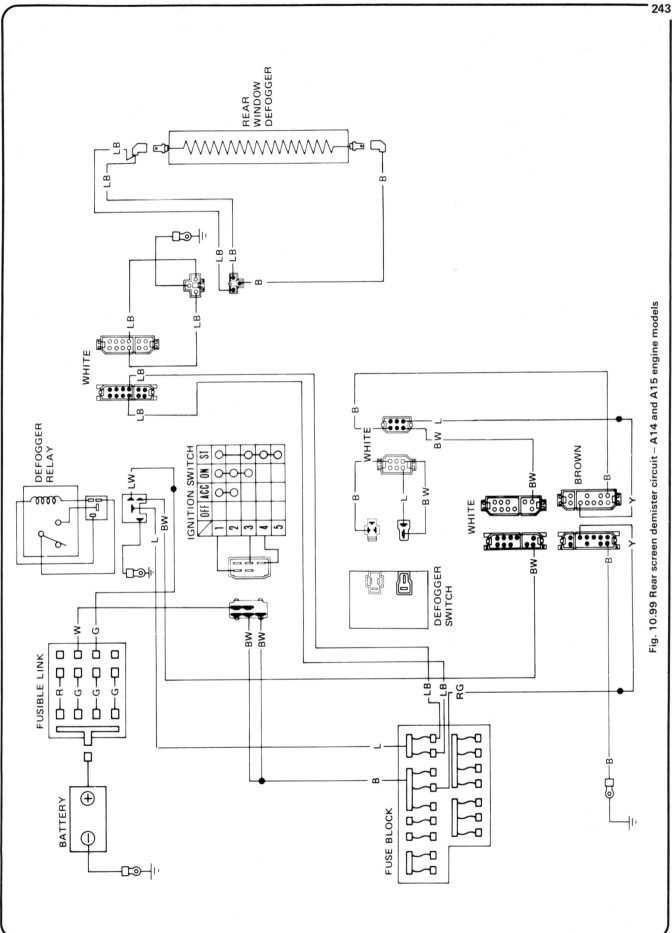

Fig. 10.99 Rear screen demister circuit – A14 and A15 engine models

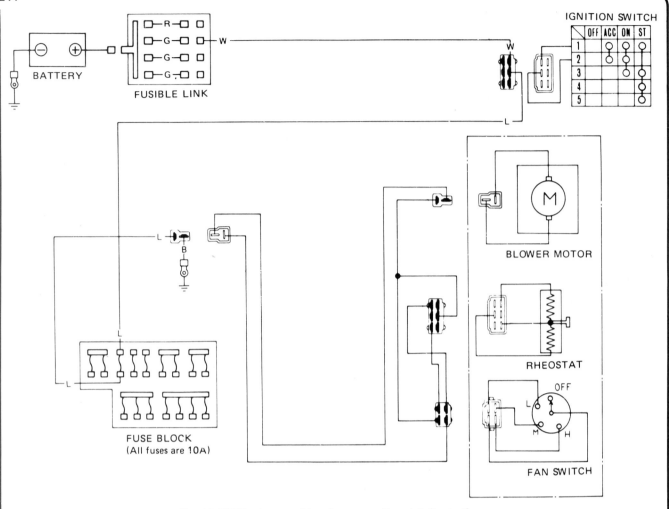

Fig. 10.100 The heater wiring diagram – all models (typical)

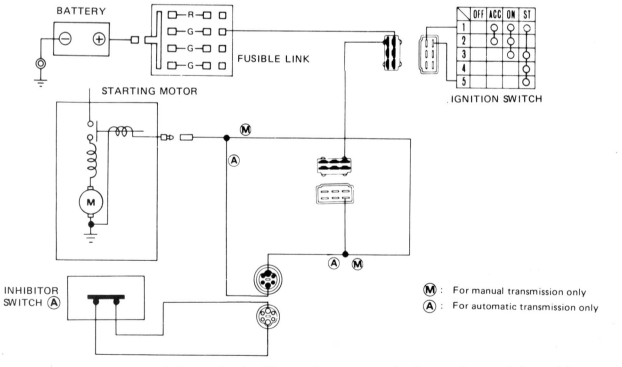

Fig. 10.101 The starter circuit diagram showing differences between manual and automatic transmission models

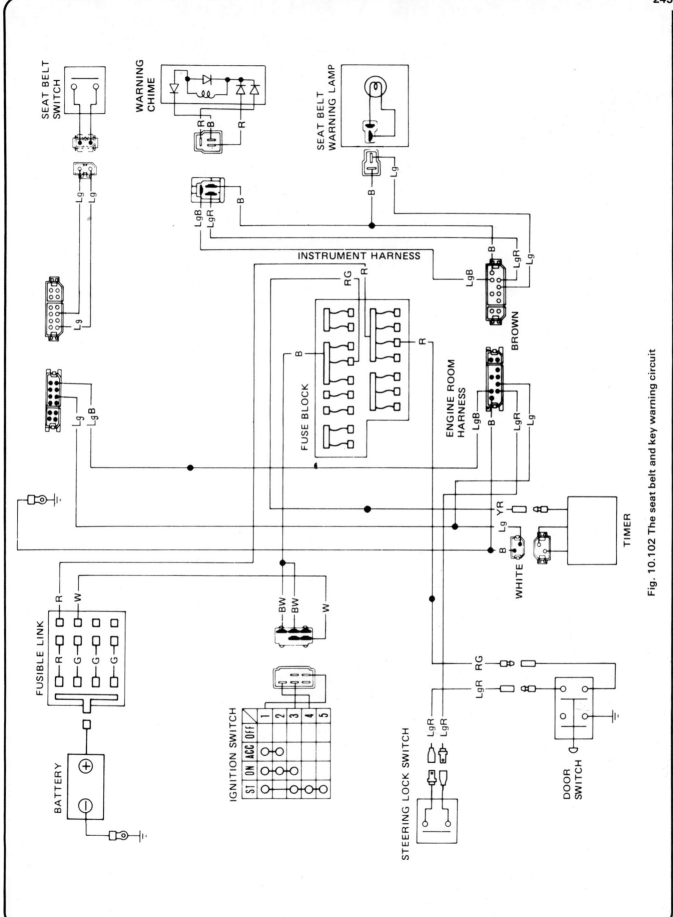

Fig. 10.102 The seat belt and key warning circuit

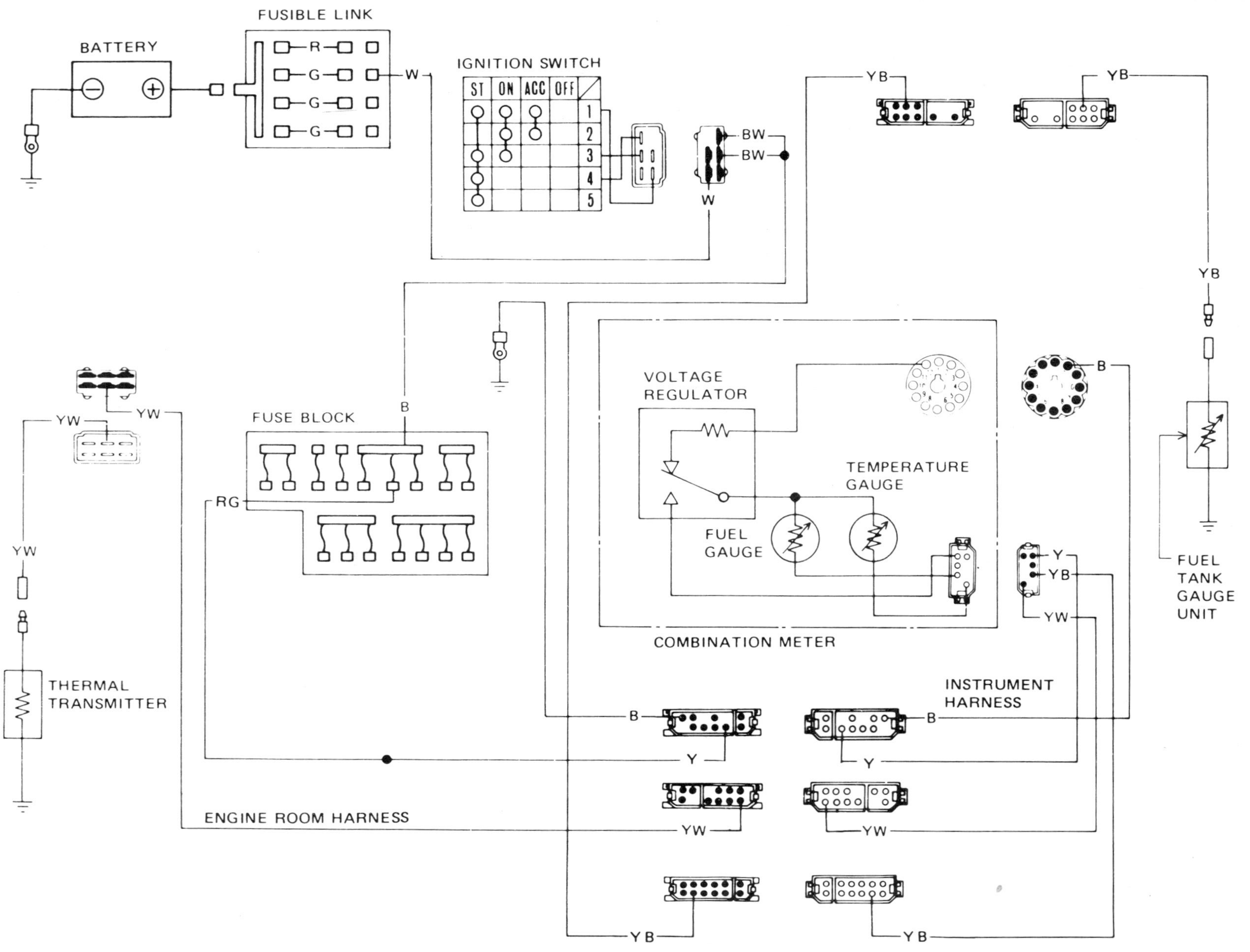

Fig. 10.103 Water temperature and fuel level gauge circuits — A14 and A15 engine models

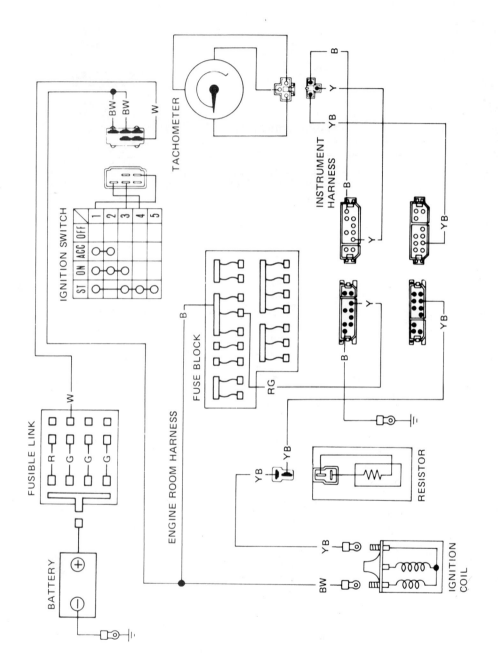

Fig. 10.104 Tachometer wiring diagram — A14 and A15 engine models

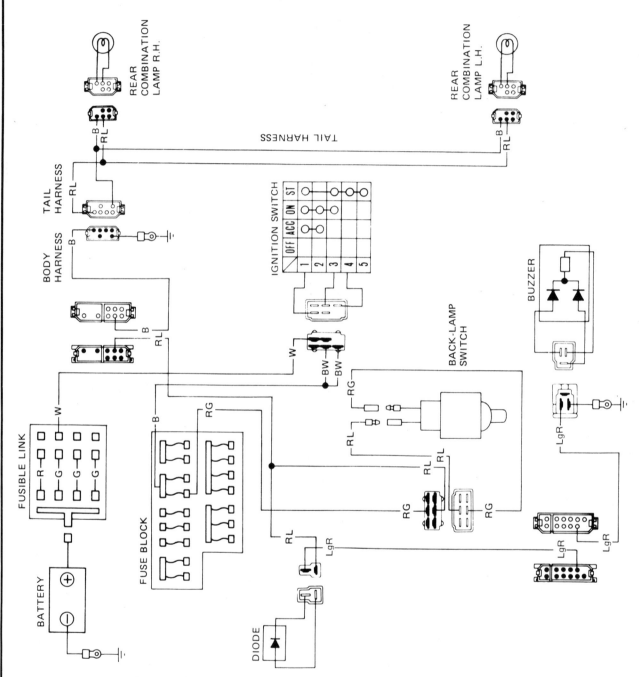

Fig. 10.105 Reversing (back-up) light wiring circuits – A14 engine models

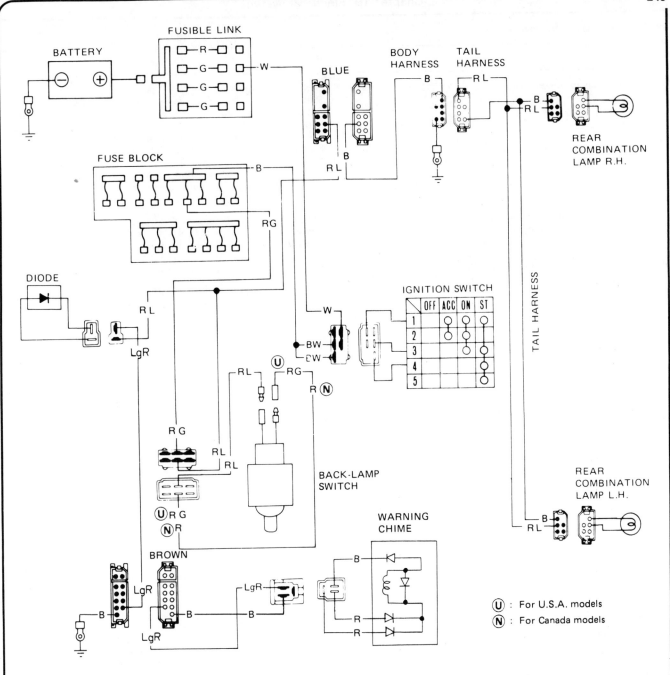

Fig. 10.106 Reversing (back-up) light wiring circuits – A15 engine models

Wiring diagram colour code

B	Black
W	White
R	Red
G	Green
Y	Yellow
L	Blue
Br	Brown
Lg	Light green

48 Fault diagnosis – electrical system

Symptom	Reason(s)
Starter motor fails to turn engine	Battery discharged Battery defective internally Battery terminal leads loose or earth lead not securely attached to body Loose or broken connections in starter motor circuit Starter motor switch or solenoid faulty Starter brushes badly worn, sticking or brush wires loose Commutator dirty, worn or burnt Starter motor armature faulty Field coils earthed
Starter motor turns engine very slowly	Battery in discharged condition Starter brushes badly worn, sticking, or brush wires loose Loose wires in starter motor circuit
Starter motor operates without turning engine	Pinion or flywheel gear teeth broken or worn
Starter motor noisy or excessively rough	Pinion or flywheel gear teeth broken or worn Starter motor retaining bolts loose
Battery will not hold charge for more than a few days	Battery defective internally Electrolyte level too low or electrolyte too weak due to leakage Plate separators no longer fully effective Battery plates severely sulphated Alternator belt slipping Battery terminal connections loose or corroded Alternator not charging properly Short in lighting circuit causing continual battery drain Regulator unit not working correctly
Ignition light fails to go out, battery runs flat in a few days	Drivebelt loose and slipping or broken Alternator faulty

Failure of individual electrical equipment to function correctly is dealt with alphabetically, item by item, under the headings listed below

Fuel gauge

Fuel gauge gives no reading	Fuel tank empty! Electric cable between tank sender unit and gauge earthed or loose Fuel gauge case not earthed Fuel gauge supply cable interrupted Fuel gauge unit broken
Fuel gauge registers full all the time	Electric cable between tank unit and gauge broken or disconnected

Horn

Horn operates all the time	Horn push either earthed or stuck down Horn cable to horn push earthed
Horn fails to operate	Blown fuse Cable or cable connection loose, broken or disconnected Horn has an internal fault Horn relay defective

Lights

Lights do not come on	If engine not running, battery discharged Poor battery connection Light bulb filament burnt out or bulbs broken Wire connections loose, disconnected or broken Light switch faulty
Lights come on but fade out	If engine not running battery discharged
Lights give very poor illumination	Lamp glasses dirty Lamps badly out of adjustment Incorrect bulb with too low wattage fitted Existing bulbs old and badly discoloured
Lights work erratically – flashing on and off, especially over bumps	Battery terminals or earth connections loose Lights not earthing properly Contacts in light switch faulty

Symptom	Reason(s)
Wiper motor	
Wiper motor fails to work	Blown fuse
	Wire connections loose, disconnected or broken
	Brushes badly worn
	Seized motor shaft or linkage pivots
Wiper motor works but blades remain stationary	Disconnected linkage or broken linkage
Wiper operating speed too slow	Brushes worn
	Linkage sticking
	Armature faulty
Incorrect parking of wiper arms	Auto-stop device incorrectly set

Chapter 11 Suspension and wheel hubs

For modifications, and information applicable to later models, see Supplement at end of manual

Contents

Specifications

Front suspension

Type .... Independent, MacPherson strut with double-acting hydraulic shock absorbers

Wheel alignment (front) – unladen:
  Camber (non-adjustable) .... 0° 15' to 1° 45'
  Caster (non-adjustable) .... 0° 25' to 1° 55'
  Toe-in .... 0 to 0.08 in (0 to 2 mm)
  Kingpin inclination .... 11° 10' to 12° 30'
Front wheel bearing preload:
  Rotational starting torque .... 6.9 to 24.3 lbf in (8 to 28 kgf cm)
  Rotational starting torque measured at hub bolt .... 3.1 to 10.8 lbf (1.4 to 4.9 kgf)
Strut unit:
  Piston rod diameter .... 0.71 in (18 mm)
  Piston diameter .... 0.98 in (25 mm)
  Stroke .... 6.14 in (156 mm)
Stabilizer bar diameter .... 0.87 in (22 mm)

Coil spring free length:

	RH	LH
UK models	14.53 in (369 mm)	14.57 in (370 mm)
USA models – 1979 and 1980	15.00 in (381 mm)	15.28 in (388 mm)
USA models – 1981	15.39 in (391 mm)	15.67 in (398 mm)
Coil spring wire diameter (all models)	0.453 in (11.5 mm)	0.441 in (11.2 mm)

Balljoint:
  Endplay .... 0.004 to 0.059 in (0.1 to 1.5 mm)
  Turning torque – new .... 26 to 87 lbf in (30 to 100 kgf cm)
  Turning torque – used (minimum) .... 8.7 lbf in (10 kgf cm)

Rear suspension

Type .... Independent, trailing arm with double-acting telescopic shock absorbers

Rear wheel alignment (unladen):
  Camber .... -15' to 1° 45'
  Toe-in .... Zero
Shock absorber stroke .... 5.71 in (145 mm)
Coil spring free length:
  UK models .... 8.94 in (227 mm)
  USA – 1979 and 1980 models .... 9.09 in (231 mm)
  USA – 1981 models .... 9.02 in (229 mm)
Wheel bearing starting torque:
  With new hub grease seal (maximum) .... 6.9 lbf in (8 kgf cm)
  Measured at hub bolt .... 3.1 lb (1.4 kg)
  With used hub grease seal (maximum) .... 3.5 lbf in (4 kgf cm)
  Measured at hub bolt .... 1.5 lb (0.7 kg)

Torque wrench settings

	lbf ft	kgf m
Front suspension		
Front hub nut	see Chapter 7	
Strut unit:		
Gland packing	58 to 116	8 to 16
Piston rod self-locking nut	46 to 53	6.3 to 7.3
Strut-to-body	11 to 17	1.5 to 2.4
Strut-to-knuckle	24 to 33	3.3 to 4.5
Balljoint:		
Stud nut (to knuckle)	22 to 29	3 to 4
Joint-to-transverse link	40 to 47	5.5 to 6.5
Caliper attachment bolts	40 to 47	5.5 to 6.5
Transverse link-to-subframe	42 to 51	5.8 to 7.0
Stabilizer-to-link	5.8 to 7.2	0.8 to 1.2
Tie (side) rod ball stud nut	40 to 47	5.5 to 6.5
Tie (side) rod locknut	27 to 34	3.8 to 4.7
Subframe-to-body	39 to 52	5.4 to 7.2
Rear suspension		
Wheel bearing locknut	29 to 33*	4.0 to 4.5*
Shock aborber locknut – top (UK models)	22 to 30	3.1 to 4.1
Shock absorber locknut – top (USA models)	5.8 to 5.7	0.8 to 1.2
Shock absorber lower attachment bolts (UK models)	14 to 18	1.9 to 2.5
Shock absorber lower attachment bolts (USA models)	11 to 17	1.5 to 2.4
Rear suspension arm bolt:		
Anchor arm bracket	36 to 43	5 to 6
Support bracket	36 to 43	5 to 6
Brake backplate attachment bolts	18 to 25	2.5 to 3.4

Initial tightening only. See text (Section 10) for full procedure

1 General description

The front suspension on all models consists of independent struts with integral shock absorbers, and transverse links. The upper end of each strut is secured to the wing structure, while the lower end is retained by a knuckle fitting bolted to the rear end of the wheel hub. Transverse links connect the lower end of each knuckle to the subframe via a balljoint and two rubber-bushed pivot points.

The rear suspension is a conventional trailing arm independent suspension, utilizing coil springs and telescopic double-acting shock absorbers. The rear hub bearings are integral with the brake drum.

2 Springs and shock absorbers – inspection

1   First check that the tyres are correctly inflated, then have an assistant bounce the car up and down while you check any movement in the top and bottom mountings of the front and rear shock absorbers.

2   The efficiency of the shock absorbers may be checked by bouncing the car at each corner. Generally speaking the body will return to its normal position and stop after being depressed. If it rises and returns on a rebound the shock absorber should be suspect. Examine also the shock absorber mounting bushes for any sign of looseness and the cylinders themselves for traces of hydraulic fluid leaks. If there is any sign of leaks the unit must be renewed.

3   Static tests of shock absorbers are not entirely conclusive and further indications of shock absorber failure are noticeable pitching, excessive rolling on fast bends, and a definite feeling of insecurity on corners, particularly if the road surface is uneven. If you are in doubt it is a good idea to drive over a roughish road and have someone follow you to watch how the wheels behave. Excessive up-and-down 'patter' of any wheel is usually quite obvious, and denotes a defective shock absorber.

3 Front wheel hub, bearings and steering knuckle – removal, inspection and refitting

1   Jack up the front of the car and support it on axle stands. Remove the roadwheels.

2   Pull out the split pin and remove the castellated hub nut and the washer (photo). This nut is very tight; it will be necessary to prevent the hub turning by bolting a length of metal to two of the wheel studs,

or some similar method. It may be possible to free the nut by temporarily refitting the roadwheels, lowering the car to the ground and having an assistant apply the brakes whilst the nut is slackened.

3   Disconnect and plug the brake hose at the brake caliper.

4   Remove the brake caliper as described in Chapter 9.

5   Attach a puller to the hub and secure it with the wheel nuts. Set the front knuckles to the straight-ahead position, so that the driveshaft constant velocity (CV) joint is not subjected to stress, and remove the wheel hub.

6   Remove the driveshaft as described in Chapter 7. When removing the driveshaft be careful not to damage the knuckle seal.

7   Remove the wheel bearings and seals from the wheel hub and knuckle. Remove the backplate.

8   To separate the brake disc from the hub, remove the securing bolts retaining the two and then drive or press the hub from the disc using a suitable drift.

9   Separate the lower balljoint and tie-rod balljoint from the knuckle as described in Chapter 8.

10   Remove the bolts securing the knuckle to the strut and detach the knuckle.

11   Drive the wheel bearing outer race and grease seal out of the knuckle with a brass drift.

12   Clean all the parts throroughly with paraffin and inspect for signs of overheating, scoring, corrosion or other damage. Check that the wheel bearings rotate freely without excess noise or any roughness.

Fig. 11.1 Check the springs and shock absorbers for wear, damage and signs of leakage (Sec 2)

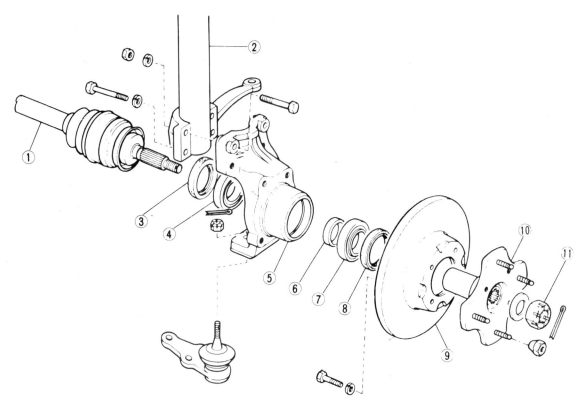

Fig. 11.2 The front hub and steering knuckle components (Sec 3)

1 Driveshaft	5 Knuckle	9 Disc
2 Strut assembly	6 Spacer	10 Wheel hub
3 Grease seal (inner)	7 Outer wheel bearing	11 Hub nut
4 Inner wheel bearing	8 Grease seal (outer)	

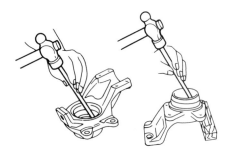

Fig. 11.3 Wheel bearing removal from knuckle (Sec 3)

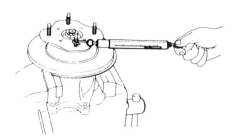

Fig. 11.4 Check the bearing preload using a spring balance (Sec 3)

Renew all defective parts. Discard the old grease seals and always fit new ones after each dismantling.

13 If new bearings have to be fitted, special tools are required to determine the thickness of the spacer. As there are eighteen different thicknesses of spacer to select from, and six different special tools are needed, take the wheel hub knuckle and driveshaft to your Datsun dealer and get him to fit the new bearings and appropriate spacer. He should then reassemble the components and check the bearing preload (see below). The bearings must be lubricated with multi-purpose grease.

14 With the hub, knuckle, brake disc and driveshaft reassembled with new bearings and oil seals, and the hub nut tightened to the specified torque, the bearing preload should be measured with a spring balance (Fig. 11.4). The acceptable values of rotational starting torque are listed in the Specifications. If the starting torque is lower than that specified, a thinner spacer must be fitted; if higher, a thicker spacer is required.

15 Refit the assembly to the front suspension strut, using new driveshaft self-locking nuts. Fit a new split pin to the hub nut (if not already done) and bend its legs around the nut.

16 Refit the brake caliper, reconnect the brake hose and bleed the brake hydraulic system (Chapter 9).

17 Refit the roadwheel, lower the car to the ground and finally tighten the wheel nuts.

4 Front suspension spring and strut assembly – removal and refitting

1 Chock the rear wheels, apply the handbrake and loosen the front wheel nuts. Raise and support the front of the vehicle using safety stands then remove the front wheel(s).

2 If the suspension spring and strut assembly are to be dismantled on removal, the spring will have to be compressed. If a spring

3.2 Front hub nut and split pin

4.5 Strut-to-knuckle retaining bolts (arrowed)

4.8 Remove cap for access to piston rod locknut

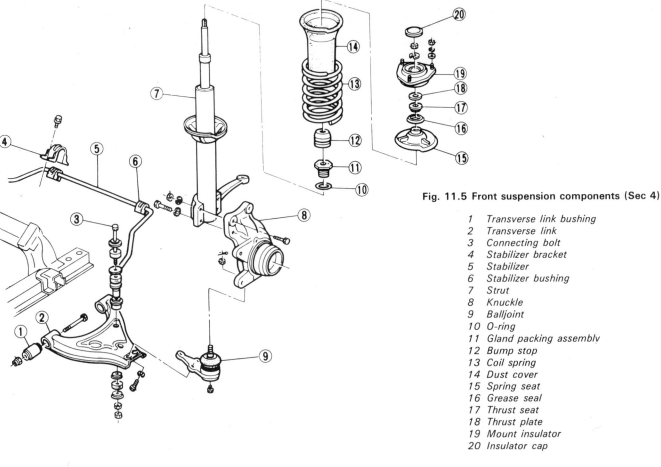

Fig. 11.5 Front suspension components (Sec 4)

   1   *Transverse link bushing*
   2   *Transverse link*
   3   *Connecting bolt*
   4   *Stabilizer bracket*
   5   *Stabilizer*
   6   *Stabilizer bushing*
   7   *Strut*
   8   *Knuckle*
   9   *Balljoint*
  10 *O-ring*
  11 *Gland packing assembly*
  12 *Bump stop*
  13 *Coil spring*
  14 *Dust cover*
  15 *Spring seat*
  16 *Grease seal*
  17 *Thrust seat*
  18 *Thrust plate*
  19 *Mount insulator*
  20 *Insulator cap*

Fig. 11.6 Compressing the coil spring (removed from the vehicle) (Sec 4)

compressor such as Datsun special tool No ST35651001 is available, the spring can be compressed when the strut unit is removed from the vehicle (see Fig. 11.6).

3   If such a tool is not available you will need to fit some retaining clips to retain the spring in the compressed position and these must be fitted at this stage. **Do not** use makeshift methods to restrain the spring – these could be highly dangerous.

4   If spring clips are to be used they should either be borrowed from your local garage or made up using some high tensile steel rod at least 0.5 in (12.70 mm) in diameter with the ends bent over. The length should accommodate as many coils as possible, with a minimum of three. Position a jack under the strut and compress the road spring by raising the jack. Fit the spring clips and tie them firmly in place with strong wire or cord, then remove the jack.

5   Remove the bolts securing the strut to the knuckle and separate the two components (photo).

6   Detach the steering tie-rod, as described in Chapter 8.

7   Disconnect the brake tube from the strut and plug the open ends.

8   Working in the engine bay, remove the cap over the top of the suspension strut and partially loosen (do not remove) the locknut securing the piston rod (photo).

9   Place a jack or suitable packing under the strut to support its weight during the next operation.

10   Working under the bonnet, undo and remove the three nuts fastening the top of the strut to the inner wing panel.

11   Carefully lower the jack or remove the packing and lift away suspension strut assembly.

12   Refitting the suspension strut assembly is the reverse sequence to removal. Tighten the respective fastenings to the specified torque settings.

13   Top up and bleed the brake system as given in Chapter 9.

---

5   Front suspension spring and strut assembly – overhaul

The front suspension spring and strut assembly can only be dismantled and overhauled on removal from the car (see previous Section). If a suitable coil spring compressor is not available or cannot be fabricated as given in Section 4, then the overhaul of the unit(s) must be entrusted to your local Datsun garage. Note that from 1981 some models are fitted with a cartridge type shock absorber. It is removed and refitted in a similar manner to that of the standard type given in this Section, but for the assembly details refer to Section 6.

1   Thoroughly clean the unit by working it in paraffin and then wiping dry with a clean non-fluffy rag.

2   Fit the coil spring compressor to the suspension unit, make sure that it is correctly positioned and then compress the spring. This is not applicable if the spring clips are in position.

3   Taking care not to scratch or score the piston rod, unscrew and remove the mounting nut and then remove the insulator, thrust plate and seal, the dust seal and spring seat, the dust cover, the coil spring (compressed) and the bump stop.

4   Push the piston rod in until it is fully retracted.

5   It is now necessary for the gland packing to be removed. Ideally a special tool should be used but it may be improvised using a wrench.

6   Remove the O-ring from the top of the piston rod guide.

7   Lift out the piston rod together with the cylinder. The piston and piston rod guide are matched with the cylinder and must only be renewed as an assembly.

8   Tilt the inner cylinder and allow the hydraulic fluid to drain out into a container. Also drain out any fluid inside the outer casing. Fresh fluid will be required during reassembly.

9   Wash all parts in solvent and wipe dry. Make quite sure no dirt is allowed to contact any internal parts.

10   Always renew the gland packing and O-ring when the strut has been dismantled.

11   Inspect the outer casing for signs of distortion, cracking or accident damage and obtain a new casing if any such condition is apparent.

12   Inspect the spindle for hair line cracks on the case or damaged threads. If evident the complete strut assembly should be renewed.

13   Inspect the rubber and metal joint for signs of damage or deterioration. Obtain new parts if evident.

14   If noise originated from the strut when driving over rough road surfaces the cause is probably due to the strut mounting bearing having worn. Obtain a new bearing assembly.

15   Before reassembly commences, make sure that every part is really clean and free from dust.

16   Fit the piston rod and cylinder into position in the outer casing.

17   Fill the assembly with the recommended grade of hydraulic fluid. For AMPCO (ATSUGI) units use 210 cc; for KYB (KAYABA) units use 220 cc. Do not deviate from the quoted amounts otherwise the operating efficiency of the unit will be altered.

18   Place the rod guide on the top of the piston rod guide and refit the O-ring and gland packing.

19   Lubricate the sealing lips with a little multi-purpose grease and tighten the gland packing to the specified torque wrench setting. This will have to be estimated if the special tool is not available. When tightening the the gland packing the piston rod must be extended approximately 4.7 in (120 mm) from the end of the outer casing to expel most of the air out of the strut.

20   It is now necessary to bleed the shock absorber by holding the

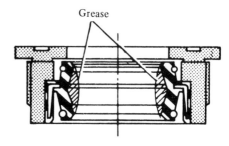

Fig. 11.7 Lubricate the gland packing seal lips (Sec 5)

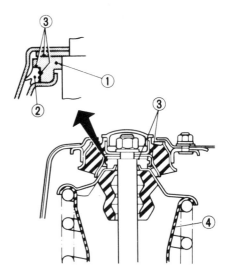

Fig. 11.8 Sectional view of strut top mounting (Sec 5)

1	*Thrust seal*	*3*	*Greasing points*
2	*Dust seal*	*4*	*Dust cover*

strut with the spindle end down and pulling the piston rod out completely.

21   Now invert the strut so that the spindle end is uppermost and push the piston rod inwards as far as it will go.

22   Repeat the procedure described in paragraph 20 several times, until an equal pressure is felt during both strokes.

23   Pull the piston rod out fully and fit the bump stop, to prevent the piston rod falling by its own weight.

24   Locate the spring on the lower spring seat with the end fitted into the recess and compress the spring with the special tool if spring clips are not fitted.

25   Refit the dust seals with the lip mounting downwards.

26   Lubricate the dust seals with a little multi-purpose grease. Fit the rest of the top mounting components as noted on removal and in

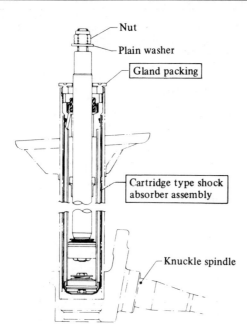

Fig. 11.9 Sectional view of the cartridge type shock absorber (Sec 6)

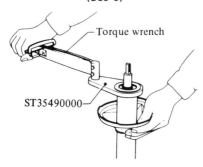

Fig. 11.10 Tightening the gland packing using the special Datsun torque wrench and adaptor (Sec 6)

Standard clearance:
About 1.8 mm (0.071 in)

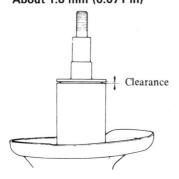

Fig. 11.11 Check gland packing-to-outer strut tube clearance (Sec 6)

accordance with Fig. 11.8.
27 Refit the piston rod self-locking nut and tighten to the specified torque wrench setting.
28 With the spring correctly located release the spring compressor. If clips have been used leave in position until the strut has been reassembled to the car.
29 Raise the bump stop until it is seated under the upper spring seat.
30 The strut assembly is now ready for refitting to the car.

6 Cartridge type shock absorber – reassembly

Although the cartridge type shock absorber is removed and refitted in a similar manner to that described for the standard type given in the previous Sections, it is assembled as follows. It cannot be dismantled and if defective must be renewed.
1 The cartridge type shock absorber is shown in Fig. 11.9. Before refitting it first check that it is in serviceable condition. If a new shock absorber is to be fitted be sure that it is of the same type as that which it replaced.
2 Carefully insert the shock absorber into position in the strut tube, then centre it by shaking it to the left and right.
3 Insert the gland packing and tighten to the specified torque. If the special torque wrench adaptor (ST35490000) is not available this will have to be estimated. When fitted and tightened check that there is sufficient clearance as shown (Fig. 11.11) between the gland packing and the outer tube.
4 The remainder of the assembly and refitting details are the same as those given for the standard shock absorber in the previous Sections.

7 Transverse link – removal, overhaul and refitting

1 Jack up the car and support it on axle stands. Remove the wheel on the side concerned.
2 Remove the three bolts securing the transverse link to the balljoint (photo).
3 Remove the stabilizer-to-transverse link retaining nut.
4 Remove the two bolts securing the transverse link to the subframe and withdraw the transverse link from under the vehicle.
5 Inspect the transverse link for evidence of cracks, corrosion or distortion. Check the bushes for ovality, cracks or other damage. Renew if necessary.
6 Renewal of the bushes calls for care as the transverse link must not be distorted during the course of removing and refitting the bushes. It is best to get the old ones out by cutting through them.
7 New bushes should be drawn in using a long nut and bolt together with a tubular spacer (on the inside of the arm) and large washers to ensure the bushes are drawn in square. Do not attempt to drive the bushes in with a hammer. When installed the bushes should project equally either side of the link. Do not get oil or grease on the bushes. Use liquid detergent as a lubricant if necessary.
8 Refitting is the reverse of removal. Fit the mounting bolts from inside the link.
9 With the transverse link under standard load conditions, (ie the car weight off the jack), tighten the bolts so as not to deform the bushing excessively. Refer to Specifications for the torque wrench settings.

8 Transverse link balljoint – removal and refitting

1 Although the normal technique for removing this particular balljoint involves removing the driveshaft beforehand, if great care is exercised it is possible to do it without this onerous task. First jack up the front of the car and support it on axle stands. Remove the roadwheel.
2 Remove the split pin and castellated locknut. Separate the joint from the knuckle. This can only be done with surety by using a claw clamp. However, it is possible to drive through but only if the knuckle is firmly supported. The joint will almost certainly be damaged in the process. Another method is to strike the side of the knuckle where the pin goes through whilst holding the head of another hammer on the opposite side. This has a squeezing out effect on the tapered pin. If any difficulty arises that looks as though it might cause damage to the driveshaft, then you must remove the driveshaft.
3 Remove the bolts securing the balljoint to the transverse link and detach the balljoint.
4 Inspect the balljoint for endplay and damage. Check the dust cover for cracks and deterioration. Should there be endplay or damage to the balljoint a new one must be fitted. Generally a new balljoint assembly is supplied complete with a dust cover.
5 Make sure that the socket groove in which the dust cover clamps securely is free from oil or grease. Wipe clean if necessary.
6 After a new dust cover is installed, move the stud until the ball surface is coated with grease evenly. Make sure that the stud rotational torque is correctly obtained. (See Specifications).

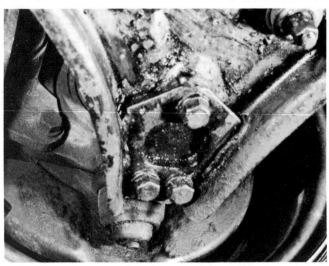

7.2 Transverse link-to-balljoint retaining bolts

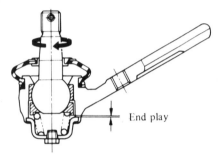

Fig. 11.12 Check balljoint for wear – end play and rotational torque (Sec 8)

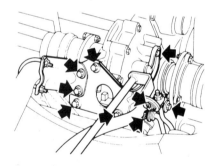

Fig. 11.13 Transmission linkages to be disconnected (Sec 9)

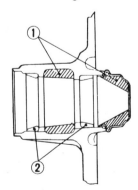

Fig. 11.14 Pack hub shaded areas with grease (Sec 10)

1 Grease	2 Bearing outer races

7   After the balljoint is installed on the vehicle, replace the plug with the grease nipple. Apply grease to the balljoint through this grease nipple until grease is forced out at the grease vent hole, then remove the nipple and refit the plug.

9   Front suspension stabilizer (anti-roll bar) – removal and refitting

1   Raise the front of the vehicle and support with axle stands. Apply the handbrake and chock the rear wheels.
2   Position a suitable jack centrally under the subframe and raise to just support it.
3   Unbolt and disconnect, but do not completely remove, the exhaust pipe from the manifold and gearbox mounting bracket.
4   Detach the gearshift and selector rod at the control rod and support rod, also the support rod at the transmission (Fig. 11.13).
5   Unscrew and remove the stabilizer-to-transverse link retaining nuts.
6   Now temporarily slacken off the subframe retaining bolts to allow the subframe to be lowered, but do not fully remove the bolts!
7   Lower the subframe just sufficiently to enable the stabilizer clamps to be detached. As the subframe is lowered, keep a careful check on the engine compartment to ensure that none of the engine/transmission attachments are damaged during this operation.
8   Withdraw the stabilizer bar.
9   Check the stabilizer bar and its bushes and fixings for signs of damage or defects. Renew where necessary.
10   Refit the stabilizer in the reverse order to removal. Tighten the respective fastenings to the specified torque wrench settings.

10   Rear hub/brake drum – removal and refitting

1   Chock the front wheels. Slacken the wheel nuts, jack up the rear of the car and support on firmly based stands. Remove the roadwheel. Release the handbrake.
2   Knock off the cap from the end of the hub, remove the split pin and adjusting cap and unscrew and remove the castellated nut, the thrust washer and outer bearing cone (photos).
3   Pull the hub assembly forward and then pull the unit from the stub axle (photo).
4   To refit the hub, first clean out all traces of old grease and repack with fresh. To do this, carefully wipe clean the stub axle and seal track. Inspect the hub seal and axle threads for wear or damage. If there are any signs of leakage onto the brake backplate fit a new seal. Remove the old seal by levering it out (photo).
5   Wipe away as much old grease as possible from the hub and then insert new grease into the bearings. Do not overfill the hub cavity. Remove any surplus grease other than that shown in Fig. 11.14.
6   Refit the hub assembly to the stub axle and secure it with the washer and castellated hub nut.
7   Using a torque wrench, tighten the nut to the specified torque setting and then rotate the hub in both directions to settle the wheel bearings.
8   Retighten the nut to the specified torque setting and then unscrew the nut a quarter of a turn (90°) or thereabouts to align it with a split pin hole in the spindle. Retighten by up to 15° if necessary to align the split pin holes and nut and adjusting cap.
9   Check that the hub is free to rotate without too much slackness or drag. A certain amount of drag may be allowed for if new brake linings have been fitted. If possible check the axial play and the wheel bearing starting torque using a spring balance as shown (Fig. 11.15). Slight adjustment of the nut may be necessary to achieve the correct setting (see Specifications).
10   With the hub adjustment correct, locate the adjusting cap over the nut and insert a new split pin. Tap the hub cap into position and refit the roadwheel to complete.

11   Rear hub – overhaul

1   Remove the rear hub as given in the previous Section.
2   Wash all internal grease from the hub using paraffin. If the bearings and seal are in good order, repack the interior of the hub and end cap with wheel bearing grease so that it occupies the area shown

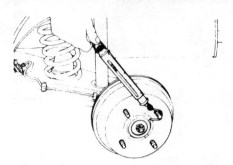

Fig. 11.15 Wheel bearing starting torque check method using a spring balance (Sec 10)

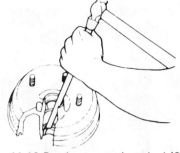

Fig. 11.16 Bearing removal method (Sec 11)

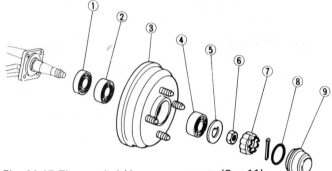

Fig. 11.17 The rear hub/drum components (Sec 11)

1	Grease seal	6	Wheel bearing nut
2	Inner wheel bearing	7	Adjusting cap
3	Brake drum	8	O-ring
4	Outer wheel bearing	9	Hub cap
5	Wheel bearing washer		

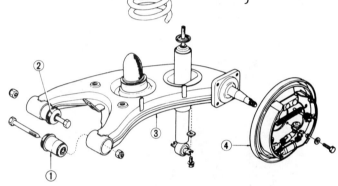

Fig. 11.19 The rear suspension arm assembly components (Sec 14)

1	Outer bushing	6	Rubber seat
2	Inner bushing	7	Shock absorber upper mounting bushes and washers
3	Rear arm		
4	Rear brake assembly		
5	Coil spring		

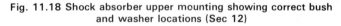

Washer

Fig. 11.18 Shock absorber upper mounting showing correct bush and washer locations (Sec 12)

in Fig. 11.14.

3   If the bearings are worn or damaged, prise out the grease seal from the inner end of the hub and extract the inner roller race. Drift out the inner and outer bearing tracks using a thin rod inserted through the two grooves within the drum in a progressive even manner (Fig. 11.16).

4   If the brake contact surface of the drum is badly scored or damaged then this should be resurfaced by machining but only to within the maximum specified tolerance allowable (see Chapter 8).

5   Fit the new bearing track using a piece of tubing as a drift. If both hubs are being dismantled at the same time, ensure that the bearings are kept as matched sets and do not mix up the races and tracks.

6   Press the new grease seal squarely into the inner end of the hub, with its lip towards the roller bearing.

7   Pack the hub with grease as described in paragraph 2.

8   Refitting is a reversal of removal, but adjust the bearing preload, as described in the preceding Section. Do not allow grease to get onto the brake contact surface of the drum or linings during refitting.

12 Rear shock absorber – removal and refitting

1   Chock the front wheels, jack the vehicle up at the rear and support it with safety stands. Remove the roadwheels.

2   Position a jack underneath the rear end of the suspension arm and raise to support it.

10.2a Remove the hub cap ...

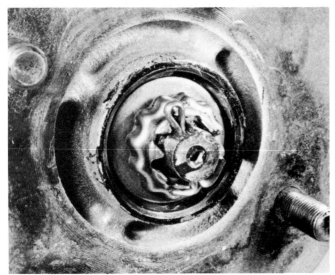

10.2b ... withdraw the split pin ...

10.2c ... and adjuster cap and nut

10.2d Remove the thrust washer ...

10.2e ... followed by the outer bearing cone

10.3 Withdrawing the hub/drum unit from the stub axle

10.4 Hub seal removal method using a cranked screwdriver blade

12.3 Rear shock absorber upper mounting nut

12.4 Rear shock absorber lower mounting bolts

14.4 Detach handbrake cable at clevis connection

3   Unscrew and remove the shock absorber upper retaining nut from within the luggage area at the rear of the car. Remove the respective washers and bushes, keeping them in order of fitting (photo).
4   Unscrew the two shock absorber-to-suspension arm retaining bolts (photo), then slowly lower the jack under the suspension arm and when clear withdraw the shock absorber.
5   If on inspection the shock absorber is damaged or ineffective it must be renewed as a unit as it cannot be repaired.
6   Refitting is the reversal of the removal procedure. Ensure that the bushes and washers at the top of the shock absorber mounting are correctly fitted as shown in Fig. 11.18.
7   Tighten the retaining bolts and nuts to the specified torque settings.

13 Rear suspension coil spring – removal and refitting

1   Chock the front wheels, jack up at the rear and support with safety stands. Remove the rear roadwheel(s).
2   Position a jack under the lower end of the rear suspension arm and raise the jack to support the arm.
3   Unscrew and remove the shock absorber upper retaining nut (from within the luggage compartment) and the lower retaining bolts.
4   Now slowly lower the jack and when the compression is released, withdraw the coil spring.
5   Renew the spring and its mountings if damaged, distorted or generally worn.
6   Refit in the reverse order to removal, ensuring that the spring is correctly located on its seating.

14 Rear suspension arm – removal and refitting

1   Chock the front wheels, jack up the rear end and support with safety stands. Remove the rear wheels.
2   Release the handbrake.
3   Unscrew the brake pipe union nut to the wheel cylinder and plug the pipe to prevent fluid leakage and the ingress of dirt.
4   Disconnect the handbrake cable at its clevis connection (photo). Remove the brake drum/hub (Section 19) and the brake backplate.
5   Position a jack under the suspension arm lower end to support it, then remove the coil spring and shock absorber (see Sections 12 and 13).
6   Unscrew and remove the suspension arm pivot bolts and nuts. Lower and remove the arm.
7   Inspect the arm for corrosion, distortion or cracks. Check the bushes for deterioration such as cracks or ovality; and check the rubber bump stop for damage.
8   If the arm is damaged it will have to be renewed.
9   Inspect the suspension arm bushes and if worn use a bolt, nut, washers and tubing to draw out the old bushes and fit new ones.
10 Refitting the rear suspension arm is the reverse sequence to removal. The following additional points should be noted:

(a) Always use new self-locking washers
(b) Finally tighten all suspension attachments when the car is resting on the ground
(c) It will be necessary to bleed the brake hydraulic system, as described in Chapter 9

15 Fault diagnosis – suspension and steering

Suspension and steering are considered together here since they are closely related for purposes of fault diagnosis. Refer to Chapter 8 for details of steering gear overhaul.

Symptom	Reason(s)
Vibration, shock or shimmy at steering wheel	Incorrect tyre pressures Wheel out of balance or buckled Worn tyre or loose wheel Worn suspension balljoint or lack of preload Steering gear out of adjustment Improper wheel alignment Worn rubber bushing in transverse link Excessive free play in steering linkage Excessive play or wear on front wheel bearing Loose steering gear Loose or inoperative shock absorber (in strut assembly)
Car pulls to one side	Incorrect tyre pressures, or loose wheel nuts Difference in right and left tyre treads, or tyre type Defective front wheel bearing Fatigued front spring, or use of incorrect spring

Symptom	Reason(s)
	Improper wheel alignment
	Brake drag (out of adjustment)
	Worn bushing in transverse link
	Deformed steering linkage or suspension link
	Defective tyre
Vehicle wanders	Incorrect tyre pressures
	Improper wheel alignment
	Excessive free play or wear on steering linkage or suspension linkage
	Steering gear out of adjustment
	Wheel buckled or out of balance
	Worn bushing in transverse link
Steering stifff	Incorrect tyre pressures
	Incorrect lubrication in steering gear housing or dirt in oil
	Improper lubrication in steering linkage, dirt in grease, or abnormal wear on steering linkage
	Seized, damaged suspension balljoint. Lack of lubrication to balljoint
	Worn or seized wheel bearing
	Steering gear out of adjustment
	Deformed steering linkage
	Improper wheel alignment
	Damaged thrust seal on upper end of strut
	Seized or damaged piston or piston rod of shock absorber (in strut)
	Power steering only:
	Fluid level low and/or air in fluid
	Hydraulic pressure low due to pump fault or leakage
	Pump drivebelt loose or broken
Excessive play at steering wheel	Steering gear out of adjustment or worn
	Worn steering linkage
	Loose steering gear
	Defective wheel bearing
	Worn bushing in transverse link
Unusual noises	Incorrect tyre pressures
	Damaged or worn suspension balljoint or steering linkage, or lack of lubrication
	Loose steering gear linkage or suspension system
	Defective shock absorber (in strut)
	Defective wheel bearing
	Worn steering linkage or steering gear
	Worn bushing in transverse link
	Broken or fatigued coil spring
	Loose mounting nut on strut mounting insulator
	Improper tightening of strut and gland packing
	Loose bolt on subframe
	Buckled wheel
	Pump defective (power steering)
Tyre squeal	Incorrect tyre pressures
	Improper wheel alignment
	Deformed knuckle, spindle or suspension
Abnormal or uneven tyre wear	Incorrect tyre pressures
	Improper wheel alignment
	Defective wheel bearing
	Brakes out of adjustment

Rear suspension

Symptom	Reason(s)
Unusual noises	Loose suspension linkages
	Tyres out of balance or incorrectly inflated
	Damaged rear arm bushing and shock absorber thrust bearings
	Defective shock absorber
	Defective coil spring
	Defective wheel bearing
Unstable running	Loose wheelnuts
	Defective rear arm rubber bushing
	Defective shock absorber
	Defective coil spring
	Faulty wheel bearings
	Brakes out of adjustment (drag)
	Incorrect tyre pressures

Chapter 12 Bodywork and fittings

Contents

1 General description

The body shells are of rigid sheet metal construction with the outer roof and body panels welded together to form an integral structure. The shells also incorporate a subframe, contributing to engine and transmission accessibility. Because of very rigid box section load-carrying members, exceptional shell rigidity is obtained. Use of the subframe keeps noise and vibration from being carried to the bodyshell.

The front wings are of bolt-on detachable type for economy of replacement in the event of accident damage.

The bonnet is locked from the vehicle interior as are the passenger rear doors. The front doors are locked externally by key.

2 Maintenance – bodywork and underframe

1 The general condition of a car's bodywork is the thing that significantly affects its value. Maintenance is easy but needs to be regular. Neglect, particularly after minor damage, can lead quickly to further deterioration and costly repair bills. It is important also to keep watch on those parts of the car not immediately visible, for instance the underside, inside all the wheel arches and the lower part of the engine compartment.

2 The basic maintenance routine for the bodywork is washing – preferably with a lot of water, from a hose. This will remove all the loose solids which may have stuck to the car. It is important to flush these off in such a way as to prevent grit from scratching the finish. The wheel arches and underframe need washing in the same way to remove any accumulated mud which will retain moisture and tend to encourage rust. Paradoxically enough, the best time to clean the underframe and wheel arches is in wet weather when the mud is thoroughly wet and soft. In very wet weather the underframe is usually cleaned of large accumulations automatically and this is a good time for inspection.

3 Periodically, it is a good idea to have the whole of the underframe of the car steam cleaned, engine compartment included, so that a thorough inspection can be carried out to see what minor repairs and renovations are necessary. Steam cleaning is available at many garages and is necessary for removal of the accumulation of oily grime which sometimes is allowed to become thick in certain areas. If steam cleaning facilities are not available, there are one or two excellent grease solvents available which can be brush applied. The dirt can then be simply hosed off.

4 After washing paintwork, wipe off with a chamois leather to give an unspotted clear finish. A coat of clear protective wax polish will give added protection against chemical pollutants in the air. If the paintwork sheen has dulled or oxidised, use a cleaner/polisher combination to restore the brilliance of the shine. This requires a little effort, but such dulling is usually caused because regular washing has been neglected. Always check that the door and ventilator opening drain holes and pipes are completely clear so that water can be drained out. Bright work should be treated in the same way as paintwork. Windscreens and windows can be kept clear of the smeary film which often appears, by adding a little ammonia to the water. If they are scratched, a good rub with a proprietary metal polish will often clear them. Never use any form of wax or other body or chromium polish on glass.

3 Maintenance – upholstery and carpets

1 Mats and carpets should be brushed or vacuum cleaned regularly to keep them free of grit. If they are badly stained remove them from the car for scrubbing or sponging and make quite sure they are dry before refitting. Seats and interior trim panels can be kept clean by a wipe over with a damp cloth. If they do become stained (which can be more apparent on light coloured upholstery) use a little liquid detergent and a soft nail brush to scour the grime out of the grain of the material. Do not forget to keep the head lining clean in the same way as the upholstery. When using liquid cleaners inside the car do not over-wet the surfaces being cleaned. Excessive damp could get into the seams and padded interior causing stains, offensive odours or even rot. If the inside of the car gets wet accidentally it is worthwhile taking some trouble to dry it out properly, particularly where carpets are involved. *Do not leave oil or electric heaters inside the car for this purpose.*

4   Minor body damage – repair

The photographic sequences on pages 270 and 271 illustrate the operations detailed in the following sub-sections.

Repair of minor scratches in the car's bodywork

If the scratch is very superficial, and does not penetrate to the metal of the bodywork, repair is very simple. Lightly rub the area of the scratch with a paintwork renovator, or a very fine cutting paste, to remove loose paint from the scratch and to clear the surrounding bodywork of wax polish. Rinse the area with clean water.

Apply touch-up paint to the scratch using a thin paint brush; continue to apply thin layers of paint until the surface of the paint in the scratch is level with the surrounding paintwork. Allow the new paint at least two weeks to harden; then blend it into the surrounding paintwork by rubbing the paintwork, in the scratch area, with a paintwork renovator or a very fine cutting paste. Finally, apply wax polish.

Where the scratch has penetrated right through to the metal of the bodywork, causing the metal to rust, a different repair technique is required. Remove any loose rust from the bottom of the scratch with a penknife, then apply rust inhibiting paint to prevent the formation of rust in the future. Using a rubber or nylon applicator fill the scratch with bodystopper paste. If required, this paste can be mixed with cellulose thinners to provide a very thin paste which is ideal for filling narrow scratches. Before the stopper-paste in the scratch hardens, wrap a piece of smooth cotton rag around the top of a finger. Dip the finger in cellulose thinners and then quickly sweep it across the surface of the stopper-paste in the scratch; this will ensure that the surface of the stopper-paste is slightly hollowed. The scratch can now be painted over as described earlier in this Section.

Repair of dents in the car's bodywork

When deep denting of the car's bodywork has taken place, the first task is to pull the dent out, until the affected bodywork almost attains its original shape. There is little point in trying to restore the original shape completely, as the metal in the damaged area will have stretched on impact and cannot be reshaped fully to its original contour. It is better to bring the level of the dent up to a point which is about $\frac{1}{8}$ in (3 mm) below the level of the surrounding bodywork. In cases where the dent is very shallow anyway, it is not worth trying to pull it out at all. If the underside of the dent is accessible, it can be hammered out gently from behind, using a mallet with a wooden or plastic head. Whilst doing this, hold a suitable block of wood firmly against the outside of the panel to absorb the impact from the hammer blows and thus prevent a large area of the bodywork from being 'belled-out'.

Should the dent be in a section of the bodywork which has double skin or some other factor making it inaccessible from behind, a different technique is called for. Drill several small holes through the metal inside the area – particularly in the deeper section. Then screw long self-tapping screws into the holes just sufficiently for them to gain a good purchase in the metal. Now the dent can be pulled out by pulling on the protruding heads of the screws with a pair of pliers.

The next stage of the repair is the removal of the paint from the damaged area, and from an inch or so of the surrounding 'sound' bodywork. This is accomplished most easily by using a wire brush or abrasive pad on a power drill, although it can be done just as effectively by hand using sheets of abrasive paper. To complete the preparation for filling, score the surface of the bare metal with a screwdriver or the tang of a file, or alternatively, drill small holes in the affected area. This will provide a really good 'key' for the filler paste.

To complete the repair see the Section on filling and re-spraying.

Repair of rust holes or gashes in the car's bodywork

Remove all paint from the affected area and from an inch or so of the surrounding 'sound' bodywork, using an abrasive pad or a wire brush on a power drill. If these are not available a few sheets of abrasive paper will do the job just as effectively. With the paint removed you will be able to gauge the severity of the corrosion and therefore decide whether to renew the whole panel (if this is possible) or to repair the affected area. New body panels are not as expensive as most people think and it is often quicker and more satisfactory to fit a new panel than to attempt to repair large areas of corrosion.

Remove all fittings from the affected area except those which will act as a guide to the original shape of the damaged bodywork (eg headlamp shells etc). Then, using tin snips or a hacksaw blade, remove all loose metal and any other metal badly affected by corrosion. Hammer the edges of the hole inwards in order to create a slight depression for the filler paste.

Wire brush the affected area to remove the powdery rust from the surface of the remaining metal. Paint the affected area with rust inhibiting paint; if the back of the rusted area is accessible treat this also.

Before filling can take place it will be necessary to block the hole in some way. This can be achieved by the use of zinc gauze or aluminium tape.

Zinc gauze is probably the best material to use for a large hole. Cut a piece to the approximate size and shape of the hole to be filled, then position it in the hole so that its edges are below the level of the surrounding bodywork. It can be retained in position by several blobs of filler paste around its periphery.

Aluminium tape should be used for small or very narrow holes. Pull a piece off the roll and trim it to the approximate size and shape required, then pull off the backing paper (if used) and stick the tape over the hole; it can be overlapped if the thickness of one piece is insufficient. Burnish down the edges of the tape with the handle of a screwdriver or similar, to ensure that the tape is securely attached to the metal underneath.

Bodywork repairs – filling and re-spraying

Before using this Section, see the Sections on dent, deep scratch, rust holes and gash repairs.

Many types of bodyfiller are available, but generally speaking those proprietary kits which contain a tin of filler paste and a tube of resin hardener are best for this type of repair. A wide, flexible plastic or nylon applicator will be found invaluable for imparting a smooth and well contoured finish to the surface of the filler.

Mix up a little filler on a clean piece of card or board – measure the hardener carefully (follow the maker's instructions on the pack) otherwise the filler will set too rapidly or too slowly.

Using the applicator apply the filler paste to the prepared area; draw the applicator across the surface of the filler to achieve the correct contour and to level the filler surface. As soon as a contour that approximates the correct one is achieved, stop working the paste – if you carry on too long the paste will become sticky and begin to 'pick up' on the applicator. Continue to add thin layers of filler paste at twenty-minute intervals until the level of the filler is just proud of the surrounding bodywork.

Once the filler has hardened, excess can be removed using a metal plane or file. From then on, progressively finer grades of sandpaper should be used, starting with a 40 grade production paper and finishing with 400 grade wet-and-dry paper. Always wrap the abrasive paper around a flat rubber, cork, or wooden block – otherwise the surface of the filler will not be completely flat. During the smoothing of the filler surface the wet-and-dry paper should be periodically rinsed in water. This will ensure that a very smooth finish is imparted to the filler at the final stage.

At this stage the dent should be surrounded by a ring of bare metal, which in turn should be encircled by the finely 'feathered' edge of the good paintwork. Rinse the repair area with clean water, until all of the dust produced by the rubbing-down operation has gone.

Spray the whole repair area with a light coat of primer – this will show up any imperfections in the surface of the filler. Repair these imperfections with fresh filler paste or bodystopper, and once more smooth the surface with abrasive paper. If bodystopper is used, it can be mixed with cellulose thinners to form a really thin paste which is ideal for filling small holes. Repeat this spray and repair procedure until you are satisfied that the surface of the filler, and the feathered edge of the paintwork are perfect. Clean the repair area with clean water and allow to dry fully.

The repair area is now ready for final spraying. Paint spraying must be carried out in warm, dry, windless and dust free atmosphere. This condition can be created artificially if you have access to a large indoor working area, but if you are forced to work in the open, you will have to pick your day very carefully. If you are working indoors, dousing the floor in the work area with water will help to settle the dust which would otherwise be in the atmosphere. If the repair area is confined to one body panel, mask off the surrounding panels; this will help to minimise the effects of a slight mis-match in paint colours. Bodywork fittings (eg chrome strips, door handles etc) will also need to be masked off. Use genuine masking tape and several thicknesses of newspaper for the masking operations.

Before commencing to spray, agitate the aerosol can thoroughly, then spray a test area (an old tin, or similar) until the technique is mastered. Cover the repair area with a thick coat of primer; the thickness should be built up using several thin layers of paint rather than one thick one. Using 400 grade wet-and-dry paper, rub down the surface of the primer until it is really smooth. While doing this, the work area should be thoroughly doused with water, and the wet-and-dry paper periodically rinsed in water. Allow to dry before spraying on more paint.

Spray on the top coat, again building up the thickness by using several thin layers of paint. Start spraying in the centre of the repair area and then, using a circular motion, work outwards until the whole repair area and about 2 inches of the surrounding original paintwork is covered. Remove all masking material 10 to 15 minutes after spraying on the final coat of paint.

Allow the new paint at least two weeks to harden, then, using a paintwork renovator or a very fine cutting paste, blend the edges of the paint into the existing paintwork. Finally, apply wax polish.

5 Major body repairs

Where serious damage has occurred or large areas need renewal due to neglect, it means certainly that completely new sections or panels will need welding in and this is best left to professionals. If the damage is due to impact it will also be necessary to completely check the alignment of the underframe structure. Owing to the principle of construction the strength and shape of the whole structure can be affected by damage to one part. In such instances the services of an official agent with specialist checking jigs are essential. If a frame is left misaligned it is first of all dangerous as the vehicle will not handle properly and secondly uneven stresses will be imposed on the steering, engine and transmission, causing abnormal wear or complete failure. Tyre wear may also be excessive.

6 Maintenance – hinges and locks

1   Oil the hinges of the bonnet, boot and doors with a drop or two of light oil periodically. A good time is after the car has been washed.
2   Oil the bonnet release catch pivot pin and the safety catch pivot pin periodically.
3   Do not over-lubricate door latches and strikers. Normally a little oil on the rotary cam spindle alone is sufficient.

7 Doors – tracing rattles and their rectification

1   Check first that the door is not loose at the hinges, and that the latch is holding the door firmly in position. Check also that the door lines up with the aperture in the body.
2   If the hinges are loose or the door is out of alignment, it will be necessary to reset the hinge position, as described in Section 13.
3   If the latch is holding the door properly, it should hold the door tightly when fully latched, and the door should line up with the body. If it is out of alignment, it needs adjustment as described in Section 13. If loose, some part of the lock mechanism must be worn out and requires renewal.
4   Other rattles from the door would be caused by wear or looseness in the window winder, the glass channels, the sill strips, the door buttons or the interior latch release mechanism. All these are dealt with in Section 13 to 17.

8 Bumpers – removal and refitting

The front and rear bumpers on European models are mounted on brackets whilst the USA bumpers are attached to impact-absorbing damper units. Removal is similar for each type.
1   Disconnect the battery earth lead.
2   Disconnect the lead connectors to the front combination lights or rear number plate light as applicable.
3   *On European models,* unscrew and remove the bumper-to-body retaining bolts (each side), then remove the bumper-to-bracket bolts and withdraw the bumper.

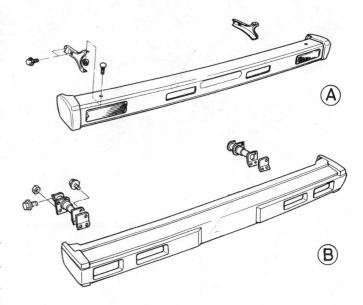

Fig. 12.1 Front bumper unit for European (A) and USA (B) models (Sec 8)

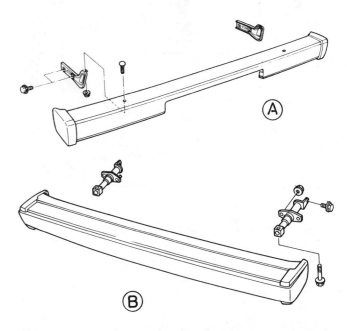

Fig. 12.2 Rear bumper unit for European (A) and USA (B) models (Sec 8)

4   *On USA models,* unscrew and remove the damper unit retaining bolts each side and withdraw the bumper(s) complete with damper units. The damper units can then be unbolted and removed from the bumper(s). Note that the damper units are gas-filled and under pressure and must not under any circumstances be dismantled. If the damper units are found to be leaking or ineffective then they must be renewed.
5   Refitting is a direct reversal of the removal procedure for all models, but ensure that the bumper is correctly aligned before fully tightening the retaining bolts.
6   On USA models the bumper height must be set as shown in Fig. 12.3. The setting is made with the car parked on a flat surface, the tyres inflated to their specified pressures, and with the car in kerb weight condition.
7   On completion, check the operation of the front combination lights or the rear licence plate light as applicable.

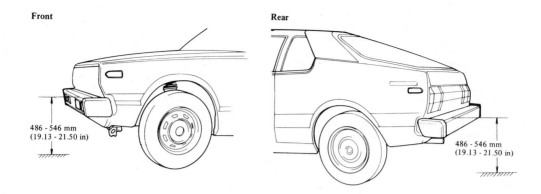

Fig. 12.3 Fitted bumper heights to be as shown on USA models (Sec 8)

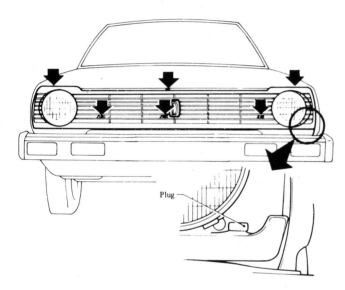

Fig. 12.4 Front grille attachment points (round headlight type)
(Sec 9)

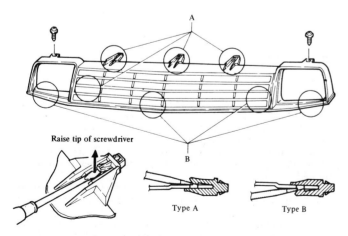

Fig. 12.5 Front grille attachment points (square headlight type)
with clip removal method shown (Sec 9)

9 Radiator grille – removal and refitting

1 The radiator grille is made of plastic and therefore care must be taken not to damage it when removing or refitting.
2 Two types of grille are fitted according to market model and these are shown in Figs. 12.4 and 12.5.
3 To remove the grille, raise and support the bonnet and then unscrew and remove the grille retaining screws from the positions indicated.
4 On USA models, use a screwdriver to lever the retaining clips free as shown to release the grille.
5 Remove the grille.
6 Refit in the reverse order to removal, engaging all of the screws and clips before fully tightening the screws.

10 Front wing – removal and refitting

1 Disconnect the battery earth cable.
2 Disconnect and remove the side marker light unit from the wing panel concerned (see Chapter 10).
3 Unbolt and remove the respective wing retaining bolts, then carefully withdraw the wing from the car, prising free of the seal where necessary.
4 Refit in the reverse order to removal. Ensure that the mating surfaces are cleaned off first before applying the seal. Align the wing correctly before fully tightening the retaining bolts. Check the operation of the side marker light on completion.

11 Bonnet – removal and refitting

1 Open the bonnet and, to act as a datum for refitting, mark the position of the hinges on the bonnet using a soft pencil.
2 With the assistance of a second person to hold the bonnet in the open position, undo and remove the bolts, spring and plain washers that hold each hinge to the bonnet. Lift away the bonnet, taking care not to scratch the top of the wing.
3 Whilst the bonnet is being lifted away take care when detaching the bonnet stay.
4 Refitting the bonnet is the reverse sequence to removal. Any adjustments necessary may be made at the hinge, catch or rubber bump pads. Lubricate the hinge pivots and lock with a little engine oil.

12 Bonnet release catch – removal and refitting

1 Raise the bonnet and support it. Detach the catch release cable from the lock (photo).
2 Working inside the car, detach and remove the lower facia panel cover on the driving side.
3 Unscrew and remove the bonnet release catch bracket retaining

Fig. 12.6 Front wing attachment bolt positions – European models
(Sec 10)

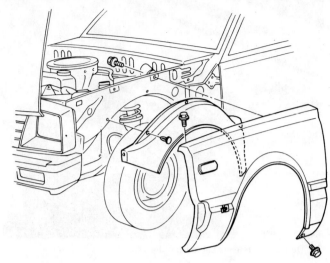

Fig. 12.7 Front wing attachment bolt positions – USA models
(Sec 10)

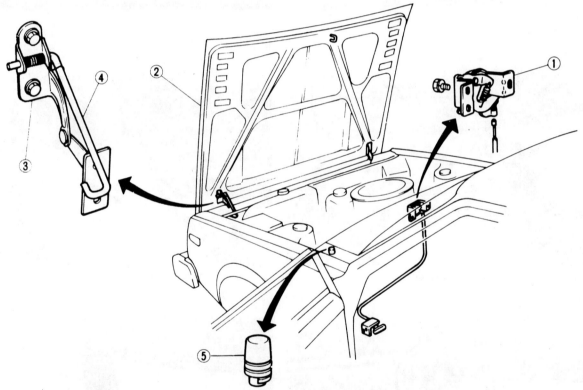

Fig. 12.8 Bonnet and fixings

1 Lock unit	2 Bonnet	3 Hinge	4 Stay rod	5 Bump rubber

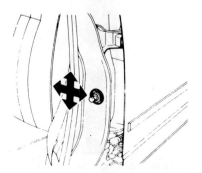

Fig. 12.9 Adjust door lock striker to suit (Sec 13)

bolts. Detach the cable clip and withdraw the cable from within the car.

4   Refitting is the reversal of removal. Lubricate the cable and catch to ensure free operation. When fully assembled, check the catch operation is satisfactory when the cable is pulled, then close the bonnet and check that it is securely locked.

13 Front and rear doors – removal, refitting and adjustment

1   Open the door to be removed and position a padded support under it to take its weight. An assistant should be enlisted to hold the door.
2   Unscrew and remove the respective bolts that secure the door hinges to the body (photo).
3   Carefully lift the door clear from the side of the car.
4   Refit in the reverse order and if necessary adjust as follows.

12.1 Detach the release cable from the lock

13.2 Door hinge and retaining bolts

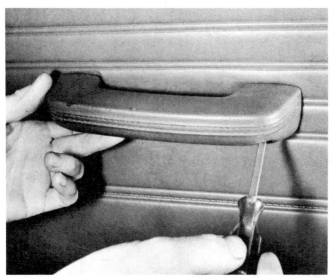

14.1 Remove the door pull retaining screws

14.2 Remove the inner catch backing

14.3 Detach the window regulator handle

14.4 Prise free the trim panel retaining clips

15.1 Door with trim panel removed and plastic sheet peeled back for access to door fittings

15.2 Remove the control catch screws

15.5 Door lock and retaining screws

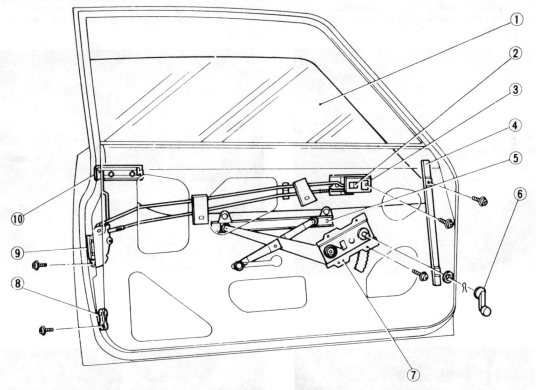

Fig. 12.10 The front door showing the component locations (Sec 15)

1 Door glass	5 Guide channel	8 Glass guide
2 Door lock knob	6 Regulator handle	9 Door lock assembly
3 Door inside handle	7 Regulator assembly	10 Door outside handle
4 Front lower sash		

Adjustment

5   Any adjustment to either the front or rear doors can be made by slackening the hinge bolts and repositioning the hinges on the body mounting locations. The door should be adjusted to give an even clearance from its periphery to the body aperture on all faces.
6   Further adjustment will probably be needed to the door lock striker and this can be moved in the direction required by simply loosening the retaining bolts. Make sure that both the hinge bolts and retaining bolts are securely tightened on completion.

14 Door trim – removal and refitting

1   Unscrew the lock knob and door pull (photo).
2   Unscrew and remove the inner door catch backing strip. Remove the strip (photo).

3   To remove the window winder handle, prise the handle and trim apart, and with a suitable wire hook reach down inside the handle and pull free the release spring from the winder pivot. Pull the handle free (photo).
4   Prise the trim carefully away from the door around the edges. The trim is retained by plastic clips (photo). The trim can now be lifted clear of the door.
5   Refitment of the trim is a direct reversal of the removal sequence, but ensure that the spring clip is correctly located to retain the window winder handle.

15 Front and rear door locks and lock controls – removal and refitting

1   Referring to the previous Section, remove the door trim panel,

This sequence of photographs deals with the repair of the dent and paintwork damage shown in this photo. The procedure will be similar for the repair of a hole. It should be noted that the procedures given here are simplified — more explicit instructions will be found in the text

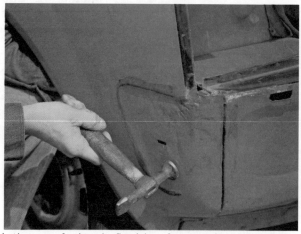

In the case of a dent the first job — after removing surrounding trim — is to hammer out the dent where access is possible. This will minimise filling. Here, the large dent having been hammered out, the damaged area is being made slightly concave

Now all paint must be removed from the damaged area, by rubbing with coarse abrasive paper. Alternatively, a wire brush or abrasive pad can be used in a power drill. Where the repair area meets good paintwork, the edge of the paintwork should be 'feathered', using a finer grade of abrasive paper

In the case of a hole caused by rusting, all damaged sheet-metal should be cut away before proceeding to this stage. Here, the damaged area is being treated with rust remover and inhibitor before being filled

Mix the body filler according to its manufacturer's instructions. In the case of corrosion damage, it will be necessary to block off any large holes before filling — this can be done with aluminium or plastic mesh, or aluminium tape. Make sure the area is absolutely clean before ...

... applying the filler. Filler should be applied with a flexible applicator, as shown, for best results; the wooden spatula being used for confined areas. Apply thin layers of filler at 20-minute intervals, until the surface of the filler is slightly proud of the surrounding bodywork

Initial shaping can be done with a Surform plane or Dreadnought file. Then, using progressively finer grades of wet-and-dry paper, wrapped around a sanding block, and copious amounts of clean water, rub down the filler until really smooth and flat. Again, feather the edges of adjoining paintwork

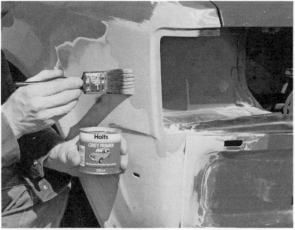

The whole repair area can now be sprayed or brush-painted with primer. If spraying, ensure adjoining areas are protected from over-spray. Note that at least one inch of the surrounding sound paintwork should be coated with primer. Primer has a 'thick' consistency, so will find small imperfections

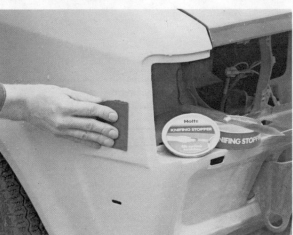

Again, using plenty of water, rub down the primer with a fine grade wet-and-dry paper (400 grade is probably best) until it is really smooth and well blended into the surrounding paintwork. Any remaining imperfections can now be filled by carefully applied knifing stopper paste

When the stopper has hardened, rub down the repair area again before applying the final coat of primer. Before rubbing down this last coat of primer, ensure the repair area is blemish-free — use more stopper if necessary. To ensure that the surface of the primer is really smooth use some finishing compound

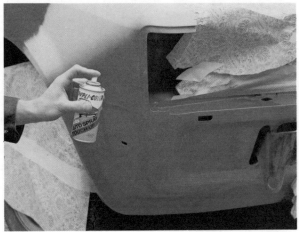

The top coat can now be applied. When working out of doors, pick a dry, warm and wind-free day. Ensure surrounding areas are protected from over-spray. Agitate the aerosol thoroughly, then spray the centre of the repair area, working outwards with a circular motion. Apply the paint as several thin coats

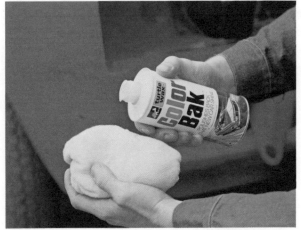

After a period of about two weeks, which the paint needs to harden fully, the surface of the repaired area can be 'cut' with a mild cutting compound prior to wax polishing. When carrying out bodywork repairs, remember that the quality of the finished job is proportional to the time and effort expended

then peel back the plastic dust sheet (photo).
2   Remove the remote control catch unit retaining screws (photo).
3   Detach the outside handle rod from the lock.
4   On the front doors, prise free the retaining clip and withdraw the lock cylinder.
5   Remove the lock retaining screws (photo), then reach through the inner door panel aperture and withdraw the door lock, simultaneously removing the outside handle.
6   Refit in the reverse order to removal, lubricating the rod pivots with grease as they are assembled.
7   To adjust the lock, set the latch to the fully locked position, then fit the lock. Fit the baseplate but do not fully tighten it yet.
8   Locate the locking knob and baseplate stop, then fit and secure the remote control unit at its forward end, but take great care not to bend or distort the door locking rod.
9   The outer handle can be adjusted for play by turning the nylon bush half a turn.
10 Finally tighten the lock baseplate and check for correct operation.

16 Front door glass and regulator – removal and refitting

1   Remove the door trim panel as given in Section 14.
2   Peel back the plastic dust sheet and then lower the door glass to its fullest extent (using the regulator handle).
3   Using a screwdriver as shown in Fig. 12.12, remove the door outer moulding.
4   Now raise the door glass so that the regulator-to-glass attachment bolts are accessible through the aperture in the inner door panel. Support the glass with one hand and unbolt the regulator, then raise and withdraw the glass upwards (photo).
5   Withdraw the regulator unit through the largest aperture in the inner door panel.

6   Refitting is the direct reversal of the removal procedure. Lubricate the regulator and glass channel sliding surfaces with grease. Before refitting the trim panel, operate the regulator to ensure that the glass winds up and down in a satisfactory manner. If adjustment is necessary proceed as follows.
7   Referring to Fig. 12.13, semi-tighten screws A and B and then fully raise the glass. Fully tighten screw B. Adjust the glass so that it is positioned centrally in the front lower sash channel. Adjust the front

16.4 Door glass-to-regulator attachment

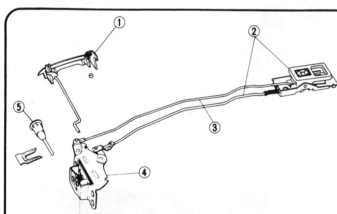

Fig. 12.11 Door lock and cylinder (Sec 15)

1   Outside handle   4   Door lock
2   Remote control   5   Lock cylinder
3   Door lock rod

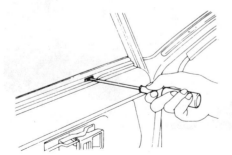

Fig. 12.12 Remove the outer moulding (Sec 16)

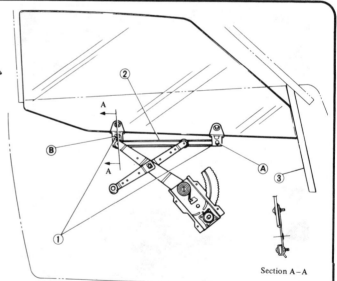

Section A–A

Fig. 12.13 Front door window regulator mechanism. For A and B see text (Sec 16)

1   Glass holder   3   Front lower sash
2   Guide chanel

Fig. 12.14 Central sash retaining screw location (rear door) (Sec 17)

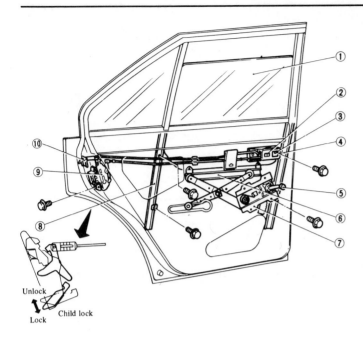

Fig. 12.15 The Saloon rear door assembly components (Sec 17)

1	Door glass	6	Guide channel
2	Inside door lock knob	7	Regulator assembly
3	Inside door handle	8	Centre sash
4	Lower sash	9	Door lock assembly
5	Regulator handle	10	Outside door handle

lower sash to give the correct fore and aft movement for the window, then tighten screw A.

8   Refit the trim panel to complete.

17 Rear door glass (4-door Saloon) – removal and refitting

1   Remove the door trim panel as given in Section 14.
2   Lower the glass and remove the outer moulding.
3   Unscrew and remove the central sash channel retaining screw (Fig. 12.14) and then pressing the sash rearwards, free the glass from the sash.
4   Unscrew and remove the central sash retaining bolts, pivot the seal forwards and then withdraw the quarterlight window together with its partitioning weatherstrip.
5   Remove the central sash and any shims fitted.
6   Position the glass so that its retaining screws are opposite the access hole in the inner panel and remove the screws. Remove the glass.

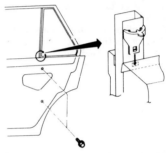

Fig. 12.16 Shim location (rear door) (Sec 17)

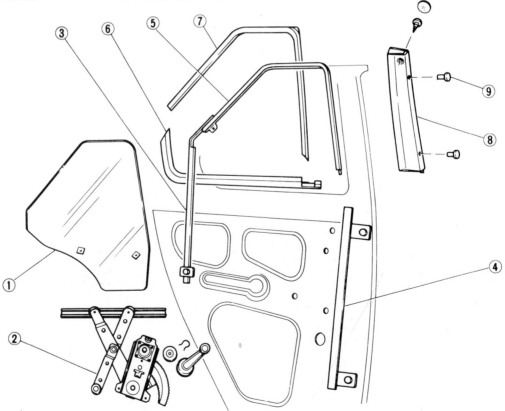

Fig. 12.17 Rear side window – Coupe (Sec 18)

1	Side window glass	4	Front sash	7	Weatherstrip
2	Regulator	5	Retainer	8	Fillet
3	Rear sash	6	Waist moulding	9	Fastener

7   Unscrew and remove the regulator attachment bolts, then withdraw the regulator through the large access aperture in the inner panel.

8   Refit in the reverse order of removal. Before fully tightening the central sash securing screws and bolts, locate the required amount of shims between the sash and the outer rear door panel as shown in Fig. 12.16.

9   Lubricate the regulator sliding surfaces with grease prior to refitting the trim panel. Adjustment for the rear door window is the same as that given for the front door in the previous Section (paragraph 7).

18 Rear side window (Coupe) – removal and refitting

1   Remove the window regulator handle in the same manner as that described for the front door (Section 14) and then carefully prise free the trim panel.

2   Refer to Fig. 12.17. Remove the waist inner weatherstrip, the outer moulding and its fillet, taking care not to damage the paintwork of the surrounding bodywork.

3   Lower the window glass so that its guide channel connection is opposite the inner panel aperture, then separate the roller from the glass channel and remove the window.

4   Unscrew its fixings and remove the regulator.

5   Refitting is a reversal of the removal procedure, but note the following:

   (a)   When refitting the fillet use suitable stainless steel self tapping screws in place of the original fastenings

   (b)   Check window movement before refitting the trim panel and if necessary adjust the guide channel by its front fixing as required to allow a satisfactory winding action

   (c)   To adjust the regulating force, loosen the rear sash fixing bolt and then adjust the sash accordingly

19 Side window (Hatchback) – removal and refitting

1   Unscrew and remove screws retaining the catch to the body.

2   Where a remote control opening device is fitted, extract the retaining pin and detach the cable from the window clevis.

3   Support the window, unscrew the hinge screws and lift the window clear.

4   To remove the remote control cable (where fitted), detach the side trim panel as given in Section 24, then disconnect the cable control.

5   Refitting is the reversal of the removal process. When refitting the remote control cable, adjust it by moving the knob forwards, then pull on the inner cable to move the glass fully, and tighten the locking screw.

20 Windscreen and rear window – removal and refitting

1   Where a windscreen is to be renewed owing to shattering, the facia air vents should be covered before attempting removal. Adhesive sheeting is useful to stick to the outside of the glass to enable large areas of crystallised glass to be removed.

2   Where the screen is to be removed intact then an assistant will be required. First release the rubber surround from the bodywork by running a blunt, small screwdriver around and under the rubber weatherstrip both inside and outside the car. This operation will break the adhesion of the sealer originally used. Take care not to damage the paintwork or cut the rubber surround with the screwdriver. Remove the windscreen wiper arms and interior mirror and place a protective cover on the bonnet.

3   Have your assistant push the inner lip of the rubber surround off the flange of the windscreen body aperture. Once the rubber surround starts to peel off the flange, the screen may be forced gently outwards by careful hand pressure. The second person should support and remove the screen complete with rubber surround and metal beading as it comes out.

4   Remove the beading from the rubber surround.

5   Before fitting a windscreen, ensure that the rubber surround is completely free from old sealant and glass fragments and has not

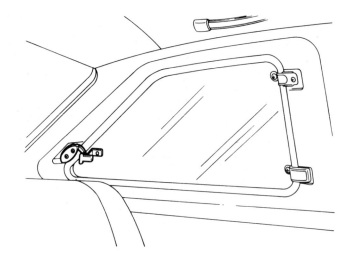

Fig. 12.18 Rear side window – Hatchback (Sec 19)

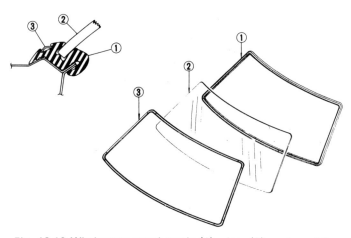

Fig. 12.19 Windscreen weatherstrip (1), glass (2), and moulding (3) (Sec 20)

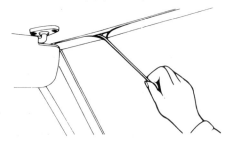

Fig. 12.20 Fitting the windscreen – pull cord to engage rubber lip over the body flange (Sec 20)

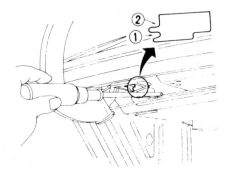

Fig. 12.21 Boot lid torsion bar setting positions (Sec 22)

1   Standard setting   2   Strong setting

21.1 Boot lid and hinge — mark hinge outline before removal

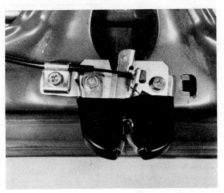

25.6 Detach the boot cable clip and disconnect the cable from the lock

29.6 Facia panel side mounting bolts (arrowed)

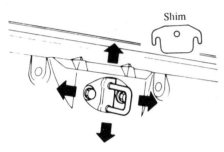

Fig. 12.22 Adjust the rear door striker position (Hatchback) (Sec 23)

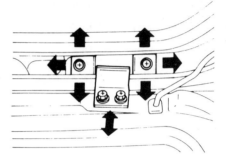

Fig. 12.23 Rear door hinge adjustment (Hatchback) (Sec 23)

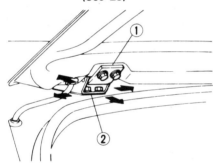

Fig. 12.24 Rear door hinge adjustment (Coupe) (Sec 23)

1   Shim A   2   Shim B

Fig. 12.25 Rear seat cushion retaining bolts — split type seat (Sec 24)

hardened or cracked. Fit the rubber surround to the glass and apply a bead of suitable sealant between the glass outer edge and the rubber.
6   Refit the bright moulding to the rubber surround.
7   Cut a piece of strong cord greater in length than the periphery of the glass and insert it into the body flange locating channel of the rubber surround.
8   Apply a thin bead of sealant to the face of the rubber channel which will eventually mate with the body.
9   Offer the windscreen to the body aperture and pass the ends of the cord, previously fitted and located at bottom centre, into the vehicle interior.
10   Press the windscreen into place; at the same time have an assistant pulling the cords to engage the lip of the rubber channel over the body flange (Fig. 12.20).
11   Remove any excess sealant with a paraffin soaked rag.
12   For removal and refitting of the heated rear window, disconnect the electrical lead and proceed in the same manner as for the windscreen.

21 Boot lid — removal and refitting

1   Open the boot lid and, using a soft pencil, mark the outline of the hinges on the lid to act as a datum for refitting (photo).

2   With the assistance of a second person hold the boot lid in the open position and then remove the two bolts, spring and plain washers from each hinge.
3   Lift away the boot lid.
4   Refitting the boot lid is the reverse sequence to removal. If necessary adjust the position of the hinges relative to the lid until the lid is centralised in the aperture.
5   To obtain a watertight fit between the boot lid and weatherstrip, move the striker up and down or side to side as necessary.

22 Boot lid torsion bar — removal and refitting

1   Open and support the boot lid with a piece of wood.
2   The torsion bars can now be detached from the lid hinge brackets using a screwdriver. Wrap the screwdriver in cloth to prevent it slipping and take care as the bar is under considerable tension.
3   Refit in the reverse order to removal. Adjust the bars as necessary as shown in Fig. 12.21.

23 Rear door/tailgate — removal, refitting and adjustment

1   Raise and support the door and then disconnect the rear window

washer tube and the rear screen demister wire.

2   Get an assistant to support the door while you detach the strut supports on each side.

3   Using a soft lead pencil, mark the hinge outlines of the door to aid correct alignment when refitting. Unscrew the hinge bolts and lift the door clear.

4   Refit in the reverse order to removal and adjust if necessary by altering the striker plate and/or hinge positions. On the Coupe model, shims can be added or subtracted accordingly to adjust the hinge positions.

24 Rear door opener (Hatchback and Coupe) – removal, refitting and adjustment

1   Open the driver's side door and remove the carpet kick plate from the sill edge. Fold back the carpet.

2   Unbolt and remove the rear seat cushion.

3   On the split type rear seat, remove the luggage floor carpet securing screw. Tilt the seat back forward and lift it out. On the bench seat, disengage the seat backrest from the hinge striker, tilt the seat back forwards 45° and slide out the backrest.

4   Remove the body and luggage side trim panels.

5   Detach and remove the luggage compartment rear trim panel.

6   Remove the fixings and withraw the back door lock, then detach the opener cable from the lock.

7   Remove the back door opener lever unit from the floor and withraw the lever unit and cable.

8   Refit in the reverse order to removal.

9   If necessary, adjust the cable rear clamp to give the required clearance between the cable end and locking lever as shown in Fig. 12.30.

25 Boot lid opener – removal, refitting and adjustment

1   Open the driver's door and detach the carpet kick plate from the sill edge.

2   Detach the cable from the operating lever bracket unit.

3   Unscrew and remove the rear seat backrest-to-seat belt anchorage bracket retaining bolts. Push up the backrest front portion and remove the backrest.

4   Unbolt and remove the rear seat cushion.

5   Detach the rear parcel shelf finisher.

6   Detach the cable end clip from the lock side (photo), disconnect

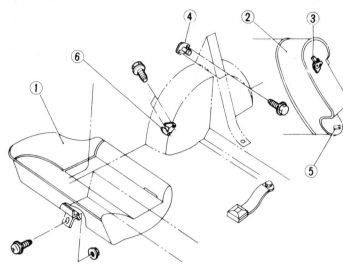

Fig. 12.26 Rear seat removal – bench type (Sec 24)

1   Cushion   4   Striker
2   Rear seat back   5   Hinge pin
3   Stopper   6   Hinge bracket

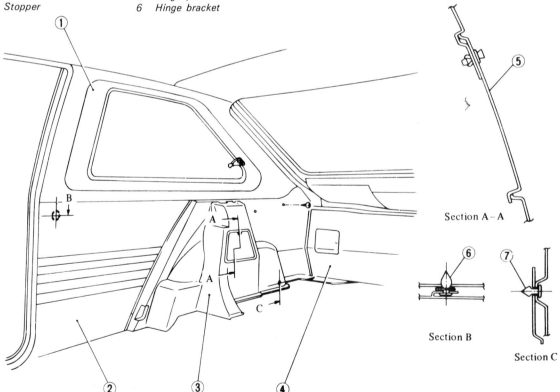

Fig. 12.27 Rear side trim and location points – Hatchback (Sec 24)

1   Side window garnish   4   Luggage rear finisher   6   Clip A
2   Rear side finisher   5   Cover   7   Clip B
3   Luggage side finisher

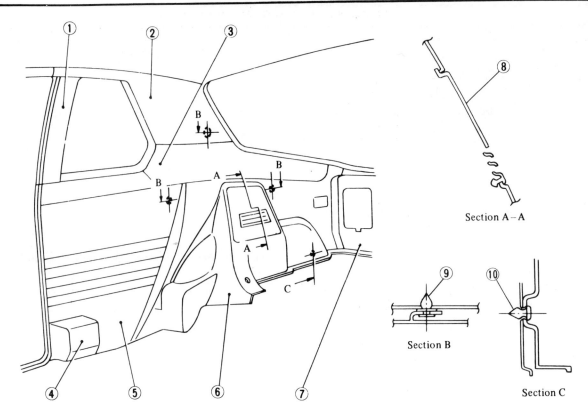

Fig. 12.28 Rear side trim and location points – Coupe (Sec 24)

1 Centre pillar garnish
2 Rear pillar finisher
3 Rear side upper finisher
4 Retractor cover
5 Rear side finisher
6 Luggage side finisher
7 Luggage rear finisher
8 Cover
9 Clip A
10 Clip B

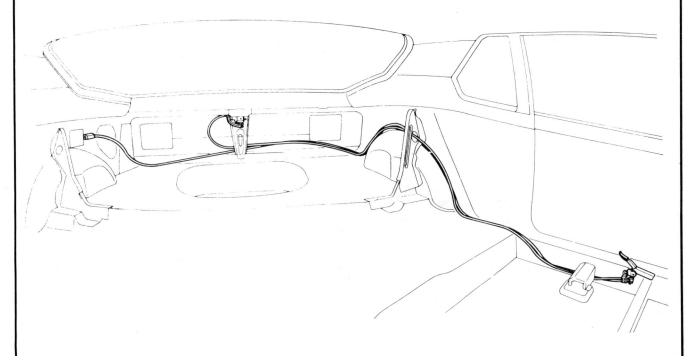

Fig. 12.29 Rear door opener and petrol filler release cables – routing round body (left-hand drive shown) (Sec 24)

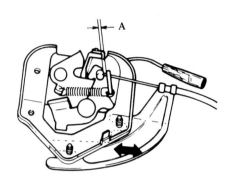

Fig. 12.30 Adjust cable at A to a clearance of 0.02 to 0.08 in (0.5 to 2.0 mm) (Sec 24)

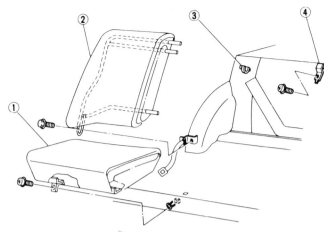

Fig. 12.31 Rear seat fastenings – 4-door Saloon (Sec 25)

| 1 | Cushion | 3 | Hook |
| 2 | Rear seat back | 4 | Stopper |

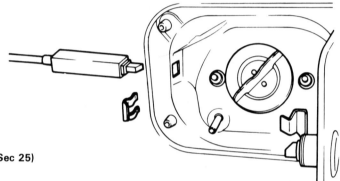

Fig. 12.33 Adjust the boot lid cable-to-lever clearance (Sec 25)

A = 0.02 to 0.08 in (0.5 to 2.0 mm)

Fig. 12.34 Fuel filler cable attachment (Sec 28)

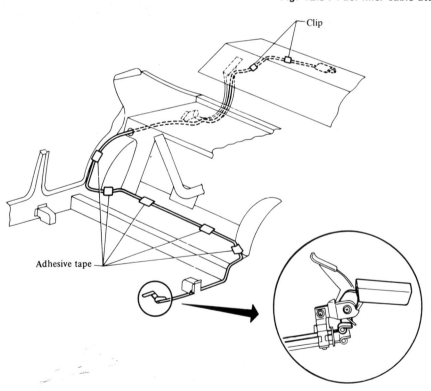

Clip

Adhesive tape

Fig. 12.32 Boot lid opener and cable location (Sec 25)

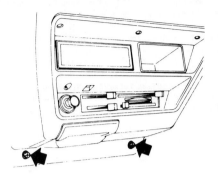

Fig. 12.35 Facia panel central retaining screw locations (Sec 29)

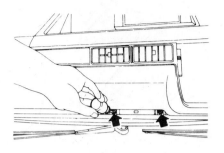

Fig. 12.36 Facia panel retaining screws are accessible for removal with the mask removed (Sec 29)

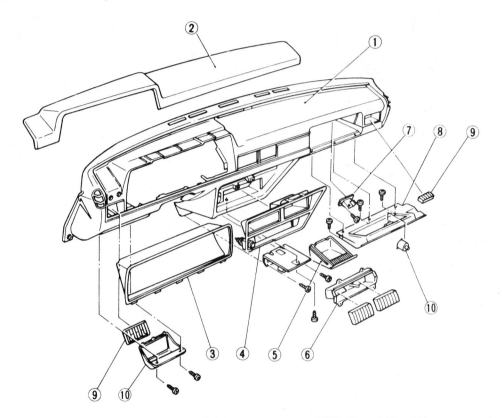

Fig. 12.37 The facia panel assembly components (LHD shown) (Sec 29)

1 Facia panel	4 Centre bezel	7 Striker	10 Key lock
2 Top pad	5 Ashtray	8 Glovebox lid	11 Coin pocket
3 Cluster lid	6 Centre ventilator	9 Side ventilator case	

the retaining clips and withdraw the cable.

7   Refit in the reverse order to removal, adjusting the cable rear clamp to give the required clearance between the locking lever and cable end as shown in Fig. 12.33 before tightening the clamp retaining bolts.

26 Boot lid lock and cylinder – removal and refitting

1   Open the boot lid and remove the lock retaining screws. Withdraw the lock unit.
2   To remove the cylinder, prise free the retaining clip on the lid inner face and withdraw the cylinder.
3   Refit in the reverse sequence to removal.

27 Rear door tailgate lock and cylinder – removal and refitting

1   Open the rear door and remove the luggage compartment rear

trim panel.
2   Unbolt and remove the door lock unit.
3   To remove the cylinder unit, prise free the retaining clip and withdraw the cylinder.
4   Refit in the reverse order to removal.

28 Fuel tank filler lid opener – removal and refitting

This is removed in a similar manner to that described for the removal of the rear door opener as given in Section 24. To detach the cable from the filler unit, simply prise free the retaining clip.

29 Facia panel (dashboard) – removal and refitting

1   Disconnect the battery earth lead.
2   Referring to Section 2 in Chapter 8, remove the steering wheel.
3   Refer to Chapter 10 and remove the instrument panel (Section

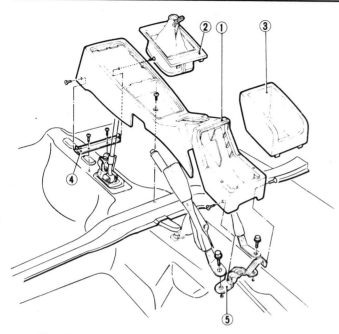

Fig. 12.38 The console assembly components (Sec 30)

1   Console box
2   Boot
3   Console pocket
4   Console box bracket A
5   Console box bracket B

26), the radio (Section 40) and the heater control panel (Section 44).

4   Remove the choke control knob and retaining nut (where applicable).

5   Disconnect any remaining wiring harness connectors to the facia panel switches, noting their location for correct refitting.

6   Unscrew and remove the right and left-hand side panel retaining bolts (photo), followed by the two lower central panel bolts.

7   Remove the two masked retaining screws above the central vents. To remove the mask, bend a piece of 1 mm diameter wire at 90° and insert it between the mask and facia pad. Pull the mask free to expose the screws.

8   Remove the panel/steering column bracket retaining bolts.

9   Check that all fittings are free and then withdraw the facia panel.

10   Refit in the reverse order to removal. Ensure that all wiring connections are securely made and check the operation of the various switches and instruments on completion.

30 Console box – removal and refitting

1   Unscrew and remove the gear lever knob.

2   Unscrew and remove the four console retaining screws, one at each corner.

3   Remove the central retaining screw from the top and then carefully lift the console over the gear lever and handbrake to withdraw it.

4   Refitting is the reversal of the removal procedure.

Chapter 13 Supplement:
Revisions and information on later models

Contents

1 Introduction

This Chapter contains information on Datsun Cherry and 310 models manufactured from October 1981 until the end of production in September 1982.

The main differences between these and earlier models lie in the all-new E-series ohc engine and related systems, improved manual and automatic transmissions and minor component revisions.

The contents of this Supplement therefore deal with the difference between these later models and earlier versions. Except for the information contained in this Chapter, all procedures contained in Chapters 1 to 12 of this manual will also be applicable to later E-series engine models.

2 Specifications

The following specifications are applicable to E-series engine models and are supplementary to the main specifications given at the beginning of each Chapter.

Engine
General

Engine type .... Four-cylinder, in-line overhead camshaft, mounted transversely at the front of the vehicle

Engine designation:
UK models .... E10 and E13
USA and Canada models E15

Engine data:	E10	E13	E15
Capacity	987 cc (60.2 cu in)	1269 cc (77.4 cu in)	1488 cc (90.8 cu in)
Bore	73.0 mm (2.87 in)	76.0 mm (2.99 in)	76.0 mm (2.99 in)
Stroke	59.0 mm (2.32 in)	70.0 mm (2.76 in)	82.0 mm (3.23 in)
Compression ratio	9.0 : 1		
Firing order	1-3-4-2		
Location of No 1 cylinder	Timing belt end		

Lubrication system

Type .... Wet sump, pressure fed
Engine oil capacity:
With filter .... 6.8 Imp pints (3.9 litres, 8.2 US pints)
Without filter .... 6.0 Imp pints (3.4 litres, 7.2 US pints)
Filter type .... Full-flow disposable canister
Oil pump .... Rotor type, driven off jackshaft
Oil pressure (at 2000 rpm) .... 47 lbf/in^2 (3.3 kgf/cm^2)
Oil pump tolerances:
Rotor side clearance .... 0.002 in (0.05 mm) maximum
Rotor tip clearance .... 0.005 in (0.12 mm) maximum
Body-to-outer rotor clearance .... 0.006 to 0.008 in (0.15 to 0.21 mm)
Body-to-rotor gap .... 0.0008 in (0.02 mm) maximum

Cylinder head

Surface flatness (maximum limit) .... 0.004 in (0.1 mm)

Valves

Valve clearances:
Inlet and exhaust (cold-assembly setting only) .... 0.009 in (0.22 mm)
Inlet and exhaust (hot) .... 0.011 in (0.28 mm)

	Inlet	Exhaust
Valve head diameter:		
E10 engines	1.38 in (35.0 mm)	1.14 in (29.0 mm)
E13 and E15 engines	1.46 in (37.0 mm)	1.18 in (30.0 mm)
Valve length:		
E10 engines	4.682 to 4.698 in (118.93 to 119.33 mm)	4.665 to 4.681 in (118.50 to 118.9 mm)
E13 and E15 models	4.665 to 4.681 in (117.85 to 118.25 mm)	4.639 to 4.655 in (118.50 to 118.90 mm)
Valve stem diameter	0.274 to 0.275 in (6.96 to 6.98 mm)	00.273 to 0.274 in (6.94 to 6.96 mm)
Valve stem-to-guide clearance	0.0006 to 0.0018 ± 0.004 in (0.015 to 0.045 ± 0.1 mm)	0.0018 to 0.0030 ± 0.004 in (0.045 to 0.075 ± 0.1 mm)

Valve spring free length .... 1.838 in (46.70 mm)
Valve guides:
Outer diameter .... 0.482 to 0.483 in (12.25 to 12.27 mm)
Inner diameter (finished size) .... 0.275 to 0.276 in (7.00 to 7.02 mm)
Cylinder head valve guide bore .... 0.480 to 0.481 in (12.20 to 12.21 mm)

	Inlet	Exhaust
Valve seats:		
Valve seat angle	45°	45°
Valve seat width	0.059 in (1.5 mm)	0.071 in (1.8 mm)

Cylinder block

Maximum allowable bore ovality .... 0.008 in (0.20 mm)
Maximum allowable bore taper .... 0.008 in (0.20 mm)

Surface flatness (maximum limit) .... 0.004 in (0.10 mm)

Pistons

	E10	E13 and E15
Diameter:		
Standard	2.872 to 2.874 in (72.96 to 73.01 mm)	2.990 to 2.992 in (75.96 to 76.01 mm)
Oversize (0.02)	2.873 to 2.875 in (72.98 to 73.03 mm)	2.991 to 2.993 in (75.98 to 76.03 mm)
Oversize (0.5)	2.892 to 2.894 in (73.46 to 73.51 mm)	3.010 to 3.012 in (76.46 to 76.51 mm)
Gudgeon pin bore diameter	0.687 to 0.688 in (17.45 to 17.46 mm)	0.748 to 0.749 in (19.00 to 19.01 mm)

Piston-to-bore clearance (all engines) .... 0.0009 to 0.0017 in (0.023 to 0.043 mm)

Piston rings

Number and type .... Two compression, one oil control
Maximum permissible ring-to-groove clearance:
    1st and 2nd rings .... 0.008 in (0.2 mm)
    Oil control ring .... 0.002 to 0.006 in (0.05 to 0.14 mm)
Maximum permissible ring gap .... 0.039 in (1.0 mm)

Gudgeon pin

	E10	E13 and E15
Diameter	0.686 to 0.687 in (17.44 to 17.47 mm)	0.747 to 0.748 in (18.99 to 19.99 mm)
Clearance in piston	0.0002 to 0.0004 in (0.006 to 0.010 mm)	0.0003 to 0.0005 in (0.008 to 0.012 mm)
Interference fit in connecting rod	0.0007 (0.0015 in) (0.017 to 0.038 mm)	0.0007 to 0.0015 in (0.017 to 0.038 mm)

Connecting rod and big-end bearings

	E10	E13 and E15
Gudgeon pin bore diameter	0.685 to 0.686 in (17.41 to 17.42 mm)	0.746 to 0.747 in (18.96 to 18.97 mm)
Maximum big-end endplay	0.20 in (0.5 mm)	0.20 in (0.5 mm)

Crankshaft and main bearings

Number of main bearings 5
Main bearing journal diameter .... 1.966 to 1.967 in (49.94 to 49.96 mm)
Big-end bearing journal diameter .... 1.573 to 1.574 in (39.95 to 39.97 mm)
Maximum permissible journal ovality .... 0.001 in (0.03 mm)
Maximum permissible journal taper .... 0.001 in (0.03 mm)
Maximum permissible crankshaft endplay .... 0.012 in (0.30 mm)
Maximum permissible main bearing shell clearance .... 0.004 in (0.10 mm)
Maximum permissible big-end bearing shell clearance .... 0.005 in (0.12 mm)

Camshaft

Number of bearings .... 5, bored in line
Drive .... Toothed rubber belt
Maximum permissible endplay .... 0.016 in (0.4 mm)
Journal diameter:
    1st, 3rd and 5th .... 1.651 to 1.652 in (41.94 to 41.96 mm)
    2nd and 4th .... 1.649 to 1.650 in (41.90 to 41.92 mm)
Bearing inner diameter .... 1.653 to 1.654 in (42.00 to 42.02 mm)
Camshaft journal-to-bearing clearance:
    1st, 3rd and 5th .... 0.001 to 0.003 in (0.03 to 0.07 mm)
    2nd and 4th .... 0.003 to 0.004 in (0.07 to 0.12 mm)

Cam lobe height:	E10 and E13	E15
Inlet	1.405 to 1.415 in (35.71 to 35.96 mm)	1.412 to 1.422 in (35.88 to 36.13 mm)
Exhaust	1.394 to 1.404 in (35.43 to 35.68 mm)	1.403 to 1.413 in 35.64 to 35.89 mm)

Jackshaft

Journal diameter:
    Front .... 1.259 to 1.260 in (31.98 to 32.00 mm)
    Rear .... 1.125 to 1.126 in (28.58 to 28.60 mm)
Bearing inner diameter:
    Front .... 1.260 to 1.263 in (32.02 to 32.08 mm)
    Rear .... 1.126 to 1.129 in (28.62 to 28.68 mm)
Jackshaft journal to bearing clearance:
    Front .... 0.0008 to 0.0019 in (0.020 to 0.048 mm)
    Rear .... 0.0008 to 0.004 in (0.020 to 0.098 mm)
Fuel pump cam height .... 1.091 to 1.094 in (27.7 to 27.8 mm)

Torque wrench settings

	lbf ft	kgf m
Cylinder head bolts:		
First stage	28 to 33	4.0 to 4.5
Second stage	51 to 54	7.0 to 7.5

	lbf ft	kgf m
Rocker shaft bolts	12 to 15	1.6 to 2.1
Connecting rod big-end nuts	23 to 27	3.2 to 3.8
Main bearing cap bolts	36 to 43	5.0 to 6.0
Flywheel bolts	58 to 65	8.0 to 9.0
Driveplate bolts	69 to 76	9.5 to 10.5
Camshaft sprocket bolt	4.3 to 5.8	0.6 to 0.8
Jackshaft sprocket bolt	4.3 to 5.8	0.6 to 0.8
Crankshaft pulley bolt	83 to 108	11.5 to 15.0
Front cover bolts	2.7 to 3.7	0.4 to 0.5
Sump nuts and bolts	2.7 to 3.7	0.4 to 0.5
Rocker cover nuts	2.9 to 5.8	0.4 to 0.8
Belt tensioner locknut	12 to 15	1.6 to 2.1
Rocker arm locknut	12 to 15	1.6 to 2.1
Oil strainer bolt	4.6 to 6.1	0.6 to 0.8
Sump drain plug	26 to 35	3.6 to 4.8
Alternator bracket bolt	6.7 to 8.7	0.9 to 1.2
Engine mounting bracket to cylinder block	22 to 29	3.0 to 4.0
Engine mounting bracket to cylinder head	12 to 15	1.6 to 2.1
Inlet and exhaust manifold nuts	12 to 15	1.6 to 2.1
Oil pump retaining nuts and bolts	6.7 to 8.7	0.9 to 1.2
Oil pump cover bolt	2.8 to 3.8	0.4 to 0.5
Pressure regulator cap nut	29 to 36	4.0 to 5.0

Fuel system
Carburettor type
E10 engines	Hitachi 217260-101
E13 engines:	
Manual transmission	Hitachi 217260-041
Automatic transmission	Hitachi 217260-051
E15 engines:	
California models	Hitachi DCR 306-140
Non-California models	Hitachi DCR 306-130
Canada models	Hitachi DCR 306-150

Carburettor specifications
E10 and E13 engines

	217260-101	217260-041	217260-051
Choke diameter:			
Primary	1.02 in (26 mm)	1.02 in (26 mm)	1.02 in (26 mm)
Secondary	1.18 in (30 mm)	1.18 in (30 mm)	1.18 in (30 mm)
Venturi diameter:			
Primary	0.71 in (18 mm)	0.75 in (19 mm)	0.75 in (19 mm)
Secondary	1.06 in (27 mm)	1.06 in (27 mm)	1.06 in (27 mm)
Main jet (standard):			
Primary	82	87	87
Secondary	150	155	155
Main air bleed:			
Primary	70	70	70
Secondary	60	60	60
Slow running jet:			
Primary	40	40	40
Secondary	55	55	55
Slow air bleed:			
Primary	80	80	80
Secondary	100	100	100
Power jet	40	40	40
Engine idle speed	750 rpm		
CO emission	1.5%		
Float chamber fuel level:			
Gap between float and body	0.59 in (15 mm)		
Bottom float position	1.77 in (45 mm)		
Fast idle adjustment clearance	0.054 ± 0.002 in (1.38 ± 0.07 mm)		
Interlock opening adjustment clearance	0.023 ± 0.012 in (5.87 ± 0.30 mm)		
Dashpot adjustment gap	0.018 ± 0.003 in (0.47 ± 0.10 mm)		
Dashpot touch speed	1700 to 2100 rpm		

E15 engines

	DCR306-140	DCR306-130	DCR306-150
Choke diameter:			
Primary	1.02 in (26 mm)	1.02 in (26 mm)	1.02 in (26 mm)
Secondary	1.18 in (30 mm)	1.18 in (30 mm)	1.18 in (30 mm)
Venturi diameter:			
Primary	0.91 in (23 mm)	0.91 in (23 mm)	0.83 in (21 mm)
Secondary	1.06 in (27 mm)	1.06 in (27 mm)	1.06 in (27 mm)
Main jet:			
Primary	114	116	100
Secondary	125	125	120

	DCR306-140	DCR306-130	DCR306-150
Main air bleed:			
Primary	60	80	70
Secondary	80	80	60
Slow running jet:			
Primary	45	45	43
Secondary	50	50	80
Slow air bleed:			
Primary	170	170	170
Secondary	80	100	100
Power jet	38	38	40
Engine idle speed	700 to 800 rpm		
CO emission	2 ± 1%		
Float chamber fuel level:			
Gap between float and body	0.47 in (12.0 mm)		
Gap between valve and float	0.051 to 0.067 in (1.3 to 1.7 mm)		
Auto-choke bi-metal setting	Centre of index mark		
Fast idle adjustment clearance (at 2nd cam step)	0.031 ± 0.002 in (0.80 ± 0.07 mm)		
Fast idle speed (at 2nd cam step):			
California models	2300 to 3100 rpm		
Non-California models	2400 to 3200 rpm		
Canada models	1900 to 2700 rpm		
Vacuum break adjustment clearance:			
California models	0.067 ± 0.003 in (1.70 ± 0.09 mm)		
Non-California models	0.067 ± 0.003 in (1.70 ± 0.09 mm)		
Canada models	0.058 ± 0.003 in (1.49 ± 0.09 mm)		
Choke unloader adjustment clearance	0.093 in (2.36 mm)		
Interlock opening adjustment clearance	0.229 ± 0.0019 in (5.83 ± 0.05 mm)		
Dashpot adjustment gap	0.029 ± 0.002 in (0.76 ± 0.07 mm)		
Throttle opener adjustment gap:			
California models	0.072 ± 0.004 in (1.84 ± 0.12 mm)		
Non-California models	0.072 ± 0.004 in (1.84 ± 0.12 mm)		
Canada models	0.022 ± 0.002 in (0.56 ± 0.07 mm)		

Accelerator cable

Cable free play at pedal pad .... 0.04 to 0.08 in (1.0 to 2.0 mm)

Ignition system
System type:
E10 and E13 engines .... Conventional contact breaker and coil
E15 engines .... Breakerless, integrated circuit

Spark plugs
Type:
    Standard (all models) .... Hitachi BPR 5 ES, or equivalent
Electrode gap:
    E10 and E13 engines .... 0.031 to 0.035 in (0.8 to 0.9 mm)
    E15 engines:
        USA models .... 0.039 to 0.043 in (1.0 to 1.1 mm)
        Canada models .... 0.031 to 0.035 in (0.8 to 0.9 mm)

Coil
Make .... Hitachi or Hanskin
Type:
    E10 and E13 engines C6R-206
    E15 engines C1T-72

Distributor
E10 and E13 engines
Make .... Hitachi
Type:
    E10 engines D410-92
    E13 engines:
        Manual transmission D412-A9
        Automatic transmission D412-B1
Direction of rotation .... Anti-clockwise
Dwell angle .... 49° to 55°
Contact breaker points gap .... 0.018 to 0.022 in (0.45 to 0.55 mm)

E15 engines
Make .... Hitachi
Type:
    California models D4R80-14
    Non-California models D4R80-13
    Canada models D4R81-08
Direction of rotation .... Anti-clockwise
Air gap .... 0.012 to 0.020 in (0.3 to 0.5 mm)

Ignition timing*
E10 engines	2° BTDC at 700 rpm
E13 engines:	
Manual transmission	2° ATDC at 750 rpm
Automatic transmission	2° ATDC at 800 rpm
E15 engines:	
USA models	0° to 4° ATDC at 700 to 800 rpm
Canada models	2° to 6° ATDC at 700 to 800 rpm

With distributor vacuum pipe disconnected and plugged

Clutch

Clutch type .... Cable operated, diaphragm spring

Clutch disc
Type:	
E10 engines	160 CBL
E13 and E15 engines	180 CBL
Disc diameter:	
E10 engines	6.30 in (160.0 mm)
E13 and E15 engines	7.09 in (180.0 mm)
Lining thickness	0.13 in (3.5 mm)

Clutch pedal
Pedal height:	
LHD models	7.15 to 7.38 in (181.5 to 187.5 mm)
RHD models	6.97 to 7.20 in (177.0 to 183.0 mm)
Pedal free travel	0.43 to 0.83 in (11.0 to 21.0 mm)
Withdrawal lever free play	0.08 to 0.16 in (2.0 to 4.0 mm)

Torque wrench settings
	lbf ft	kgf m
Clutch cover bolts	12 to 15	1.6 to 2.1
Clutch cable bracket bolt	5.8 to 8.0	0.8 to 1.1
Clutch cable adjusting locknuts	14 to 19	1.9 to 2.6
Pedal stopper bolt locknut	12 to 19	1.6 to 2.6

Transmission

Manual transmission
Transmission identification:	
Four-speed	RN4F30A
Five-speed	RS5F30A
Gear ratios:	
1st	3.333 : 1
2nd	1.955 : 1
3rd	1.286 : 1
4th	0.902 : 1
5th	0.756 : 1
Reverse	3.417 : 1
Final drive ratio:	
E10 engines	4.471 : 1
E13 engines	4.056 : 1
E15 engines:	
Four-speed	3.650 : 1
Five-speed	3.895 : 1
Gear clearances:	
Endplay:	
Main 1st gear	0.007 to 0.012 in (0.18 to 0.31 mm)
Main 2nd to 4th gear	0.007 to 0.015 in (0.20 to 0.40 mm)
Input 5th gear	0.007 to 0.016 in (0.18 to 0.41 mm)
Maximum permissible baulk ring to gear clearance	0.028 in (0.7 mm)
Rotary frictional force:	
Differential only	43 to 65 lbf in (50 to 75 kgf cm)
Total geartrain	65 to 95 lbf in (75 to 110 kgf cm)
Lubrication:	
Lubricant capacity:	
Four-speed	4 Imp pints (2.3 litres, 4.8 US pints)
Five-speed	4.7 Imp pints (2.7 litres, 5.7 US pints)

Automatic transmission
Transmission type	Three-speed, fully automatic, hydraulic control
Transmission identification	RN3F01A
Gear ratios:	
1st	2.826 : 1
2nd	1.543 : 1

3rd	1.000 : 1	
Reverse	2.364 : 1	
Throttle wire stroke	1.07 to 1.23 in (27.4 to 31.4 mm)	
Fluid capacity	5.2 Imp pints (3.0 litres, 6.34 US pints)	

Torque wrench settings

	lbf ft	kgf m
Manual transmission		
Clutch housing to engine	12 to 15	1.6 to 2.1
Rear mounting to body:		
M8 bolts	12 to 15	1.6 to 2.1
M10 bolts	22 to 29	3.0 to 4.0
Right side mounting to body:		
M8 bolts	12 to 15	1.6 to 2.1
M10 bolts	22 to 29	3.0 to 4.0
Clutch cable locknut	14 to 19	1.9 to 2.6
Speedometer pinion gear	2.7 to 3.7	0.38 to 0.51
Gear linkage control rod to transmission	4.6 to 6.1	0.64 to 0.85
Gear linkage support rod to transmission	22 to 29	3.0 to 4.0
Gearchange control assembly to body	6.7 to 8.7	0.93 to 1.2
Clutch housing to transmission case	12 to 15	1.6 to 2.1
Case cover to transmission case	4.6 to 6.1	0.64 to 0.85
Bearing retainer to clutch housing	12 to 15	1.6 to 2.1
Control bracket to clutch housing	4.6 to 6.1	0.64 to 0.85
5th/reverse check plug	14 to 18	1.9 to 2.5
5th/reverse check assembly to housing	4.6 to 6.1	0.64 to 0.85
Final gear to differential case	54 to 65	7.5 to 9.0
Filler and drain plugs	18 to 25	2.5 to 3.5
Reverse and neutral switches	14 to 22	2.0 to 3.0
Switch plug	11 to 14	1.5 to 2.0

Automatic transmission

	lbf ft	kgf m
Torque converter to driveplate	36 to 51	5.0 to 7.0
Converter housing to engine	12 to 16	1.6 to 2.2
Throttle wire securing nut	3.6 to 5.1	0.5 to 0.7
Control cable securing nut	5.8 to 8.0	0.8 to 1.1
Oil cooler pipes to transmission	22 to 36	3.0 to 5.0

Driveshafts

	lbf ft	kgf m
Front hub nut	87 to 145	12 to 20

Steering

	lbf ft	kgf m
Power steering pump mounting bolts	23 to 31	3.2 to 4.3
Adjusting bolt lockbolt	23 to 31	3.2 to 4.3
High and low pressure hoses to rack and pinion gear	36 to 51	5.0 to 7.0
High pressure hose to pump	22 to 36	3.0 to 5.0

Electrical system

Battery

Capacity:	
UK models	45 Ah
USA models	60 Ah
Canada models	65 Ah

Alternator

Make	Hitachi
Type:	
UK models:	
Manual transmission	LR150-99B
Automatic transmission	LR150-53
USA and Canada models	LR150-125B

Starter motor

Make	Hitachi
Type:	
UK models:	
Manual transmission	S114-315
Automatic transmission	S114-317
USA models	S114-315
Canada models:	
Manual transmission	S114-316
Automatic transmission	S114-318
Commutator minimum outer diameter:	
S114-315	1.26 in (32.0 mm)
S114-316, 317 and 318	1.54 in (39.0 mm)
Minimum brush length	0.43 in (11.0 mm)
Brush spring tension	4.0 to 4.9 lbs (1.8 to 2.2 kgs)
Gap between pinion and pinion stopper	0.012 to 0.098 in (0.3 to 2.5 mm)

Suspension

Front suspension
Coil spring free length:
     UK models .... 14.41 in (366.0 mm)
     USA and Canada models .... 14.76 in (375.0 mm)
Coil spring wire diameter .... 0.425 in (10.8 mm)

Rear suspension
Coil spring free length:
     UK models .... 8.31 in (211.0 mm)
     USA and Canada models .... 9.02 in (229.0 mm)
Coil spring wire diameter:
     UK models .... 0.504 in (12.8 mm)
     USA and Canada models .... 0.453 in (11.5 mm)

3   Vehicle identification numbers

1   The location of the engine, manual transmission or automatic transmission identification numbers on models powered by the E-series engine are as shown in the accompanying illustrations.

4   Routine maintenance

1   The service schedule given at the beginning of this manual is still applicable to E-series engine models. There have, however, been some revisions to component specifications and their locations which directly affect the maintenance operations. The following paragraphs and accompanying illustrations describe these revisions and where applicable further details will be found in the appropriate sections of this Chapter.

Drivebelts
2   Fig. 13.4 shows the location of the alternator, power steering and air conditioner drivebelts and the appropriate tension point for checking the deflection. The tension should be checked using moderate finger pressure and the deflection should be as follows:

	New belt	Used belt
Alternator	0.39 to 0.55 in	0.51 to 0.67 in
	(10.0 to 14.0 mm)	(13.0 to 17.0 mm)
Power steering	0.25 to 0.33 in	0.28 to 0.35 in
	(6.5 to 8.5 mm)	(7.0 to 9.0 mm)
Air conditioning	0.28 to 0.35 in	0.35 to 0.43 in
	(7.0 to 9.0 mm)	(9.0 to 11.0 mm)

Engine lubrication
3   The location of the oil filter, engine sump drain plug and oil filter cap are as shown in Fig. 13.5.

Transmission lubrication
4   The location of the manual and automatic transmission drain and filler plugs is shown in Figs. 13.6 to 13.9.

Power steering
5   The combined dipstick and reservoir cap and the critical areas to check for leaks in the system are shown in Figs. 13.10 and 13.11.

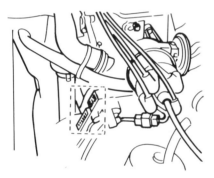

Fig. 13.1 Engine serial number location (Sec 3)

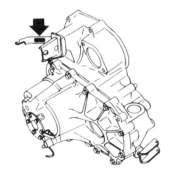

Fig. 13.2 Manual transmission serial number location (Sec 3)

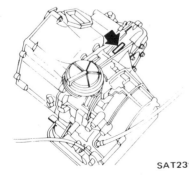

SAT23

Fig. 13.3 Automatic transmission serial number location (Sec 3)

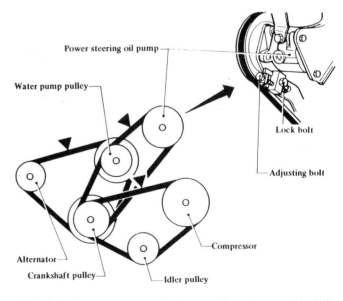

Power steering oil pump

Water pump pulley

Lock bolt

Adjusting bolt

Compressor

Alternator

Crankshaft pulley

Idler pulley

Fig. 13.4 Alternator, power steering and air conditioner drivebelt locations and tension checking points (Sec 4)

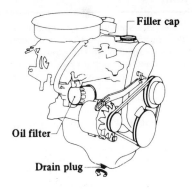

Filler cap

Oil filter

Drain plug

Fig. 13.5 Engine oil filler cap, filter and drain plug locations (Sec 4)

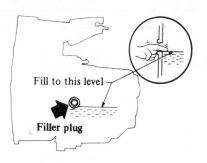

Fill to this level

Filler plug

Fig. 13.6 Manual transmission filler plug location (Sec 4)

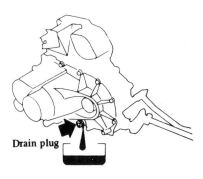

Drain plug

Fig. 13.7 Manual transmission drain plug location (Sec 4)

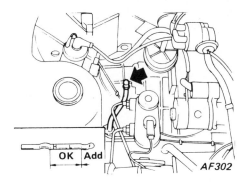

OK Add

AF302

Fig. 13.8 Automatic transmission filler tube and dipstick location (Sec 4)

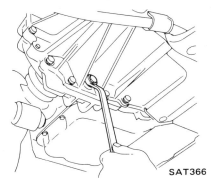

SAT366

Fig. 13.9 Automatic transmission drain plug location (Sec 4)

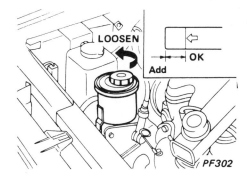

LOOSEN

Add OK

PF302

Fig. 13.10 Power steering fluid reservoir and dipstick (Sec 4)

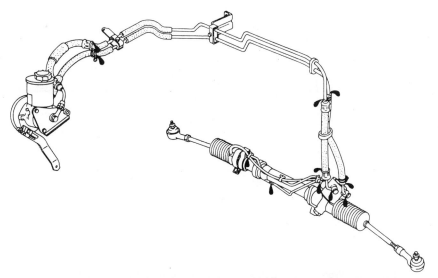

Fig. 13.11 Power steering hydraulic system showing potential leak areas (Sec 4)

5   Engine

PART A: GENERAL INFORMATION AND REMOVAL PROCEDURES

Description

1   The E-series engine fitted to UK market models is either the E10 series of 987cc capacity or the E13 series of 1269cc capacity. USA market models are equipped with the E15 series having a capacity of 1488cc. All three engines are of the in-line, single overhead camshaft, water-cooled design with alterations to the bore and stroke to give the different capacities.

2   The cylinder head is of the crossflow type incorporating hemispherical combustion chambers. The camshaft is mounted within the cylinder head and operates the inclined valves via rocker arms. Camshaft drive is by a toothed rubber belt mounted externally on the front of the engine and driven by a sprocket on the crankshaft.

3   An idler sprocket is used to maintain correct tension on the belt which also drives a jackshaft. The externally mounted oil pump and the fuel pump are operated by the jackshaft while the ignition distributor, which is attached to the flywheel end of the cylinder head, is driven directly off the end of the camshaft.

4   The pistons are of aluminium alloy with flat crowns and incorporating two compression rings and one oil control ring. The connecting rods are of forged steel with gudgeon pins which are an interference fit in the connecting rod small-ends, but fully floating in the pistons.

5   The crankshaft is supported in the cylinder block by five renewable shell bearings. Endfloat is controlled by thrustwashers which are an integral part of the centre main bearing shells.

6   The water pump, alternator and additional engine ancillaries are driven by V-belts from the crankshaft pulley, the number of belts and their arrangement being dependent on equipment fitted and export territory.

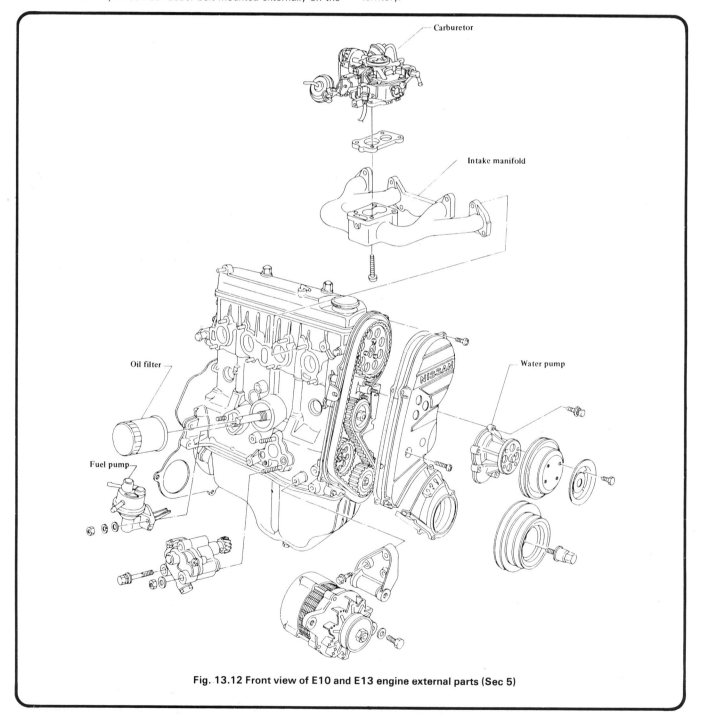

Fig. 13.12 Front view of E10 and E13 engine external parts (Sec 5)

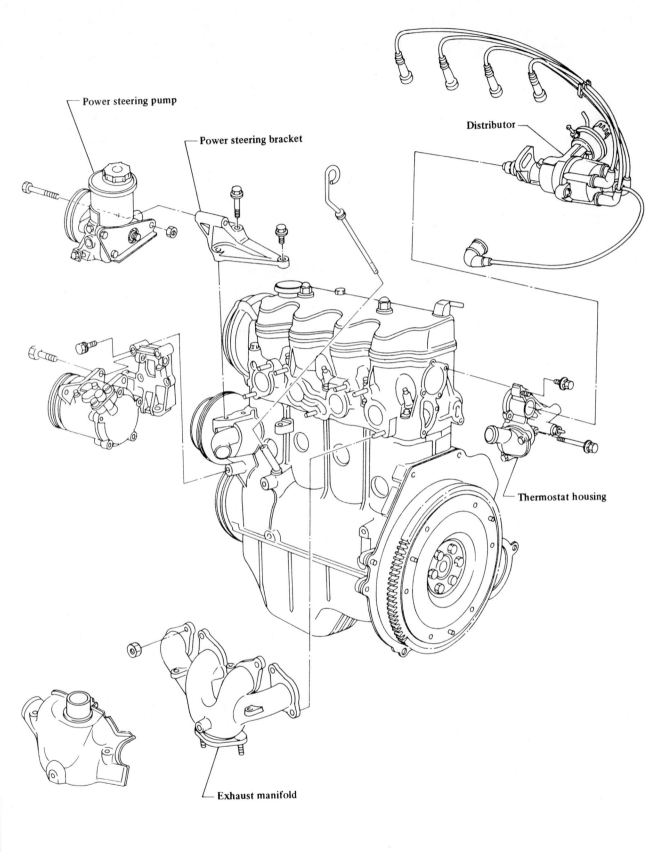

Power steering pump

Power steering bracket

Distributor

Thermostat housing

Exhaust manifold

Fig. 13.13 Rear view of E10 and E13 engine external parts (Sec 5)

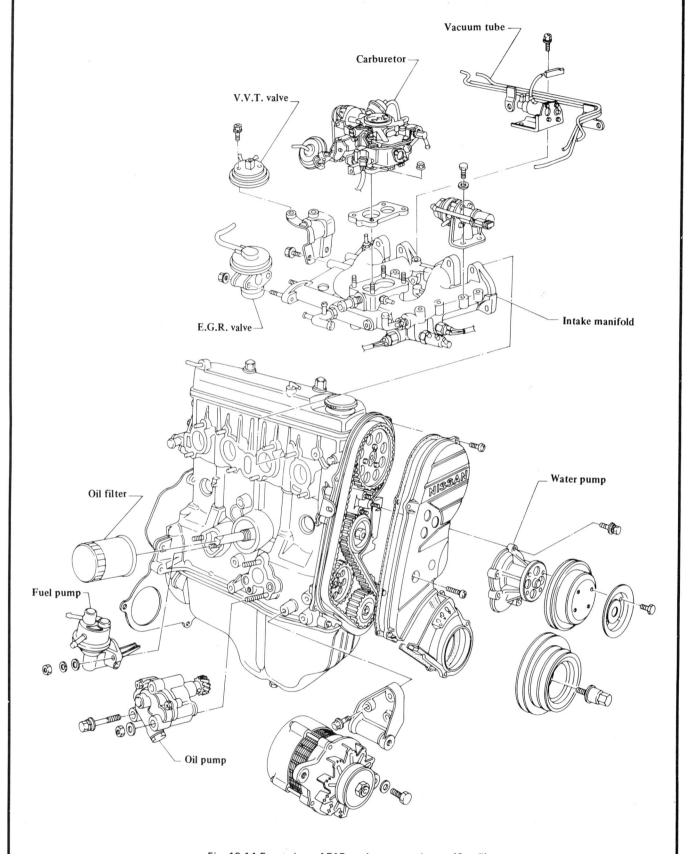

Fig. 13.14 Front view of E15 engine external parts (Sec 5)

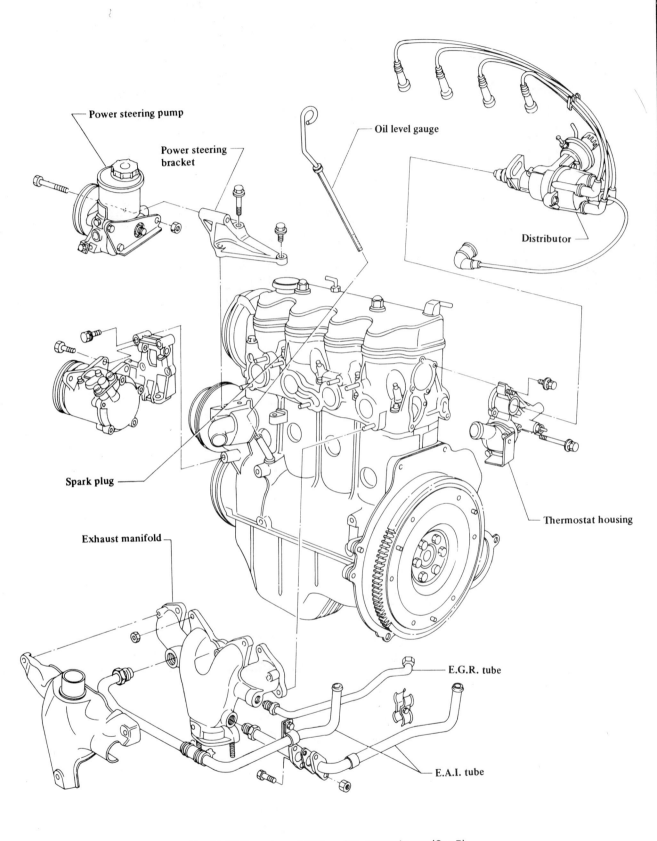

Fig. 13.15 Rear view of E15 engine external parts (Sec 5)

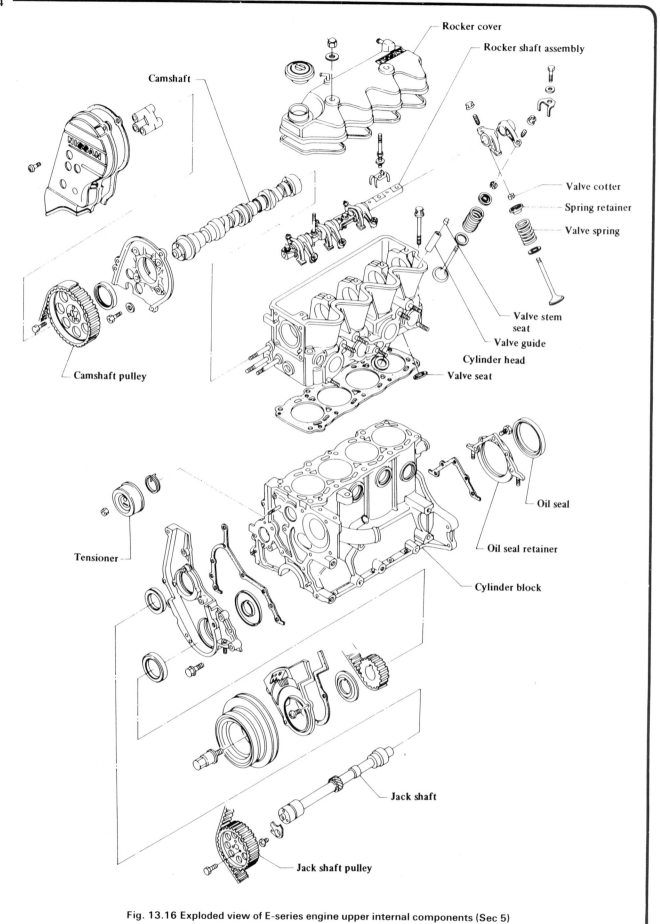

Fig. 13.16 Exploded view of E-series engine upper internal components (Sec 5)

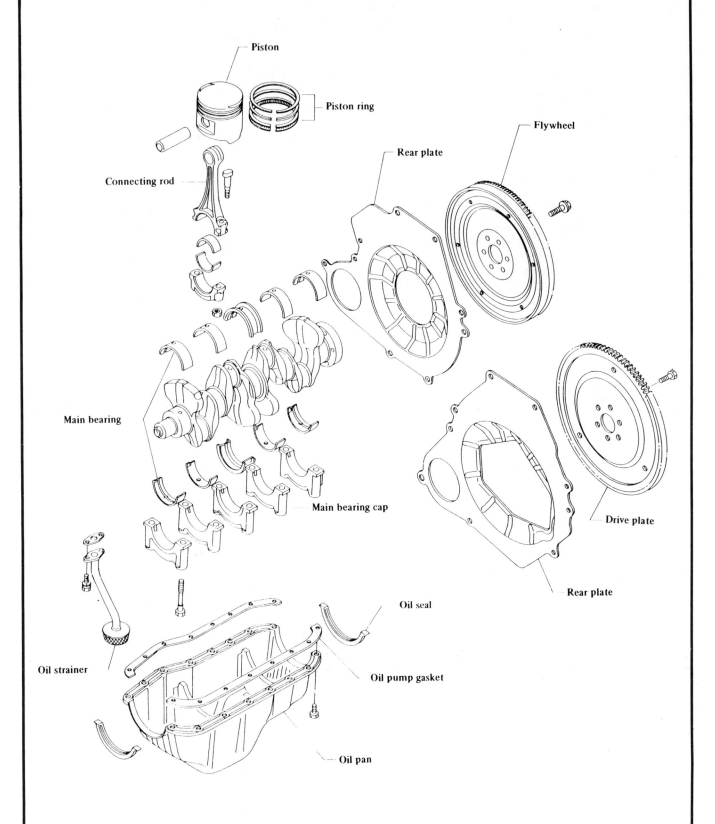

Fig. 13.17 Exploded view of E-series engine lower internal components (Sec 5)

Major operations possible with the engine in the vehicle

7   The following major operations can be carried out on the engine
with it in place in the car:

   (a)   Removal and refitting of the timing belt
   (b)   Removal and refitting of the rocker shaft assembly
   (c)   Removal and refitting of the cylinder head
   (d)   Removal and refitting of the oil pump
   (e)   Removal and refitting of the engine mountings

8   The camshaft can be removed after removal of the cylinder head.

Major operations requiring engine removal

9   The following major operations require the removal of the
engine/transmission assembly from the car:

   (a)   Removal and refitting of the main bearings
   (b)   Removal and refitting of the crankshaft
   (c)   Removal and refitting of the flywheel (or alternatively, after
         removal of the transmission)
   (d)   Removal and refitting of the jackshaft
   (e)   Removal and refitting of the sump, pistons, connecting rods
         and big-end bearings

10   Although it is physically possible to remove the sump for access to
the big-end bearings with the engine in the car, this is not
recommended due to the confined working conditions and the
possibility of dirt entry.

Method of engine removal

11   The engine and transmission are removed as a complete assembly
from above. After removal, the transmission can then be separated to
allow work to proceed on the engine.
12   A sturdy hoist will be required and two axle stands if an inspection
pit is not available. It will also be helpful if there is someone to assist,
particularly in the latter stages of the operation.

Engine – removal

13   Open the bonnet and place suitable covers over the front wings.
14   Using a pencil, mark the outline of the bonnet hinges on each side
as a guide to refitting. With the help of an assistant remove the hinge-
to-bonnet retaining bolts and lift away the bonnet.
15   Disconnect the battery negative (–) and positive (+) terminals,
release the clamp bracket and lift out the battery.
16   Remove the battery support bracket.
17   Refer to Section 7 and remove the air cleaner assembly.
18   Referring to Section 6, drain the cooling system and then remove
the radiator and cooling fan.
19   On models equipped with power steering, slacken the pump upper
mounting bolt and the adjuster lockbolt. Unscrew the adjuster until the
drivebelt can be slipped off the pulley. Remove the upper mounting
bolt and suspend the pump out of the way using string or wire. Do not
detach the fluid hoses.
20   On models equipped with air conditioning, slacken the idler pulley
locknut then unscrew the adjusting bolt until the drivebelt can be
slipped off the pulleys. Remove the idler pulley completely, noting the
position of the spacers and washers. Remove the bolts, top and
bottom, securing the compressor to its mounting bracket. Move the
compressor to one side and support it, the right way up, with a suitable
rope. Do not detach any of the hoses of this system.
21   Disconnect the accelerator cable and choke control cable at the
carburettor.
22   Detach the brake servo vacuum hose and the heater inlet and
outlet water hoses.
23   Slacken the clutch cable adjusting nuts and disconnect the cable
from the clutch operating lever and bracket.
24   Make a careful note of the location of all electrical wiring and
harness connectors between the engine and body. Then disconnect
them. Also note the position of all vacuum and air hoses for the
emission control equipment then detach them as well.
25   Disconnect the fuel hoses from the fuel pump. Plug the hoses after
removal.
26   Remove the bolt securing the speedometer pinion assembly to the
transmission and withdraw the pinion complete with cable.
27   Jack up the front of the car and support it securely on axle stands.
Remove the front roadwheels.
28   Working under the car remove the nuts securing the exhaust front
pipe to the manifold. Slacken the bolt securing the front pipe to its
mounting bracket.

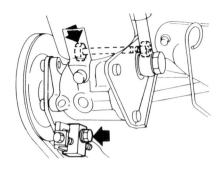

Fig. 13.18 Power steering pump upper mounting bolt and adjuster
lockbolt (Sec 5)

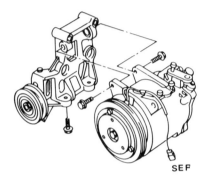

Fig. 13.19 Air conditioner compressor mounting bolts and idler
pulley assembly (Sec 5)

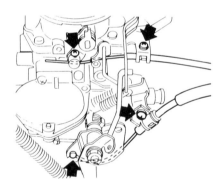

Fig. 13.20 Accelerator and choke cable attachments at carburettor
– E10 and E13 engines (Sec 5)

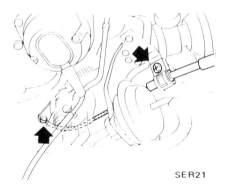

Fig. 13.21 Accelerator cable attachment at carburettor – E15
engine (Sec 5)

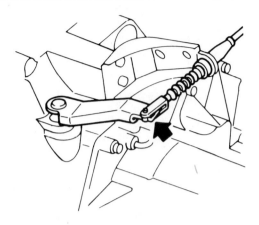

Fig. 13.22 Clutch cable-to-operating lever attachment (Sec 5)

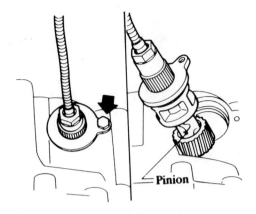

Fig. 13.23 Removal of the speedometer and pinion assembly (Sec 5)

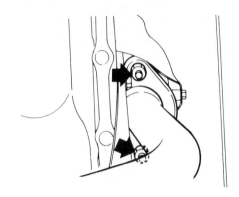

Fig. 13.24 Exhaust pipe to manifold securing nuts viewed from below (Sec 5)

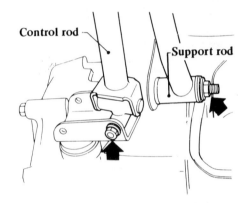

Fig. 13.25 Gearchange control rod and support rod attachments at manual transmission (Sec 5)

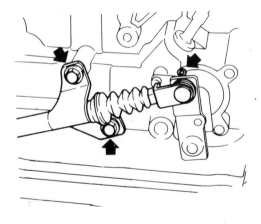

Fig. 13.26 Control cable attachments at automatic transmission unit (Sec 5)

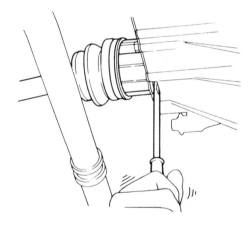

Fig. 13.27 Use of a screwdriver to release the driveshaft inner joint from the transmission (Sec 5)

29 On manual transmission models remove the bolt securing the gearchange control rod to the transmission linkage and disconnect the support rod from the transmission bracket.
30 On automatic transmission models remove the two bolts, retaining clip and clevis pin securing the control cable to the transmission.
31 Disconnect the reversing light switch wires, the neutral wires (where fitted) and, on automatic transmission models, the inhibitor switch wires.
32 Remove the drain plug from the transmission and allow the oil, or automatic transmission fluid, to drain into a suitable container. Refit the plug after draining.
33 Remove the three bolts securing the left-hand side front

suspension lower balljoint to the transverse link. Remove the nut securing the steering tie-rod balljoint to the steering arm. Release the joint from the arm using a clamp claw separator. Pull the suspension assembly outwards and release the driveshaft inner joint from the transmission using a screwdriver or suitable lever. After removal place a suitable bar, such as a short length of broom handle, into the transmission to retain the differential side gears in position. Repeat this procedure for the right-hand driveshaft and suspension assembly.
34 Attach suitable chains or rope slings around the engine/transmission, or alternatively secure home made lifting brackets to the cylinder head and attach the chains on ropes to these. Secure the tackle to a hoist and just take the weight of the power unit.

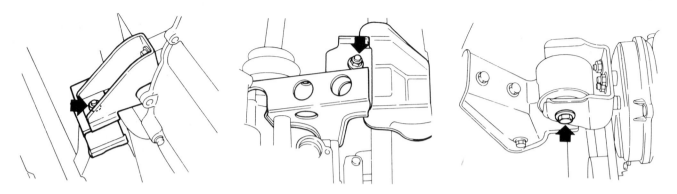

Fig. 13.28 Front, rear and right-hand side engine mounting retaining bolt locations (Sec 5)

35 Remove the nuts and through-bolts securing the front, rear, and right-hand side engine mounting brackets to the rubber insulator blocks.

36 Make a careful check above and below that all cables, wires, hoses and pipes have been disconnected and that all removed ancillaries are clear of the engine/transmission unit.

37 Carefully raise the unit until it is high enough to clear the front grille panel. Guide it clear of the car and lower the assembly to the ground.

Engine – separation from transmission

38 With the power unit removed from the car the transmission can be separated from the engine, according to type, as follows.

Manual transmission

39 Remove the two retaining bolts and lift off the starter motor.

40 Remove the bolts securing the engine steady brackets to the transmission casing.

41 Remove the bolts securing the clutch housing to the engine and carefully withdraw the transmission from the engine. Take care not to allow the weight of the transmission to hang unsupported on the input shaft.

Automatic transmission

42 Remove the converter housing dust cover.

43 Suitably mark the relationship of the torque converter to the driveplate to ensure correct refitment.

44 Turn the crankshaft by means of the front pulley bolt until one of the torque converter-to-driveplate retaining bolts is accessible through the dust cover in the same manner.

45 Remove the two retaining bolts and lift off the starter motor.

46 Remove the bolts securing the converter housing to the engine and carefully withdraw the transmission. Ensure that the torque converter stays in place on the transmission during removal. Do not remove or partially withdraw the torque converter from the transmission once the engine is removed. To ensure that it stays in position bolt a suitable bar across the face of the converter housing, using the engine-to-transmission bolt holes as attachment points.

PART B: DISMANTLING

Dismantling – general

1 It is best to mount the engine on a dismantling stand, but if one is not available, then stand the engine on a strong bench so as to be at a comfortable working height. Failing this, the engine can be stripped down on the floor.

2 During the dismantling process the greatest care should be taken to keep the exposed parts free from dirt. As an aid to achieving this, it is a sound scheme to thoroughly clean down the outside of the engine, removing all traces of oil and congealed dirt, if it has not been done already.

3 Use paraffin or a good grease solvent. The latter compound will make the job much easier, as, after the solvent has been applied and allowed to stand for a time, a vigorous jet of water will wash off the solvent and all the grease and filth. If the dirt is thick and deeply embedded, work the solvent into it with a wire brush.

4 Finally wipe down the exterior of the engine with a rag and only then, when it is quite clean, should the dismantling process begin. As

the engine is stripped, clean each part in a bath of paraffin or petrol.

5 Never immerse parts with oilways in paraffin, eg the crankshaft, but to clean, wipe down carefully with a petrol-dampened rag. Oilways can be cleaned out with wire. If an air line is present all parts can be blown dry and the oilways blown through as an added precaution.

6 Re-use of old engine gaskets is false economy and can give rise to oil and water leaks, if nothing worse. To avoid the possibility of trouble after the engine has been reassembled **always** use new gaskets throughout.

7 Do not throw the old gaskets away as it sometimes happens that an immediate replacement cannot be found and the old gasket is then very useful as a template. Hang up the old gaskets as they are removed on a suitable hook or nail.

8 To strip the engine it is best to work from the top down. The sump provides a firm base on which the engine can be supported in an upright position. When the stage where the sump must be removed in an upright position. When the stage where the sump must be removed is reached, the engine can be turned on its side and all other work carred out with it in this position.

9 Wherever possible, refit nuts, bolts and washers finger tight fom wherever they were removed. This helps avoid later loss and muddle. If they cannot be refitted then lay them out in such a fashion that it is clear from where they came.

Ancillary components – removal

10 With the engine removed from the car and separated from the transmission, the ancillary components should now be removed before dismantling of the engine unit commences.

11 **Alternator:** Remove the bolts securing the alternator to its mounting bracket and to the adjusting arm. Lift off the alternator and also remove the adjusting arm from its attachment on the front of the engine. Recover the drivebelt.

12 **Distributor:** Detach the spark plug leads from the spark plugs and, where emission control equipment is fitted, detach the distributor vacuum advance and retard hoses. Suitably mark the relationships of the distributor flange to the thermostat housing, remove the retaining nut and washer and withdraw the distributor.

13 **Emission control equipment:** The type and number of components fitted will vary according to model and export territory. Reference should be made to Chapter 3 and also Section 7 of this Chapter for details and removal procedures.

14 **Water pump:** Remove the four bolts and lift off the pulley. Remove the five bolts and withdraw the pump together with the gasket.

15 **Thermostat housing:** Remove the retaining bolts, noting the different lengths and ease the housing from its location at the rear of the cylinder head. Recover the gasket.

16 **Oil filter:** Unscrew the oil filter, using a strap wrench if it is tight, from the side of the cylinder block. Have some old rags handy as there is likely to be some oil spillage.

17 **Oil pump:** Remove the bolts and nuts securing the pump to the cylinder block and withdraw the unit.

18 **Fuel pump:** Remove the two nuts and lift away the pump. Note the arrangement of gaskets and spacer block where fitted.

19 **Exhaust manifold:** First remove the three bolts securing the heat box to provide access to the retaining nuts. Unscrew these and

withdraw the manifold. Note that the centre retaining nut is of a larger diameter than the others.

20 **Inlet manifold**: Remove the retaining nuts and lift off the manifold, complete with carburettor.

21 **Clutch assembly**: On cars with manual transmission progressively remove, in a diagonal sequence, the clutch cover retaining bolts. Lift away the cover assembly and the clutch disc.

Timing belt – removal and refitting (engine in car)

22 Disconnect the battery negative (–) terminal.

23 On models equipped with air conditioning slacken the idler pulley locknut then unscrew the adjusting bolt until the drivebelt can be slipped off the pulleys.

24 On models equipped with power steering slacken the pump upper mounting bolt and the adjuster lockbolt. Unscrew the adjuster until the drivebelt can be slipped off the pulley.

25 Slacken the alternator mounting bolts and the adjusting arm bolt. Move the alternator toward the engine and lift off the drivebelt. Remove the alternator adjusting arm from its mounting on the front of the engine.

26 Remove the four bolts and withdraw the water pump pulley.

27 Spring back the retaining clips, or remove the two screws, and lift off the distributor cap.

28 Using a socket on the crankshaft pulley bolt, rotate the crankshaft until the notch on the pulley is aligned with the O-mark on the timing scale, and the distributor rotor arm is pointing toward the No 1 segment in the cap.

29 To prevent the crankshaft turning while the pulley bolt is undone, put the transmission in gear and securely apply the handbrake. Alternatively remove the starter motor and engage a screwdriver with the flywheel ring gear teeth. On automatic transmission models this can be done through the torque converter housing dust cover. Using a socket again, remove the crankshaft pulley retaining bolt and ease off the pulley using two screwdrivers as levers. If the pulley is very tight, draw it off with a two or three-legged puller.

30 Remove the retaining bolts and lift off the upper and lower timing belt covers. Recover the gasket.

31 Slacken the timing belt tensioner locknut and slacken the tensioner by inserting a screwdriver into the slot and turning clockwise. Hold the tensioner in this position and retighten the locknut.

32 Slide the timing belt off the three sprockets and tensioner.

33 Rotate the crankshaft and camshaft as necessary to align the timing marks. The mark on the crankshaft sprocket tooth must be adjacent to the mark on the lower face of the front cover. The mark on the camshaft must be adjacent to the mark on the upper face of the front cover.

34 With the crankshaft and camshaft sprockets correctly aligned slip on a new timing belt, making sure that it is taut along the jackshaft sprocket inside.

35 Slacken the tensioner locknut and allow the tensioner to tension the belt. Using a suitable bar or screwdriver, turn the camshaft sprocket a quarter of a turn to take up all the slack in the belt on the jackshaft side.

36 With a screwdriver inserted into the slot of the tensioner to hold it in position, tighten the tensioner locknut.

37 Rotate the crankshaft one complete turn and again bring the timing mark on the sprocket into alignment with the mark on the front cover. Check that the mark on the camshaft is also in alignment and not 'one tooth out' as is often the case after the tensioner is adjusted. If the marks are not aligned, remove the belt again, move it one tooth as necessary on the camshaft sprocket and repeat the procedure in paragraphs 35 to 37 inclusive.

38 The remainder of the reassembly is a straightforward reversal of the removal sequence. Observe the correct torque settings as shown in the Specifications and ensure that the alternator, power steering and air conditioning drivebelts (where applicable) are correctly tensioned as described at the beginning of this Chapter.

Cylinder head – removal (engine in car)

39 Remove the air cleaner as described in Section 7, and drain the cooling system as described in Section 6.

40 Refer to the previous Section and carry out the operations described in paragraphs 22 to 32 inclusive.

41 Mark the relationship of the distributor base to the thermostat

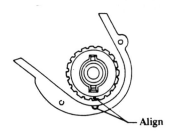

Fig. 13.29 Crankshaft sprocket and front cover valve timing marks in alignment (Sec 5)

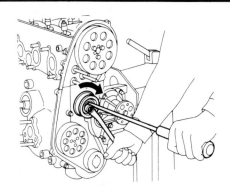

Fig. 13.31 Tighten the belt tensioner locknut while holding the tensioner with a screwdriver (Sec 5)

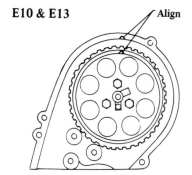
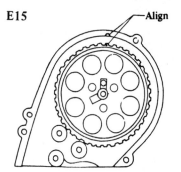

Fig. 13.30 Camshaft sprocket and front cover valve timing marks in alignment (Sec 5)

housing as a guide to refitment. Remove the spark plug leads and distributor retaining nut and withdraw the unit from the head.

42 Remove the exhaust manifold heat box.

43 From under the car detach the exhaust front pipe mounting from its retaining bracket.

44 Remove the nuts securing the exhaust manifold to the cylinder head, noting the larger diameter of the centre retaining nut.

45 Ease the exhaust manifold away from the cylinder head just sufficiently to clear the mounting studs and secure it in this position using a length of string or wire. On vehicles equipped with emission control equipment detach any hoses or pipes, as necessary, to allow sufficient movement of the manifold.

46 Remove the nuts securing the inlet manifold to the cylinder head. Ease the manifold, complete with carburettor, off the mounting studs and suitably support it just clear of the cylinder head. On models equipped with emission control equipment, detach any pipes, hoses or control units as necessary to enable the inlet manifold to be moved clear of the cylinder head. Also remove any equipment that may impede removal of the head from the engine. Make a careful note of the location of all disconnected items and where necessary refer to Chapter 3, or Section 7 of this Chapter.

47 Detach the radiator coolant and heater hoses from the thermostat housing.

48 Detach all electrical wires and connectors from the cylinder head, making a note of their locations.

49 Remove the two retaining nuts and washers and lift away the rocker cover and gasket.

50 Progressively loosen the cylinder head retaining bolts in two or three stages in the order shown in Fig. 13.32.

51 Remove the cylinder head bolts and lift the head off the engine. If it is stuck do not attempt to prise it off with a screwdriver, but tap it all round using a rubber or hide mallet. Remove the cylinder head gasket.

Cylinder head – removal (engine out of car)

52 The procedure for removing the cylinder head with the engine out of the car and on the bench is similar to that for removal when the engine is in the car, with the exception of disconnecting the controls and services. Refer to the previous section and follow the sequence given in paragraphs 39 to 51, as applicable.

Cylinder head – dismantling

53 With the cylinder head removed from the car and on the bench, remove the three retaining bolts and lift off the camshaft sprocket.

54 Remove the four screws securing the front cover to the head and withdraw the cover. Take care not to damage the oil seal lips.

55 Remove the bolts securing the rocker shaft assembly in position, noting the location of the two longer central studs and the positioning of the rockers and spacers. Lift the assembly off the cylinder head.

56 Carefully withdraw the camshaft, taking care not to scratch the bearing journals with the sharp edges of the cam lobes.

57 The valves can be removed from the cylinder head by the following method. Compress each spring in turn with a valve spring compressor until the two halves of the collet can be removed. Release the compressor and remove the retaining cap, spring and seat.

58 If, when the valve spring compressor is screwed down, the valve spring retaining cap refuses to free to expose the slit collet, do not continue to screw down on the compressor as there is a likelihood of damaging it.

59 Gently tap the top of the tool directly over the cap with a light hammer. This will free the cap. To avoid the compressor jumping off the valve spring retaining cap when it is tapped, hold the compressor firmly in position with one hand.

60 Slide the rubber oil control seal off the top of each valve stem and then drop out each valve through the combustion chamber.

61 It is essential that the valves are kept in their correct sequence unless they are so badly worn that they are to be renewed.

Sump – removal

62 If not already done, remove the sump drain plug and drain the oil into a suitable container. Refit the plug after draining.

63 Turn the engine on its side and remove the sump retaining bolts. Lift away the sump and recover the gaskets.

64 The gauze strainer and oil suction pipe are now exposed and can be detached by removing the two flange retaining bolts.

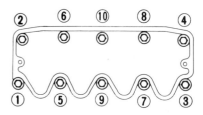

Fig. 13.32 Cylinder head bolt loosening sequence (Sec 5)

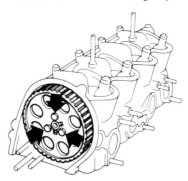

Fig. 13.33 Camshaft sprocket retaining bolts (Sec 5)

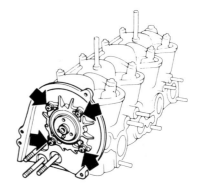

Fig. 13.34 Cylinder head front cover retaining screws (Sec 5)

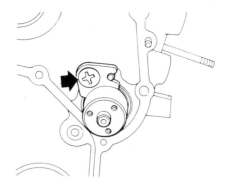

Fig. 13.35 Jackshaft locating plate and retaining screw (Sec 5)

Jackshaft – removal

65 Remove the three retaining bolts and withdraw the jackshaft sprocket.

66 Withdraw the crankshaft timing sprocket and spacer.

67 Remove the front cover retaining bolts and lift off the front cover and gasket. Recover the oil slinger from the front of the crankshaft, noting which way it is fitted.

68 Remove the retaining screw and take out the jackshaft locating plate.

69 Carefully slide the jackshaft out of its bearings in the cylinder block.

Flywheel and rear oil seal — removal

70 Using a suitable socket and bar, remove the six bolts securing the flywheel, or driveplate, to the crankshaft. Insert a suitable block of wood between one of the crankshaft throws and the cylinder block to prevent the crankshaft turning as the bolts are undone.

71 Lift off the flywheel, or driveplate, followed by the engine backplate.

72 The three screws securing the rear oil seal retainer can now be removed and the retainer, complete with oil seal, lifted away.

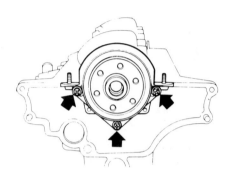

Fig. 13.36 Rear oil seal retainer securing screws (Sec 5)

Pistons and connecting rods — removal

73 With the cylinder head and sump removed, undo the big-end retaining bolts.

74 The connecting rods and pistons are lifted out from the top of the cylinder block, after the carbon or 'wear' ring at the top of the bore has been scraped away.

75 Remove the big-end caps one at a time, taking care to keep them in the right order and the correct way round. Also ensure that the shell bearings are kept with their correct connecting rods and caps unless they are to be renewed. Normally, the numbers 1 to 4 are stamped on adjacent sides of the big-end caps and connecting rods, indicating which cap fits on which rod and which way round the cap fits. If no numbers or lines can be found, then, with a sharp screwdriver or file, scratch mating marks across the joint from the rod to the cap. One line for connecting rod No. 1, two for connecting rod No 2 and so on. This will ensure there is no confusion later as it is most important that the caps go back in the correct position on the connecting rods from which they were removed.

76 If the big-end caps are difficult to remove they may be gently tapped with a soft hammer.

77 To remove the shell bearings, press the bearing opposite the groove in the connecting rod and the connecting rod caps, and the bearings will slide out easily.

78 Withdraw the pistons and connecting rods upwards and ensure they are kept in the correct order for refitting in the same bore. Refit the connecting rod caps to the rods to prevent the caps and rods getting mixed up. Keep the bearing shells with their respective rods and cap if they are to be re-used.

Piston rings — removal

79 If the same piston rings are to be refitted, care must be taken that the rings are not broken when being removed. Starting with the top ring (all rings must be removed from the top of the piston), ease one end out of its groove and place a thin piece of metal (eg an old feeler blade) behind it.

80 Then move the metal strip carefully behind the ring, at the same time easing the ring upward so that it rests on the surface of the piston above the grooves, until the whole ring is clear and can be slid off. With the second and third rings which must come off from the top, arrange the strip of metal to carry them over the other grooves.

81 Identify the rings so that they can be refitted to the same pistons, by piercing a piece of paper with each ring, showing its location, top 1, middle 1, etc.

Gudgeon pins — removal

82 The gudgeon pins are an interference fit in the connecting rod small-ends.

83 To separate the pistons from the connecting rods considerable

pressure is required to press out the gudgeon pins and this requires a proper press. Attempts with other methods will probably result in bent connecting rods or broken pistons. Therefore this is a job best left to your local Datsun dealer, as in the event of new pistons being needed it is necessary to heat the connecting rod when refitting the gudgeon pins and this requires experience to prevent distortion of the connecting rod.

Main bearings and crankshaft — removal

84 Gradually slacken the main bearing cap retaining bolts in two or three stages in the sequence shown in Fig. 13.37. Ensure that each main bearing cap is numbered 1 to 5, starting at the timing belt end and that arrows pointing toward the timing belt end of the engine are present. If these identification marks are not visible, mark the caps to ensure correct orientation when refitting.

85 Withdraw the main bearing bolts followed by the caps, complete with shells.

86 Lift the crankshaft out of the cylinder block and remove the main bearing upper halves.

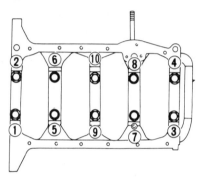

Fig. 13.37 Main bearing cap retaining bolt loosening sequence (Sec 5)

Lubrication system — description

87 The engine lubrication system is of the pressure feed type, oil being circulated by a rotor type pump mounted on the right-hand side of the engine and driven in by a skew gear from the jackshaft.

88 Oil is drawn from the sump through a filter screen and tube by the pump, whereby the oil passes through a full-flow filter to the main crankshaft oil gallery.

89 The main oil gallery supplies oil to the crankshaft main and big-end bearings through drillings, and a regulated quantity of oil, ejected from small holes in the connecting rods, lubricates the gudgeon pins and cylinder walls.

90 The jackshaft and camshaft are lubricated with oil from the main gallery. The rocker shaft and valve gear obtain their lubrication through a drilling from the camshaft centre bearing.

Oil pump — inspection and servicing

91 Having removed the oil pump, as previously described, unscrew and remove the bolts securing the pump cover to the pump body.

92 Withdraw the outer rotor from the pump body.

93 Remove the oil pressure regulator cap, washer, spring and valve.

94 Thoroughly clean all the parts in paraffin, or a suitable solvent, and dry with a lint-free cloth or air line.

95 Examine all the parts for damage, scoring or excessive wear. Check the inner rotor shaft for looseness in the pump body and the skew gear for wear or ridging of the teeth.

96 Check the following clearances using a feeler gauge and straight edge:

(a) Side clearance between inner and outer rotors
(b) Clearance between outer rotor and pump body
(c) Rotor tip clearance
(d) Gap between body and rotor

If the clearances exceed the limits given in the Specifications at the beginning of this Chapter, the pump must be renewed as a complete assembly as individual parts are not available.

97 Reassembly of the pump is the reverse of the dismantling procedure. Ensure that all the parts are thoroughly lubricated with clean engine oil during reassembly.

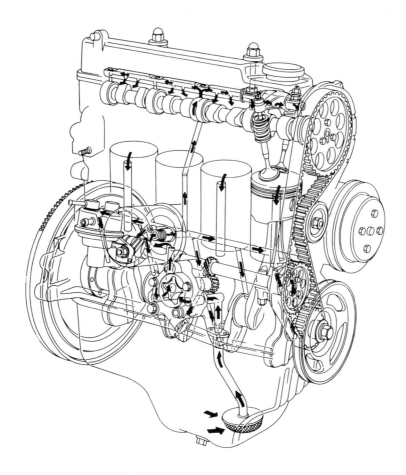

Fig. 13.38 Engine lubrication circuit diagram (Sec 5)

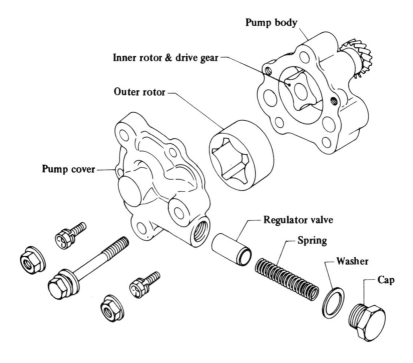

Pump body

Inner rotor & drive gear

Outer rotor

Pump cover

Regulator valve

Spring

Washer

Cap

Fig. 13.39 Exploded view of the oil pump components (Sec 5)

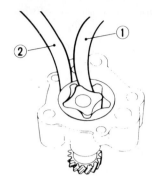

Fig. 13.40 Check the oil pump rotor tip clearance (1) and body-to-outer rotor clearance (2) (Sec 5)

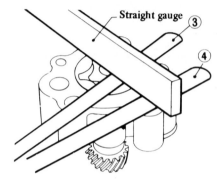

Fig. 13.41 Check the oil pump rotor side clearance (3) and gap between body and rotor (4) (Sec 5)

PART C: INSPECTION AND RENOVATION

1   Owing to the similarities between the internal components of the E-series engines and the earlier A-series units, the procedures for inspection and renovation are the same as described in Chapter 1, Sections 23 to 35 inclusive, with the exception of Sections 32 and 34. Where reference is made to sizes, clearance and tolerances the Specifications at the beginning of this Chapter should be consulted.
2   Additionally the following components must be inspected.

Jackshaft and jackshaft bearings
3   The procedure for inspection and renovation is the same as described for the camshaft in Chapter 1.

Timing belt, tensioner and sprockets
4   Carefully inspect the timing belt for signs of cracks or fraying and for indications of wear, particularly around the teeth. Renew the belt if doubtful about its condition.
5   Check for wear around the teeth of the drive sprockets.
6   Check that the tensioner turns smoothly with no sign of roughness or excessive free play. Renew if necessary.

Oil seals
7   It is a good idea to renew all the engine oil seals as a matter of course. Tap out the old seals using a tube of suitable diameter and refit the new seals in the same manner. Note the direction of each seal and make sure the new seals are fitted the same way.

PART D: REASSEMBLY

Engine reassembly – general
1   Before commencing reassembly ensure that all parts have been thoroughly cleaned, with all traces of old gaskets removed and all oilways and passages clear.
2   During reassembly liberally lubricate all bearing and other working surfaces with clean engine oil. Make sure that where applicable all nuts and bolts are tightened to the specified torque settings.
3   Apart from the normal tools, a supply of clean rags, an oil can filled with clean engine oil, a torque wrench, new gaskets and a tube of jointing compound should be available.

Cylinder head – reassembly
4   Using a tube of suitable diameter, install the valve stem oil seals in position over the valve guides.
5   Lubricate the valve stems and fit the valves into their respective guides in the cylinder head.
6   Fit a valve spring seat, spring and spring retainer to each valve. Where the valve springs are of the uneven pitch type, the narrow coils must be towards the cylinder head.
7   Fit the valve spring compressor over the valve head and compress the spring until the collets can be fitted to the grooves in the valve stem. Release the compressor and repeat for the remaining valves. When all the collets have been fitted, tap the valve stems with a soft-faced mallet to seat all the parts.
8   Liberally lubricate the camshaft bearings and bearing journals and carefully insert the camshaft into the cylinder head.
9   Lubricate the sealing lip of the front cover oil seal and place the cover in position. Take care not to damage the oil seal on the camshaft journal. Secure the front cover with the four retaining screws.
10 Refit the camshaft sprocket and retaining bolts.
11 Lubricate the rocker shaft and internal bore of each rocker and assemble the rockers to the shaft. Place the spacers and retaining bolts in position, noting that the oil hole in the shaft faces downward and the cut-out in the centre spacer faces the exhaust manifold side of the cylinder head when installed.
12 Lower the assembled shaft into the cylinder head and tighten the retaining bolts to the specified torque.
13 The valve clearances can now be adjusted using the procedure described later in this Section. Note that this is only an initial setting to allow the engine to be started. A final adjustment must be carried out with the engine hot.
14 Turn the camshaft by means of the sprocket until the timing mark on the sprocket aligns with the mark on the front cover. In this position valve numbers 1, 2, 3 and 6 can be adjusted. To adjust valves 4, 5, 7 and 8 turn the camshaft through 180° so that the timing mark on the sprocket is facing downwards, and repeat the valve clearance adjustment procedure.
15 After adjustment, turn the camshaft back so that the timing marks are aligned prior to refitting the cylinder head to the engine.

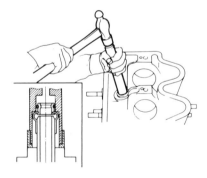

Fig. 13.42 Use a hammer and suitable tube to install the valve stem oil seals (Sec 5)

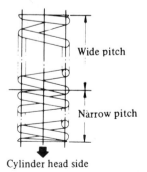

Fig. 13.43 Correct positioning of uneven pitch type valve springs (Sec 5)

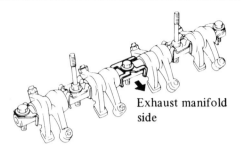

Fig. 13.44 Cut-out in rocker shaft centre spacer must face exhaust manifold when fitted (Sec 5)

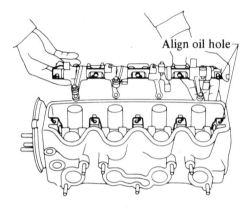

Fig. 13.45 Oil hole in rocker shaft must face downward when fitted (Sec 5)

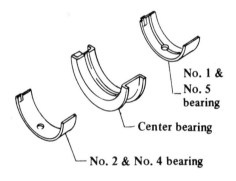

Fig. 13.46 Main bearing shell identification (Sec 5)

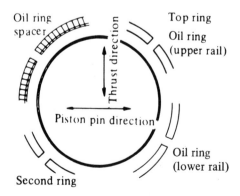

Fig. 13.48 Piston ring gap arrangement (Sec 5)

Crankshaft and main bearings – refitting

16 Install the bearing shells into their crankcase locations and also into the bearing caps. Note that the centre bearing shell is the flanged type, bearings number one and five have an oil groove, and bearings number two and four are plain.

17 Liberally lubricate the bearing shells, and lower the crankshaft into position in the crankcase. Fit the main bearing caps, complete with shells, in their original locations with the figure stamped on the cap toward the front of the engine.

18 Refit the bearing cap retaining bolts and tighten the bolts progressively in two or three stages, in the sequence shown in Fig. 13.47, to the specified torque setting.

19 Check that the crankshaft rotates smoothly, and recheck the crankshaft endfloat.

Pistons and connecting rods – refitting

20 The pistons, piston rings, and connecting rods, having been assembled with new big-end bearings and gudgeon pins as required, can now be fitted in the cylinders. Arrange the piston ring gaps as shown in Fig. 13.48. Liberally lubricate the rings and pistons. Fit a piston ring compressor on the piston to compress the rings and insert the connecting rod and piston into the cylinder bore. Ensure that it is the correct piston/connecting rod assembly for that particular bore and that the mark stamped on the piston head faces to the front of the engine.

21 The piston will slide into the cylinder only as far as the piston ring clamp. Gently tap the piston into the bore with a hammer shaft. This should drive the piston and rod assembly into the bore. If this action does not have the desired effect then either the piston rings have not been sufficiently compressed with the piston ring compressor, or the connecting rod has jammed on the crankshaft.

22 Connect each big-end to its appropriate crankshaft journal and fit the big-end cap complete with shells. The caps and rods are numbered 1 to 4 commencing at the timing gear end of the engine and when correctly fitted will have the cap and rod numbers adjacent. Tighten the big-end bolt nuts to the torque given in the Specifications. Use plenty of oil when fitting the connecting rods to the crankshaft and turn the crankshaft so that each big-end bearing is engaged when the respective crankshaft journal is at its lowest point.

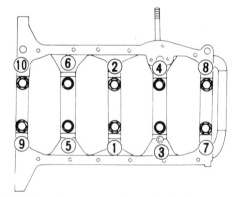

Fig. 13.47 Tightening sequence for main bearing cap retaining bolts (Sec 5)

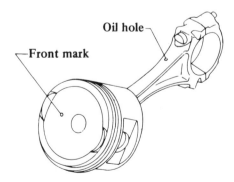

Fig. 13.49 Correct orientation of piston/connecting rod assemblies. The mark on the piston crown must face the front of the engine (Sec 5)

Flywheel and rear oil seal — refitting

23 Lubricate the sealing lip of the rear oil seal and also the rear boss of the crankshaft.

24 Place a new gasket on the oil seal retainer and fit the retainer and seal to the rear face of the crankcase. Take care not to damage the lip of the seal when fitting.

25 Refit the seal retainer securing bolts and tighten fully.

26 With the engine backplate in position, place the flywheel, or driveplate, on the crankshaft boss and refit the retaining bolts. With a block of wood preventing the crankshaft turning, tighten the retaining bolts to the specified torque setting.

Jackshaft — refitting

27 Lubricate the jackshaft bearings and bearing journals and carefully insert the jackshaft into the cylinder block. Refit the locating plate and secure with the retaining bolt.

28 Refit the crankshaft oil slinger, followed by the front cover with new gasket. Tighten the cover bolts to the specified torque.

29 Place the crankshaft timing sprocket on the crankshaft, noting that the recessed side must face the engine.

30 Refit the jackshaft sprocket and secure with the three bolts. Temporarily refit the timing belt tensioner ensuring that the spring tang engages with the locating hole. Refit the retaining nut.

Sump — refitting

31 Refit the oil strainer and suction pipe, using a new gasket between the pipe flange and crankcase. Tighten the bolts to the specified torque.

32 Position new front and rear half-seals into their location in the sump, holding them in place with a little jointing compound. Smear jointing compound along the sump side flanges and particularly over the edges of the half-seals. Lay the two sump gaskets in place.

33 Position the sump on the crankshaft, taking care not to dislodge the gaskets. Refit the retaining bolts and progressively tighten them, in a diagonal sequence and in at least three stages, to the specified torque setting.

Cylinder head — refitting

34 With the cylinder head assembled, as previously described, turn the camshaft sprocket until the timing mark on the sprocket is aligned with the mark on the front cover.

35 Lubricate each cylinder bore with engine oil and then turn the crankshaft until pistons No 1 and 4 are at TDC and the timing mark on the crankshaft sprocket is aligned with the mark on the front cover.

36 Wipe away all traces of oil and grease from the mating faces of the cylinder block and head. Ensure both surfaces are spotlessly clean.

37 Place a new cylinder head gasket in position on the block face, with the identification markings facing upward. Do not use any jointing compound on the gasket on block and head faces.

38 Carefully lower the cylinder head onto the gasket and refit the retaining bolts.

39 Tighten the cylinder head bolts in two stages to the specified torque setting in the sequence shown in Fig. 13.54. Refit the rocker cover.

40 The timing belt can now be refitted using the procedure described earlier in this Chapter.

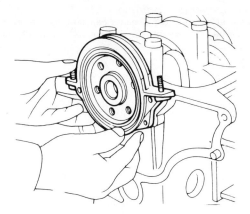

Fig. 13.50 Refitting the rear oil seal and retainer (Sec 5)

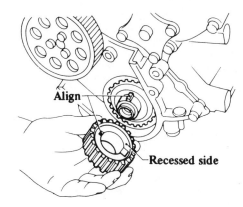

Fig. 13.51 The recessed side of the crankshaft sprocket must be toward the engine (Sec 5)

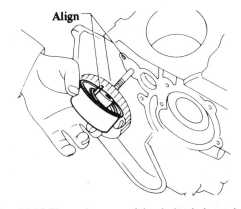

Fig. 13.52 The spring tang of the timing belt tensioner must engage with the locating hole (Sec 5)

○ : Sealing points

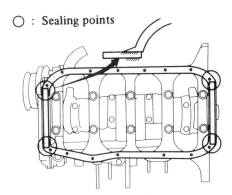

Fig. 13.53 Apply jointing compound as shown before fitting the sump (Sec 5)

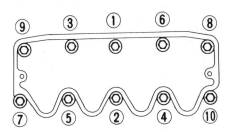

Fig. 13.54 Cylinder head tightening sequence (Sec 5)

Ancillary components – refitting

41 The following ancillary components can now be refitted to the engine using the reverse of the previously described removal procedure:

(a) Clutch assembly
(b) Inlet manifold and carburettor
(c) Exhaust manifold
(d) Fuel pump
(e) Oil pump
(f) Oil filter
(g) Thermostat housing
(h) Water pump
(i) Emission control equipment
(j) Distributor
(k) Alternator

Where applicable ensure that new gaskets are used, and that the correct torque settings are observed. if necessary reference should be made to the more detailed refitting procedures contained in the relevant section of this Chapter, and in earlier Chapters of this manual.

Engine – refitting to transmission

42 This is a straightforward reverse of the separation procedure contained in Part A of this Chapter.

Engine – refitting

43 This is also a reversal of the removal procedure contained in Part A of this Chapter, but the following points should be noted.

(a) Refill the radiator with coolant, as described in Chapter 2
(b) Refill the sump with the correct grade of engine oil
(c) Refill the transmission with the correct grade of lubricant as described at the beginning and in Section 10 of this Chapter
(d) Ensure that all drivebelts are correctly tensioned
(e) Adjust the accelerator and choke cables, as described in Section 7 of this Chapter
(f) Observe the correct torque settings where applicable

Engine – adjustments after major overhaul

44 With the engine refitted to the car give a final visual check to see that everything has been reconnected and that no loose rags or tools have been left within the engine compartment.
45 Restarting the engine may take a little longer than usual as the fuel pump and carburettor will be empty and need initial filling.
46 As soon as the engine starts, push the choke in (manual choke models) until the engine runs at a fast tickover. Check the engine for leaks particularly at water hose, fuel line and oil filter unions.
47 Where the engine has reached normal operating temperature adjust the valve clearances, as described in the following Section.
48 After the car has been taken for a road test and any necessary minor adjustments carried out, the cylinder head bolts must be retorqued. This should be done with the engine hot. Undo each head bolt, one at a time in the sequence shown in Fig. 13.54, by half a turn, and retighten it to the correct torque setting.
49 After making final adjustments recheck and, if necessary, top up all fluid levels.

Valve clearances – adjustment

50 Valve clearance adjustment is carried out with the engine at normal operating temperature.
51 Remove the valve rocker cover and the distributor cap.
52 Turn the crankshaft over, by means of a socket on the crankshaft pulley bolt, until No 1 cylinder is at TDC on its firing stroke and the distributor rotor arm is pointing toward the No 1 spark plug lead segment in the cap.
53 With the engine in this position valve numbers 1, 2, 3 and 6 can be adjusted (Fig. 13.55). Note that the clearance is the same for both the inlet and exhaust valves.
54 To carry out the adjustment insert a feeler blade of the specified size between the stem of the valve and the adjusting screw of the rocker arm. Insert a screwdriver into the adjusting screw slot and release the locknut with a spanner. Tighten the adjusting screw until the feeler blade is a tight sliding fit, and tighten the locknut. Withdraw the feeler blade and repeat the procedure on the other three valves.
55 After adjusting valve Nos 1, 2, 3 and 6, turn the crankshaft one complete turn so that the distributor rotor arm is pointing towards No

4 spark plug lead segment in the distributor cap. Valve Nos 4, 5, 7 and 8 can be adjusted using the foregoing procedure.
56 After completing the adjustment, refit the rocker cover and distributor cap.

Engine mountings – renewal

57 The procedure for renewal of the engine mountings is basically the same as described in Chapter 1. Fig. 13.57 shows the location and method of attachment of the various mountings.

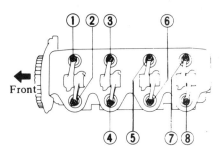

Fig. 13.55 Valve rocker identification (Sec 5)

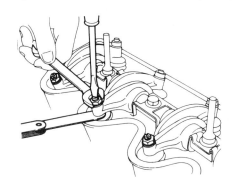

Fig. 13.56 Valve clearance adjustment (Sec 5)

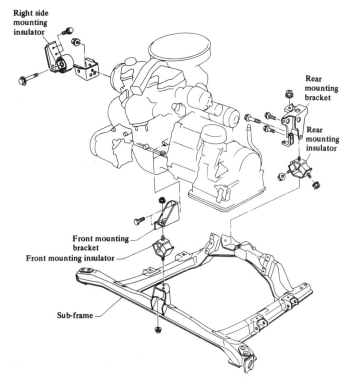

Fig. 13.57 Location and attachments of the engine mountings (Sec 5)

6 Cooling system

Cooling system – general

1   The cooling system consists of the radiator, top and bottom water hoses, water pump, cylinder head and block water jackets, radiator cap, thermostat, cooling fan and water heated inlet manifold. On models equipped with the E15 engine, an auxiliary fan is used to reduce under bonnet temperatures in particularly hot climates. This fan and the radiator cooling fan are activated by temperature sensing switches located in the radiator outlet adaptor.

2   The principles of operation of the cooling system are described in detail in Chapter 2, and only those components or procedures which are unique to E-series engine models are described in this Chapter.

Cooling system – draining, flushing and refilling

3   The procedures described in Chapter 2 are applicable to E-series engines, but it should be noted that a cylinder block drain plug is not provided.

Radiator – removal and refitting

4   Drain the cooling system, referring to Chapter 2 if necessary.

5   On models equipped with power steering, slacken the pump upper mounting bolt and the adjuster lockbolt. Unscrew the adjuster until the drivebelt can be slipped off the pulley. Remove the upper mounting

bolt and suspend the pump out of the way using string or wire. Do not disconnect the fluid hoses.

6   Disconnect the radiator upper and lower hoses and remove the lower hole adaptor.

7   On models equipped with automatic transmission, disconnect the fluid pipe unions at the base of the radiator. Plug, or tape over, the pipe unions to prevent fluid loss and dirt entry.

8   Disconnect the fan motor wiring harness connector.

9   Remove the radiator retaining bolts and carefully withdraw the radiator from the engine compartment.

10   Refitting is the reverse sequence to removal, bearing in mind the following points:

   (a) Refill the cooling system, as described in Chapter 2
   (b) On models equipped with power steering, adjust the drivebelt as detailed earlier in this Chapter
   (c) On models equipped with automatic transmission, top up the fluid level, as described in Section 10

Thermostat – general

11   The thermostat is located in a housing attached to the rear of the cylinder head. Access to the unit is gained after draining off a quantity of coolant, detaching the radiator upper hose and then removing the three housing cover bolts.

12   The description and the testing and refitting procedures described in Chapter 2 are also applicable to E-series engines.

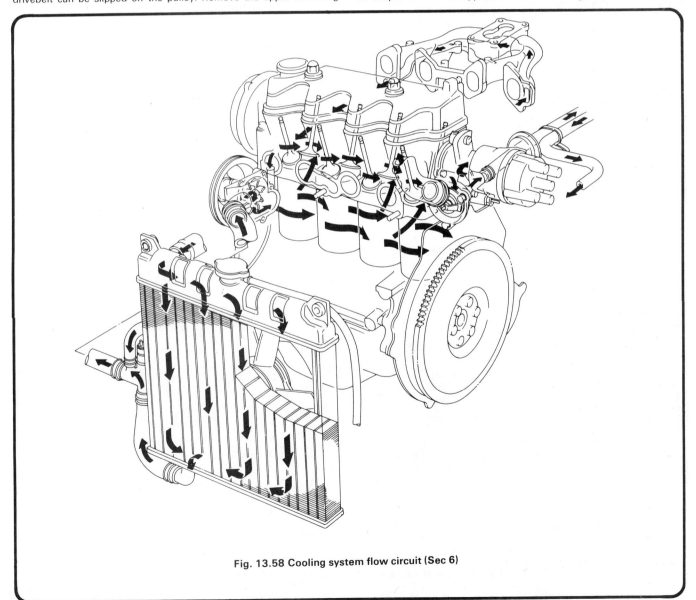

Fig. 13.58 Cooling system flow circuit (Sec 6)

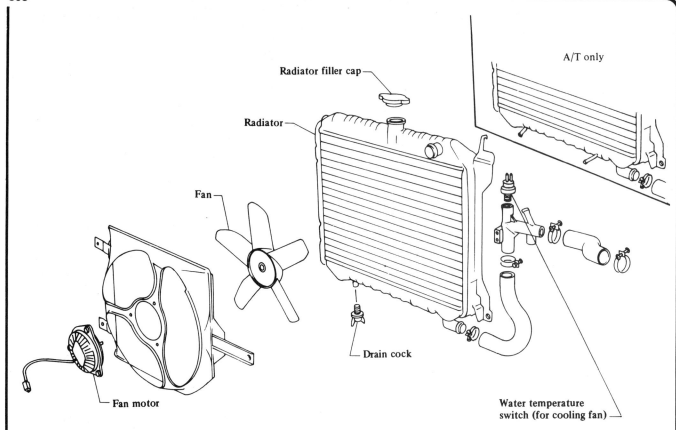

Radiator filler cap

A/T only

Radiator

Fan

Water temperature
switch (for cooling fan)

Drain cock

Fan motor

Fig. 13.59 Radiator and cooling fan assembly (Sec 6)

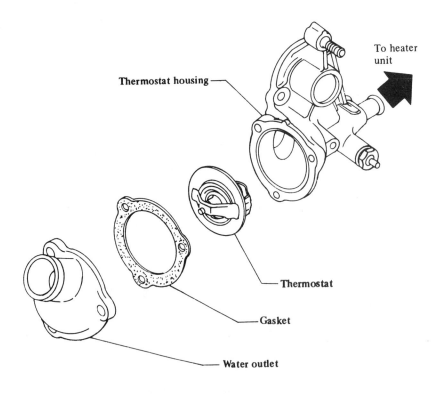

To heater
unit

Thermostat housing

Thermostat

Gasket

Water outlet

Fig. 13.60 The thermostat and housing components (Sec 6)

Water pump – removal and refitting

13 Drain the cooling system, as described previously.

14 On models equipped with power steering, slacken the pump upper mounting bolt and the adjuster lockbolt. Unscrew the adjuster until the drivebelt can be slipped off the pulley. Remove the upper mounting bolt and suspend the pump out of the way using string or wire. Do not disconnect the fluid hoses.

15 Slacken the bolts securing the alternator to its mounting bracket and to the adjusting arm. Move the alternator toward the engine and slip the drivebelt off the pulleys.

16 Remove the four bolts securing the water pump pulley to the pump and lift off the pulley.

17 Remove the five bolts securing the pump to the engine and withdraw the pump with gasket.

18 The water pump cannot be repaired and must therefore be renewed if there are any signs of coolant leakage from the gland, roughness or slackness of the bearings, excessive endfloat of the impeller shaft, or signs of corrosion on the body or impeller.

19 Refitting is the reverse sequence to removal, bearing in mind the following points:

(a) Ensure that the mating faces of the pump and engine are thoroughly clean, with all traces of old gasket when refitting

(b) Tighten the pump and pulley retaining bolts to the specified torque settings (see Chapter 2)

(c) Adjust the alternator and, where fitted, the power steering drivebelts, as detailed earlier in this Chapter

(d) Refill the cooling system, as detailed in Chapter 2

7 Fuel, exhaust and emission systems

PART A: FUEL AND EXHAUST SYSTEMS

Air cleaners – general

1 The standard air cleaner fitted to E10 and E13 engines is now equipped with an idle compensator. This device is a thermostatic valve which introduces air directly from the air cleaner to the inlet manifold to compensate for abnormal enrichment of the mixture at a high idling temperature. The idle compensator is also used on the air cleaner fitted to earlier A14 and A15 engines, and full details appear in Chapter 3.

2 The automatic temperature control (ATC) air cleaner fitted to E15

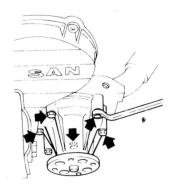

Fig. 13.61 Location of the water pump retaining bolts (Sec 6)

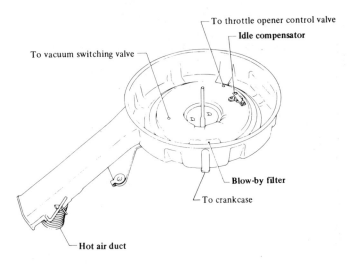

Fig. 13.62 The standard air cleaner as used on E10 and E13 engines (Sec 7)

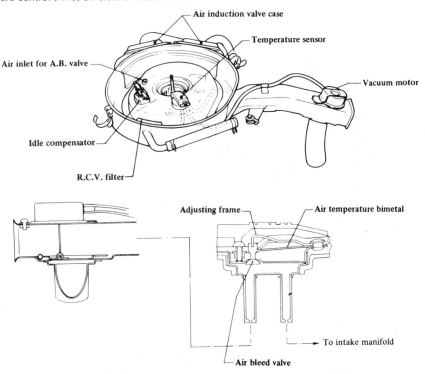

Fig. 13.63 The automatic temperature control (ATC) air cleaner as used on E15 engines (Sec 7)

engine models is also the same as used on A14 and A15 engines. Although slight relocation of the components within the air cleaner body has taken place, the description and checking procedures contained in Chapter 3 are still valid.

Fuel pump – general
3   A fuel pump of sealed design is used on E-series engines. The removal, refitting and checking procedures are as described in Chapter 3, however, the pump cannot be dismantled for repair and if faulty must be renewed.

Accelerator cable – adjustment
4   Although the removal and refitting procedure remains unchanged from earlier models, the method of adjustment differs slightly and is as follows.
5   When the cable is correctly adjusted there should be the specified amount of free play at the accelerator pedal, measured at the centre of the pedal pad.
6   If adjustment is necessary, disconnect the battery earth terminal and remove the air cleaner.
7   On automatic choke models open the choke flap by hand while turning the throttle lever so that the choke stays in the fully open position.
8   On all models, adjust the cable length by slackening the outer cable clamp at the carburettor, and moving the outer cable to give the necessary pedal free play.
9   After adjustment, refit the air cleaner and reconnect the battery.

Carburettor (E10 and E13 engines) – description
10   The Hitachi carburettor used on E10 and E13 engines is similar in design and operation to the DCG type described in Chapter 3. The main difference is the operation of the secondary throttle valve which is controlled by a vacuum diaphragm assembly. A dashpot is used on automatic transmission models to dampen the effect of sudden deceleration, and on certain models a servo diaphragm is linked to the primary throttle and controls exhaust emission during deceleration.

Idling speed and mixture (E10 and E13 engines) – adjustment
11   Run the engine until normal operating temperature is obtained, and then turn the throttle adjusting screw to obtain the specified idle speed.
12   Run the engine at 2000 to 3000 rpm for 30 seconds to clear the inlet manifold of excess fuel. Do this every 30 seconds during the following adjustment procedure.
13   Turn the idle adjusting screw as necessary to obtain the fastest possible speed consistent with even running. After adjustment reset the idle speed to the specified setting by means of the throttle adjusting screw.
14   On certain models the idle adjusting screw is covered by a metal 'tamperproof' cap. This is to prevent adjustment of the mixture by unauthorised persons in countries where strict emission control regulations are in force. Where legislation is not so stringent it is permissible to make adjustments; however, a special tool will be required. The tool is a screwdriver with a V slot cut in the blade and when inserted through the slot in the tamperproof cap, will locate in the adjusting screw. A tool specially made for this purpose is available from Dee and Jay Tools of Sheffield, England.

Carburettor (E10 and E13 engines) – removal and refitting
15   Removal and refitting procedures are the same as described in Chapter 3 for the DCG series carburettor.

Carburettor (E10 and E13 engines) – dismantling and reassembly
16   Dismantling and reassembly procedures are also as described in Chapter 3; however, reference should be made to Fig. 13.67 for details of the slight differences in component locations.

Float chamber fuel level (E10 and E13 engines) – checking and adjustment
17   The fuel level in the carburettor can be checked by viewing the float chamber sight glass. With the car standing on level ground, the

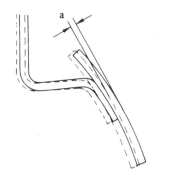
Fig. 13.64 Accelerator pedal free play (a) (Sec 7)

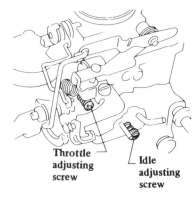
Fig. 13.65 Carburettor throttle and idle adjusting screws (Sec 7)

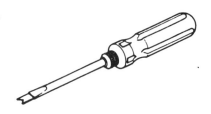
Fig. 13.66 Typical idle adjusting tool for use on carburettors with tamperproof adjusting screws (Sec 7)

fuel level should be up to the mark etched on the sight glass. If the level is too low or too high adjust as follows.
18   Remove the carburettor, as previously described.
19   Disconnect the choke connecting rod, accelerator pump lever and return spring.
20   Remove the retaining screws and carefully lift the carburettor choke chamber off the centre body. Take care not to damage the gasket.
21   Turn the choke chamber upside down and check that dimension 'H' in Fig. 13.68 with the float hanging under its own weight. Now move the float upwards to the full extent of its travel and check the dimension 'h' in Fig. 13.69. Adjustment to correct either of these dimensions is carried out by carefully bending the float stopper tag.

Interlock opening of primary and secondary throttle valves (E10 and E13 engines) – checking and adjustment
22   With the carburettor removed from the car, open the primary throttle until the adjusting plate on the linkage contacts the lock lever at point 'A' in Fig. 13.70. The clearance between the throttle valve and chamber wall can now be checked. Carefully bend the tongue of the adjusting plate if adjustment is required.

Fast idle (E10 and E13 engines) – adjustment
23   With the carburettor removed from the car, rotate the choke linkage so that the choke valve is fully closed.
24   Referring to Fig. 13.71, check the clearance between the primary

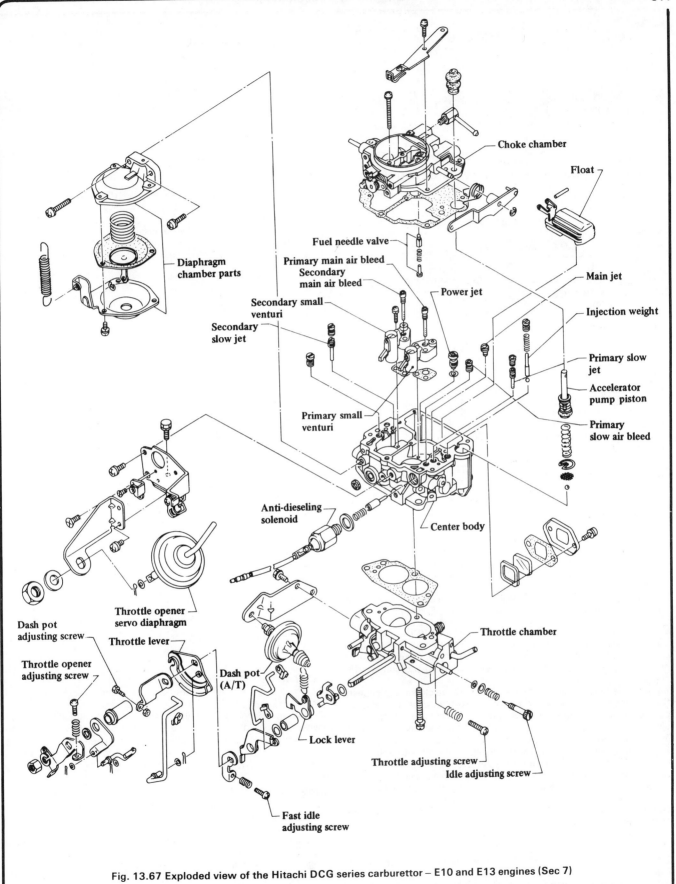

Fig. 13.67 Exploded view of the Hitachi DCG series carburettor – E10 and E13 engines (Sec 7)

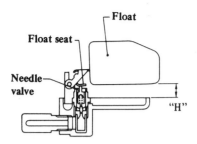

Fig. 13.68 Float level adjustment – E10 and E13 engines
(Sec 7)

H = 0.59 in (15.0 mm)

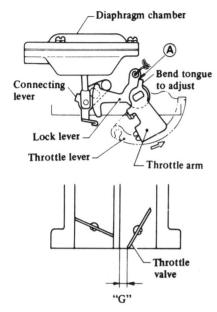

Fig. 13.70 Interlock opening adjustment clearance – E10 and E13
engines (Sec 7)

A Adjusting plate in contact with lock lever
G = 0.23 ± 0.012 in (5.87 ± 0.30 mm)

throttle valve and the chamber wall. Adjust as necessary, by turning
the fast idle adjusting screw, to achieve the specified dimension.

Dashpot (E10 and E13 engines) – adjustment
25 On models equipped with automatic transmission a dashpot may
be fitted to give a progressive closure of the throttle. Adjustment may
be carried out with the carburettor removed or in position on the
engine.
26 If the carburettor has been removed, check the clearance between
the primary throttle valve and chamber wall with the dashpot stem just
contacting the throttle arm. If the clearance is outside the specified
dimension range, slacken the dashpot locknut and screw the dashpot
in or out as necessary. Tighten the locknut after adjustment.
27 If the carburettor is in place on the engine, open the throttle valve
by hand with the engine running until the dashpot stem is just
contacting the throttle arm. At this point the engine speed should be
as shown in the Specifications. If adjustment is required, slacken the
locknut and screw the dashpot in or out as necessary. Tighten the
locknut and check that the engine speed drops smoothly from 2000 to
1000 rpm in approximately 2 seconds.

Carburettor (E15 engines) – description
28 The Hitachi DCR 306 series carburettor used on E15 engines is
identical to the unit described in Chapter 3 with the exception of the
jet sizes and minor settings. All carburettor operations described in
Chapter 3 are therefore applicable, but reference should be made to
the Specifications at the beginning of this Chapter for the relevant
dimensions and tolerances.

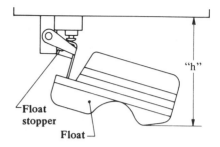

Fig. 13.69 Bottom float position – E10 and E13 engines
(Sec 7)

h = 1.77 in (45.0 mm)

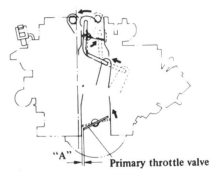

Fig. 13.71 Fast idle adjustment clearance – E10 and E13 engines
(Sec 7)

A = 0.054 ± 0.002 in (1.38 ± 0.07 mm)

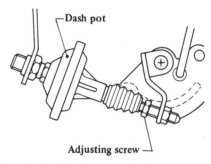

Fig. 13.72 Dashpot retaining and adjusting screws – E10 and E 13
models (Sec 7)

Exhaust system – general
29 The type of exhaust system fitted is dependent on the territory to
which the car was originally supplied and the accompanying
illustrations show the various types. Removal and refitting of the
system, or individual parts of the system, is quite straightforward and
follows the same procedure as described in Chapter 3.

PART B: EMISSION CONTROL SYSTEMS

Emission control systems – general
1 Three types of emission control systems are used; crankcase
emission control, exhaust emission control and an evaporative
emission control system.
2 To ensure that noxious emissions are kept to a minimum, periodic
inspection and servicing of these systems should be carried out.
Regular checks should also be made of the engine, ignition, fuel and
exhaust systems as these play an important part in reducing harmful
emissions.
3 The following Sections contain details of the three systems and
their associated components, some or all of which may be fitted,
depending on model and export territory.

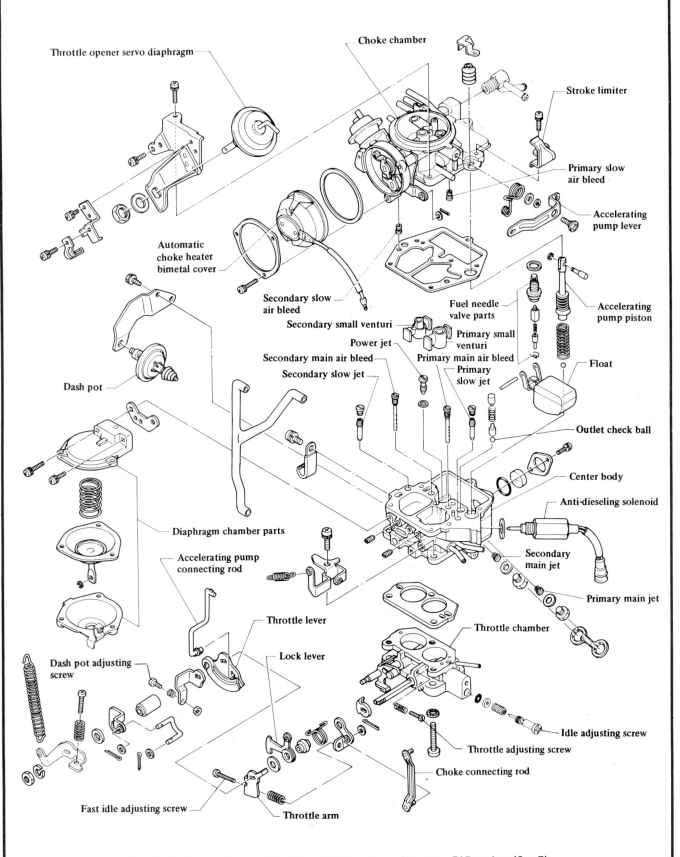

Fig. 13.73 Exploded view of the Hitachi DCR series carburettor – E15 engines (Sec 7)

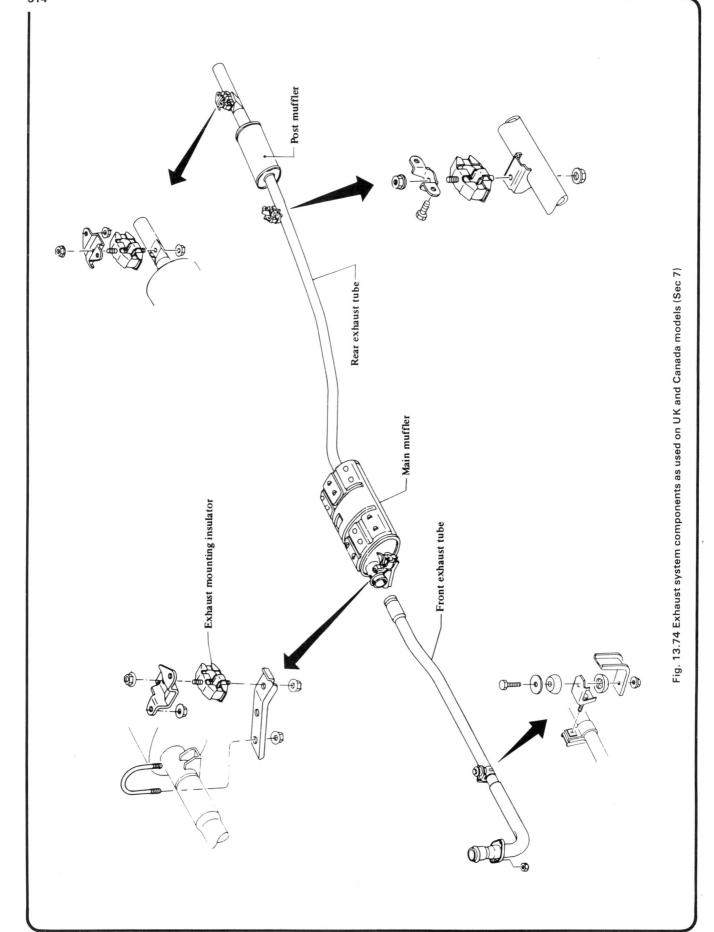

Fig. 13.74 Exhaust system components as used on UK and Canada models (Sec 7)

Post muffler

Rear exhaust tube

Main muffler

Exhaust mounting insulator

Front exhaust tube

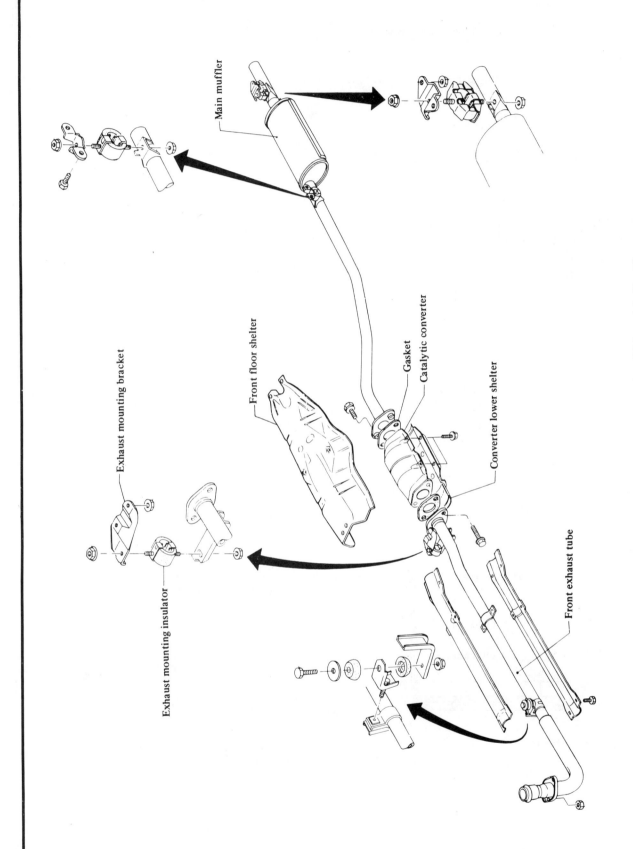

Main muffler

Front floor shelter

Exhaust mounting bracket

Exhaust mounting insulator

Gasket

Catalytic converter

Converter lower shelter

Front exhaust tube

Fig. 13.75 Exhaust system components as used on USA models (Sec 7)

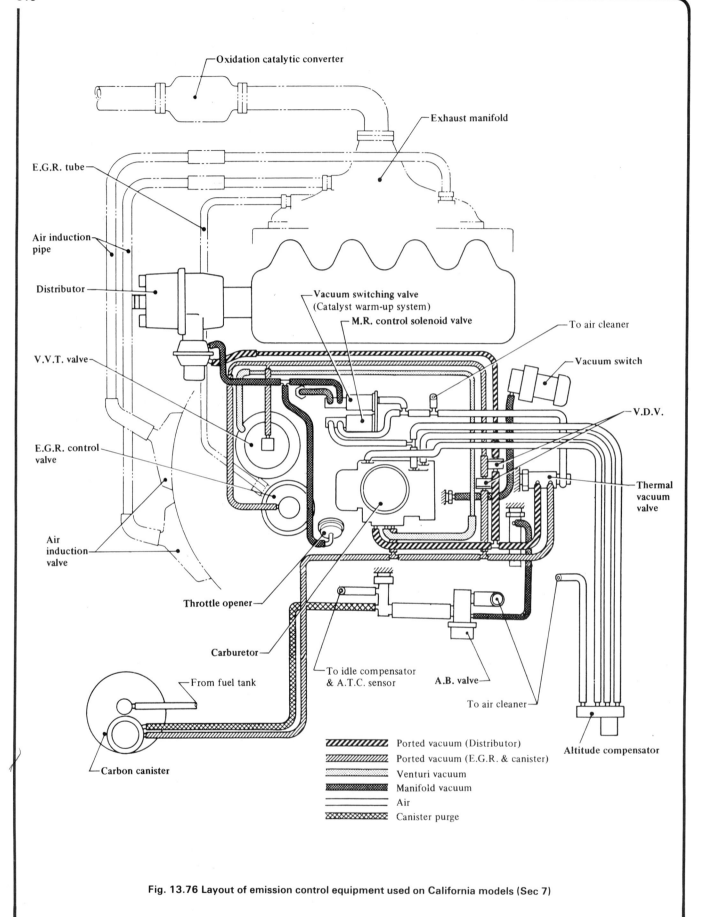

Oxidation catalytic converter

Exhaust manifold

E.G.R. tube

Air induction pipe

Distributor

Vacuum switching valve (Catalyst warm-up system)

M.R. control solenoid valve

To air cleaner

Vacuum switch

V.V.T. valve

V.D.V.

E.G.R. control valve

Thermal vacuum valve

Air induction valve

Throttle opener

Carburetor

To idle compensator & A.T.C. sensor

A.B. valve

To air cleaner

From fuel tank

Altitude compensator

Carbon canister

Ported vacuum (Distributor)
Ported vacuum (E.G.R. & canister)
Venturi vacuum
Manifold vacuum
Air
Canister purge

Fig. 13.76 Layout of emission control equipment used on California models (Sec 7)

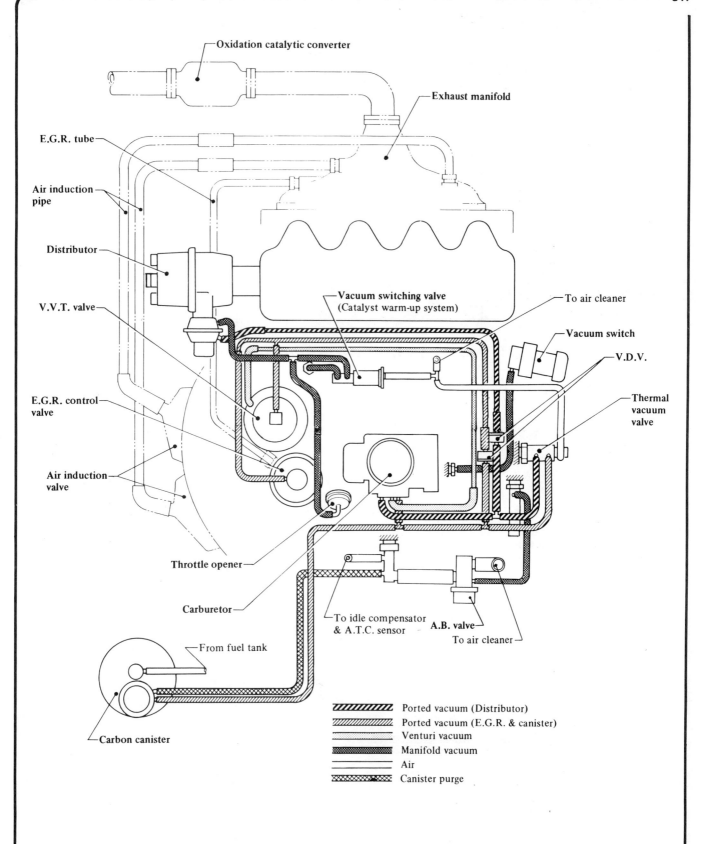

Oxidation catalytic converter

Exhaust manifold

E.G.R. tube

Air induction pipe

Distributor

Vacuum switching valve (Catalyst warm-up system)

To air cleaner

Vacuum switch

V.D.V.

V.V.T. valve

Thermal vacuum valve

E.G.R. control valve

Air induction valve

Throttle opener

Carburetor

To idle compensator & A.T.C. sensor

A.B. valve

To air cleaner

From fuel tank

Carbon canister

▨▨▨	Ported vacuum (Distributor)
▨▨▨	Ported vacuum (E.G.R. & canister)
▨▨▨	Venturi vacuum
▨▨▨	Manifold vacuum
──	Air
▨▨▨	Canister purge

Fig. 13.77 Layout of emission control equipment used on non-California models (Sec 7)

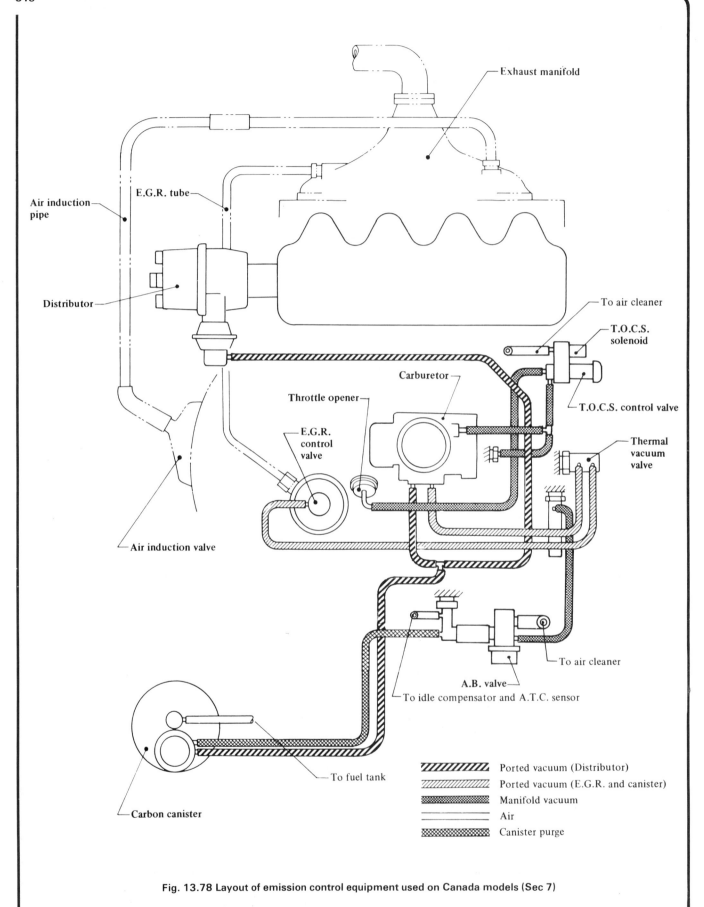

Fig. 13.78 Layout of emission control equipment used on Canada models (Sec 7)

Crankcase emission control system – description

4   This system returns crankcase fumes to both the air cleaner and inlet manifold under the control of a positive crankcase ventilation valve (PCV valve). Under partial throttle conditions the high manifold vacuum draws fumes from the crankcase through the valve and also fresh air from the air cleaner. The fresh air is drawn from the air cleaner through a connecting hose and into the rocker cover where it mixes with the crankcase fumes. Under conditions of low manifold vacuum such as during full throttle acceleration, the PCV valve will close and all crankcase fumes will pass through the connecting hose, in the reverse direction, to the air cleaner. On cars with excessively high crankcase pressure some of the fumes will pass to the air cleaner under all throttle conditions.

Exhaust emission control system – description

5   The exhaust emission control system consists of the following sub-systems, some or all of which are used, according to model and export territory:

   (a)   Air induction system (AIS)
   (b)   Exhaust gas recirculation system (EGR)
   (c)   Mixture ratio rich-lean exchange system
   (d)   Fuel shut-off system
   (e)   Catalyst warm-up system
   (f)   Spark timing control system
   (g)   Throttle opener control system (TOCS)
   (h)   Catalytic converter

6   In addition to the above sub-systems, the anti-dieseling solenoid, altitude compensator (if fitted) and temperature controlled air cleaner can be regarded as exhaust emission control items. These are described elsewhere in this Chapter, and in Chapter 3.

7   A brief description of the above listed systems and their functions is as follows.

Air induction system (AIS)

8   The function of the air induction system is to supply secondary air to the exhaust manifold during pulses of vacuum within the manifold. This then assists in reducing the harmful CO and HC exhaust emissions. The secondary air is supplied via the air induction valve and an interconnecting pipe from the air cleaner to the exhaust manifold. The air induction valve, which is a simple reed valve, is located in the air cleaner and opens to admit secondary air when the pressure in the

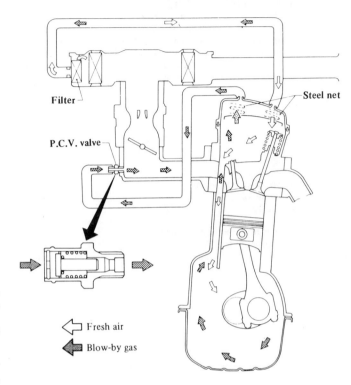

Fig. 13.79 Crankcase emission control system (Sec 7)

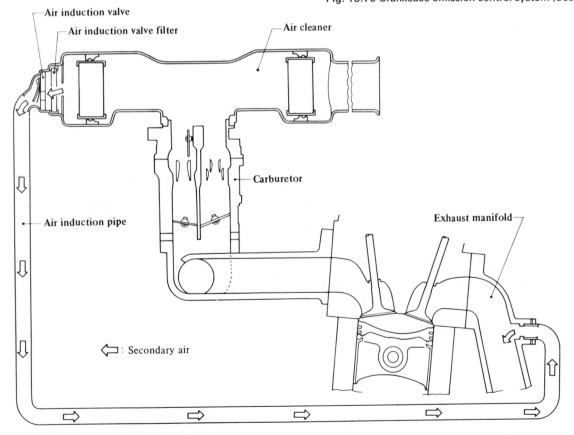

Fig. 13.80 Air induction system (AIS) (Sec 7)

exhaust system drops below atmospheric pressure. The system also incorporates an anti-backfire (AB) valve to prevent after burning in the exhaust system during initial moments of deceleration.

Exhaust gas recirculation system (EGR)
9   The function of this system is to lower the flame temperature during combustion, so reducing the nitrogen oxide content of the exhaust gases. This it achieves by returning a small amount of exhaust gas to the combustion chambers, the amount of gas being regulated by the EGR control valve. The gas being recirculated is directed to the inlet manifold and it is then drawn into the combustion chambers in the normal manner. A very complex system of vacuum and electrically operated valves is necessary to enable this system to function efficiently under all throttle and engine temperature conditions. The following are the valves and switches used for this purpose:

   (a)   *Exhaust gas recirculation (EGR) valve*
   (b)   *Venturi vacuum transducer (VVT) valve*
   (c)   *Thermal vacuum valve*
   (d)   *Vacuum delay valve*
   (e)   *Vacuum switching valve*
   (f)   *Vacuum switch*
   (g)   *One-way valve*

Mixture ratio rich-lean exchange system
10   This system controls the air/fuel mixture ratio in the carburettor to improve fuel economy and performance, whilst reducing harmful exhaust emissions. The operation of the system is dependent on the car's roadspeed and engine coolant temperature. A speed detecting switch and amplifier located in the speedometer operate a mixture ratio control solenoid valve which is interconnected with the engine coolant temperature switch. According to roadspeed and/or engine temperature the mixture ratio control solenoid valve regulates an airflow passage from the air cleaner to the carburettor main air bleed, thus regulating the mixture ratio.

Fuel shut-off system
11   The fuel shut-off system enables the fuel supply to be cut off during deceleration from high speeds, and is actuated by high manifold vacuum. The system works in conjunction with the anti-dieseling solenoid and the speed detecting switch described previously. When the vacuum within the inlet manifold drops below a certain level, the vacuum switch reactivates the anti-dieseling solenoid valve and the fuel flow is allowed to continue. Switches on the clutch and transmission and a number of electrical relays are also used on this system.

Catalyst warm-up system
12   This system is designed to increase engine speed during warm-up periods, thereby reducing exhaust emissions. This is achieved by an electrically operated vacuum switching valve which operates the throttle opener servo diaphragm on the carburettor, and also alters the ignition timing accordingly. The system is operated by water temperature switches in conjunction with a neutral switch on the transmission and associated relays. A vacuum delay valve is used in the distributor vacuum line to give a more progressive alteration of ignition timing.

Spark timing control system
13   This system utilizes a thermal vacuum valve and vacuum delay valve to control the distributor vacuum advance under varying conditions of engine speed and load. This effectively reduces exhaust emissions and also gives improved fuel economy. The system is controlled by engine coolant temperature and works in conjunction with the EGR system described previously.

Throttle opener control system (TOCS)
14   As this system is directly linked to the carburettor, reference should be made to the applicable section in Part A dealing with the E15 engine carburettor.

Catalytic converter
15   This device is fitted in the exhaust system and speeds up the chemical reaction of the hydrocarbons and carbon monoxide present in the gases, so that they change into harmless carbon dioxide and water.

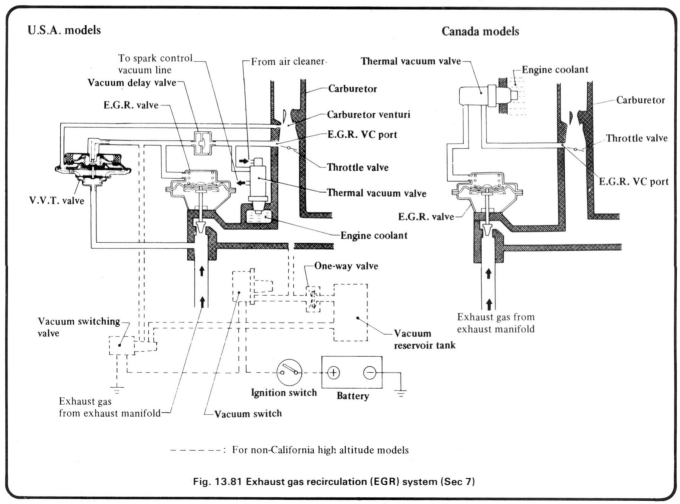

Fig. 13.81 Exhaust gas recirculation (EGR) system (Sec 7)

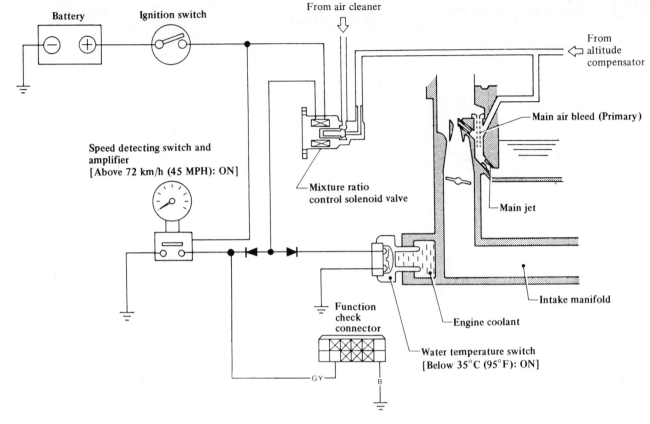

Fig. 13.82 Mixture ratio rich-lean control system (Sec 7)

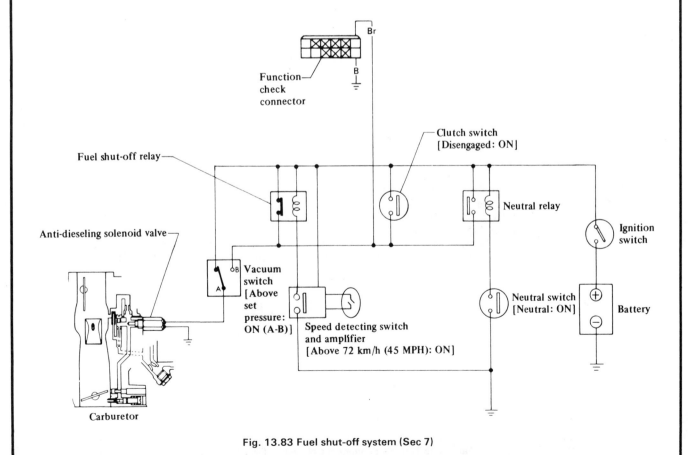

Fig. 13.83 Fuel shut-off system (Sec 7)

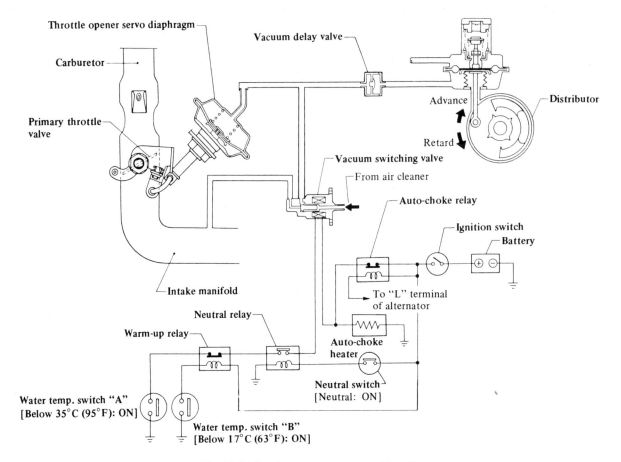

Fig. 13.84 Catalyst warm-up system (Sec 7)

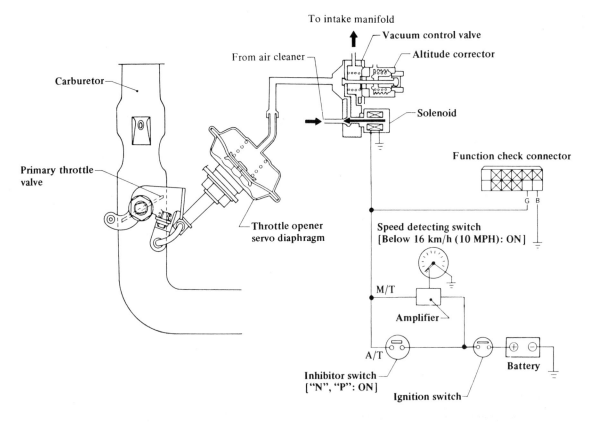

Fig. 13.85 Throttle opener control system (TOCS) (Sec 7)

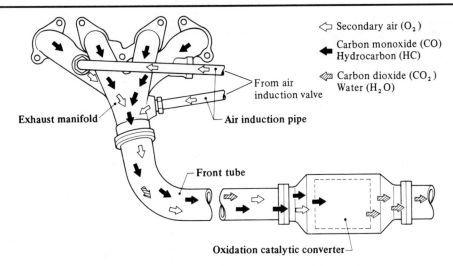

Secondary air (O₂)

Carbon monoxide (CO)
Hydrocarbon (HC)

Carbon dioxide (CO₂)
Water (H₂O)

Fig. 13.86 Catalytic converter (Sec 7)

Emission control system – maintenance and general procedures

16 The emission control components can only operate efficiently if the engine and its associated parts are in good condition and correctly adjusted. If the maintenance schedules given in the preliminary Sections of this manual and at the beginning of this Chapter are observed then this should be the case. In particular check that the valve clearances are correct, the fuel lines are secure and the fuel filter is changed at the specified mileage. The carburettor air filter and emission control air filters in the air cleaner must be renewed regularly and the carburettor correctly adjusted. In the ignition circuit, make sure that the distributor and ignition timing are in correct adjustment and that the spark plug electrode gaps are as specified.

17 Check that all emission control vapour lines and their respective connections are secure and in good condition.

18 Renew the positive crankcase ventilation (PCV) valve filter at the prescribed mileage/time interval and check the valve for correct operation.

19 Renew the air induction valve filter at the prescribed mileage/time interval and check the operation of the valve, and also the anti-backfire valve.

20 Thoroughly check all the hoses, connections, fittings and components of the exhaust gas recirculation (EGR) system for damage or deterioration. Check also the operation of the EGR valve and thermal vacuum valve.

21 Specialised equipment is necessary to test the remainder of the systems and to confirm any suspected faults. Therefore, apart from the above mentioned items and the following service information, any more complex repair or overhaul of the emission control system components should be left to a Datsun dealer who has the specialised knowledge and equipment to deal with such problems.

22 Before removing any of the components or carrying out any of the procedures in the following Sections, make a careful note of the location of all vacuum or air lines and electrical connections. As a general guide the following colour coding is used to identify the function and purpose of the hoses:

  Yellow – Vacuum line to distributor
  White – Vacuum line for EGR system
  Green – Manifold vacuum line
  Pink – Atmospheric pressure
  Blue – Venturi vacuum line to VVT valve

Crankcase emission control system – maintenance and testing

23 Maintenance of the system involves the renewal of the PCV valve filter and a general inspection of the condition of hoses. Access to the filter is gained after removal of the air cleaner cover. The filter can then be removed from its location in the air cleaner body and a new filter fitted.

24 To test the operation of the PCV valve, remove the ventilator hose from the valve with the engine idling. A hissing noise will be heard

from the valve if it is working. This can be confirmed by placing a finger over the valve. A strong vacuum should be felt. If this is not the case the valve must be renewed.

Air induction system – maintenance and testing

25 Inspect the system hoses for security, distortion and general condition. Renew any hoses which are defective.

26 Test the air induction valve and filter in the air cleaner by detaching the induction hose at the induction pipe and then blow or suck through the hose to ensure that the air only flows to the induction pipe side.

27 Check the induction valve and filter by removing them from the air cleaner body, to which they are attached by retaining screws.

28 Extract the filter and if blocked, or very dirty, renew it. The filter must be renewed at the specified mileage/time interval irrespective of condition.

29 Inspect the induction reed valve for binding, or signs of damage, and renew if necessary.

30 To test the anti-backfire (AB) valve, warm up the engine to normal operating temperature then detach the hose from the air cleaner and place a finger near the outlet. Run the engine at approximately 3000 rpm then quickly return it to idle. A suction force should be felt on your

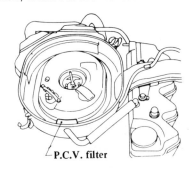

P.C.V. filter

Fig. 13.87 Location of the PCV valve filter (Sec 7)

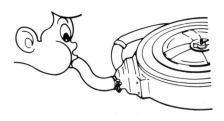

Fig. 13.88 Checking the AIS valve and filter (Sec 7)

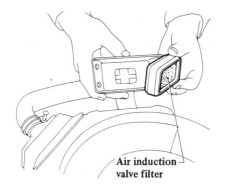

Fig. 13.89 Location of the AIS valve and filter assembly (Sec 7)

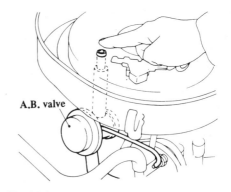

Fig. 13.90 Testing the anti-backfire valve (Sec 7)

finger if the valve is working normally. If no suction is felt the AB valve is defective and must be renewed.

Exhaust gas recirculation (EGR) system – maintenance and testing

31 Check the complete system for damaged or insecure hoses. Renew, or tighten, as appropriate.

32 With the engine stationary move the diaphragm of the EGR valve upwards with the fingers and check that it does not stick or bind.

33 With the engine cold, check that the EGR valve does not operate as the engine speed is increased from idle to between 3000 and 3500 rpm, again with a finger on the diaphragm.

34 With the engine at normal operating temperature repeat the test described in the previous paragraph and ensure that this time the valve does operate.

35 If the EGR valve does not operate as described, detach the vacuum hose at the valve and increase the engine speed from idle to between 3000 and 3500 rpm. Vacuum should be felt at the end of the hose. If the vacuum is weak, or non-existent, renew the thermal vacuum valve. If vacuum is present check the EGR valve, or, where fitted, the VVT valve.

36 If renewal of the thermal vacuum valve is necessary, you will need to partially drain the coolant. When renewing the valve unit, take care, as it is made of plastic and is easily damaged.

37 To check the EGR control valve, remove it from the engine and connect a length of hose to its port. When suction is applied the valve should move to its fully extended position and retain this attitude for at least 30 seconds after the vacuum ceases. If this is not the case, or if the valve shows any signs of damage or deformity, it must be renewed.

38 The vacuum delay valve can be tested by blowing into the EGR side port of the valve. Air should flow through. Now blow through the other (VVT valve) side, and in this case a greater resistance to flow should be felt.

39 The one-way valve can be tested by blowing through first on the inlet manifold side and then on the vacuum tank (white face) side. Airflow should be through the vacuum tank side only.

40 To test the vacuum switching valve, disconnect the electrical connector and connect an independent 12 volt supply to the terminals. Using a length of hose, check that air flows through the valve when the supply is connected and stops when it is disconnected.

41 Special equipment is required to test the VVT valve and vacuum switch. If the condition of these components is suspect the work should be left to a Datsun dealer.

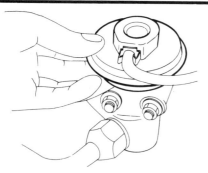

Fig. 13.91 Checking the EGR valve operation (Sec 7)

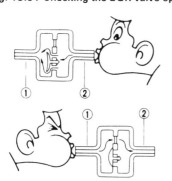

Fig. 13.93 Checking airflow through the vacuum delay valve (Sec 7)

1   To EGR valve   2   To VVT valve

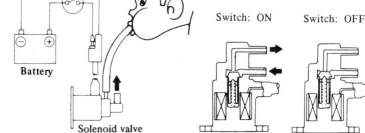

Fig. 13.92 Testing the EGR valve (Sec 7)

Fig. 13.94 Using an independent 12 volt supply to check the function of the two port vacuum switching valve (Sec 7)

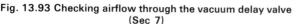

Catalyst warm-up system – maintenance and testing
42 Maintenance of this system consists of a visual check to ensure that all components are secure and in good condition.
43 To check the system operation, start the engine from cold and with it well below normal operating temperature, move the gear lever through all gear positions. Engine speed should increase noticeably in neutral. As the engine warms up and approaches 35°C (95°F), the engine speed should decrease in neutral and remain unchanged through all other gear positions.
44 If the engine speed does not vary during these tests, disconnect the vacuum switching valve connector and connect an independent 12 volt supply to the terminals. The engine speed should now increase and the ignition timing retard. If this does not happen, check the vacuum switching valve, throttle opener, servo diaphragm and all vacuum hoses and connections.
45 To check the vacuum switching valve, disconnect the electrical connector and connect an independent 12 volt supply to the terminals. Using a length of hose, check the airflow through the valve which should be as follows:
Switch on:
    Air flows from the vacuum delay valve into the switching valve port and out of the outer port to the inlet manifold.
Switch off:
    Air flows into the switching valve port and out of the air cleaner connecting pipe port.
46 The vacuum delay valve can be tested as described previously in this Section.
47 Testing of the water temperature switches and relays is best entrusted to your Datsun dealer.

Catalytic converter – testing, removal and refitting
48 The operation of the catalytic converter can be checked by noting the variation in CO percentage as follows.
49 Initially make a visual inspection of the catalytic converter and check for damage, cracks and security.
50 With the engine at normal operating temperature, check and, if necessary, adjust the throttle and idle adjusting screws, as described earlier in this Section and in Chapter 3, to obtain the specified CO percentage.
51 Rev up the engine to between 2000 and 3000 rpm two or three times and then allow it to idle again. If the idling speed has altered, readjust by means of the throttle adjusting screw.
52 Run the engine at 2000 rpm for four minutes and then at idling speed for one minute. Now recheck the CO percentage.
53 If the CO percentage is less than 0.3% the catalytic converter is serviceable.
54 If the CO percentage is more than 0.3% check the air induction system and renew the air induction valve.
55 Repeat the tests again and if the CO percentage is still more than 0.3% renew the catalytic converter as follows.
56 Jack up the car and support it securely on axle stands. Ensure that the catalytic converter is cold.
57 Remote the retaining screws and lift away the lower guard plate.
58 Undo the flange retaining bolts and withdraw the catalytic converter from the exhaust system.
59 Refitting is the reverse sequence to removal.

Evaporative emission control system – maintenance and testing
60 The system is designed to prevent vapour from the fuel tank escaping into the atmosphere and is fitted to vehicles operating in areas where stringent anti-pollution regulations are in force.
61 The system consists of a positive sealing fuel tank filler cap, a fuel check valve, a carbon canister, a vapour vent line, vacuum signal line and canister purge line. Additionally a thermal vacuum valve may be fitted, depending on operating territory.
62 The fuel vapours within the sealed tank are directed to the carbon canister which is filled with activated charcoal to absorb the vapours when the engine is idling or stopped.
63 When the engine speed increases, vacuum in the signal line opens the purge control valve and fuel vapours in the canister are drawn into the inlet manifold via the purge line. Where a thermal vacuum valve is fitted this prevents the purge control valve from opening until a specific engine temperature is reached.

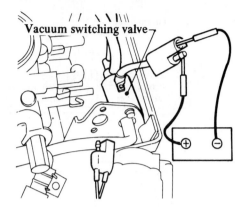
Fig. 13.95 Testing the three port vacuum switching valve in position (Sec 7)

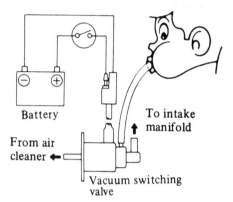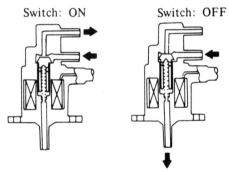
Fig. 13.96 Air flow through the three port vacuum switching valve in ON and OFF positions (Sec 7)

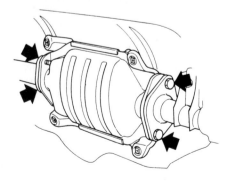
Fig. 13.97 Catalytic converter retaining bolts (Sec 7)

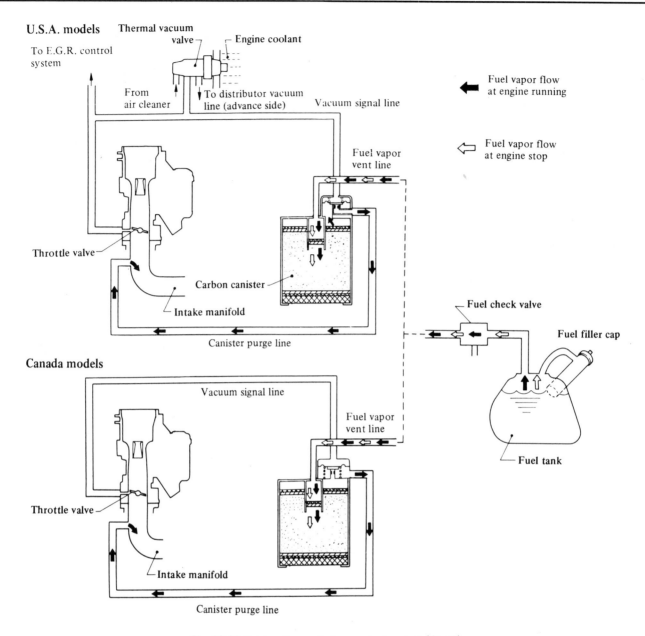

Fig. 13.98 Evaporative emission control system (Sec 7)

64 Periodic preventative maintenance of the system should be carried out. Inspect all hoses and the fuel filler cap for damage or deterioration. If the fuel cap is suspected of leaking, have it checked by your Datsun dealer.

65 At the specified maintenance intervals, remove and renew the carbon canister filter.

66 The fuel check valve is fitted above the fuel filler pipe to the tank within the body side panel. To remove the valve for checking prise free the inner panel for access, then detach the respective hoses and withdraw the valve.

67 To check the valve, refer to Fig. 13.100 and blow through the fuel tank connector. A resistance should be felt whilst some air should be felt to emerge from the engine side connectors. Now blow the air through from the engine side connector and check that air exits freely from the fuel tank port connection. Renew the valve unit if it is suspected of malfunction.

68 Check the carbon canister purge control valve for signs of leakage. Check the distributor vacuum line and the purge control diaphragm also. To do this, detach the rubber hose in the line at the T-connector (to carbon canister) and suck air through a rubber hose connected to a vacuum port in the canister. There should be no sign of leakage, but

if there is, remove the purge control valve top cover and inspect the diaphragm for signs of cracks or damage. If the diaphragm is found to be defective it must be renewed together with its retainer and spring.

69 The thermal vacuum valve is as used on the EGR system which is described earlier in this Section.

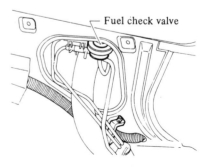

Fig. 13.99 Fuel check valve location in body side panel (Sec 7)

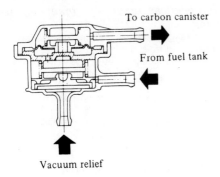

Fig. 13.100 Fuel check valve port identification (Sec 7)

8   Ignition system

Ignition system – general

1   The ignition system of E-series engines is identical to that used on the earlier A-series unit apart from modifications to the distributors. E10 and E13 engines utilize a conventional contact breaker points distributor, whilst E15 engines for the North American market are equipped with electronic ignition and a breakerless distributor. Both these units are of a slightly different design than previously used.

2   Apart from the procedures described in the following sections and

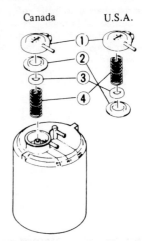

Fig. 13.101 Carbon canister purge control valve components (Sec 7)

| 1 | Cover | 3 | Retainer |
| 2 | Diaphragm | 4 | Diaphragm spring |

the information contained in the Specifications, all repair operations and instructions contained in Chapter 4 are also applicable to E-series engines.

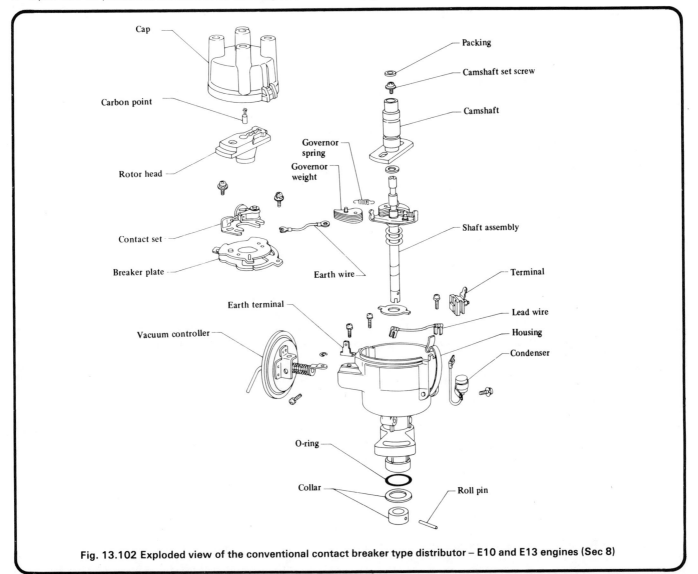

Fig. 13.102 Exploded view of the conventional contact breaker type distributor – E10 and E13 engines (Sec 8)

Distributor (all types) – removal and refitting

3   The distributor is mounted on the rear face of the cylinder head and is driven directly off the camshaft. Drive is by means of a slot in the distributor shaft which engages with a peg on the end of the camshaft. Consequently there is no rotational movement of the distributor shaft during removal or refitting, caused by the meshing action of the drive gears, as is the case on earlier engines. Apart from this, the removal and refitting procedures are as described in Chapter 4.

Distributor (contact breaker type) – dismantling, inspection and reassembly

4   Although the distributor is of a modified design, the layout of the components and therefore their dismantling and reassembly sequence is the same as on earlier engines. If reference is made to the accompanying illustrations, no problems should arise using the procedures given in Chapter 4.

Distributor (breakerless type) – dismantling, inspection and reassembly

5   Remove the retaining screws and lift off the distributor cap. Withdraw the rotor head from the shaft.
6   Remove the two retaining screws and withdraw the vacuum controller from the housing. Note the electrical connector tag retained by the upper screw.
7   Note the position of the leads and remove the wiring harness from the housing.
8   Using a suitable screwdriver, ease the reluctor upwards and off the distributor shaft. Recover the locating roll pin.
9   Remove the retaining screws and lift out the breaker plate assembly.
10 Remove the retaining screws and lift off the IC ignition unit from the breaker plate. Note the two spacers between the ignition unit and breaker plate.
11 The two screws securing the magnet and stator to the breaker plate can now be removed and these components withdrawn.

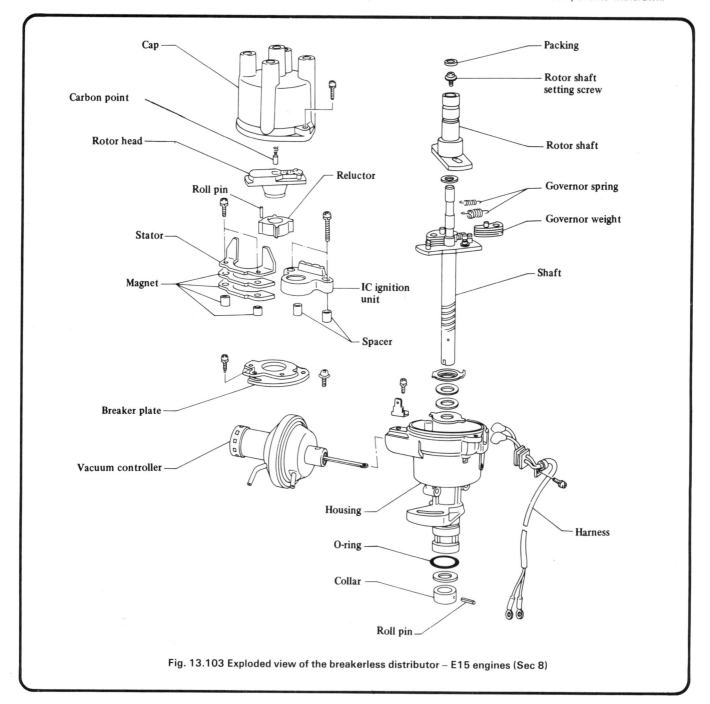

Fig. 13.103 Exploded view of the breakerless distributor – E15 engines (Sec 8)

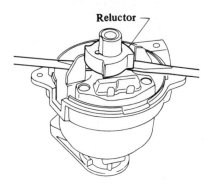

Fig. 13.104 Removal of the reluctor using two screwdrivers as levers – E15 engines (Sec 8)

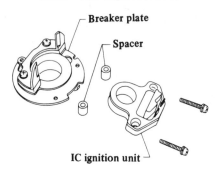

Fig. 13.105 Breaker plate and IC unit assembly – E15 engines (Sec 8)

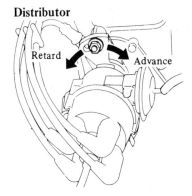

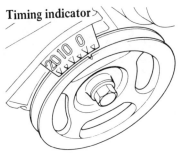

Fig. 13.106 Orientation of distributor and location of timing marks for ignition timing adjustment (Sec 8)

12 At the base of the distributor shaft, knock out the roll pin using a suitable punch and slide off the collar. The shaft assembly can now be withdrawn from the housing.
13 Before dismantling the centrifugal advance mechanism components, examine them for signs of damage and wear. If they are found to be in good condition then further dismantling is not necessary, or advised. Should any of the components be defective, dismantle the assembly as follows.
14 Mark the relative positions of the drive and rotor shafts. Extract the packing from the top of the rotor, remove the retaining screw and separate the two shafts.
15 Mark for positional identification a governor spring and its bracket and a governor weight and its pivot. The respective governor springs and weights can now be unhooked and removed. Take care not to stretch and distort the springs as they are unhooked.
16 Clean all parts and inspect for wear and damage. If wear in the shaft, bushes, governor weight pivots or holes is excessive, then the distributor should be renewed on an exchange basis. Check the distributor cap for tracking, indicated by a thin black line between the segments. Renew the cap if any sign of tracking is apparent. If the vacuum advance unit or IC ignition unit is suspected of malfunction they cannot be repaired and should therefore be renewed.
17 Reassembly is the reverse of dismantling. Align the match marks so that parts are reassembled in their original positions and note the following special points.
18 Smear the governor weights and springs with grease before assembly. Also lubricate the top of the rotor shaft with grease as it is assembled.
19 When refitting the pinion or collar it should be set at its original position on the shaft.
20 Check that the reluctor is correctly repositioned on the shaft.
21 Centralise the stator and reluctor before tightening the retaining screws.
22 Readjust the air gap, as described in Chapter 4, to the specified setting.
23 When refitting the IC ignition unit, ensure that its mating surfaces with the distributor are perfectly clean and dry.
24 Before refitting the distributor into the engine, check that the governor action is satisfactory by supporting the drive pinion and

twisting the rotor a fraction against the spring tension. When released it should return to its original position. Check that the rotor and driveshaft rotate freely without binding or excessive slackness.

9   Clutch

Description
1 All manual transmission models are fitted with a diaphragm spring, single dry plate clutch assembly, actuation on all models being by cable.
2 The clutch assembly is conventional, consisting of a one piece clutch cover pressure plate and diaphragm, clutch friction disc and ball-race type release bearing.
3 Unlike the assembly fitted to earlier A-series engine models, the complete transmission unit must be removed to provide access to the clutch components.

Clutch pedal height and free play – checking and adjustment
4 The clutch pedal height and withdrawal lever free play must be checked and, if necessary, adjusted at the specified routine maintenance intervals.
5 With the clutch pedal fully released, check the pedal-to-floor clearance, measured from the top of the pedal pad.
6 To adjust the pedal height, slacken the locknut and turn the pedal stopper as required until the specified height is obtained.
7 After adjusting the pedal height check the withdrawal lever free play as follows.
8 At the transmission end of the clutch cable, alter the position of the locknuts on the outer cable until all free play at the withdrawal lever is removed.
9 Fully depress and release the clutch pedal two or three times. Alter the position of the locknuts on the outer cable again to give the specified amount of free play at the withdrawal lever.

Clutch pedal and cable – removal and refitting
10 Slacken the clutch cable locknuts at the bracket on the transmission and release the inner cable end from the withdrawal lever.
11 Remove the instrument panel lower cover.

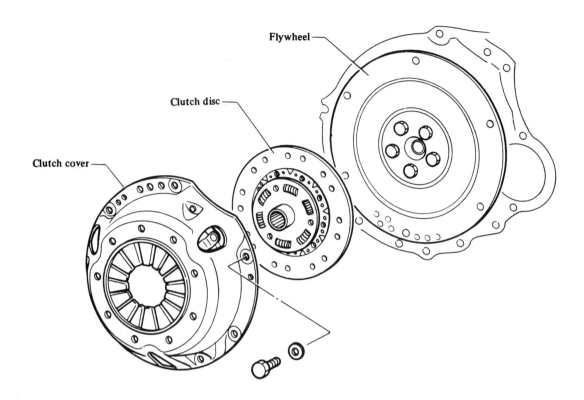

Fig. 13.107 Exploded view of the clutch assembly (Sec 9)

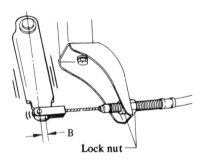

Fig. 13.109 Clutch withdrawal lever free play (B) and adjusting locknuts (Sec 9)

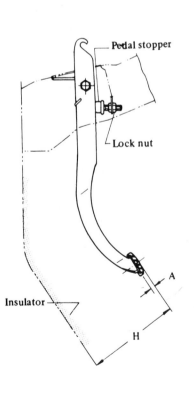

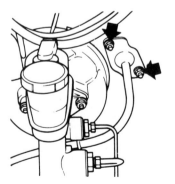

Fig. 13.108 Clutch pedal height and free travel adjustment (Sec 9)

Fig. 13.110 Clutch cable-to-engine bulkhead retaining nuts (Sec 9)

A = Pedal free travel *H = Pedal height*

12 Remove the circlip and clevis pin securing the cable to the clutch pedal.

13 Remove the two nuts securing the cable to the engine bulkhead and withdraw the cable from the car.

14 Remove the E-ring circlip securing the pedal to the fulcrum and withdraw the pedal and return spring.

15 Refitting is the reverse of the removal procedure. Apply grease to the clutch pedal fulcrum and bushes before fitting. Check the clutch pedal height and free play, when fitted, as described previously.

Clutch unit — removal and refitting

16 Access to the clutch unit can only be gained after removing the transmission assembly, as described elsewhere in this Chapter.

17 With the transmission removed suitably mark the clutch cover in relation to the flywheel.

18 Progressively slacken the clutch cover retaining bolts half a turn at a time, in a diagonal sequence. Remove the bolts when all the tension has been relieved from the diaphragm spring.

19 With the bolts removed, lift the cover assembly off the locating dowels. The clutch disc will fall out at this stage as it is not attached to either the cover assembly or the flywheel. Carefully note which way round it is fitted.

20 It is important that no oil or grease is allowed to come into contact with the clutch disc friction linings, or the pressure plate and flywheel faces. It is advisable to handle the parts with clean hands and to wipe down the pressure plate and flywheel faces with a clean dry rag before inspection or refitting commences.

21 To refit the clutch assembly begin by placing the clutch disc against the flywheel with the raised centre boss of the hub facing outward.

22 Position the clutch cover over the locating dowels with, if the original unit is being refitted, the previously made marks in alignment. Refit the six retaining bolts finger tight so that the clutch disc is gripped, but can still be moved.

23 It is now necessary to centralise the clutch disc so that the input shaft will pass freely through the splines and locate in the spigot bearing in the crankshaft. If possible use a clutch aligning tool, or a dowel with stepped diameters to fit the clutch disc hub and crankshaft spigot bearing. Alternatively, a long screwdriver can be used to move the disc up and down or from side to side as necessary. When viewed through the diaphragm fingers of the clutch cover, the clutch disc boss must be directly in line with the spigot bearing.

24 With the disc correctly centralised, tighten the clutch cover retaining bolts one turn at a time in a diagonal sequence to the specified torque setting.

25 The transmission can now be refitted.

Clutch unit — inspection

26 Examine the clutch disc friction linings for wear, and loose or broken springs and rivets. The linings must be proud of the rivets and light in appearance, with the material structure visible. If the linings are dark in appearance, further investigation is necessary as this is a sign of oil contamination, caused by oil leaking past the crankshaft rear oil seal or transmission input shaft oil seal.

27 Check the faces of the flywheel and pressure plate for signs of grooving or deep scoring. If apparent, the flywheel and pressure plate must be machined until smooth, or preferably renewed. If the pressure plate is cracked or split or if any of the diaphragm spring fingers are distorted, loose, or broken, the cover assembly must be renewed.

28 Place the clutch disc on the transmission input shaft and check that it is free to slide up and down the splines without binding.

29 Check the release bearing for smoothness of operation. There should be no harshness or slackness in it. Check that it spins freely with no sign of roughness from the bearing.

30 Should either the release bearing, clutch disc or clutch cover assembly require renewal, practical experience has shown that whenever possible all three units should be renewed together. Renewal of individual clutch components separately can often cause judder, squeal and a general roughness of the clutch, as new components do not easily bed into old ones. However, cost is a major consideration and it is left to the owner's discretion as to which course of action he chooses.

31 Before refitting the clutch assembly apply a smear of lithium or molybdenum disulphide grease to the transmission input shaft. Slide the clutch disc over the input shaft several times and then wipe away any excess. Take great care not to allow any grease to contact the friction material of the disc.

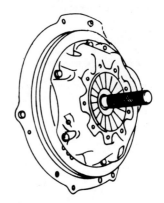

Fig. 13.111 Clutch aligning tool in position (Sec 9)

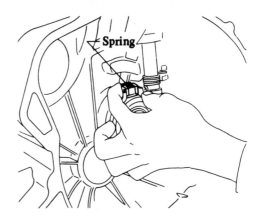

Fig. 13.112 Removal of the clutch release bearing-to-fork retaining spring clips (Sec 9)

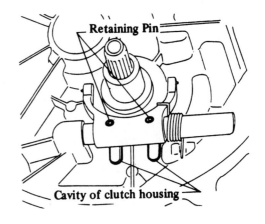

Fig. 13.113 Clutch release fork-to-shaft retaining pins (Sec 9)

Clutch release bearing — removal and refitting

32 With the transmission removed from the engine, disconnect the retaining spring clips securing the bearing to the release fork. Withdraw the bearing from the fork and off the input shaft.

33 To remove the release mechanism align the release fork retaining pins with the cavities in the clutch housing cover.

34 Using a suitable parallel pin punch drive out the two roll pins securing the release fork to the shaft. Slide the shaft out of the housing and withdraw the release fork and return spring.

35 Refitting is the reverse sequence to removal, bearing in mind the following points:

(a) Apply lithium or molybdenum disulphide grease to the release shaft, inner groove of the release bearing, and the contact surfaces of the bearing and withdrawal fork. Use the grease sparingly.

(b) Ensure that the release fork return spring is fitted as shown in Fig. 13.114

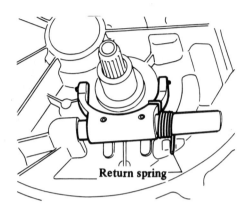

Fig. 13.114 Correct positioning of the clutch release fork return spring (Sec 9)

10 Transmission

PART A: MANUAL TRANSMISSION

Description
1   The manual transmission fitted to vehicles powered by the E-series engine is of an entirely different design from that used on earlier models. Because of the more compact dimensions of the E-series engine, the transmission is attached to the rear face of the cylinder block allowing the transmission input shaft to engage directly into the clutch disc hub. This arrangement obviates the need for transfer coupling gears necessary on earlier models where the transmission was situated below the engine.
2   The transmission is fairly conventional in design and is available in either four-speed or five-speed versions. The final drive to the differential is by helically cut spur gears allowing the differential assembly to form an integral part of the transmission unit.
3   Gear selection is by a floor mounted, remote control lever operating through a linkage. The linkage consists of a remote control housing, gear selection rod and support rod.

Transmission – removal and refitting
4   The transmission can be removed from the vehicle as a unit with the engine, as described earlier in this Chapter, or as a separate item. When removing the transmission separately the procedure entails withdrawing the unit from the engine and lifting it upwards out of the engine compartment. As the transmission assembly consists of the gearbox and differential units, considerable weight is involved. The use of a crane or other overhead lifting gear will therefore be necessary.

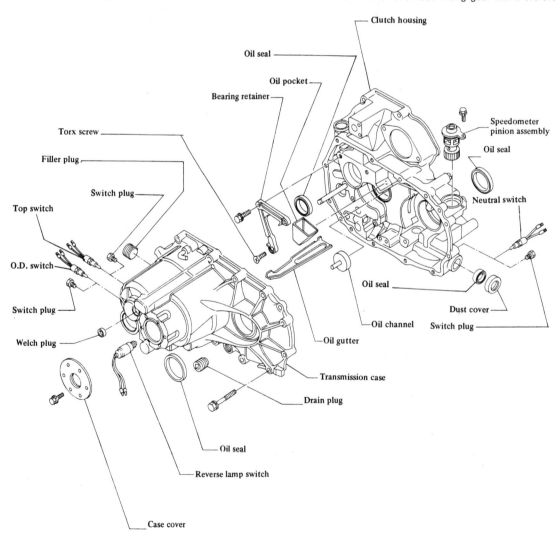

Fig. 13.115 Exploded view of the transmission case components (Sec 10)

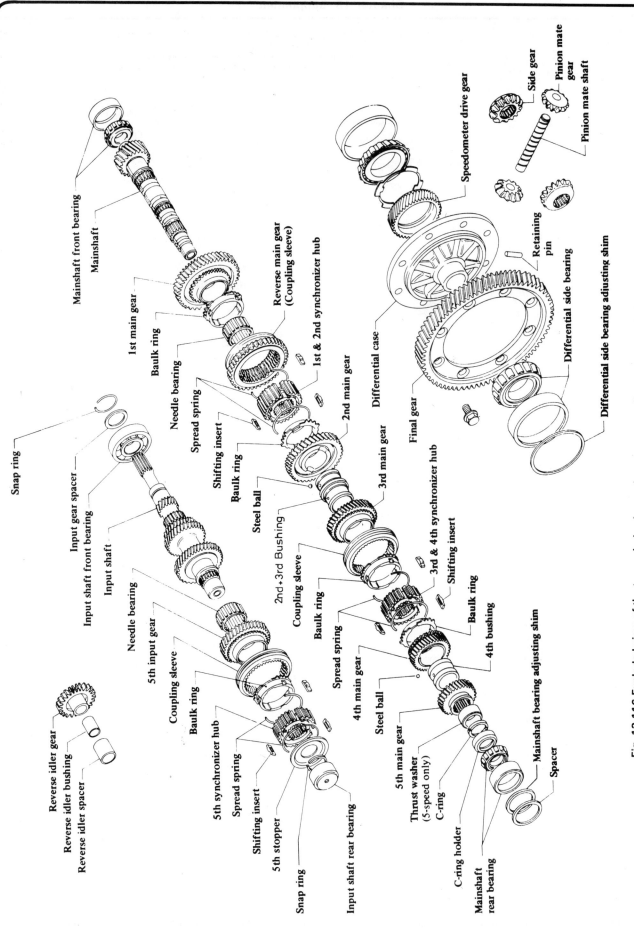

Fig. 13.116 Exploded view of the transmission internal components – five-speed model illustrated (Sec 10)

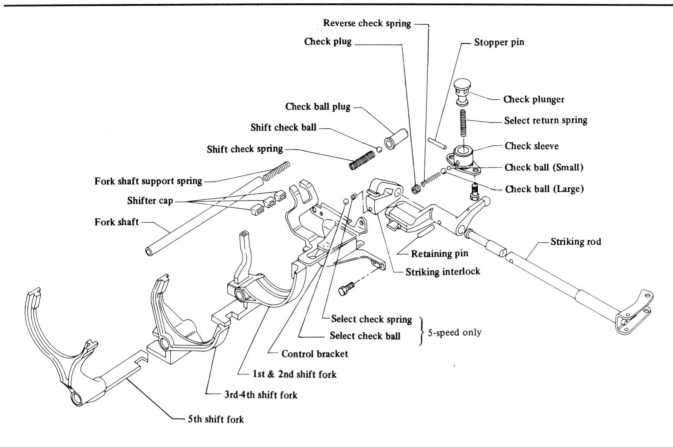

Fig. 13.117 Exploded view of the gear selector mechanism – five-speed model illustrated (Sec 10)

5   Begin by disconnecting the battery terminals and then remove the battery from its carrier.
6   Place a suitable container beneath the transmission drain plug. Remove the plug and allow the oil to drain. Refit the plug after draining.
7   Refer to Section 8, and remove the distributor.
8   Where applicable remove the air induction tube, EGR tube and exhaust manifold cover. Refer to Section 7, if necessary.
9   Remove the heater hose clamp.
10 Release the clutch cable from the withdrawal lever and from its mounting bracket.
11 Remove the bolts securing the starter motor to the clutch housing. Withdraw the motor and place it to one side.
12 Remove the speedometer cable from the drive pinion housing.
13 Jack up the front of the car and support it on axle stands. Remove the front roadwheels.
14 Remove the three bolts securing the left-hand side front suspension lower balljoint to the transverse link. Remove the nut securing the steering tie-rod balljoint to the steering arm. Release the joint from the arm using a clamp claw separator. Pull the suspension assembly outwards and release the driveshaft inner joint from the transmission using a screwdriver or suitable lever. After removal place a suitable bar, such as a short length of broom handle, into the transmission to retain the differential side gears in position. Repeat this procedure for the right-hand driveshaft and suspension assembly.
15 Working underneath the car, remove the bolt securing the gearchange control rod to the transmission linkage and disconnect the support rod from the transmission bracket.
16 Remove the exhaust front pipe mounting.
17 Disconnect the reversing light switch wires and (where fitted) the neutral switch wires.
18 Place a jack with interposed block of wood beneath the engine sump and just take the weight of the engine and transmission assembly.
19 Place a second jack beneath the transmission and just take the weight of this unit also.
20 Remove the bolts securing the engine gusset steady brackets to the transmission.

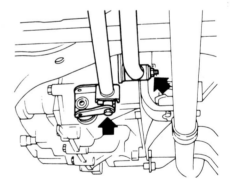

Fig. 13.118 Gearchange control rod and support rod-to-transmission retaining bolts (Sec 10)

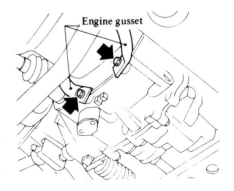

Fig. 13.119 Engine gusset steady bracket retaining bolts (Sec 10)

21 Remove the engine right-hand side mounting bracket and insulator (five-speed models only), and the rear mounting bracket and insulator.
22 Attach suitable lifting gear to the transmission and support its weight. The clutch cable mounting bracket may be used for this purpose.
23 Remove the bolts securing the transmission to the engine and draw the transmission sideways until the input shaft is clear of the clutch assembly. On five-speed models it will also be necessary to move the engine slightly to the right to provide sufficient clearance for removal. During this process ensure that the transmission is well supported and that no undue strain is placed on the input shaft. When the transmission is clear, lift it up and out of the engine compartment.
24 Refitting the transmission is the reverse sequence to removal, bearing in mind the following points:

(a) Ensure that the cylinder block and clutch housing mating faces are perfectly clean
(b) Smear the transmission input shaft with a trace of lithium or molybdenum disulphide grease before fitting
(c) Tighten all nuts and bolts to the specified torque settings as given in this, and other relevant Chapters, of this manual
(d) Fill the gearbox with the specified grade of oil after installation
(e) Adjust the clutch cable as described earlier in this Chapter

Transmission dismantling – general
25 Before commencing dismantling refer to Chapter 6, Part A, Section 3.

Transmission – dismantling
26 The following procedure is applicable to both four-speed and five-speed units. Any differences between the two will be detailed where applicable.
27 Prior to dismantling, clean off all external dirt and grease using a suitable solvent. After cleaning support the unit on a stand or on a bench. The housing is made of aluminium alloy, so care must be taken as it is easily damaged.
28 Begin dismantling by removing the clutch release bearing and release mechanism, as described earlier in this Chapter.
29 Remove the bolts securing the transmission case to the clutch housing. Using a plastic or hide mallet tap the case free and lift it off the housing. On five-speed units tilt the case slightly while lifting to clear the 5th speed shift fork.
30 If it is wished to dismantle the transmission case further proceed as follows, otherwise proceed to paragraph 37.
31 Unscrew the top, overdrive and reversing light switches (where applicable) and remove them from the case.
32 Remove the oil gutter.
33 To remove the input shaft rear bearing from the case, first drive out the welch plug using a suitable drift.
34 Again using a suitable drift, tap out the rear bearing through the hole from which the welch plug was removed.
35 Unscrew the retaining bolts and lift off the case cover, spacer and mainshaft bearing adjusting shim. Using a drift or tube of suitable diameter, drive out the mainshaft bearing outer race.
36 To remove the differential side bearing outer race an outward facing two-legged puller and a bit of improvisation will be needed. The

accompanying illustrations show the procedure. However, unless the race is definitely in need of renewal, it is best left in position.
37 To dismantle the clutch housing and associated gear trains first lift out the reverse idler spacer and shift fork shaft.

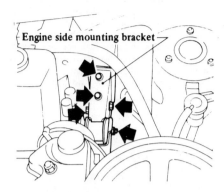
Fig. 13.120 Right-hand side engine mounting retaining bolts (Sec 10)

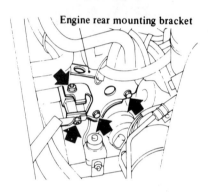
Fig. 13.121 Engine rear mounting bracket retaining bolts (Sec 10)

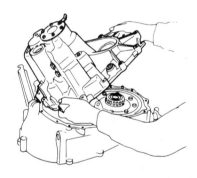
Fig. 13.122 Removal of the transmission case from the clutch housing (Sec 10)

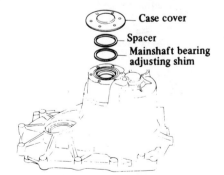
Fig. 13.123 Removal of the transmission case cover, spacer and adjusting shim (Sec 10)

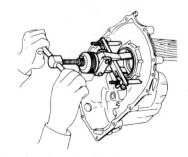
Fig. 13.124 Using a suitable puller to remove the differential side bearing outer race (Sec 10)

38 Lift out the 5th speed (where applicable) and 3rd/4th speed shift fork. Take care not to lose the small shifter caps located in the striking slots of the forks.

39 Remove the retaining bolts and carefully withdraw the control bracket, together with the 1st/2nd shift fork. Again take care not to lose the shifter caps; on five-speed units recover the select check ball and check spring. These will be released when the control bracket bolts are removed, so be prepared to catch them.

40 Unscrew the two bolts and one Torx screw securing the bearing retainer bracket to the housing. Note that a cranked Torx driver, as shown in the accompanying illustration, will be required owing to the lack of clearance between the screw and reverse idler gear. If the correct tool cannot be obtained it should not be too difficult to devise a suitable substitute. After removal of the bolts and screw, lift out the retainer bracket.

41 Turn the clutch housing on its side and, using a plastic or hide mallet, carefully tap out the input shaft, together with the mainshaft. During this operation keep the two shafts straight to avoid damaging the resin oil channel in the housing. Also take care not to allow the differential assembly to fall out as the shafts are withdrawn.

42 The reverse idler gear can now be withdrawn and the differential carefully lifted out.

43 If it is wished to dismantle the selector mechanism proceed as follows.

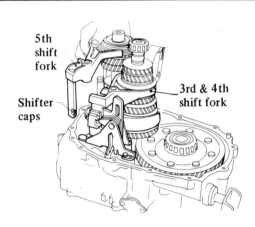

Fig. 13.125 Removal of the 5th, and 3rd/4th shift forks (Sec 10)

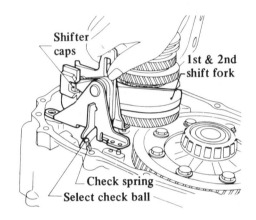

Fig. 13.126 Removal of the control bracket together with the 1st/2nd shift forks (Sec 10)

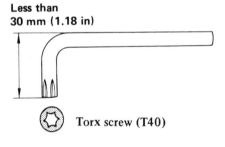

Fig. 13.127 Dimension of Torx driver tool for removal of bearing retainer bracket screw (Sec 10)

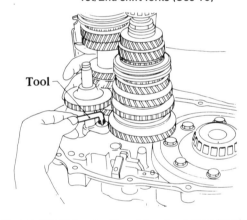

Fig. 13.128 Using the Torx driver to remove bearing retainer bracket screw (Sec 10)

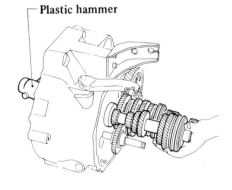

Fig. 13.129 Removal of the geartrains from the clutch housing (Sec 10)

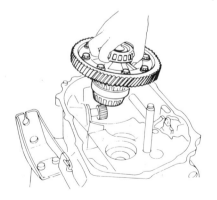

Fig. 13.130 Lifting out the differential assembly (Sec 10)

44 Remove the oil pocket, shift check ball, check spring and check ball plug.

45 Turn the striking rod so that there is clearance below the striking lever retaining roll pin and drift out the pin using a suitable punch. Now withdraw the rod and lift out the lever and striking interlock.

46 Remove the reverse and 5th speed check plug, then withdraw the check spring and two check balls, one large, one small.

47 Unscrew the retaining bolts and lift out the reverse and 5th speed check assembly, including check plunger and select return spring.

48 Check to see if the shift fork shaft support spring is still in its location in the casing and if so remove it. It is possible that the spring stayed in place in the shift fork shaft when this component was removed.

49 Removal of the mainshaft and differential side bearing outer races requires the use of an outward facing two-legged puller. The previous illustrations show the procedure and it should not be too difficult to improvise a suitable alternative. However unless the outer races are definitely in need of renewal they are best left in position.

50 Finally remove the oil channel from the housing.

Mainshaft — dismantling

51 Before dismantling the mainshaft, check the endplay of the gears using feeler gauges, as shown in the accompanying illustration. If the endplay is excessive between any of the gears a careful check must be made after dismantling to determine the condition of any worn parts.

Fig. 13.132 Using a punch to drift out the striking lever roll pin (Sec 10)

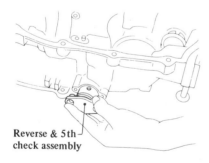

Reverse & 5th check assembly

Fig. 13.134 Removal of the 5th/reverse check assembly (Sec 10)

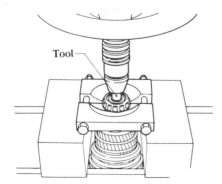

Tool

Fig. 13.136 Removal of the mainshaft front bearing inner race (Sec 10)

52 Using a bearing remover, support the mainshaft front bearing inner race and press the mainshaft out. Repeat this procedure for the rear bearing inner race. If a bearing remover is not available, support the underside of the bearings using two strips of angle iron placed across open vice jaws. Using a soft metal drift, drive the mainshaft out of the bearings.

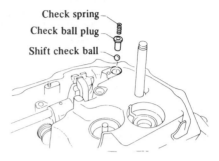

Check spring
Check ball plug
Shift check ball

Fig. 13.131 Removal of the shift check components (Sec 10)

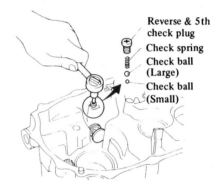

Reverse & 5th check plug
Check spring
Check ball (Large)
Check ball (Small)

Fig. 13.133 Removal of the 5th/reverse check plug, spring and balls (Sec 10)

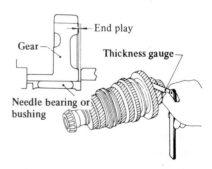

End play
Gear
Thickness gauge
Needle bearing or bushing

Fig. 13.135 Using feeler gauges to measure the endplay of the gears (Sec 10)

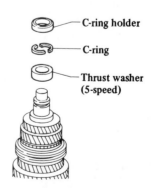

C-ring holder
C-ring
Thrust washer (5-speed)

Fig. 13.137 Mainshaft rear retaining components (Sec 10)

53 At the rear of the mainshaft, remove the C-ring holder and C-rings, and on five-speed units, lift off the thrust washer.

54 On five-speed units draw off 5th gear using a bearing remover engaged under the lip of the bearing flange. Press the mainshaft out of the bearing. Alternatively this can be done using two strips of angle iron as used for removal of the mainshaft bearings.

55 Slide off 4th gear and 4th gear bushing. Recover the small steel ball used to locate the bushing from the mainshaft.

56 Using a gear puller or suitable alternative, draw off the 3rd/4th gear synchroniser unit complete with 3rd gear. Slide out the 2nd/3rd bushing, recover the steel ball and slide out 2nd gear.

57 Again using the puller, or an alternative, draw off the 1st/2nd gear synchroniser together with 1st gear, then slide out the 1st gear needle bearing.

58 If it is wished to dismantle the synchroniser units first make a careful note of the location and orientation of the spread springs and mark the hub and coupling sleeve at one end with paint. This will ensure correct reassembly of the components.

59 Remove the spread springs, slide the hub out of the sleeve and recover the shifting inserts.

Input shaft — dismantling

60 Using circlip pliers remove the input shaft front bearing retaining snap-ring and lift off the spacer. Note that on reassembly a new snap-ring of the correct thickness must be used. Press or drive off the front bearing.

61 Measure the endplay of the gears on the input shaft as described in paragraph 51.

62 Using circlip pliers extract the 5th gear assembly retaining snap-ring and lift off the 5th stopper.

63 Using a gear puller, or an alternative, draw off the 5th gear synchroniser unit together with 5th gear and needle bearing.

Differential — dismantling

64 Before commencing dismantling, measure the endplay of the side gears using a dial gauge, as shown in the accompanying illustration, or

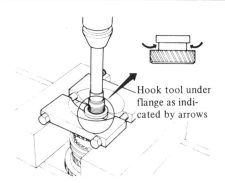

Fig. 13.138 Removal of 5th gear from the mainshaft (Sec 10)

Hook tool under flange as indicated by arrows

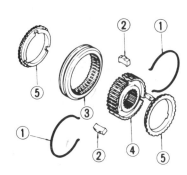

Fig. 13.139 Synchroniser unit components (Sec 10)

1 Spread springs   4 Synchro hub
2 Shifting insert   5 Baulk ring
3 Coupling sleeve

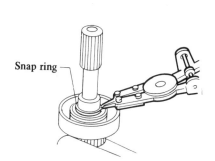

Snap ring

Fig. 13.140 Input shaft front bearing snap-ring removal (Sec 10)

Fig. 13.141 Removal of the input shaft front bearing using a puller (Sec 10)

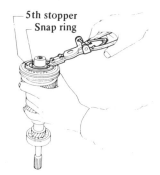

5th stopper
Snap ring

Fig. 13.142 Removal of the 5th gear snap-ring from the input shaft (Sec 10)

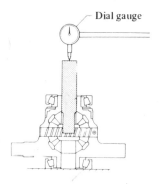

Dial gauge

Fig. 13.143 Arrangement of dial gauge and suitable bar for differential side gear endplay measurement (Sec 10)

with feeler gauges. If the endplay exceeds the specified amount the complete differential must be renewed. Note also that if the side bearing inner races are removed, reassembly will involve a critical setting up procedure requiring a dial gauge, depth micrometer and a good deal of skill.

65 If the unit is to be dismantled first remove the bolts securing the final drive gear to the differential case. Lift off the gear.

66 Using a suitable punch, drive out the pinion mate shaft lockpin and draw out the pinion mate shaft. Remove the pinion mate gears and side gears.

67 Remove the differential side bearing inner races using a gear puller. Identify the left and right bearings to avoid confusion during reassembly.

68 Lift off the speedometer stopper and draw off the speedometer gear.

Transmission components – inspection and checking

69 The inspection and checking procedure is the same as described in Chapter 6, Part A, Section 9. Reference should be made to the Specifications at the beginning of this Chapter for applicable dimensions and tolerances.

Differential – reassembly

70 Refit the speedometer gear followed by the stopper.

71 Press the side bearing inner races onto the differential case. If a proper press is not available use a hammer and block of wood or tube of suitable diameter.

72 Refit the pinion mate shaft and pinion mate gears then retain the shaft using a new lockpin. Ensure that the lockpin is flush with the differential case when fitted.

73 Insert the two side gears into engagement with the pinion mates.

74 Refit the final gear to the case and secure with the retaining bolts. Use a locking sealant on the bolt threads and tighten them to the specified torque setting.

75 Where applicable, adjust the differential rotary frictional force as described in the following paragaphs.

Differential – adjustment

76 It will be necessary to adjust the differential rotary frictional force

if any of the following components have been renewed:

Differential case
Differential side bearings
Clutch housing
Transmission case

77 Thoroughly clean the mating faces of the clutch housing and transmission case.

78 Install the differential side bearing outer race into the clutch housing using a hammer and tube of suitable diameter.

79 Lubricate the side bearing inner race on the differential and carefully lay the unit in position in the clutch housing. Place the other side bearing outer race over the inner race and, while applying hand pressure to the outer race, turn the differential. This will settle the bearings.

80 It is now necessary to take an accurate measurement of the distance between the clutch housing mating face and the upper surface of the side bearing outer race. The accompanying illustrations show the Datsun special tool and a depth micrometer being used to obtain this dimension. Any flat strip of metal or suitable alternative can be used, providing that it is absolutely flat and level and can be

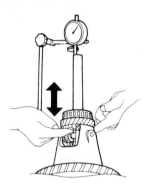

Fig. 13.144 Checking the differential side gear endplay (Sec 10)

Fig. 13.145 Removal of the differential pinion mate shaft lockpin (Sec 10)

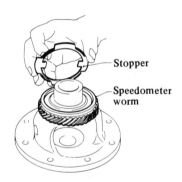

Fig. 13.146 Removal of the speedometer stopper and worm gear (Sec 10)

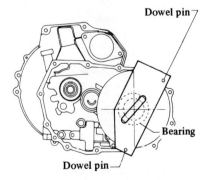

Fig. 13.147 Positioning of datum plate for differential outer race depth measurement (Sec 10)

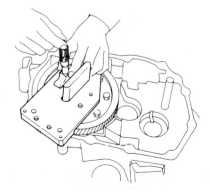

Fig. 13.148 Using a depth micrometer and datum plate to obtain differential bearing outer race dimension (Sec 10)

supported securely. Don't forget to take into account the thickness of the material being used when taking the measurement. Record the measurement which will be referred to as dimension A.

81 Using this same procedure take a similar measurement between the mating face of the transmission case and the land in which the side bearing adjusting shim rests. This will be dimension B.

82 The thickness of adjusting shim required to give the necessary side bearing pre-load can be calculated as follows:

$$\text{Shim thickness} = (B-A) + 0.012 \text{ in } (0.3 \text{ mm})$$

Shims of varying thicknesses are available from Datsun dealers. Note that it may be necessary to use more than one shim to achieve the specified pre-load.

83 As a final check that the correct shim(s) has been selected, assemble the shim(s) and side bearing outer race into the transmission case and, with the differential unit in place, bolt the clutch housing and transmission case together.

84 Using a slotted bar engaged with the pinion mate shaft turn the differential through at least ten revolutions to settle the bearings.

85 If the Datsun special tool can be borrowed the actual turning torque of the differential can be checked and compared with tthe specified figure. However if the differential turns smoothly without binding and with minimal resistance no problems in service should be encountered. There should of course be no trace of endfloat which would indicate that the shims selected are too thin.

86 After carrying out this check dismantle the clutch housing and transmission case again to allow fitment of the gear trains and components.

Input shaft – reassembly

87 Liberally lubricate all the input shaft components and begin reassembly by placing 5th gear and its needle bearing on the shaft.

88 Place the baulk rings on either side of the assembled 5th gear synchroniser. Using a press or hammer and tube of suitable diameter, drive the synchroniser onto the input shaft.

89 Refit the 5th stopper followed by a new selected snap-ring. A snap-ring of sufficient thickness to reduce the groove clearance to a minimum must be used.

90 At the other end of the input shaft press or drive on the front bearing followed by the spacer and selected snap-ring. Again ensure that the snap-ring groove clearance is kept to a minimum.

Mainshaft – reassembly

91 Liberally lubricate all the mainshaft components and begin reassembly by placing the 1st gear needle bearing on the mainshaft. Now slide on 1st gear.

92 Place the baulk rings on either side of the assembled 1st/2nd synchroniser. Using a press or hammer and tube of suitable diameter, drive the synchroniser onto the mainshaft. Note the correct fitting direction of the synchroniser as shown in Fig. 13.149.

93 Apply some grease to the steel ball that locates the 2nd/3rd bushing and insert the ball in its mainshaft location.

94 Slide on 2nd gear followed by the 2nd/3rd bushing. Push the bush through the gear and rotate it until the groove on its inner bore locates over the steel ball. Place the 3rd gear over the other half of the bushing.

95 Place the baulk rings on either side of the assembled 3rd/4th synchroniser and drive the synchroniser onto the mainshaft.

96 Apply some grease to the remaining steel ball and insert the ball into the mainshaft. Slide on the 4th bushing, engaging its groove with the ball, followed by 4th gear.

97 Where applicable, drive 5th gear onto the mainshaft followed by the thrust washer. Refit the two selected C-rings and the C-ring holder. C-rings of sufficient thickness to reduce the groove clearance to a minimum must be used.

98 Refit the front and rear bearings using a press or hammer and suitable tube.

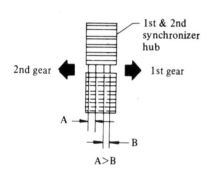

Fig. 13.149 Correct positioning of 1st/2nd synchroniser assembly on mainshaft (Sec 10)

Fig. 13.150 Assembly of mainshaft gear components (Sec 10)

Fig. 13.151 2nd/3rd gear bushing showing steel ball locating groove (Sec 10)

Fig. 13.152 Assembly of 4th bushing and steel ball (Sec 10)

Transmission – reassembly

99 Refit the oil channel to the clutch housing ensuring that the oil groove faces the oil pocket.

100 If previously removed, refit the mainshaft bearing and differential side bearing outer races using a hammer and suitable tube.

101 Refit the oil pocket, fill it with oil and ensure that it flows out of the oil channel.

102 Refit the reverse and 5th check assembly including check plunger and select return spring. Secure the assembly with the two retaining bolts.

103 Place the small check ball into the hole in the housing directly above the check assembly. Follow this with the large check ball, check spring and finally the check plug. Apply locking sealant to the check plug threads before fitting.

104 Lubricate the lips of the striking rod oil seal and very carefully insert the striking rod. Push the rod in halfway and then place the striking lever and striking interlock over it. Align the holes in the lever and rod and secure the two with a new retaining roll pin.

105 Refit the shift check ball, check spring and check ball plug.

106 Carefully lower the differential assembly into the housing.

107 Refit the mainshaft, input shaft and reverse idler gear assemblies, taking care not to damage the oil seals as the shafts are inserted. Using a plastic or hide mallet, top the input shaft fully home.

108 Refit the bearing retainer and secure with the two bolts and one Torx screw. Apply locking sealant to the threads of the Torx screw and stake its head at two points after tightening.

109 On five-speed units refit the spring and select check ball into the hole in the striking interlock. Retain the ball in place with a little grease.

110 With the shifter caps in place refit the control bracket together with the 1st/2nd shift fork. Secure the assembly with the retaining bolts.

111 Refit the 3rd/4th and, where applicable, the 5th shift forks.

112 Apply grease to the fork shaft support spring and insert the spring into the shaft. Slide the shaft through the forks and into position.

113 Refit the reverse idler spacer.

114 Refit the mainshaft bearing and differential side bearing outer races to the transmission case using a hammer and tube of suitable diameter.

115 If the input shaft rear bearing was removed from the case, refit the welch plug using a suitable drift. Coat the plug with sealant before fitting. Refit the input shaft bearing from the inside of the case using a hammer and tube.

116 Apply sealant to the threads of the top, overdrive and reversing light switches (where applicable) and refit them to the transmission case.

117 Refit the oil gutter.

118 Apply an even, unbroken coat of gasket sealant to the mating face of the transmission case and place the case in position over the gears and clutch housing. Refit the retaining bolts and tighten them progressively to the specified torque setting.

119 If any of the following components have been renewed it will be necessary to adjust the mainshaft rotary frictional force:

Mainshaft
Mainshaft bearings
Clutch housing
Transmission case

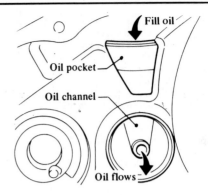

Fig. 13.153 Checking oil flow from oil pocket to oil channel (Sec 10)

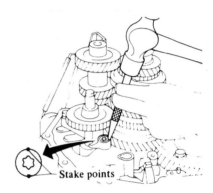

Fig. 13.154 Stake the bearing retainer bracket Torx screw at two points after fitting (Sec 10)

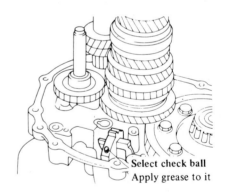

Fig. 13.155 Refit the select check ball into the hole in the striking interlock (Sec 10)

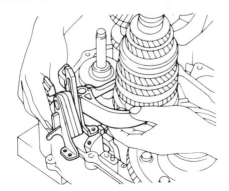

Fig. 13.156 Refit the control bracket together with the 1st/2nd shift fork (Sec 10)

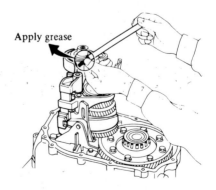

Fig. 13.157 Insert the fork shaft support spring into the end of the shaft before fitting the shaft (Sec 10)

If these original components are being refitted, proceed to paragraph 123, otherwise carry out the following procedure.

120 Place the mainshaft rear bearing spacer (not the shim) over the outer race and gently tap the spacer and outer race onto the bearing to ensure they are properly seated.

121 Using a depth micrometer, measure the distance from the surface of the transmission case to the spacer and record the measurement.

122 A shim must now be selected equal to the measured distance plus 0.008 in (0.2 mm).

123 Place the mainshaft adjusting shim between the bearing outer race and the spacer. Apply gasket sealant evenly to the transmission case cover, place the cover in position and secure with the retaining bolts tightened to the specified torque setting. Note that the raised centre faces outward.

124 Refer to Fig. 13.159 and select top gear by moving the striking rod accordingly.

125 Turn the transmission input shaft by hand and ensure that the geartrain turns smoothly with minimal resistance and without binding.

If this is not the case, recheck the mainshaft rotary frictional force as previously described in paragraphs 120 to 122.

126 Move the striking rod through all gear positions and check that all gears and neutral can be selected. There may be some roughness during this check due to the lack of oil in the transmission.

127 The clutch release bering and mechanism can now be refitted as described in Section 9 of this Chapter.

Gearchange linkage – removal, inspection and refitting

128 From inside the car, detach the gear lever rubber boot from its floor fixing.

129 Slacken the gear lever retaining locknut and unscrew the lever from the lower control lever.

130 Jack up the front of the car and support it on axle stands.

131 From under the car remove the nut and through-bolt securing the control rod to the transmission striking rod bracket. Also remove the nut and bolt securing the support rod to the transmission.

132 Remove the bolts securing the control lever bracket to the car

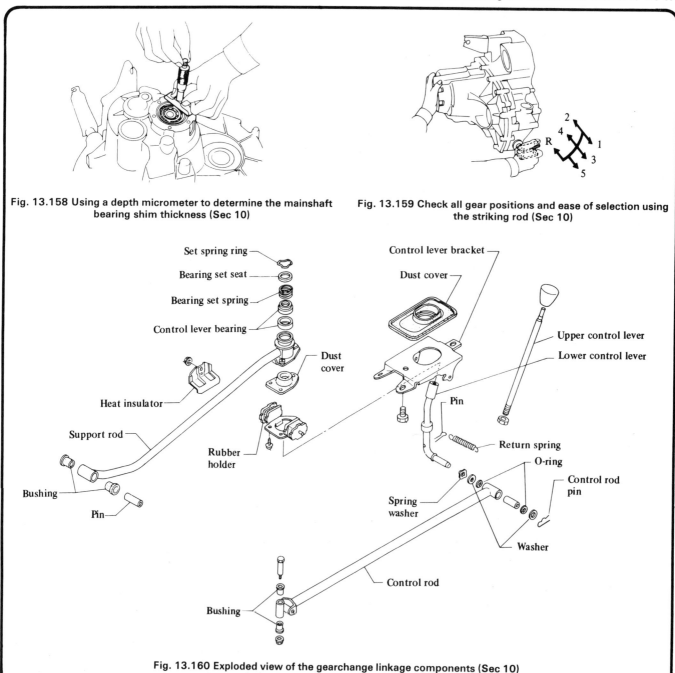

Fig. 13.158 Using a depth micrometer to determine the mainshaft bearing shim thickness (Sec 10)

Fig. 13.159 Check all gear positions and ease of selection using the striking rod (Sec 10)

Fig. 13.160 Exploded view of the gearchange linkage components (Sec 10)

underbody and lower the complete linkage assembly to the ground.
133 It should only be necessary to dismantle the linkage for renewal of the rubber bushes or bearing seats. Dismantling the linkage is straightforward and if reference is made to the accompanying illustrations, no problems should be encountered. The bushes can be renewed by pressing them out in a vice using tubes of suitable diameter as supports. When refitting, apply a multi-purpose grease to all contact surfaces and striking points.
134 Refitting the linkage is the reverse sequence to removal.

PART B: AUTOMATIC TRANSMISSION

Description
1   A three-speed fully automatic transmission is available as an option on models powered by the E-series engine.
2   The unit consists of three main assemblies, namely the hydraulic torque converter, the planetary gear sets and clutches and the hydraulic control unit.
3   Owing to the complexity of the automatic transmission unit, it is imperative that overhaul be left to a Datsun garage or a specialist with the equipment and knowledge required for diagnosis and rectification of faults. The contents of the following Sections are therefore limited to the minor adjustment and routine maintenance tasks that can be carried out by the home mechanic.

Automatic transmission fluid – level checking and renewal
4   The procedure for level checking and fluid renewal is the same as described in Chapter 6, Part B, Section 21. Note, however, that fluid renewal is not a service requirement on the fully automatic transmission and should only be necessary if the fluid appears contaminated. This will be indicated by a darker than normal colour of the fluid, together with a burnt smell. If the fluid exhibits these properties the clutches and brake bands may need attention.

Throttle wire – adjustment
5   The adjustment of the throttle wire (often known as a kick-down cable) should be checked periodically or after removal, refitting or adjustment of the carburettor.
6   To adjust the cable, slacken the two locknuts securing the outer cable to its mounting bracket at the carburettor.
7   Open the throttle fully by hand and retain it in this position. Pull the outer cable away from the carburettor as far as it will go and screw up the lower locknut to hold the cable in this position. Undo the lower locknut by half a turn and screw the upper locknut down to secure the cable. Release the throttle.
8   With quick drying paint mark the inner cable at the throttle closed and throttle fully open positions. Measure the distance between the two marks and check that it is within the throttle wire stroke dimension as given in the Specifications.

Control cable – adjustment
9   Jack up the front of the car and support it on axle stands.
10 Place the gear selector lever in the 'P' position.
11 From under the car slacken the two locknuts securing the cable to the gear selector lever trunnion. Pull the cable through the trunnion as far as it will go and tighten the locknuts.
12 Move the selector lever through all gear positions, returning to the 'P' position. Check that the operating lever on the transmission does not move slightly out of the 'P' position under the tension of the cable.
13 Apply grease to the exposed selector mechanism and cable then lower the car to the ground.

Automatic transmission – removal and refitting
14 The automatic transmission can only be removed as a complete assembly in unit with the engine. After removal from the car they can be separated. Full details of these procedures will be found earlier in this Chapter.
15 Note that any suspected fault must be referred to a Datsun dealer or transmission specialist before unit removal, as with this type of transmission accurate fault diagnosis can only be carried out with the transmission in the car.

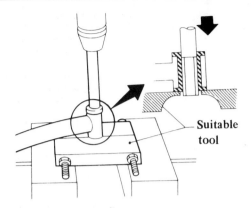

Fig. 13.161 Using a press to remove the gearchange linkage bushes (Sec 10)

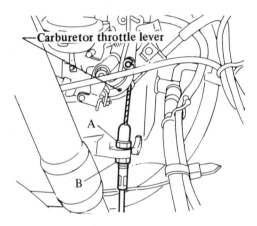

Fig. 13.162 Automatic transmission throttle wire adjusting nuts (A and B) at carburettor (Sec 10)

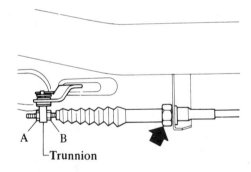

Fig. 13.163 Automatic transmission control cable adjusting nuts (A and B) at selector lever trunnion (Sec 10)

11 Driveshafts

Driveshaft modifications
1   Models equipped with the E-series engine utilize driveshafts with a modified inner constant velocity joint. As this inner joint engages directly with the transmission differential side gears a revised removal and refitting procedure must be used, as described in the following paragraphs.
2   Apart from the rubber boots, individual replacement parts are not available for the driveshaft joints and if worn or defective, these parts can only be renewed as complete assemblies. The procedure for removal of the joints and rubber boots from the driveshaft is the same as described in Chapter 7.

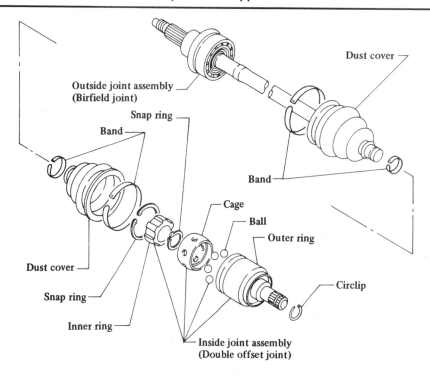

Fig. 13.164 Exploded view of the driveshaft and inner joint assembly (Sec 11)

Driveshaft – removal and refitting

3   Jack up the front of the car and support it on axle stands. Remove the appropriate roadwheel.

4   Place a suitable container beneath the transmission drain plug. Unscrew the plug and allow the oil, or fluid to drain. Refit the plug after draining.

5   Extract the split pin securing the driveshaft retaining nut and then slacken the nut using a suitable socket. Use a bar placed between two wheel studs, with the nuts in place, to prevent the hub and driveshaft rotating. Do not unscrew the nut completely at this stage.

6   Remove the three bolts securing the lower balljoint to the transverse link.

7   Extract the split pin and remove the tie-rod outer balljoint retaining nut. Using a claw clamp extractor separate the balljoint from the steering arm.

8   Move the front hub assembly outwards and release the driveshaft inner joint from the transmission. Prise it out carefully using a long screwdriver or bar as a lever if it will not pull out by hand. With the inner joint removed, place a tube or dowel (a short length of broom handle will do) of suitable diameter into the transmission to retain the differential side gears in position.

9   Unscrew the metal pipe-to-flexible hose union at the suspension strut. Plug the hose and pipe to prevent excessive loss of fluid and dirt entry.

10 Remove the two bolts securing the steering knuckle to the suspension strut. Now withdraw the driveshaft complete with steering knuckle, hub and brake caliper.

11 Remove the hub nut and, using a hide or plastic mallet, carefully tap the driveshaft out of the hub. If the shaft is tight attach a universal hub puller to the wheel studs and push the shaft out by tightening the central screw of the tool.

12 Refitting is the reverse sequence to removal, bearing in mind the following points.

   (a) *Always renew the circlip located on the end of the inner constant velocity joint*

   (b) *Lubricate the oil seals in the steering knuckle and transmission with multi-purpose grease before fitting the driveshaft*

   (c) *Tighten all nuts and bolts to the specified torque settings*

   (d) *Bleed the braking system as described in Chapter 9 after refitting*

   (e) *Refill the transmission with the correct grade and quantity of*

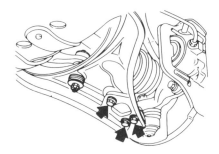

Fig. 13.165 Lower balljoint to transverse link retaining bolts (Sec 11)

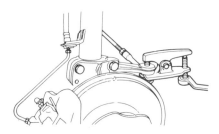

Fig. 13.166 Using a claw clamp extractor to separate the tie-rod outer balljoint (Sec 11)

oil or automatic transmission fluid, as applicable. Refer to Recommended Lubricants and Fluids and the appropriate Chapters of this manual for details

12 Steering, wheels and tyres

Power steering system – general

1   E-series engine models equipped with power steering utilize the IPRP 15L system described in Chapter 8. However, due to the revised

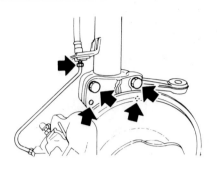

Fig. 13.167 Steering knuckle-to-suspension strut retaining bolts and brake pipe-to-hose union location (Sec 11)

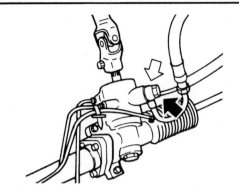

Fig. 13.169 High and low pressure hose unions at power steering rack and pinion unit (Sec 12)

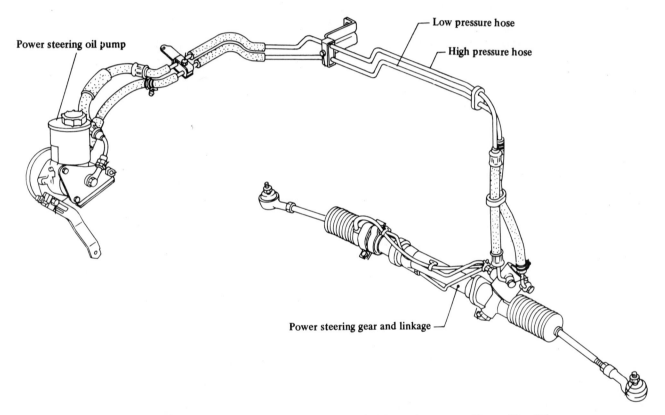

Fig. 13.168 Layout of the power steering rack and pinion unit, pump and hoses (Sec 12)

layout of the E-series engine, the removal and refitting procedures for the rack and pinion unit and the pump assembly have been amended, and the pump itself now incorporates the fluid reservoir tank. Apart from these changes, which are described in the following paragraphs, the remainder of the information contained in Chapter 8 is still applicable.

Power steering fluid – draining, refilling and bleeding

2   Place a suitable container beneath the high and low pressure hose unions on the rack and pinion unit. Wipe clean the area around the unions, then unscrew the unions from the rack. Take care not to lose the copper sealing washers.

3   When the system has drained completely, refit the unions.

4   To refill and bleed the system first jack up the front of the car so that the wheels are clear of the ground and support the car on axle stands.

5   Half fill the pump reservoir with fresh fluid of the specified type.

6   With the engine switched off, quickly turn the steering wheel from

lock to lock ten times. Add fluid as necessary while doing this so that the level is not allowed to fall below the low level mark on the dipstick.

7   Start the engine and allow it to idle. Turn the steering wheel from lock to lock to bring the fluid to normal operating temperature. Keep the reservoir topped up during this operation.

8   Stop the engine and add fluid as necessary.

9   Start the engine again and allow it to idle for five seconds then switch off the recheck the fluid level.

10   With the engine switched off turn the steering from lock to lock ten times whilst continually checking the fluid level.

11   Repeat paragraphs 9 and 10 until the fluid level remains constant and there are no air bubbles in the fluid.

12   If the fluid level continues to fall and air bubbles are still apparent turn the steering from lock to lock, with the engine running, five to ten times. Hold the steering on full lock for a maximum of five seconds while at the same time inspecting the system for leaks. If a leak is found, take the necessary corrective action and repeat the full bleeding procedure.

13   On completion switch off the engine, check the fluid level once

more and refit the reservoir cap. Lower the car to the ground and carry
out a short test drive.

Rack and pinion unit (power steering) – removal and refitting

14 Jack up the front of the car and support it on axle stands. Remove
the front roadwheels.

15 Remove the joint cover at the base of the steering column and
slacken the bolt securing the column to the lower joint.

16 Remove the bolt securing the lower joint to the pinion gear shaft
and ease the joint off the shaft.

17 Extract the split pins and remove the nuts securing the tie-rod end
balljoints to the steering arms. Release the balljoints from the steering
arms using a clamp claw separator.

18 Wipe clean the area around the high and low pressure hose unions
on the rack and pinion unit. Place a suitable container beneath the
hoses and unscrew the unions. Take care not to lose the copper
sealing washers. When all the fluid has drained, seal the union orifices
to prevent dirt entry.

19 Remove the bolts securing the rack and pinion unit mounting
clamps and lift off the clamps.

20 Carefully withdraw the rack and pinion from the side of the car.

21 Refitting is the reverse sequence to removal, bearing in mind the
following points:

  (a) *Before fitting the lower joint to the pinion shaft, ensure that
       the wheels are in the straight-ahead position and the steering
       wheel spokes are horizontal*

  (b) *Tighten all nuts and bolts to the specified torque settings*

  (c) *Bleed the system as described in the previous sub-section*

Power steering pump – removal and refitting

22 Slacken the power steering pump adjusting bolt locknut and
mounting bolts. Unscrew the adjusting bolt sufficiently to allow the
drivebelt to be slipped off the pulley.

23 Place a suitable container beneath the pump, remove the high
pressure hose union at the rear of the unit and drain the reservoir. Take
care not to lose the copper washers.

24 Slacken the low pressure hose clamp at the pump and detach the
hose.

25 Completely remove the pump assembly mounting bolts and
withdraw the pump from the engine.

26 Refitting is the reverse sequence to removal, bearing in mind the
following points:

  (a) *Adjust the drivebelt tension by means of the adjusting bolt to
       give the specified deflection. (See Routine Maintenance at
       the beginning of this Chapter)*

  (b) *Bleed the system as described earlier in this Section*

13 Electrical system

Electrical system – general

1   The electrical system on models powered by the E-series engine is
virtually identical to that of earlier models, apart from the uprating of
certain components.

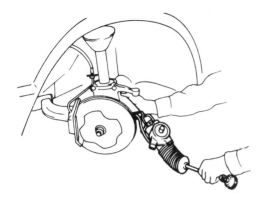

**Fig. 13.173 Removal of the rack and pinion unit from the car
(Sec 12)**

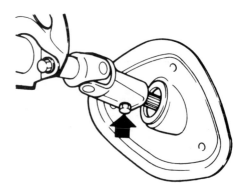

Fig. 13.170 Steering column-to-lower joint retaining bolt (Sec 12)

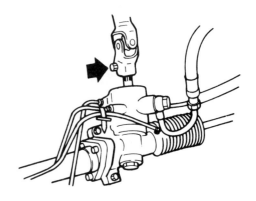

Fig. 13.171 Lower joint-to-pinion gear shaft retaining bolt (Sec 12)

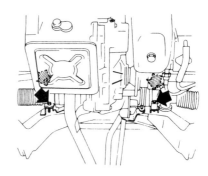

**Fig. 13.172 Rack and pinion unit mounting clamp locations
(Sec 12)**

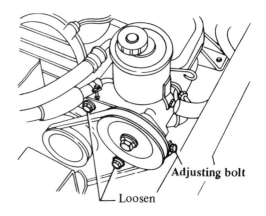

**Fig. 13.174 Location of the power steering pump adjusting and
mounting bolts (Sec 12)**

2   Starter motors of improved performance are fitted, and on models equipped with air conditioning, the layout of the components has been altered slightly.

3   The accompanying illustrations show the revisions to these components, but all repair and servicing procedures remain unchanged, and are as described in Chapter 10.

4   Where component specifications have changed, these are shown at the beginning of this Chapter.

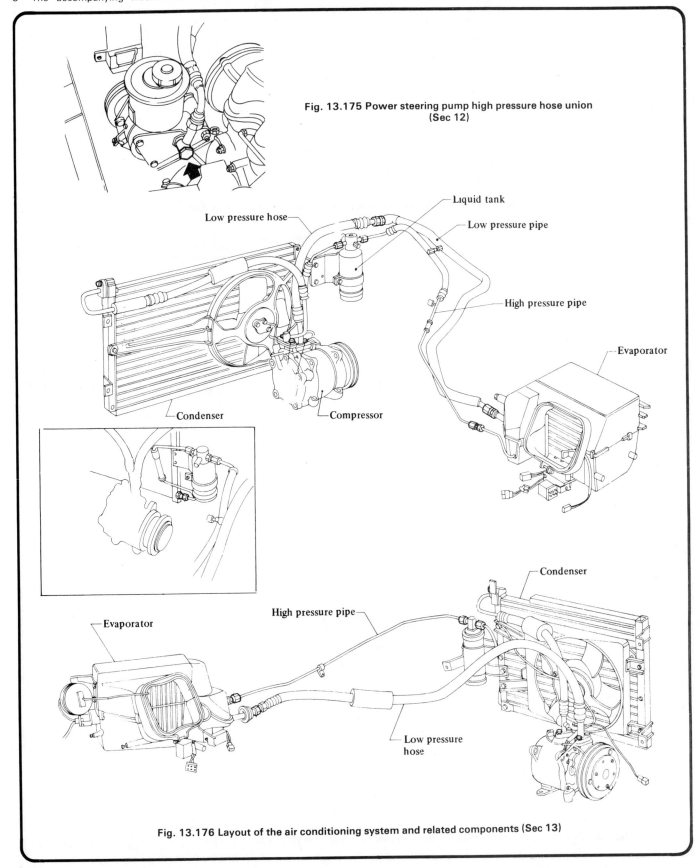

Fig. 13.175 Power steering pump high pressure hose union (Sec 12)

Fig. 13.176 Layout of the air conditioning system and related components (Sec 13)

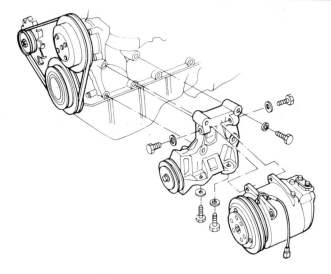

Fig. 13.177 Air conditioning compressor, mounting bracket and idler pulley mountings (Sec 13)

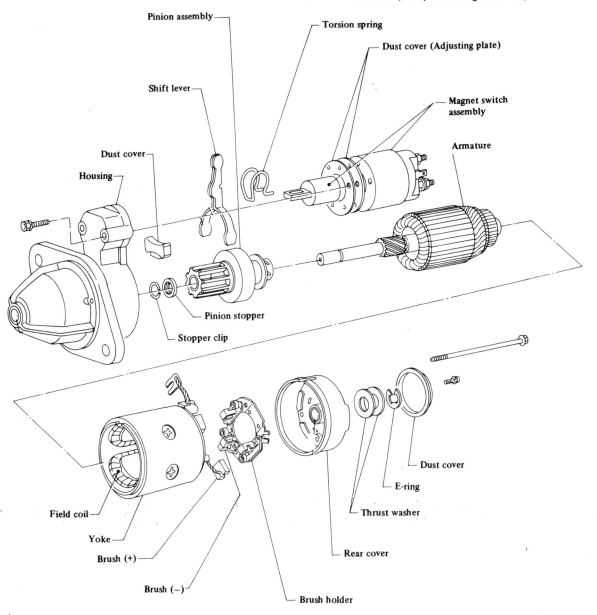

Fig. 13.178 Exploded view of the non-reduction gear type starter motor – manual transmission models (Sec 13)

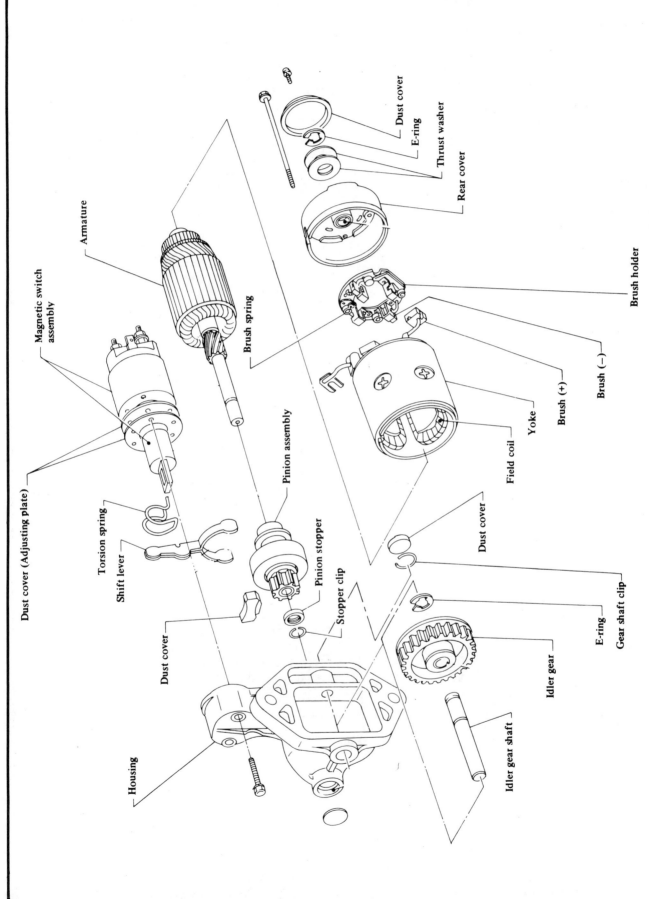

Magnetic switch assembly

Dust cover (Adjusting plate)

Torsion spring

Shift lever

Dust cover

Housing

Armature

Brush spring

Pinion assembly

Pinion stopper

Stopper clip

Field coil

Dust cover

Idler gear

Idler gear shaft

E-ring

Gear shaft clip

Dust cover

E-ring

Thrust washer

Rear cover

Brush holder

Brush (+)

Brush (−)

Yoke

Fig. 13.179 Exploded view of the reduction gear type starter motor – automatic transmission models (Sec 13)

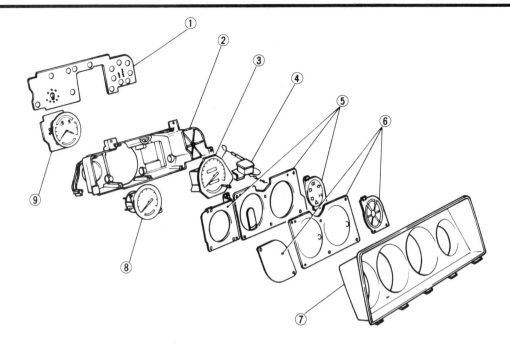

Fig. 13.180 Cone type instrument panel components (Sec 13)

1	Printed circuit board	4	Speed switch amplifier	6	Front cover
2	Lower housing		(where applicable)	7	Cluster lid
3	Speedometer	5	Upper housing	8	Tachometer

9 Water temperature and fuel gauges

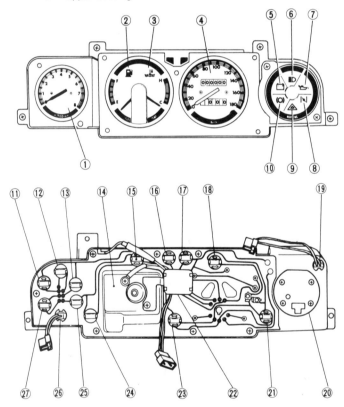

Fig. 13.181 Layout of instruments and warning lights on cone type instrument panel (Sec 13)

1	Tachometer	9	Hazard indicator lamp	16	Turn signal indicator	22	Speed switch amplifier
2	Fuel gauge	10	Brake warning lamp		lamp (RH)		(where applicable)
3	Water temperature gauge	11	Oil pressure warning lamp	17	Turn signal indicator	23	Illumination lamp
4	Speedometer	12	High beam warning lamp		lamp (LH)	24	Illumination lamp
5	Charge warning lamp	13	Charge warning lamp	18	Illumination lamp	25	Brake warning lamp
6	High beam warning lamp	14	Speedometer	19	Illumination lamp	26	Hazard indicator lamp
7	Oil pressure warning lamp	15	Illumination lamp	20	Tachometer	27	Choke warning lamp
8	Choke warning lamp			21	Illumination lamp		

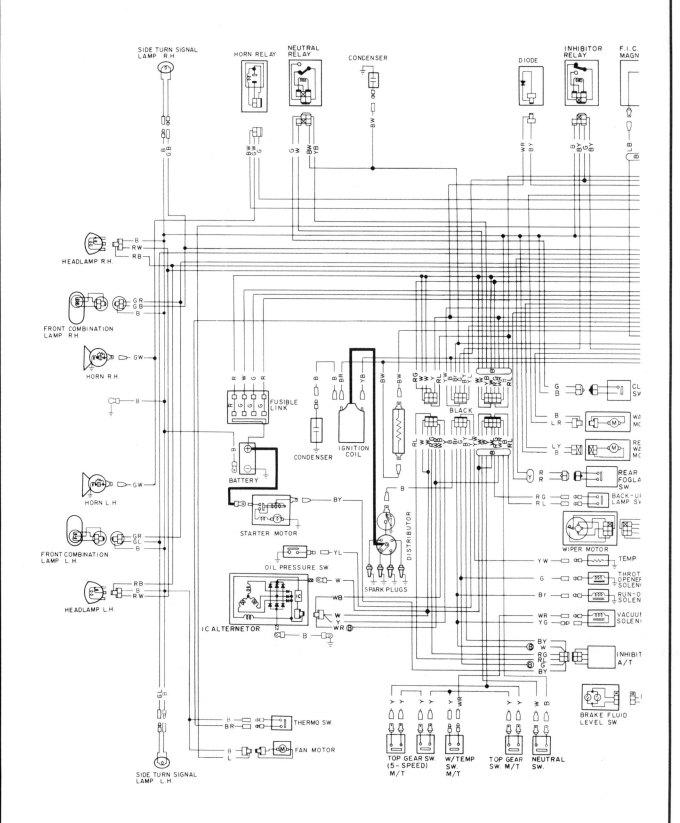

Fig. 13.182 Wiring diagram for 1981/82 models – right-hand drive

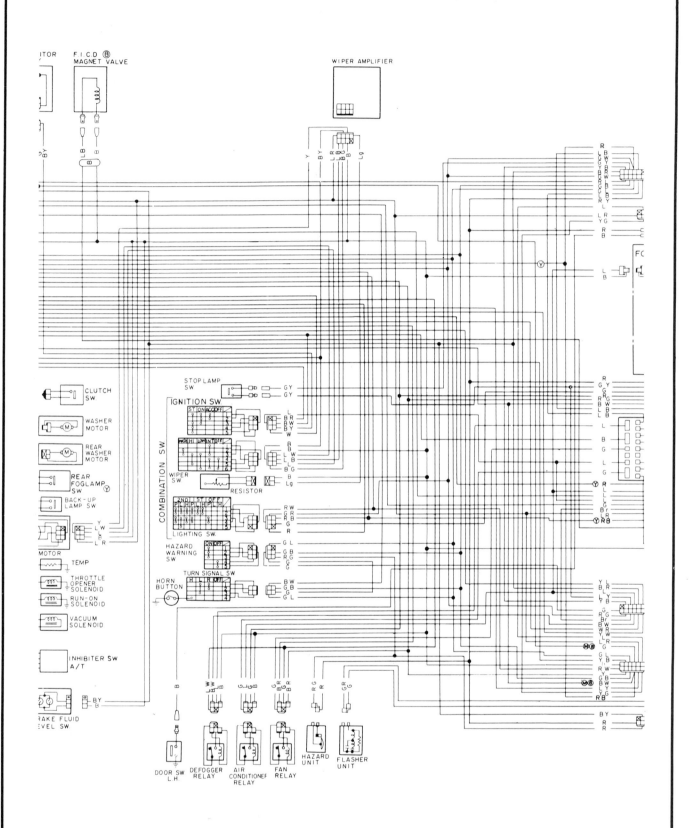

Fig. 13.182 Wiring diagram for 1981/82 models – right-hand drive (cont)

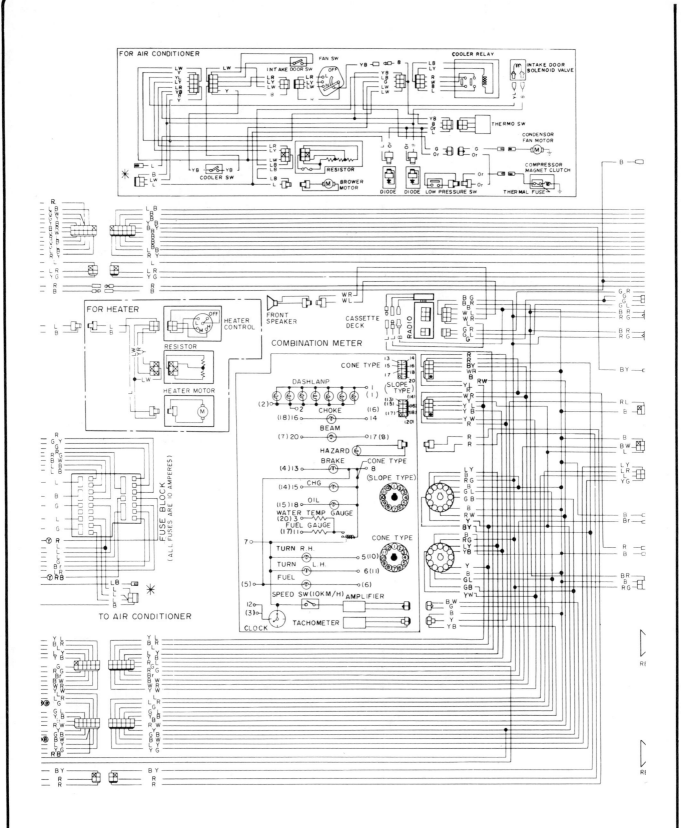

Fig. 13.182 Wiring diagram for 1981/82 models – right-hand drive (cont)

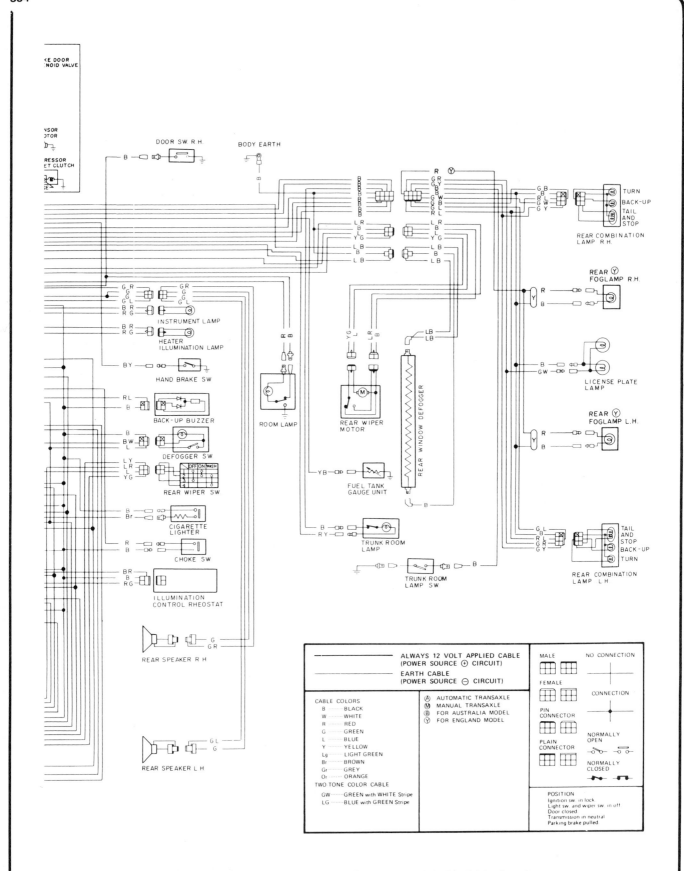

Fig. 13.182 Wiring diagram for 1981/82 models – right-hand drive (cont)

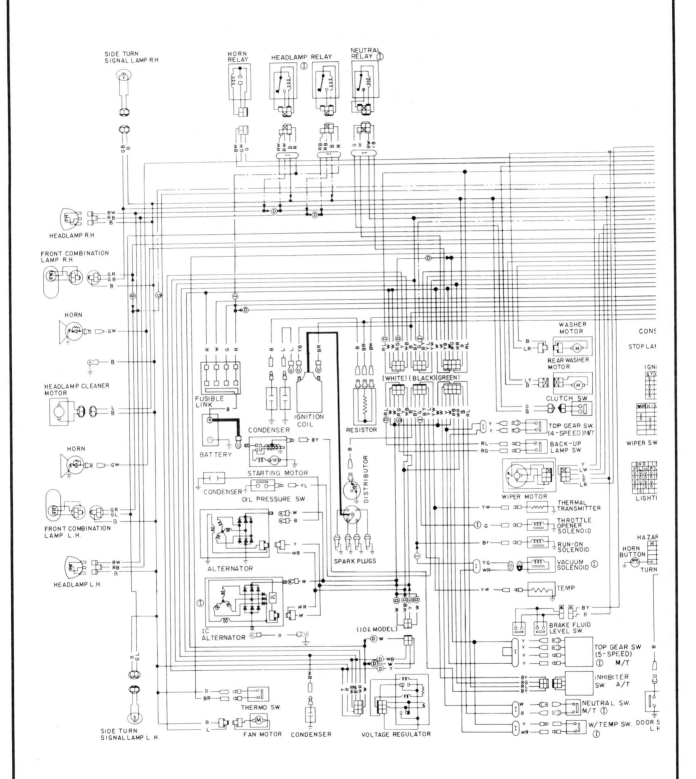

Fig. 13.183 Wiring diagram for 1981/82 models – left-hand drive

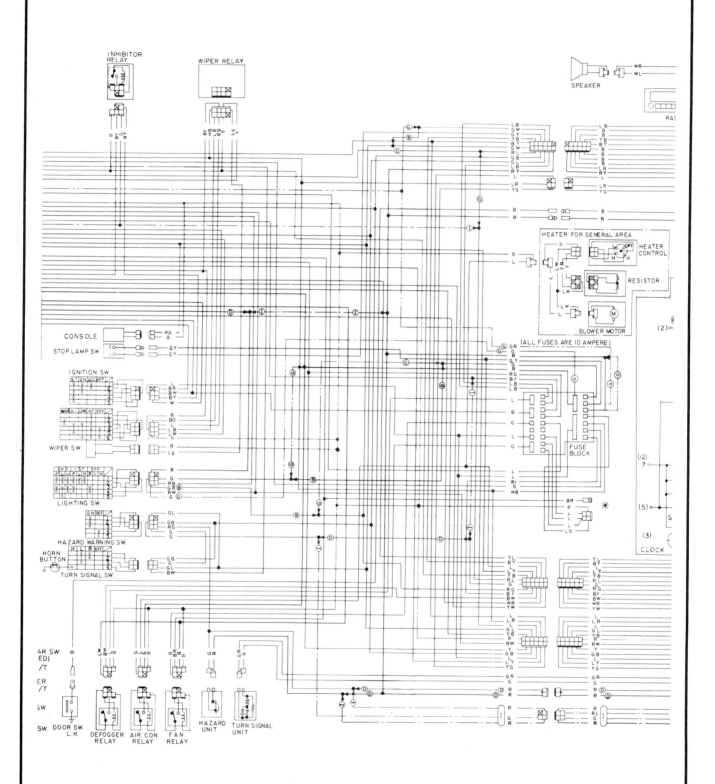

Fig. 13.183 Wiring diagram for 1981/82 models – left-hand drive (cont)

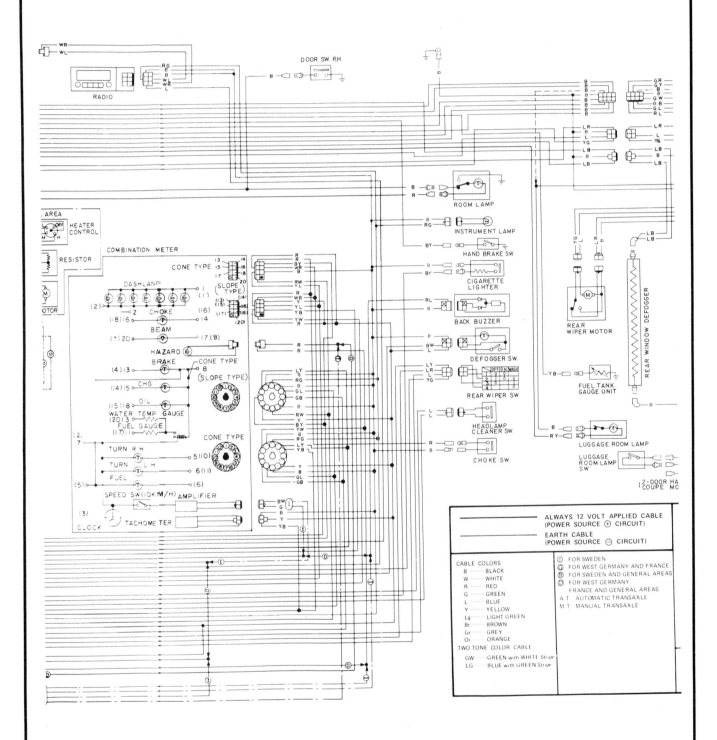

Fig. 13.183 Wiring diagram for 1981/82 models – left-hand drive (cont)

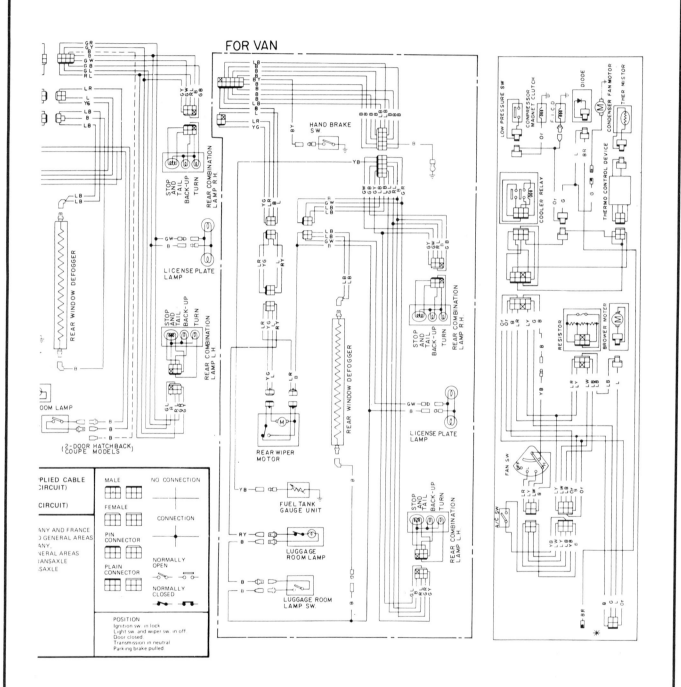

Fig. 13.183 Wiring diagram for 1981/82 models – left-hand drive (cont)

Conversion factors

Length (distance)

Inches (in)	X	25.4	= Millimetres (mm)	X	0.0394	= Inches (in)
Feet (ft)	X	0.305	= Metres (m)	X	3.281	= Feet (ft)
Miles	X	1.609	= Kilometres (km)	X	0.621	= Miles

Length (distance):

Inches (in) X 25.4 = Millimetres (mm) — X 0.0394 = Inches (in)
Feet (ft) X 0.305 = Metres (m) — X 3.281 = Feet (ft)
Miles X 1.609 = Kilometres (km) — X 0.621 = Miles

Volume (capacity)

Cubic inches (cu in; in^3) X 16.387 = Cubic centimetres (cc; cm^3) — X 0.061 = Cubic inches (cu in; in^3)
Imperial pints (Imp pt) X 0.568 = Litres (l) — X 1.76 = Imperial pints (Imp pt)
Imperial quarts (Imp qt) X 1.137 = Litres (l) — X 0.88 = Imperial quarts (Imp qt)
Imperial quarts (Imp qt) X 1.201 = US quarts (US qt) — X 0.833 = Imperial quarts (Imp qt)
US quarts (US qt) X 0.946 = Litres (l) — X 1.057 = US quarts (US qt)
Imperial gallons (Imp gal) X 4.546 = Litres (l) — X 0.22 = Imperial gallons (Irnp gal)
Imperial gallons (Imp gal) X 1.201 = US gallons (US gal) — X 0.833 = Imperial gallons (Imp gal)
US gallons (US gal) X 3.785 = Litres (l) — X 0.264 = US gallons (US gal)

Mass (weight)

Ounces (oz) X 28.35 = Grams (g) — X 0.035 = Ounces (oz)
Pounds (lb) X 0.454 = Kilograms (kg) — X 2.205 = Pounds (lb)

Force

Ounces-force (ozf; oz) X 0.278 = Newtons (N) — X 3.6 = Ounces-force (ozf; oz)
Pounds-force (lbf; lb) X 4.448 = Newtons (N) — X 0.225 = Pounds-force (lbf; lb)
Newtons (N) X 0.1 = Kilograms-force (kgf; kg) — X 9.81 = Newtons (N)

Pressure

Pounds-force per square inch (psi; lbf/in^2; lb/in^2) X 0.070 = Kilograms-force per square centimetre (kgf/cm^2; kg/cm^2) — X 14.223 = Pounds-force per square inch (psi; lbf/in^2; lb/in^2)
Pounds-force per square inch (psi; lbf/in^2; lb/in^2) X 0.068 = Atmospheres (atm) — X 14.696 = Pounds-force per square inch (psi; lbf/in^2; lb/in^2)
Pounds-force per square inch (psi; lbf/in^2; lb/in^2) X 0.069 = Bars — X 14.5 = Pounds-force per square inch (psi; lbf/in^2; lb/in^2)
Pounds-force per square inch (psi; lbf/in^2; lb/in^2) X 6.895 = Kilopascals (kPa) — X 0.145 = Pounds-force per square inch (psi; lbf/in^2; lb/in^2)
Kilopascals (kPa) X 0.01 = Kilograms-force per square centimetre (kgf/cm^2; kg/cm^2) — X 98.1 = Kilopascals (kPa)

Torque (moment of force)

Pounds-force inches (lbf in; lb in) X 1.152 = Kilograms-force centimetre (kgf cm; kg cm) — X 0.868 = Pounds-force inches (lbf in; lb in)
Pounds-force inches (lbf in; lb in) X 0.113 = Newton metres (Nm) — X 8.85 = Pounds-force inches (lbf in; lb in)
Pounds-force inches (lbf in; lb in) X 0.083 = Pounds-force feet (lbf ft; lb ft) — X 12 = Pounds-force inches (lbf in; lb in)
Pounds-force feet (lbf ft; lb ft) X 0.138 = Kilograms-force metres (kgf m; kg m) — X 7.233 = Pounds-force feet (lbf ft; lb ft)
Pounds-force feet (lbf ft; lb ft) X 1.356 = Newton metres (Nm) — X 0.738 = Pounds-force feet (lbf ft; lb ft)
Newton metres (Nm) X 0.102 = Kilograms-force metres (kgf m; kg m) — X 9.804 = Newton metres (Nm)

Power

Horsepower (hp) X 745.7 = Watts (W) — X 0.0013 = Horsepower (hp)

Velocity (speed)

Miles per hour (miles/hr; mph) X 1.609 = Kilometres per hour (km/hr; kph) — X 0.621 = Miles per hour (miles/hr; mph)

Fuel consumption*

Miles per gallon, Imperial (mpg) X 0.354 = Kilometres per litre (km/l) — X 2.825 = Miles per gallon, Imperial (mpg)
Miles per gallon, US (mpg) X 0.425 = Kilometres per litre (km/l) — X 2.352 = Miles per gallon, US (mpg)

Temperature

Degrees Fahrenheit = (°C x 1.8) + 32

Degrees Celsius (Degrees Centigrade; °C) = (°F - 32) x 0.56

*It is common practice to convert from miles per gallon (mpg) to litres/100 kilometres (l/100km), where mpg (Imperial) x l/100 km = 282 and mpg (US) x l/100 km = 235

Index

W

Printed by
Haynes Publishing Group
Sparkford Yeovil Somerset
England